ORDINARY DIFFERENTIAL EQUATIONS

A Blaisdell Book in Pure and Applied Mathematics

CONSULTING EDITOR
George Springer · *Indiana University*

ORDINARY DIFFERENTIAL EQUATIONS

SECOND EDITION

Garrett Birkhoff

HARVARD UNIVERSITY

Gian-Carlo Rota

MASSACHUSETTS INSTITUTE OF TECHNOLOGY

BLAISDELL PUBLISHING COMPANY

A Division of Ginn and Company

WALTHAM, MASSACHUSETTS / TORONTO / LONDON

Preface

The theory of differential equations is distinguished for the wealth of its ideas and methods. Although this richness makes the subject attractive as a field of research, it has frequently been the cause of confusion on the part of the student. For many students the transition from the elementary theory of differential equations to the study of advanced methods and techniques has been too abrupt. One of the chief purposes of the present text is to fill this gap.

We present what seem to us to be the most important key ideas of the subject in their simplest context, often that of second-order equations. We have deliberately avoided the systematic elaboration of these key ideas, feeling that this is often best done by the student himself. After one has grasped the underlying methods, one of the best ways to develop technique is to generalize (say, to higher-order equations or systems) by one's own efforts.

The exposition presupposes primarily a knowledge of the advanced calculus and some experience with the formal manipulation of elementary differential equations. Beyond this, only an acquaintance with vectors, matrices, and elementary complex functions is assumed in most of the book. Familiarity with the concepts of pole and branch point is assumed in Chapter 9, and in Chapter 11 Euclidean vector spaces are used freely.

The book falls broadly into three parts. Chapters 1 through 4 constitute a review of material to which, presumably, the student has already been exposed in elementary courses. This has a twofold purpose: to fill the inevitable gaps in the student's knowledge of the beginnings of the subject and to give a rigorous presentation of the material. The first part covers elementary methods of integration of first-order, second-order linear, and nth-order linear constant-coefficient differential equations. Besides reviewing elementary methods, it includes rigorous discussions of comparison theorems and the method of majorants. Finally, a brief introduction is given to the concepts of transfer function and Nyquist diagram and their relation to the Laplace transform. Although widely used in electrical engineering for many years, these concepts seem not to have previously found their way into textbooks on differential equations.

Chapters 5 through 8 deal with systems of nonlinear differential equations. Chapter 5 treats plane autonomous systems, including the classification of nondegenerate critical points, and introduces the important notion of stability and Liapunov's method, which is then applied to some of the simpler types of nonlinear oscillations. Chapter 6 includes theorems of existence, uniqueness, and continuity, both in the small and in the large, and introduces the perturbation equations. Chapters 7 and 8 provide a brief survey of the theory of effective numerical integration.

Finally, Chapters 9 through 11 are devoted to the study of second-order linear differential equations. Chapter 9 develops the theory of regular singular points, with applications to some important special functions. Chapter 10 is devoted to Sturm-Liouville theory and related asymptotic formulas, for both finite and infinite intervals. Chapter 11 establishes the completeness of the eigenfunctions of regular Sturm-Liouville systems, without assuming the Lebesgue integral.

Throughout the book, the properties of various important special functions—notably Bessel functions, hypergeometric functions, and the more common orthogonal polynomials—are derived from their defining differential equations and boundary conditions. In this way we illustrate the theory of ordinary differential equations and show its power.

This textbook can be used either in a one-term survey course or as a leisurely one-year course. In a one-term course, the instructor would normally omit starred sections. Or he might try to cover thoroughly a selection of chapters, developing each in full, for example Chapters 1–3, 5 and 6, and 9–11—or, in a more elementary course, Chapters 1–8.

In a year's course, the book can be used as an introduction to more advanced and systematic treatments, such as those found in the well-known treatises of Cesari, Coddington and Levinson, Ince, and Nemytskii and Stepanoff. Another possibility is to use the book as a continuation of an elementary text on differential equations.

This text contains several hundred exercises of varying difficulty, which in all cases should be an important part of the course. The most difficult exercises are starred.

It is a pleasure to extend our thanks to John Barrett, Fred Brauer, Thomas Brown, Lamberto Cesari, Abol Ghaffari, Andrew Gleason, Carl

Langenhop, Norman Levinson, Robert Lynch, Laurence Markus, Frank Stewart, Feodor Theilheimer, and J. L. Walsh for their comments, criticisms, and help in eliminating errors. We also thank John Freeman, Nick Metas, Richard Moroney, David Morrison, Norton Starr, Fred Van Vleck, John Wells, and Michael Wilber for assistance in proofreading.

Cambridge, Massachusetts   GARRETT BIRKHOFF
                                                          GIAN-CARLO ROTA

Contents

1

FIRST-ORDER DIFFERENTIAL EQUATIONS

2

SECOND-ORDER LINEAR EQUATIONS

3

POWER SERIES SOLUTIONS

4

LINEAR EQUATIONS WITH CONSTANT COEFFICIENTS

5

PLANE AUTONOMOUS SYSTEMS

6

EXISTENCE AND UNIQUENESS THEOREMS

7

APPROXIMATE SOLUTIONS

8

EFFICIENT NUMERICAL INTEGRATION

9

REGULAR SINGULAR POINTS

10

STURM-LIOUVILLE SYSTEMS

11

EXPANSIONS IN EIGENFUNCTIONS

APPENDIX: LINEAR SYSTEMS

BIBLIOGRAPHY   *355*

INDEX   *361*

ORDINARY DIFFERENTIAL EQUATIONS

First-Order Differential Equations

1 Introduction

A *differential equation* is an equation between specified derivatives of a function, its values, and known quantities. Many laws of physics are most simply and naturally formulated as differential equations (or DE's, as we shall write for short). For this reason, DE's have been studied by the greatest mathematicians and mathematical physicists since the time of Newton.

Ordinary differential equations are DE's whose unknowns are functions of a single variable; they arise most commonly in the study of dynamic systems and electric networks. They are much easier to treat than partial differential equations, whose unknown functions depend on two or more independent variables.

Ordinary DE's are classified according to their order. The *order* of a DE is defined as the largest positive integer, n, for which an nth derivative occurs in the equation. This Chapter will be restricted to *real first-order* DE's of the form

$$\phi(x, y, y') = 0. \tag{1}$$

Given the function ϕ of three real variables, the problem is to determine all real functions $y = f(x)$ which satisfy the DE, that is, all solutions of (1) in the following sense.

■ DEFINITION. *A solution of* (1) *is a differentiable function $f(x)$ such that $\phi(x, f(x), f'(x)) = 0$ for all x in the interval where $f(x)$ is defined.*

EXAMPLE 1. In the first-order DE

$$x + yy' = 0, \tag{2}$$

the function ϕ is a polynomial function $\phi(x, y, z) = x + yz$ of the three variables involved. The solutions of (2) can be found by considering the identity $d(x^2 + y^2)/dx = 2(x + yy')$. From this identity, one sees that $x^2 + y^2 = C$ is a constant if $y = f(x)$ is any solution of (2).

The equation $x^2 + y^2 = C$ defines y *implicitly* as a two-valued function of x, for any positive constant C. Solving for y, we get *two* solutions, the (single-valued†) functions $y = \pm \sqrt{C - x^2}$, for each positive constant C. The *graphs* of these solutions, the so-called *solution curves*, form two families of semicircles, which fill the upper half-plane $y > 0$ and the lower half-plane $y < 0$, respectively.

On the x-axis, where $y = 0$, the DE (2) implies that $x = 0$. Hence the DE has no solutions which cross the x-axis, except possibly at the origin. This fact is easily overlooked, because the solution curves *appear* to cross the x-axis to form full circles, as in Figure 1.1. However, these

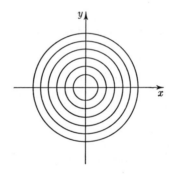

FIGURE 1.1   Integral Curves of $x + yy' = 0$.

circles have infinite slope where they cross the x-axis; hence y' does not exist, and the DE (2) is *not* satisfied there.

The preceding difficulty also arises if one tries to solve the DE (2) for y'. Dividing through by y, one gets $y' = -x/y$, an equation which cannot be satisfied if $y = 0$. The preceding difficulty is thus avoided if one restricts attention to regions where the DE (1) is normal, in the following sense.

■ DEFINITION.   *A normal first-order DE is one of the form*

$$y' = F(x, y). \tag{3}$$

---

† In this book, the word "function" will always mean single-valued function, unless the contrary is expressly specified.

In the normal form $y' = -x/y$ of the DE (2), the function $F(x, y)$ is continuous in the upper half-plane $y > 0$ and in the lower half-plane where $y < 0$; it is undefined on the x-axis.

2 Fundamental theorem of the calculus

The most familiar class of differential equations consists of the first-order DE's of the form

$$y' = g(x). \tag{4}$$

Such DE's are normal; their solutions are described by the fundamental theorem of the calculus, which reads as follows.

■ FUNDAMENTAL THEOREM OF THE CALCULUS.   *Let the function $g(x)$ in DE (4) be continuous in the interval $a \leq x \leq b$. Given a number c, there is one and only one solution $f(x)$ of the DE (4) in the interval such that $f(a) = c$. This solution is given by the definite integral*

$$f(x) = c + \int_a^x g(t)\, dt, \qquad c = f(a). \tag{5}$$

This basic result serves as a model of rigorous formulation in several respects. First, it specifies the region under consideration, as a vertical strip $a \leq x \leq b$ in the xy-plane. Second, it describes in precise terms the class of functions $g(x)$ considered. And third, it asserts the *existence* and *uniqueness* of a solution, given the "initial condition" $f(a) = c$. We recall that the definite integral

$$\int_a^x g(t)\, dt = \lim_{\max \Delta t_k \to 0} \sum g(t_k)\, \Delta t_k, \qquad \Delta t_k = t_k - t_{k-1}, \tag{5'}$$

is defined for each fixed x as a limit of Riemann sums; it is not necessary to find a formal expression for the indefinite integral $\int g(x)\, dx$ to give meaning to the definite integral $\int_a^x g(t)\, dt$, provided only that $g(t)$ is continuous. Such functions as the *error function* $\operatorname{erf} x = (2/\sqrt{\pi}) \int_0^x e^{-t^2}\, dt$ and the *sine integral function* $\operatorname{SI}(x) = \int_x^\infty [(\sin t)/t]\, dt$ are indeed commonly *defined* as definite integrals; cf. Chapter 3, §1.

To formulate and prove analogous theorems for more general first-order normal DE's, we need some technical concepts. We define a *domain*† as a nonempty *open connected* set. A function $\phi = \phi(x_1, \ldots, x_r)$ is said to be *of class $\mathscr{C}^n$* in a domain D, when all its derivatives $\partial \phi / \partial x_i$, $\partial^2 \phi / \partial x_i\, \partial x_j$, $\cdots$ of orders $1, \cdots, n$ exist and are continuous in D. One writes this condition in symbols as $\phi \in \mathscr{C}^n$ in D, or $\phi \in \mathscr{C}^n(D)$. When ϕ

---

† Some authors say *region* where we say domain. We will call the closure of a domain a *closed domain*.

is merely assumed to be continuous in D, one writes $\phi \in \mathscr{C}$ in D, or $\phi \in \mathscr{C}(D)$.

Intervals appear so frequently in analysis that they are referred to by a special notation. Thus, the *closed* interval $a \leq x \leq b$, which is not a domain (why not?) is denoted by $[a, b]$, the *open* interval $a < x < b$ by (a, b), the positive semi-axis $0 \leq x < +\infty$ by $[0, +\infty)$, and so on. Generally, a round bracket indicates that the endpoint adjacent to it is excluded from the interval, and a square bracket that the adjacent endpoint is included.

Given $F(x)$, the notation $F \in \mathscr{C}^2[1, +\infty)$ thus means that F is twice continuously differentiable in the semi-infinite line $[1, +\infty)$. Considered as a function of the two variables x and y, F is of class $\mathscr{C}^2$ in the *closed* domain including the vertical line $x = 1$ and all points to the right of it in the xy-plane. Likewise, $F \in \mathscr{C}[0, 1]$ means that F is continuous in the vertical strip $0 \leq x \leq 1$. Where there is any question of just what domain is referred to below, the domain will be described in words as well as in symbols.

There are a number of obvious facts about the differentiability of solutions of DE's. Such facts about differentiability will be used without special comment where they are irrelevant to the main idea of a proof. For instance, if $g \in \mathscr{C}^n(a, b)$, and $y = f(x)$ is any solution of the DE $y' = g(x)$, then $y \in \mathscr{C}^{n+1}(a, b)$. Again, if $\phi \in \mathscr{C}^n$ and $\psi \in \mathscr{C}^n$ in a domain D, and $F(u, v) \in \mathscr{C}^n$ in the entire uv-plane, then $G(x, y) = F(\phi(x, y), \psi(x, y)) \in \mathscr{C}^n(D)$.

3   Solutions and integrals

According to the definition given in §1, a *solution* of a DE is always a *function*. For example, the solutions of the DE $x + yy' = 0$ in Example 1 are the functions $y = \pm\sqrt{C - x^2}$, whose graphs are semicircles of arbitrary diameter, centered at the origin. The graph of the solution curves are, however, more easily described by the equation $x^2 + y^2 = C$, describing a family of circles centered at the origin. In what sense can such a family of curves be considered as a solution of the DE? To answer this question, we require a new notion.

■ DEFINITION. *An* integral *of DE (1) is a function of two variables,* $u(x, y)$, *which assumes a constant value whenever the variable y is replaced by a solution $y = f(x)$ of the DE.*

In the above example, the function $u(x, y) = x^2 + y^2$ is an integral of the DE $x + yy' = 0$, because, upon replacing the variable y by any function $\pm\sqrt{C - x^2}$, we obtain $u(x, y) = C$.

The second-order DE,

$$\frac{d^2x}{dt^2} = -x, \tag{2'}$$

becomes a first-order DE equivalent to (2) after setting $dx/dt = y$:

$$y\frac{dy}{dx} = -x. \tag{2}$$

As we have seen, the curves $u(x, y) = x^2 + y^2$ are integrals of this DE. When the DE (2') is interpreted as an equation of motion under Newton's second law (see, for example, the discussion in Chapter 5, §7), the integrals $C = x^2 + y^2$ represent curves of constant energy C. This illustrates an important principle: an integral of a DE representing some kind of motion is a quantity that remains unchanged through the motion.

The relationship between *solutions* and *integrals* of the DE (1) will be made clear by the following theorem.

■ IMPLICIT FUNCTION THEOREM.† *Let $u(x, y)$ be a function of class $\mathscr{C}^n$ in a domain containing the point (x_0, y_0), and let $\partial u(x_0, y_0)/\partial y \neq 0$. Then there exists a unique function $y = f(x, C)$ of class $\mathscr{C}^n$, defined in some open interval (a, b) containing x_0, such that $y_0 = f(x_0, C)$ and $u(x, f(x, C)) = C$ for all x in (a, b) and for all C in an open interval.*

By the Implicit Function Theorem, every integral $u(x, y)$ of class $\mathscr{C}^1$ of the DE (1) defines a family of solutions near any point (x, y) where $\partial u(x, y)/\partial x \neq 0$, obtained by solving the equation $u(x, y) = C$ for the variable y.

The notion of integral has been defined in terms of a solution of a DE. For several classes of DE's, however, it is possible to verify that a function $u(x, y)$ is an integral without first finding any solution. For example, a function $u(x, y)$ of class $\mathscr{C}^1$ is an integral of the *quasilinear* DE

$$\phi(x, y, y') = M(x, y) + N(x, y)y' = 0$$

whenever

$$M(x, y)\frac{\partial u}{\partial y} - N(x, y)\frac{\partial u}{\partial x} = 0,$$

provided that $\partial u/\partial y \neq 0$, as can be verified from the familiar formula $dy/dx = -(\partial u/\partial x)/(\partial u/\partial y)$.

---

† Courant, Vol. 2, p. 114; Widder, p. 55. Here and below, page references to authors refer to the books listed in the selected bibliography on pp. 355–357.

A similar method can be applied to DE's of finite *degree* in the derivative y', namely, when the function $\phi(x, y, y')$ is a polynomial in the variable y' (see §8).

Parametric Solutions. A pair of functions $x = g(t)$, $y = h(t)$ of the parameter t describe a *curve* in the xy-plane. Such a curve is a *parametric solution* of DE (1) whenever the function $h(t) = f(g(t))$ for every solution $y = f(x)$ of the DE, as t ranges over the interval of definition of the functions g and h. If $u(g(t), h(t))$ is constant, then the function $u(x, y)$ is an integral of the DE.

Thus we see that there are three different notions of "solution" of a first-order DE (1): a *function* $y = f(x)$, and *integral* $u(x, y) = C$, corresponding to an *implicit solution*, and a parametric *curve* $x = g(t)$, $y = h(t)$.

4   Regular and normal curve families

Let the function $u(x, y)$ be of class $\mathscr{C}^1$ in a region of the xy-plane. The points in the region where both partial derivatives of u vanish are called *critical points*. We shall always assume in this book (unless the contrary is explicitly stated) that the function u has but a finite number of critical points. This implies that the critical points of u are isolated. The reason for this assumption is that it allows us to study the contour lines of u in the neighborhood of a critical point.

For example, the function $u = x^2 + y^2$ has just one critical point in the entire plane; this is at the origin, through which indeed no contour line passes. The contour lines $u = C$ satisfy the following three conditions in any domain D not containing any critical points: (i) one and only one curve of the family passes through each point of D, (ii) each curve of the family has a tangent at every point, and (iii) the tangent direction is a continuous function of position.

We call *any* curve family which satisfies conditions (i)–(iii) a *regular* curve family. The contour lines of any function $u(x, y) \in \mathscr{C}^1$ form a regular curve family in any domain that contains no critical points.

In Example 1, the families of *solution* curves $y = \pm\sqrt{C - x^2}$ are not only a regular curve family in each half-plane but, in addition, the functions $f(x, C) = \sqrt{C - x^2}$ and $g(x, C) = -\sqrt{C - x^2}$ satisfy $\partial f/\partial C = 1/2y > 0$ when $y > 0$, and $\partial g/\partial C = -1/2y > 0$ when $y < 0$, respectively. They constitute a *normal* curve family, as in the following.

■ DEFINITION. *In a domain D of the xy-plane, a* normal *curve family is a family of curves defined explicitly as the graphs of functions $y = f(x, c)$,*

$f \in \mathscr{C}^1(D)$, *which depend on a parameter* $c = c(x, y)$ *which is defined on D and satisfies* $\partial c / \partial y \neq 0$ *there.*

Since, for fixed x, $(\partial f / \partial c)(\partial c / \partial y) = 1$, it is equivalent to require that $\partial f / \partial c \neq 0$.

The relationship of regular and normal curve families to first-order DE's is given by the following result.

■ THEOREM 1.   *For curve families in a domain D of the xy plane:*
  (i) *every normal curve family is regular;*
 (ii) *a regular curve family is normal in any domain where no tangent to any curve of the family is vertical;*
(iii) *the functions* $y = f(x, c)$ *defining a normal curve family are the solutions of a normal first-order DE;*
 (iv) *the functions* $u(x, y) = C$ *defining any regular curve family are the solutions of a first-order* partial *DE*

$$M(x, y) \frac{\partial u}{\partial y} - N(x, y) \frac{\partial u}{\partial x} = 0;$$

  (v) *in any domain where a regular curve family is normal, the curves of the family are the* integrals *of the quasilinear* DE

$$M(x, y) + N(x, y)y' = 0. \tag{6}$$

The proof is essentially contained in the preceding discussion. Statement (i) is an immediate consequence of the definition of a normal curve family. Statement (ii) is a consequence of the Implicit Function Theorem, stated in the preceding Section.

Statement (iii) is seen to be true as follows. By definition of a normal curve family, we have $\partial f / \partial c \neq 0$; applying the implicit function theorem to solve this equation for the parameter c, we find that there is a function $c = g(x, y)$ of class $\mathscr{C}^1$ for which $y = f(x, g(x, y))$. Differentiating $y = f(x, c)$ relative to x, we find that

$$y' = \partial f(x, g(x, y)) / \partial x = F(x, y),$$

as was to be shown.

Statement (iv) follows by setting $M(x, y) = \partial u(x, y) / \partial x$ and $N(x, y) = \partial u(x, y) / \partial y$, and statement (v) follows from the identity

$$\frac{dy}{dx} = - \frac{\partial u / \partial x}{\partial u / \partial y}.$$

EXAMPLE 2.   In Example 1, the curves $u(x, y) = x^2 + y^2 = c$ form a regular curve family of integrals of the implicit DE $x = -y y'$.

The curves $y = +\sqrt{c - x^2}$, for $c > 0$, form a *normal* family of curves, solutions of the DE in normal form

$$y' = -x/y$$

in the domain D consisting of the upper half-plane. There is only one critical point, namely the origin.

We have already seen that the solution curves $y = c + f(x)$ for $y' = g(x)$ form a normal curve family in the strip $a \leq x \leq b$ if $g \in \mathscr{C}[a, b]$, with $\partial y/\partial c = 1$. See Figure 1.2, which depicts solution curves for the DE $y' = e^{-x^2}$.

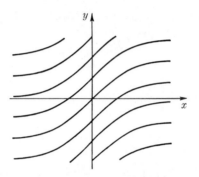

FIGURE 1.2   Solution Curves of $y' = e^{-x^2}$.

It is important to notice that, on the basis of the preceding theorem, we can construct DE's whose solution curves behave in any desired way: we simply draw on a region of the plane a normal family of curves.

EXAMPLE 3.   Let $y' = g(x)h(y)$ be any DE with "separable variables" (and g, h continuous). Then the indefinite integrals $\phi(x) = \int g(x)dx$ and $\psi(y) = \int dy/h(y)$ exist in any horizontal strip $y_1 < g(x) < y_2$ between successive zeros of $h(y)$. The implicit equation $u(x, y) = \phi(x) - \psi(y) = c$ defines a regular family of integral curves in each such strip since $\partial u/\partial y = 1/h(y) \neq 0$ has constant sign there.

In (6), the points where $M = N = 0$ are the critical points; they are points where the tangent direction is indeterminate, because (6) reduces to $y' = 0/0$ there. Thus, in Example 1, the origin is such a point, and we see that no integral "curve" passes through it. The behavior of solutions near critical points will be discussed in Chapter 5; it can be very complicated.

Moreover until Chapter 6, §14, we will not even prove the basic fact that, if $F \in \mathscr{C}^1(D)$, the solution curves of $y' = F(x, y)$ form a normal curve family in D. For the present, in order to give precise formulations and proofs of theorems in a reasonably short space, we shall have to content ourselves with much less sweeping conclusions.

5 Exact differentials; integrating factors

A differential $M\,dx + N\,dy$ ($M, N \in \mathscr{C}(D)$) is called *exact* in a domain D when the line integral

$$\int_\tau M(x, y)\,dx + N(x, y)\,dy$$

is the same for all paths of integration τ in D which have the same endpoints. It is shown in the calculus† that $M\,dx + N\,dy$ is exact if and only if there exists a continuously differentiable function $u(x, y)$ such that $M = \partial u / \partial x$ and $N = \partial u / \partial y$, that is, such that the total differential $du = (\partial u / \partial x)dx + (\partial u / \partial y)dy$ is $M\,dx + N\,dy$. For *continuously differentiable* M, N, a necessary condition for $M\,dx + N\,dy$ to be exact is that M and N satisfy the partial DE $\partial M / \partial y = \partial N / \partial x$; if D is simply connected, this condition is also sufficient.

We now consider first-order DE's of the form

$$\phi(x, y, y') = M(x, y) + N(x, y)y' = 0 \tag{7}$$

with M, $N \in \mathscr{C}$ in a domain D. Dividing by N, we obtain the algebraically equivalent normal form

$$y' = F(x, y) = -M(x, y)/N(x, y) \tag{7'}$$

except on the closed set where N vanishes, i.e., where $\partial \phi / \partial y' = 0$. This set (the x-axis in Example 1) divides the domain D into a number of subdomains, in each of which the normal form (7′) is equivalent to (7).

It is often stated that the solution curves of the DE (7) are the contour lines $u(x, y) = C$, whenever $M\,dx + N\,dy = du$ is an exact differential. But this is not true, as Example 1 shows. A correct statement of the relation in question is the following.

■ THEOREM 2.   *If $M(x, y)\,dx + N(x, y)\,dy$ is an exact differential du in a domain D, then the contour lines $u(x, y) = C$ are integral curves of (7) for any constant C. These contour lines form a regular curve family in the domain D^*, consisting of D with the critical points where $M = N = 0$ (that is, where grad $u = 0$) deleted.*

The proof is immediate, for any continuous M, N. Along any solution curve $y = f(x)$, we have

$$du/dx = \partial u/\partial x + y'\,\partial u/\partial y = M(x, y) + N(x, y)y' = 0.$$

---

† Courant, Vol. 2, p. 352; Widder, p. 251.

The regularity of the family of contour lines follows directly from the implicit function theorem. They form a normal family in any sub-domain where N does not vanish.

When the differential $M\,dx + N\,dy$ is not exact, one can often find a function $\mu(x, y)$ such that the product

$$(\mu M)\,dx + (\mu N)\,dy = du$$

is an exact differential. The contour lines $u(x, y) = C$ will then again be integral curves of the DE $M\,(x, y) + N\,(x, y)y' = 0$ because $du/dx = \mu(M + Ny') = 0$; and segments of these contour lines between points of vertical tangency will be solution curves. Such a function μ is called an integrating factor.

■ DEFINITION. *An* integrating factor *for a differential* $M(x, y)\,dx + N(x, y)\,dy$ *is a nonvanishing function* $\mu(x, y)$ *such that the product* $(\mu M)\,dx + (\mu N)\,dy$ *is an exact differential.*

For example, consider the DE $xy' = y$. The differential $x\,dy - y\,dx$ which is associated with it is not exact, but it has the integrating factor $1/(x^2 + y^2)$ in the right half-plane $x > 0$. In fact, the function $\theta(x, y)$ defined by the line integral

$$\theta(x, y) = \int_{(1, 0)}^{(x, y)} (x\,dy - y\,dx)/(x^2 + y^2)$$

is the angle made with the positive x-axis by the vector (x, y). That is, it is just the polar angle θ when the point (x, y) is expressed in polar coordinates. Thus, the integral curves of $xy' = y$ in the domain $x > 0$ are the radii $\theta = C$, where $-\pi/2 < \theta < \pi/2$; the solution curves are the same.

Note that the differential $(x\,dy - y\,dx)/(x^2 + y^2)$ is not exact in the punctured plane, consisting of the xy-plane with the origin deleted. For θ changes by 2π in going around the origin. This is possible, even though $\partial[x/(x^2 + y^2)]/\partial x = \partial[-y/(x^2 + y^2)]/\partial y$, because the punctured plane is not a simply connected domain.

EXERCISES A

1. Plot the integral curves of the DE $y' = y^2/x^2$. In which regions of the plane do they form a regular curve family? A normal curve family?
2. Find equations describing all solutions of $y' = (x + y)^2$.
3. Find equations describing all solutions of $y' = (2x + y)^{-1}$.
4. Show that if a normal curve family is invariant under horizontal translation, then the curves of the family are the solution curves of a DE of the form $y' = f(y)$.
5. Find all functions $f(x)$ whose definite integral between 0 and any x equals the reciprocal of $f(x)$. [HINT: DE is $y' = -y^3$.]
6. For what pairs of positive integers n, r is the function $|x|^n$ of class $\mathscr{C}^r$?

7. In what domains do the level lines $x^3 + 3x^2y + y^3 = c$ form a regular curve family? A normal curve family?

8. Same question as Exercise 7 for $x^3 - 3x^2y + y^3 = c$.

9. Find all integral curves of $(x^n + y^n)y' - x^{n-1}y = 0$. [HINT: Set $u = y/x$.]

10*. Let $f(x)$ and $g(y) \neq 0$ be continuous in the rectangle $a < x < b$, $c < y < d$. Prove that the DE $y' = f(x)g(y)$ has a unique solution through each point of the rectangle.†

11*. Show that each solution of Exercise 10 can be continued up to the boundary of the rectangle.

12. Solve the DE $yy' + x = 0$ by the method of separation of variables, deducing rigorously the domains in which the method gives normal families of solutions.

13*. Same question as Exercise 12 for the DE $y' = xy - xy^3$.

6 First-order linear equations

The first-order *linear* DE is

$$a(x)y' + b(x)y + c(x) = 0. \tag{8}$$

It is called *homogeneous* if $c(x) \equiv 0$, and *inhomogeneous* otherwise.

Let the coefficient functions a, b, c be continuous. In any interval I where $a(x)$ does not vanish, the linear DE (8) can be reduced to the normal form

$$y' = -p(x)y - q(x), \tag{9}$$

with continuous coefficient-functions $p = b/a$ and $q = c/a$.

The homogeneous linear case $y' = -p(x)y$ of (9) is solved easily, if not rigorously, as follows. We separate variables, $dy/y = -p(x)\,dx$; then we integrate (by quadratures), $\ln|y| = -\int p(x)\,dx + C$. Exponentiating both sides, we obtain $|y| = Ke^{-\int p(x)\,dx}$, where $K = e^C$ and any indefinite integral $P(x) = \int p(x)\,dx$ may be used.

This heuristic reasoning suggests that, if $P'(x) = p(x)$, then $ye^{P(x)}$ is a constant. Though this result was derived heuristically, it is easily verified rigorously:

$$d[ye^{P(x)}]/dx = y'e^{P(x)} + p(x)ye^{P(x)} = e^{P(x)}[y' + p(x)y] = 0.$$

In short, $e^{P(x)}$ is an *integrating factor* for $y' + p(x)y$, provided that $P'(x) = p(x)$. And the existence of such a $P(x)$, and hence of a positive $e^{P(x)} \in \mathscr{C}^1$, follows from the Fundamental Theorem of the Calculus (§2).

We now verify that $e^{P(x)}$ is also an integrating factor for the normal linear DE (9). For, the expression

$$[e^{P(x)}q(x) + e^{P(x)}p(x)y]\,dx + e^{P(x)}\,dy$$

is an exact differential, with the integral

$$u = ye^{P(x)} + \int e^{P(x)}q(x)\,dx. \tag{10}$$

---

† The more difficult exercises are starred throughout this book.

The existence of the integral on the right side of (10) again follows from the Fundamental Theorem of the Calculus. Formula (10) implies that

$$ye^{\int p\,dx} + \int[qe^{\int p\,dx}]\,dx = C. \tag{10'}$$

By Theorem 2, the contour lines $u(x, y) = C$ are integral curves of (9), where any indefinite integral is chosen in (10). Solving for y, we obtain, for any $x_0 \in I$, the equivalent equation

$$y = Ce^{-P(x)} - e^{-P(x)} \int_{x_0}^{x} e^{P(t)}q(t)\,dt, \qquad P(x) = \int p(t)\,dt, \tag{11}$$

where C is an arbitrary constant. Namely, we have shown that, if $y = f(x)$ is any solution of (9), then the left side of (10') is constant. Conversely, for any constant C, the function (11) defines a solution of (9). This proves the following.

■ **THEOREM 3.** *If $p(x)$ and $q(x)$ are continuous, the solutions of the normal linear DE (9) are the functions (11).*

For this reason, formula (11) is said to define the *general solution* of (9).

In formula (11), the right side is a function $y = f(x, C)$ of class $\mathscr{C}^1$ in any vertical strip $a < x < b$ where the functions p, q are continuous; this follows from the Fundamental Theorem of the Calculus. Moreover, since any power of e is positive, $\partial f/\partial C = e^{-P(x)} > 0$. From this follows a useful corollary.

■ **COROLLARY.** *Let $p, q \in \mathscr{C}$ in any open interval (a, b) of the x-axis. Then the solutions (11) of (9) form a normal curve family in the vertical strip $a < x < b$ in the xy-plane.*

In particular, for any "initial value" y_0, the choice in (11) of

$$C = e^{P(x_0)}y_0$$

gives one and only one solution of (9) satisfying the "initial condition" $f(x_0) = y_0$.

Quadrature. In the Fundamental Theorem of the Calculus, if the function g is nonnegative, the definite integral in (5) is the area under the curve $y = g(x)$ in the vertical strip between a and x. For this reason, the integration of (4) is called a *quadrature*. Formula (11) reduces the solution of any first-order linear DE to the performance of a sequence of quadratures. Using Tables of Indefinite Integrals,† the solutions can

---

† See the books by Peirce and Foster and by Dwight listed in the Bibliography. Kamke's book listed there contains an extremely useful catalog of solutions of DE's not of the form $y' = g(x)$. For a bibliography of function tables, see Fletcher, Miller, and Rosenhead.

therefore often be expressed in closed form, in terms of well-known functions whose numerical values have been tabulated ("tabulated functions").

EXERCISES B

1. Find all solutions of the DE $|x| + |y|\, y' = 0$. In which regions of the plane is the differential on the left side exact?
2. (a) Reduce the *Bernoulli* DE $y' + p(x)y = q(x)y^n$ to a linear first-order DE by the substitution $u = y^{1-n}$.
   (b) Express its general solution, using indefinite integrals.
3. Show that, if $\mu(x, y)$ and $\nu(x, y)$ are integrating factors of class $\mathscr{C}^1$ for the same DE $M(x, y) + N(x, y)y' = 0$ with $M, N \in \mathscr{C}^2$, then the quotient $h(x, y) = \mu(x, y)/\nu(x, y)$ is an integral of the DE whenever $\nu(x, y) \neq 0$.

In Exercises 4–7, describe domains in which the solutions of the DE's specified form regular curve families:

4. $y' = \dfrac{y}{x} - \dfrac{x}{\log|x|}$.

5. $y' = \dfrac{y}{x} - \cos(\log|x|)$.

6. $\dfrac{dr}{d\theta} = r^2 \sin \dfrac{1}{r}$ (polar coordinates).

7. $\dfrac{dr}{d\theta} = 2 \log r$.

7   The linear fractional equation

An important first-order DE is the *linear fractional equation*

$$\frac{dy}{dx} = \frac{cx + dy}{ax + by}, \qquad ad \neq bc, \tag{12}$$

which is the normal form of

$$(ax + by)y' - (cx + dy) = 0. \tag{12'}$$

It is understood that the coefficients a, b, c, d are constants.

The integration of the DE (12) can be reduced to a quadrature by the substitution $y = vx$. This substitution replaces (12) by the DE

$$xv' + v = (c + dv)/(a + bv),$$

in which the variables x and v can be separated. Transposing v, we are led to the separation of variables

$$\frac{(a + bv)\, dv}{bv^2 + (a - d)v - c} + \frac{dx}{x} = 0.$$

Since the integrands are rational functions, this can be integrated in terms of elementary functions. Thus x can be expressed as a function of $v = y/x$: we have $x = CG(y/x)$, where

$$G(v) = \exp\left\{- \int [(a + bv)/(bv^2 + (a - d)v - c)]\, dv\right\}. \tag{13}$$

The preceding manipulations can be rigorously justified, provided that $x \neq 0$, $ax + by \neq 0$, and $bv^2 + (a - d)v \neq c$. These loci divide the xy-plane into at most eight sectors.

Another good way to obtain solutions of (12) is to introduce polar coordinates, setting $x = r \cos \theta$, $y = r \sin \theta$. If $\psi = \gamma - \theta$ is the angle between the tangent direction γ and the radial direction θ, then

$$\frac{1}{r}\frac{dr}{d\theta} = \cot \psi = \frac{\cot \gamma \cot \theta + 1}{\cot \theta - \cot \gamma}.$$

Since $\tan \gamma = y' = (cx + dy)/(ax + by) = (c + d \tan \theta)/(a + b \tan \theta)$, the final expression in the preceding equation is equal to

$$[(a + b \tan \theta) \cot \theta + (c + d \tan \theta)]/[(c + d \tan \theta) \cot \theta - (a + b \tan \theta)].$$

Multiplying numerator and denominator by $\sin \theta \cos \theta$, we reduce the linear fractional DE (12) to

$$\frac{1}{r}\frac{dr}{d\theta} = \frac{a \cos^2 \theta + (b + c) \sin \theta \cos \theta + d \sin^2 \theta}{c \cos^2 \theta + (d - a) \sin \theta \cos \theta - b \sin^2 \theta} = Q(\theta). \tag{14}$$

This can also be integrated by a quadrature. The solution is

$$r(\theta) = r(0) \exp\left\{\int_0^\theta Q(\theta)\, d\theta\right\}, \tag{14'}$$

which is well-defined by the Fundamental Theorem of the Calculus as long as the denominator of $Q(\theta)$ does not vanish.

Invariant radii. The radii along which the denominator of $Q(\theta)$ vanishes are those where (12) is equivalent to $d\theta/dr = 0$. Hence they are particular solution curves of (12); they are called *invariant radii*. They are the solutions $y = \tau x$, for constant $\tau = \tan \theta$. Therefore, they are the radii $y = \tau x$ for which $y' = \tau = (c + d\tau)/(a + b\tau)$, by (12), and so their slopes τ are the roots of the quadratic equation

$$b\tau^2 + (a - d)\tau = c. \tag{15}$$

This equation can also be obtained by setting the denominator of (14) equal to zero, and dividing through by $\cos^2 \theta$.

If $b \neq 0$, Equation (15) has zero, one, or two real roots according as its discriminant is negative, zero, or positive. This discriminant is

$$\Delta = (a - d)^2 + 4bc = (a + d)^2 - 4(ad - bc). \tag{16}$$

In the sectors between invariant radii, $d\theta/dr$ has constant sign; this fact facilitates the sketching of solution curves. Together with the invariant radii, the solution curves (14') form a regular curve family in the *punctured plane*, consisting of the xy-plane with the origin deleted.

8 Graphical integration

The simplest way to sketch approximate solution curves of a given first-order normal DE $y' = F(x, y)$ proceeds as follows. Draw a short segment with slope $\lambda_i = F(x_i, y_i) = \tan \theta_i$ through each point (x_i, y_i) of a set of sample points sprinkled fairly densely over the domain of interest. Then draw smooth curves so as to have at every point a slope y' approximately equal to the average of the $F(x_i, y_i)$ at nearby points, weighting the nearest points most heavily (i.e., using graphical interpolation). Methods of doing this systematically are called schemes of *graphical integration*.

The preceding construction also gives a graphical representation of the direction field associated with a given normal first-order DE. This is defined as follows.

■ DEFINITION. *A direction field in a region D of the plane is a function which assigns to every point (x, y) in D a direction. Two directions are considered the same if they differ by an integral multiple of $180°$ or π radians.*

Direction fields are defined by many DE's that are not normal. Thus, for the DE $M(x, y) + N(x, y)y' = 0$ with continuous M and N, we can draw a short segment through points (x_i, y_i) parallel to the vector $(N(x_i, y_i), -M(x_i, y_i))$, through any point not a critical point where $M = N = 0$, and proceed as before. Such segments can be vertical, whereas this is impossible for normal DE's.

It is very easy to integrate graphically the linear fractional equation (14), because the direction is constant along each radius $y = vx$, $v = $ constant. We need only draw segments having the right direction fairly densely on radii spaced at intervals of, say, $30°$. After tracing one approximate integral curve through the direction field by the graphical method described above, we can construct others by similarity, taking advantage of the following

Similarity Property. Each solution of the linear fractional DE (12) is transformed into another solution when x and y are both multiplied by the same nonzero constant k. The reason is that both sides of the DE $y' = F(x, y)$ are "homogeneous of degree zero" in this case: they are unchanged by the substitution $(x, y) \to (kx, ky)$. In polar coordinates, if $r = f(\theta)$ is a solution of (14), then so is $r = kf(\theta)$. Since the transformation $(x, y) \to (kx, ky)$ is a similarity transformation of the xy-plane for any fixed k, it follows that the solution curves in the sector between any two adjacent invariant lines are all *geometrically similar* (and similarly placed). This fact is apparent in the drawings of Figure 1.3.

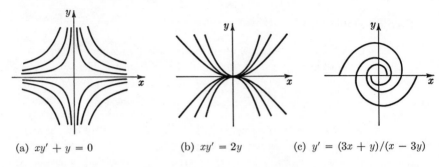

(a) $xy' + y = 0$ (b) $xy' = 2y$ (c) $y' = (3x + y)/(x - 3y)$

FIGURE 1.3   Integral curves

EXERCISES C

1. Sketch the integral curves of the DE's in Exercises B4–B7 in the neighborhood of the origin of coordinates.

2. Represent graphically the direction fields of the following linear fractional DE's, and sketch typical solution curves:

(a) $y' = -x/2y$,   (b) $y' = 1 + y/x$,   (c) $y' = (2x + y)/(2x - y)$.

3. (a) Show that the inhomogeneous linear fractional DE

$$(cx + dy + e)dx - (ax + by + f)dy = 0, \quad ad \neq bc$$

can be reduced to the form (12) by a translation of coordinates.

  (b) Using this idea, integrate $(x + y + 1)dx = (2x - y - 1)dy$.

  (c) For what constants a, b, c, d, e, f, is the DE exact?

4. Express in closed form all solutions of the following DE's:

   (a) $y' = (x^2 - y^2)/(x^2 + y^2)$,   (b) $y' = \sin(y/x)$.

5. Show that the solutions of any homogeneous DE $y' = g(y/x)$ have the Similarity Property described in §8.

6. Show that the solution curves of $y' = G(x, y)$ cut those of $y' = F(x, y)$ at a constant angle β if and only if $G = (\tau + F)/(1 - \tau F)$, where $\tau = \tan \beta$.

7. Let A, B, C be constants, and K a parameter. Show that the coaxial conics $Ax^2 + 2Bxy + Cy^2 = K$, satisfy the DE $y' = -(Ax + By)/(Bx + Cy)$.

8. (a) Show that the differential $(ax + by)dy - (cx + dy)dx$ is exact if and only if $a + d = 0$, and that in this case the integral curves form a family of coaxial conics.

  (b) Using Exercises 6 and 7, show that if $\tan \beta = (a + d)/(c - b)$, the curves cutting the solution curves of the linear fractional DE $y' = (cx + dy)/(ax + by)$ at an angle β form a family of coaxial conics.

9. Sketch sample curves of the family of graphs of

$$y = f(x, c) = \begin{cases} -x^2 + c + 1, & c < -1, \\ cx^2, & -1 \leq c \leq 1, \\ x^2 + c - 1, & 1 < c. \end{cases}$$

Do the above curves form a normal curve family in the punctured plane, with the origin deleted? Do they form a regular curve family in this domain?

10. (a) Show that the functions in Exercise 9 satisfy the DE

$$y' = F(x, y) = \begin{cases} -2x & \text{if } y < -x^2, \\ 2y/x & \text{if } -x^2 \leq y \leq x^2, \\ 2x & \text{if } y > x^2. \end{cases} \quad (*)$$

  (b) Is F continuous? Justify your answer.

(c) Find a two-parameter family of curves satisfying the above. [HINT: See the discussion of Example 4 below.]

11. For the linear fractional DE (12), show that

$$y'' = (ad - bc)[cx^2 - (a - d)xy - by^2]/(ax + by)^3.$$

Discuss the domains of convexity and concavity of solutions.

12. Find an integrating factor for $y' + (2y/x) = a$, and integrate the DE by quadratures.

13. Find all integral curves of $y' = -(2x + y - 1)/(x + 2y - 1)$, and make a sketch of the regular family of these curves. [HINT: See Exercise 3c.]

*9 Equations of higher degree

A first-order polynomial DE of the form

$$\phi(x, y, y') = y'^n + \sum_{k=1}^{n} M_k(x, y)y'^{n-k} = 0 \tag{17}$$

is said to be of degree n when it is of degree n considered as a polynomial in y'. For given x, y, it is satisfied by at most n values of y'. This observation leads one to define the *degree* of a first-order DE $\phi(x, y, y') = 0$ generally, as the largest number of values of y' compatible with given values of x and y.

The reduction of a first-order DE of degree $n > 1$ to normal form may be accomplished as follows.

Let ϕ be of class $\mathscr{C}^1$ in a domain D of three-dimensional x,y,y'-space. The locus $\partial\phi/\partial y' = 0$ is then a closed set, called the *singular locus*. Thus, for the DE $M(x, y) + N(x, y)y' = 0$, the singular locus is the set $N = 0$ where the normal form is undefined. In each subdomain where $\partial\phi/\partial y' \neq 0$, the DE $\phi(x, y, y') = 0$ is equivalent to a set of normal DE's by the implicit function theorem. We illustrate this situation by an example.

EXAMPLE 4. Consider Euler's quadratic DE

$$(1 - x^2)y'^2 = (1 - y^2), \tag{18}$$

for which ϕ is $(1 - x^2)y'^2 - (1 - y^2)$ in (1). In the region of the xy-plane where $(1 - x^2)$ and $(1 - y^2)$ have opposite signs, (1.18) has no real solution because y'^2 is never negative. In the region where they have the same sign, solving (1.18) for y' gives the two alternative normal forms

$$y' = \sqrt{(1 - y^2)/(1 - x^2)} = F_1(x, y)$$

and

$$y' = -\sqrt{(1 - y^2)/(1 - x^2)} = F_2(x, y). \tag{18'}$$

---

* Sections marked with an asterisk (starred section) can be skipped without loss of continuity.

The solutions of these DE's can be found by the method of separation of variables, as follows.

In the square $|x| < 1$, $|y| < 1$, Equations (18′) are equivalent to

$$dy/\sqrt{1 - y^2} = \pm dx/\sqrt{1 - x^2}.$$

In the domain $|x| > 1$, $|x| > 1$, they are equivalent to

$$dy/\sqrt{y^2 - 1} = \pm dx/\sqrt{x^2 - 1}.$$

Taking the indefinite integrals of all terms, we get four families of solutions:

$$\sin^{-1}y \pm \sin^{-1}x = C \quad \text{on} \quad |x| < 1, |y| < 1, \tag{18a}$$

and

$$\cosh^{-1}y \pm \cosh^{-1}x = C \quad \text{on} \quad |x| > 1, |y| > 1, \tag{18b}$$

where C is an arbitrary constant or *parameter*.

Actually, the solution curves are conics. To show this, set $x = \sin u$ and $y = \sin v$. Then, on the solution curves $v \pm u = C$ of (18a), we have

$$\sqrt{(1 - x^2)(1 - y^2)} \mp xy = \cos(v \pm u)) = C.$$

Transposing the term in xy, squaring both sides of the resulting equation, and cancelling x^2y^2, we obtain $x^2 \pm 2Cxy + y^2 = 1 - C^2$ thus a conic with 45° axes. Similar calculations can be made from (18b); typical solution curves are sketched in Figure 1.4. Two such curves pass through each point (x_0, y_0) in the regions where real solutions

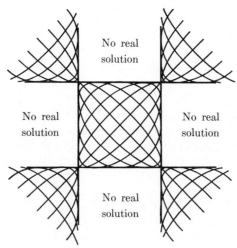

FIGURE 1.4   Integral curves of Euler's quadratic DE.

exist. The number of curves through each point is equal to the degree of the DE (18), regarded as a polynomial equation expressing the unknown y' implicitly as a function of x and y.

Note that the function $y \equiv 1$, which clearly satisfies the DE (18), is a solution for which $dy/\sqrt{y^2 - 1}$ and $dy/\sqrt{1 - y^2}$ are undefined. Finally, the solutions are exhibited in (18a) and (18b) not as explicit functions $y = f(x)$ of the independent variable x, but only as implicit functions (integrals) $u(x, y) = $ constant.

Clairaut equation. Another equation of higher degree is the Clairaut DE

$$y = xy' + h(y'),$$

where h is an arbitrary function. Solutions can be obtained by inspection, as a one-parameter family,

$$y = Cx + h(C),$$

of nonparallel straight lines.

For example, if $h(y') = -y'^2/2$, the straight lines so obtained are the tangents to the parabola $y = x^2/2$. This parabola, which is an *envelope* of the straight line solutions, is also a solution since it has the "right" slope at every point. One can also verify analytically that $y = x^2/2$ satisfies the DE $y = xy' - y'^2/2$. The parabola is called a *singular* solution of the Clairaut DE; it is the singular locus where $\partial\phi/\partial y' = 0$ in the given DE.

EXERCISES D

1. Show that the confocal ellipses $x^2/\lambda + y^2/(1 + \lambda) = 1, 0 < \lambda < +\infty$, form a regular curve family in the domain exterior to the interval $-1 \leqq y \leqq 1$ of the y-axis.

2. Show that the ellipses of Exercise 1 satisfy the DE

$$y'^2 + [(x^2 - y^2 + 1)/xy]y' = 1. \tag{*}$$

3. Show that the hyperbolas $x^2/\lambda + y^2/(1 + \lambda) = 1, -1 < \lambda < 0$, form a family of curves which satisfy (*) and are orthogonal to the ellipses of Exercise 1. Describe the domain in which the curve family is regular.

4. Show that the tangents to the parabola $y = x^2$ are the lines $y = \lambda(x - \lambda/2)$. In which domains of the plane, if any, do these lines form a regular curve family?

5. Show that the family of straight lines in Exercise 4 satisfies the Clairaut DE $y = xy' - y'^2/4$. Find a two-parameter family of solutions of this DE. (See the discussion of Example 4 above.)

6. Show that the integral curves of Example 3 are ellipses and hyperbolas with diagonal axes, tangent to four straight lines (the "singular solutions" $y = \pm 1$, $x = \pm 1$), as in Figure 1.4.

7. Integrate and find the singular solutions of the DE

$$y'^2 - 2x\sqrt{y}\,y' + 4y\sqrt{y} = 0 \qquad \text{(Boole)}.$$

[HINT: Reduce to a Clairaut DE by setting $u = \sqrt{y}$.]

8*. Reduce the following DE's to normal form, specifying for each normal form a domain of regularity in (x, y, y'):

   (a) $y'^3 + 3xy' = y$,   (b) $2xy(1 + y'^2) - (xy' + y)^2 = 0$ (Abbé Moigno),
   (c) $xy^2y'^2 - y^3y' + a^2x = 0$ (Schlömilch).

10   Initial value problems

For any normal first-order differential equation $y' = F(x, y)$ and any "initial" x_0 (think of x as time), the *initial value problem* consists in finding the solution or solutions of the DE, for $x \geq x_0$, which assume a given initial value $f(x_0) = c$. In geometric language, this amounts to finding the solution curve or curves which issue from the point (x_0, c) to the right in the xy-plane.

When $F(x, y) = g(x)$ depends on x alone, the initial-value problem is solved by the Fundamental Theorem of the Calculus (§ 2). Given $x_0 = a$ and $y_0 = c$, the initial value problem for the DE $y' = g(x)$ has one and only one solution, given by the definite integral (5).

The initial value problem is said to be *well-set* in a domain D when there is one and only one solution $y = f(x, c)$ in D of the given DE for each given $(x_0, c) \in D$, and when this solution varies continuously with c. To show that the initial value problem is well-set, therefore, requires proving theorems of *existence* (there is a solution), *uniqueness* (there is only one solution), and *continuity* (the solution depends continuously on the initial value). The term *well-set* is applied to boundary value problems for DE's generally. As was pointed out by Hadamard, solutions which do not have the properties specified are useless physically because no physical measurement is exact. The concept of a well-set initial value problem gives a precise mathematical interpretation of the physical concept of *determinism* (cf. Chapter 6, § 5).

From the definition of a normal curve family (§ 3), it follows that the initial-value problem is well-set in any domain D where the solution curves constitute a normal curve family. Thus, it is well-set for the linear DE $y' + p(x)y = q(x)$ in any vertical strip $a < x < b$ where p and q are continuous. The initial value problem is also well-set for the linear fractional DE (12) in each of the half-planes $ax + by > 0$ and $ax + by < 0$.

For the solutions of a DE to form a normal curve family in a domain D, and hence for the initial value problem to be well-set there, it is sufficient that $F \in \mathscr{C}^1$ in D. But it is not sufficient that $F \in \mathscr{C}$: though the continuity of F implies the existence of at least one solution through every point (cf. Chapter 6, § 13), it does not necessarily imply uniqueness, as the following example shows.

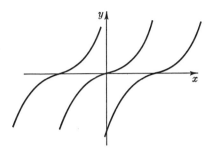

FIGURE 1.5   Solution curves of $y' = 3y^{2/3}$

EXAMPLE 5.   Consider the curve family $y = (x - C)^3$, sketched in Figure 1.5. It is regular but not normal: $\partial y/\partial C$ vanishes when $y = 0$, on the x-axis. Moreover, for fixed C, we have

$$y' = \partial y/\partial x = 3(x - C)^2 = 3y^{2/3}, \qquad (19)$$

a DE whose right side is a continuous function of position (x, y). Through every point (x_0, c) of the plane passes just one curve $y = (x - C)^3$ of the family, for which $C = x_0 - c^{1/3}$ depends continuously on (x_0, c). Hence, the initial value problem for the DE (19) always has one and only one solution of the form $y = (x - C)^3$. But there are also other solutions.

Thus, the function $y = 0$ also satisfies (19). Its graph is the envelope of the curves $y = (x - C)^3$. In addition, for any $\alpha < \beta$, the function defined by the three equations

$$y = \begin{cases} (x - \alpha)^3, & x < \alpha, \\ 0, & \alpha \leq x \leq \beta, \\ (x - \beta)^3, & x > \beta, \end{cases}$$

is a solution of (19). Hence, the first-order DE $y' = 3y^{2/3}$ has a *two-parameter* family of solutions, depending on the parameters α and β.

11   Uniqueness and continuity

Example 5 shows that mere continuity of $F(x, y)$ does not suffice to ensure the uniqueness of solutions $y = f(x)$ of $y' = F(x, y)$ with given $f(a) = c$. However, it is sufficient that $F \in \mathscr{C}^1(D)$. We shall prove this and continuity at the same time, using for much of the proof the following generalization of the standard Lipschitz condition.

■ THEOREM 4.   *A function $F(x, y)$ satisfies a one-sided Lipschitz condition in a domain D when, for some finite constant L,*

$$y_2 > y_1 \quad implies \quad F(x, y_2) - F(x, y_1) \leq L(y_2 - y_1) \qquad (20)$$

identically in D. It satisfies a Lipschitz condition† *in D, when, for some nonnegative constant L (Lipschitz constant), it satisfies the inequality*

$$|F(x, y) - F(x, z)| \leq L|y - z| \tag{20'}$$

for all point pairs (x, y) and (x, z) in D having the same x-coordinate.

The same function F may satisfy Lipschitz conditions with different Lipschitz constants, or no Lipschitz conditions at all, as the domain D under consideration varies. For example, the function $F(x, y) = 3y^{2/3}$ of the DE in Example 5 satisfies a Lipschitz condition in any strip $|y| \geq \epsilon, \epsilon > 0$, with $L = 2\epsilon^{-1/3}$. More generally, one can prove the following.

■ LEMMA 1.   *Let F be continuously differentiable in any bounded closed convex‡ domain D. Then it satisfies a Lipschitz condition there, with $L = \sup_D |\partial F/\partial y|$.*

Proof — The domain being convex, it contains the entire vertical segment joining (x, y) with (x, z). Applying the Law of the Mean to $F(x, \eta)$ on this segment, considered as a function of η, we have

$$|F(x, y) - F(x, z)| = |y - z| \, |\partial F(x, \eta)/\partial \eta|,$$

for some η between y and z. The inequality (20'), with $L = \sup_D |\partial F/\partial y|$, follows. — A similar argument shows that (20) holds with $L = \max_D \partial F/\partial y$.

The case $F(x, y) = g(x)$ of ordinary integration, or "quadrature," is easily identified as the case when $L = 0$ in (20'). A Lipschitz condition is satisfied even if $g(x)$ is discontinuous.

■ LEMMA 2.   *Let σ be a differentiable function satisfying the differential inequality*

$$\sigma'(x) \leq K\sigma(x), \qquad a \leq x \leq b, \tag{21}$$

where K is a constant. Then

$$\sigma(x) \leq \sigma(a)e^{K(x-a)} \quad for \quad a \leq x \leq b. \tag{21'}$$

Proof. — Multiply both sides of (21) by e^{-Kx} and transpose, getting

$$0 \geq e^{-Kx}[\sigma'(x) - K\sigma(x)] = \frac{d}{dx}\{\sigma(x)e^{-Kx}\}.$$

---

† R. Lipschitz, *Bull. Sci. Math.* 10 (1876), p. 149; the idea of the proof is due to Cauchy (1839). See Ince, p. 76, for a historical discussion.
‡ A set of points is called *convex* when it contains, with any two points, the line segment joining them.

The function $\sigma(x)e^{-Kx}$ thus has a nonpositive derivative and so is non-increasing for $a \leq x \leq b$. Therefore, $\sigma(x)e^{-Kx} \leq \sigma(a)e^{-Ka}$, q.e.d.

■ LEMMA 3. *The one-sided Lipschitz condition (20) implies that*

$$[g(x) - f(x)][g'(x) - f'(x)] \leq L[g(x) - f(x)]^2$$

for any two solutions $f(x)$ and $g(x)$ of $y' = F(x, y)$.

Proof — Setting $f(x) = y_1$, $g(x) = y_2$, we have

$$[g(x) - f(x)][g'(x) - f'(x)] = (y_2 - y_1)[F(x, y_2) - F(x, y_1)]$$

from the DE. If $y_2 > y_1$, then, by hypothesis (20), the right side of this equation has the upper bound $L(y_2 - y_1)^2$. Since all expressions are unaltered when y_1 and y_2 are interchanged, we see that the inequality of Lemma 3 is true in any case.

We now prove that solutions of $y' = F(x, y)$ depend continuously (and hence uniquely) on their initial values, provided that a one-sided Lipschitz condition holds.

■ THEOREM 5. *Let $f(x)$ and $g(x)$ be any two solutions of the first-order normal* DE $y' = F(x, y)$ *in a domain D where F satisfies (20). Then*

$$|f(x) - g(x)| \leq e^{L(x-a)}|f(a) - g(a)| \quad if \quad x > a. \tag{22}$$

Proof — Consider the function

$$\sigma(x) = [g(x) - f(x)]^2.$$

Computing the derivative by elementary formulas, we have

$$\sigma'(x) = 2[g(x) - f(x)] \cdot [g'(x) - f'(x)].$$

By Lemma 3, this implies that $\sigma'(x) \leq 2L\sigma(x)$; and by Lemma 2, this implies $\sigma(x) \leq e^{2L(x-a)}\sigma(a)$. Taking the square root of both sides of this inequality (which are nonnegative), we get (22), completing the proof.

As the special case $f(a) = g(a)$ of Theorem 5, we get uniqueness for the initial value problem: in any domain where F satisfies the one-sided Lipschitz condition (20), there is at most one solution of $y' = F(x, y)$ for $x \geq a$ which satisfies $f(a) = c$. However, we do not get uniqueness or continuity for *decreasing* x. We now prove that we have uniqueness and continuity in both directions when the Lipschitz condition (20') holds.

■ THEOREM 6. *If (20') holds in Theorem 5, then*

$$|f(x) - g(x)| \leq e^{L|x-a|}|f(a) - g(a)|. \tag{23}$$

In particular, the DE $y' = F(x, y)$ *has at most one solution curve passing through any point* $(a, c) \in D$.

Proof — Since (20′) implies (20), we know that the inequality (20) holds; from Theorem 5, this gives (23) for $x \geqq a$. Since (20′) also implies (20) when x goes to $-x$, we have by Theorem 5

$$|f(x) - g(x)| \leqq e^{L(a-x)} |f(a) - g(a)| = e^{L|x-a|} |f(a) - g(a)|,$$

giving (23′) also for $x < a$, and completing the proof.

EXERCISES E

1. In which domains do the following functions satisfy a Lipschitz condition?
   (a) $F(x, t) = 1 + x^2$,   (b) $F(x, t) = 1 + t^2$,
   (c) $F(x, t) = 1/(1 + x^2)$,   (d) $F(x, t) = t/(1 + x^2)$.
2. In which domains of the plane does $|xy|$ satisfy a Lipschitz condition? Find all solutions of $y' = |xy|$.
3. Same question for

$$F(x, t) = \begin{cases} 0 & \text{if } x \text{ is rational,} \\ 1 & \text{if } x \text{ is irrational.} \end{cases}$$

4. Let f and g be solutions of $y' = F(x, y)$, where F is a continuous function. Show that the functions m and M, defined as $m(x) = \min (f(x), g(x))$ and $M(x) = \max (f(x), g(x))$, satisfy the same DE. [HINT: Discuss separately the cases $f(x) = g(x)$, $f(x) < g(x)$, and $f(x) > g(x)$.]
5. Let $\sigma(t)$, positive and of class $\mathscr{C}^1$ for $a \leqq t \leqq a + \epsilon$, satisfy the differential inequality $\sigma'(t) \leqq K\sigma(t) \log \sigma(t)$. Show that $\sigma(t) \leqq \sigma(a) \exp [K(t - a)]$.
6. Let $F(x, y) = y \log (1/y)$ for $0 < y < 1$, $F(y) = 0$ for $y = 0$. Show that $y' = F(x, y)$ has at most one solution satisfying $f(0) = c$ even though F does not satisfy a Lipschitz condition.
7. (*Peano uniqueness theorem*). For each fixed x, let $F(x, y)$ be a nonincreasing function of y. Show that, if $f(x)$ and $g(x)$ are two solutions of $y' = F(x, y)$, and $b > a$, then $|f(b) - g(b)| \leqq |f(a) - g(a)|$. Infer a uniqueness theorem.
8. Discuss uniqueness and nonuniqueness for solutions of the DE $y' = -y^{1/3}$ [HINT: Use Exercise 7.]
9. (a) Prove a uniqueness theorem for $y' = xy$ on $-\infty < x, y < + \infty$.
   (b)* Prove the same result for $y' = y^{2/3} + 1$.
10. (*Generalized Lipschitz condition.*) Let $F \in \mathscr{C}$ satisfy

$$|F(x, y) - F(x, z)| \leq k(x)|y - z|,$$

identically on the strip $0 < x < a$. Show that, if the improper integral $\int_0^a k(x)\, dx$ is finite, then $y' = F(x, y)$ has at most one solution satisfying $y(0) = 0$.
11*. Let F be continuous and satisfy

$$|F(x, y) - F(x, z)| \leq K|y - z| \log(|y - z|^{-1}), \qquad \text{for } |y - z| < 1.$$

Show that the solutions of (3) are unique.

12 The comparison theorem

Since most DE's cannot be solved in terms of elementary functions, it is important to be able to compare the unknown solutions of one DE with the known solutions of another. It is also often useful to compare functions satisfying the *differential inequality*

$$f'(x) \leq F(x, f(x)) \tag{24}$$

with exact solutions of the DE (1). The following theorem gives such a comparison.

■ THEOREM 7.   *Let F satisfy a Lipschitz condition for $x \geq a$. If the function f satisfies the differential inequality (24) for $x \geq a$, and if g is a solution of $y' = F(x, y)$ satisfying the initial condition $g(a) = f(a)$, then $f(x) \leq g(x)$ for $x \geq a$.*

Proof — Suppose that $f(x_1) > g(x_1)$ for some x_1 in the given interval, and define x_0 to be the largest x in the interval $a \leq x \leq x_1$ such that $f(x) \leq g(x)$. Then $f(x_0) = g(x_0)$. Letting $\sigma(x) = f(x) - g(x)$, we have $\sigma(x) \geq 0$ for $x_0 \leq x \leq x_1$; and, also for $x_0 \leq x \leq x_1$,

$$\sigma'(x) = f'(x) - g'(x) \leq F(x, f(x)) - F(x, g(x)) \leq L(f(x) - g(x)) = L\sigma(x),$$

where L is the Lipschitz constant for the function F. That is, the function σ satisfies the hypothesis of Lemma 2 of § 11 on $x_0 \leq x \leq x_1$, with $K = L$. Hence $\sigma(x) \leq \sigma(x_0)e^{L(x-x_0)} = 0$, and so σ, being nonnegative, vanishes identically. But this contradicts the hypothesis $f(x_1) > g(x_1)$. We conclude that $f(x) \leq g(x)$ for all x in the given interval, q.e.d.

■ THEOREM 8 (Comparison Theorem).   *Let f and g be solutions of the DE's*

$$y' = F(x, y), \qquad z' = G(x, z) \tag{25}$$

respectively, where $F(x, y) \leq G(x, y)$ in the strip $a \leq x \leq b$ and F or G satisfies a Lipschitz condition. Let also $f(a) = g(a)$. Then $f(x) \leq g(x)$ for all $x \in [a, b]$.

Proof — Let G satisfy a Lipschitz condition. Since $y' = F(x, y) \leq G(x, y)$, the functions f and g satisfy the conditions of Theorem 7 with G in place of F. Therefore, the inequality $f(x) \leq g(x)$ for $x \geq a$ follows immediately.

If F satisfies a Lipschitz condition, then the functions $u = -f(x)$ and $v = -g(x)$ satisfy the DE's $u' = -F(x, -u)$ and

$$v' = -G(x, -v) \leq -F(x, -v).$$

Theorem 7, applied to the functions v, u and $H(u, v) = -F(x, -v)$ now yields the inequality $v(x) \leq u(x)$ for $x \geq a$, or $g(x) \geq f(x)$, as asserted.

The inequality $f(x) \leq g(x)$ in this Comparison Theorem can often be replaced by a strict inequality. Either f and g are identically equal for $a \leq x \leq x_1$, or else $f(x_0) < g(x_0)$ for some x_0 in the interval (a, x_1). By the Comparison Theorem, the function $\sigma_1(x) = g(x) - f(x)$ is non-negative for $a \leq x \leq x_1$, and moreover $\sigma_1(x_0) > 0$. Much as in the preceding proof,

$$\sigma_1'(x) = G(x, g(x)) - F(x, f(x)) \geq G(x, g(x)) - G(x, f(x)) \geq -L\sigma_1.$$

Hence $[e^{Lx}\sigma_1(x)]' = e^{Lx}[\sigma_1' + L\sigma_1] \geq 0$, whence $e^{Lx}\sigma_1(x)$ is a non-decreasing function on $a \leq x \leq x_1$. Consequently, we have

$$\sigma_1(x) \geq \sigma_1(x_0)e^{-L(x-x_0)} > 0,$$

which gives a strict inequality. This proves

■ COROLLARY 1.   *In Theorem 7, for any $x_1 > a$, either $f(x_1) < g(x_1)$, or $f(x) \equiv g(x)$ for $a \leq x \leq x_1$.*

Theorem 8 can also be sharpened in another way, as follows.

■ COROLLARY 2.   *In Theorem 8, assume that F, as well as G, satisfies a Lipschitz condition and, instead of $f(a) = g(a)$, that $f(a) < g(a)$. Then $f(x) < g(x)$ for $x > a$.*

Proof — The proof will be by contradiction. If we had $f(x) \geq g(x)$ for some $x > a$, there would be a first $x = x_1 > a$ where $f(x) \geq g(x)$. The two functions $y = \phi(x) = f(-x)$ and $z = \psi(x) = g(-x)$ satisfy the DE's $y' = -F(-x, y)$ and $z' = -G(-x, z)$ as well as the respective initial conditions $\phi(-x_1) = \psi(-x_1)$. Since $-F(-x, y) \geq -G(-x, y)$, we can apply Theorem 8 in the interval $[-x_1, -a]$, knowing that the function $-F(-x, y)$ satisfies a Lipschitz condition. We conclude that $\phi(-a) \geq \psi(-a)$, that is, that $f(a) \geq g(a)$, a contradiction.

EXERCISES F

1. Let $f(u)$ be continuous and $a + bf(u) \neq 0$ for $p \leq u \leq q$. Show that the DE $y' = f(ax + by + c)$ (a, b, c are constants) has a solution passing through every point of the strip $p < ax + by + c < q$.
2. Find all solutions of the DE $y' = |x^3y^3|$.
3. Show that, if M and N are homogeneous functions of the same degree, then (7) has the integrating factor $(xM + yN)^{-1}$ in any simply connected domain where $xM + yN$ does not vanish.
4. Show that (7) has the integrating factor $(M^2 + N^2)^{-1}$ in any simply connected domain if $M_x = N_y$, $M_y = -N_x$.
5. Let $g(x)$ be continuous for $0 \leq x < \infty$, $\lim_{x \to \infty} g(x) = b$ and $a > 0$. Show that, for every solution $y = f(x)$ of $y' + ay = g(x)$, we have $\lim_{x \to \infty} f(x) = b/a$.

6. Show that if $a < 0$ in Exercise 5, then there exists one and only one solution of the DE such that $\lim_{x \to \infty} f(x) = b/a$.

7*. (*Osgood's Uniqueness Theorem.*) Suppose that $\phi(u)$ is a continuous increasing function defined and positive for $u > 0$, such that $\int_\epsilon^1 du/\phi(u) \to \infty$ as $\epsilon \to 0$. If $|F(x, y) - F(x, z)| < \phi(|y - z|)$, then the solutions of the DE (3) are unique. [HINT: Use Exercise E4].

8. Let F, G, f, g be as in Theorem 8, and $F(x, y) < G(x, y)$. Show that $f(x) < g(x)$ for $x > a$, without assuming that F or G satisfies a Lipschitz condition.

9*. Let $f'(x) < F(x, f(x))$ for $x \geqq a$, and let F be continuous. Show that $f(x) < g(x)$ when g is any solution of (3) such that $f(a) < g(a)$.

In Exercises 10–11, $G(x, u)$ is a nonnegative continuous function, nondecreasing in u for fixed x, such that the DE $u' = G(x, u)$ has a *unique* solution $g(x)$ satisfying $g(0) = 0$.

10*. Let $h \in \mathscr{C}^1$ satisfy $h(0) \leqq 0$ and the differential *inequality* $h'(x) \leqq G(x, h(x))$. Show that $h(x) \leqq g(x)$ for $x > 0$.

11*. Let $G(x, 0) = 0$. Show that if F satisfies Kamke's inequality

$$2|y - z| \cdot |F(x, y) - F(x, z)| \leqq G(x, |y - z|^2),$$

then $y' = F(x, y)$ has at most one solution satisfying $y(0) = c$.

12*. Infer Osgood's Uniqueness Theorem (Exercise 7) from Exercises 10 and 11.

2 | *Second-Order Linear Equations*

I Basic definitions

The most intensively studied class of ordinary differential equations is that of second-order linear DE's, of the form

$$p_0(x)\frac{d^2u}{dx^2} + p_1(x)\frac{du}{dx} + p_2(x)u = p_3(x). \tag{1}$$

The coefficient-functions $p_i(x)$ [$i = 0, 1, 2, 3$] are assumed continuous and real-valued on an interval I of the real axis, which may be finite or infinite. The interval I may include one or both of its endpoints, or neither of them. The central problem is to find and describe the unknown functions $u = f(x)$ on I satisfying this equation, the *solutions* of the DE. The present chapter will be devoted to second-order linear DE's and the behavior of their solutions.

Dividing through (1) by the leading coefficient $p_0(x)$, one obtains the *normal form*

$$d^2u/dx^2 + p(x)\,du/dx + q(x)u = r(x), \tag{1'}$$

$$p = p_1/p_0, \quad q = p_2/p_0, \quad r = p_3/p_0.$$

This DE is equivalent to (1) so long as $p_0(x) \neq 0$; if $p_0(x_0) = 0$ at some point $x = x_0$, then the functions p and q are not defined at the point x_0. One therefore says that the DE (1) has a *singular point*, or *singularity*, at the point x_0, when $p_0(x_0) = 0$.

There is a basic difference between linear and nonlinear DE's. The singular points of nonlinear DE's can be arbitrary curves in the xy-plane. For example, the DE $(x - y)y' = x + y$ is singular on the line $x = y$, whereas the singular points of linear DE's correspond to fixed values of x, and hence to vertical lines in the xy-plane. This justifies the following definition.

■ DEFINITION.   *The normal* DE (1′) *is* regular *on an interval I of the x-axis when p(x), q(x), and r(x) are continuous on I. A* solution *of* (1) *is a twice differentiable function u = f(x) which satisfies* (1) *at every point of I.*

It is understood that, when I contains an endpoint, the solution need only have a one-sided derivative there.

In the rest of this chapter, we will be concerned only with second-order linear DE's which are regular in specified intervals. The study of singular points of DE's will be taken up in Chapter 9.

Linear operators. The operation of transforming a given function f into a function g by the rule

$$g = p_0 f'' + p_1 f' + p_2 f$$

(for continuous p_i) is a transformation from one family of functions (in our case, the family $\mathscr{C}^2(I)$ of continuously twice-differentiable functions on a given interval I) to another family of functions (in our case, $\mathscr{C}(I)$). Such a functional transformation is called an *operator*, and is written in operator notation

$$L[f] = p_0 f'' + p_1 f' + p_2 f.$$

In our case, the operator L is *linear*; that is, it satisfies

$$L[cf + dg] = cL[f] + dL[g]$$

for any constants c and d.

As a special case (setting $c = 1$, $d = -1$), if u and v are any two solutions of the inhomogeneous linear DE (1), then their difference $u - v$ satisfies

$$L[u - v] = L[u] - L[v] = p_3(x) - p_3(x) = 0.$$

That is, their difference is a solution of the *homogeneous* second-order linear DE

$$p_0(x) \frac{d^2 u}{dx^2} + p_1(x) \frac{du}{dx} + p_2(x)u = 0. \tag{2}$$

The preceding simple observations, whose proofs are immediate, have the following result as an immediate consequence.

■ LEMMA 1.   *If the function u(x) is any particular solution of the inhomogeneous* DE (1), *then the general solution of* (1) *is obtained by adding to u(x) the general solution of the corresponding homogeneous linear* DE (2).

More generally, we have the following.

■ LEMMA 2.   *If $u(x)$ is a solution of $L[u] = r(x)$, if $v(x)$ is a solution of $L[u] = s(x)$, and if c, d are constants, then $w = cu(x) + dv(x)$ is a solution of the* DE $L[u] = cr(x) + ds(x)$.

The proof is trivial, but the result describes the fundamental property of linear operators.

The homogeneous DE (2), obtained by dropping from the given inhomogeneous DE the *forcing term* $p_3(x)$, is called the *reduced* equation of (1).

A fundamental property of the homogeneous linear DE (2) is the following *Superposition Principle*. Given two solutions $f_1(x)$ and $f_2(x)$ of (2), and any two constants c_1 and c_2, the function

$$f(x) = c_1 f_1(x) + c_2 f_2(x) \tag{3}$$

is also a solution of (2). This property is characteristic of homogeneous linear equations; the function f is called a *linear combination* of the functions f_1 and f_2 with constant coefficients c_1 and c_2.

Notice that DE (2) always has the trivial solution $u \equiv 0$. This is true of all homogeneous linear DE's; solutions not vanishing identically are called *nontrivial*.

EXAMPLE 1.   The trigonometric DE $u'' + k^2 u = 0$ has the general solution

$$A \cos k(x - x_1) = c_1 \cos kx + c_2 \sin kx, \tag{4}$$

where $A = (c_1{}^2 + c_2{}^2)^{1/2}$ is the *amplitude* and x_1 is the *phase* constant.

EXAMPLE 2.   The *Bessel* DE of order† n is the DE

$$u'' + \frac{1}{x} u' + \left(1 - \frac{n^2}{x^2}\right) u = 0. \tag{5}$$

This second-order linear DE has its only singular point at $x = 0$; its solutions will be described in Chapter 3, §4.

The trigonometric and Bessel DE's are commonly written in normal form; the following DE is not.

EXAMPLE 3.   The *Legendre* DE is

$$\frac{d}{dx}\left[(1 - x^2)\frac{du}{dx}\right] + n(n + 1)u = 0; \tag{6}$$

its solutions will be described (as power series) in Chapter 3, § 2. This DE has singular points at $x = \pm 1$.

---

† Note that the Bessel DE of "order" n is still a "second-order" DE.

2 Initial value problems

In differential equations arising from physical problems, one is often interested in particular solutions satisfying additional "boundary conditions." Thus one may know the state of a given physical system at some initial time, $t = a$, and wish to predict its state at later times. Consider, for instance, the following mass-spring system.

EXAMPLE 4.   Let $u(t)$ be the vertical displacement of a mass m, at time t, from its equilibrium position when suspended on a spring. Then the linear DE with constant coefficients,

$$m \frac{d^2u}{dt^2} = -mp \frac{du}{dt} - mqu, \tag{7}$$

expresses Newton's Third Law of Motion for an elastic restoring force mqu proportional to the displacement from the equilibrium position $u = 0$, and an idealized viscous damping force $mp\, du/dt$.

Physical intuition suggests that it should be possible to predict the motion of the mass at all future times from the law (7), whenever the initial position and velocity are known. These initial conditions amount to prescribing $f(a) = u_0$ and $f'(a) = u_0'$. One then refers to the *initial conditions* $f(a) = u_0$, $f'(a) = u_0'$; the problem of integrating DE's like (1), subject to given initial conditions, is called the *initial value problem*.

Thus, physical intuition leads one to conjecture the truth of *existence* and *uniqueness* theorems for the initial value problem for (1), at least in the special case (7). It can be proved that this intuition is justified as regards the initial value problem for regular linear DE's, in intervals free from singular points. However, as will be shown in § 9 below, it is not true for "two-endpoint problems," in which $f(a)$ and $f(b)$ are assumed given at the two endpoints of a given interval $[a, b]$.

The *uniqueness* of solutions of initial-value problems for second-order linear DE's will be proved now; *existence* will be proved in Chapter 3 (for analytic coefficient-functions) and in Chapter 6 (for continuous coefficient-functions), where the continuous dependence of solutions on their initial values will also be proved. In short, the initial-value problem for regular second-order linear DE's is a *well-set* problem.

■ THEOREM 1 (Uniqueness Theorem).   *If p and q are continuous, then at most one solution of (1') can satisfy given initial conditions $f(a) = c_0$ and $f'(a) = c_1$.*

Proof — Let v and w be any two solutions; their difference $u = v - w$ satisfies (1') by Lemma 1, with $r(x) = 0$. It also satisfies the initial conditions $u = u' = 0$ when $x = a$. Now consider the nonnegative function $\sigma(x) = u^2 + u'^2$. By definition, $\sigma(a) = 0$. Differentiating, we have, since $r(x) = 0$,

$$\sigma'(x) = 2u'(u + u'') = 2u'[u - p(x)u' - q(x)u]$$
$$= -2p(x)u'^2 + 2(1 - q(x))uu'.$$

Since $(u \pm u')^2 \geqq 0$, it follows that $|2uu'| \leqq u^2 + u'^2$. Hence

$$2(1 - q(x))uu' \leqq (1 + |q(x)|)(u^2 + u'^2),$$

and

$$\sigma'(x) \leqq [1 + |q(x)|]u^2 + [1 + |q(x)| + |2p(x)|]u'^2.$$

Therefore, if $K = 1 + \max(|q(x)| + 2|p(x)|)$, the maximum being taken over any finite closed interval $[a, b]$, we obtain

$$\sigma'(x) \leqq K\sigma(x), \qquad K < +\infty.$$

By Lemma 2 of Chapter 1, § 11, it follows that $\sigma(x) = 0$ for all $x \in [a, b]$. Hence $u(x) \equiv 0$ and $v(x) \equiv w(x)$ on the interval, as claimed.

The Uniqueness Theorem just proved implies an important extension of the Superposition Principle stated in § 1.

■ **THEOREM 2.** *Let f and g be two solutions of the homogeneous second-order linear DE*

$$u'' + p(x)u' + q(x)u = 0, \qquad p, q \in \mathscr{C}. \tag{8}$$

For some $x = x_0$, let $(f(x_0), f'(x_0))$ and $(g(x_0), g'(x_0))$ be linearly independent vectors. Then every solution of this DE is equal to some linear combination $h(x) = cf(x) + dg(x)$ of f and g with constant coefficients c, d.

In other words, the *general solution* of the given homogeneous DE (8) is $cf(x) + dg(x)$, where c and d are arbitrary constants.

Proof — By the Superposition Principle, any such $h(x)$ satisfies (8). Conversely, suppose the function $h(x)$ satisfies the given DE (8). Then, at the given point x_0, constants c and d can be found such that

$$cf(x_0) + dg(x_0) = h(x_0), \qquad cf'(x_0) + dg'(x_0) = h'(x_0).$$

In fact, the constants c and d are given by Cramer's Rule, as

$$c = (h_0 g_0' - g_0 h_0')/(f_0 g_0' - g_0 f_0'),$$
$$d = (f_0 h_0' - h_0 f_0')/(f_0 g_0' - g_0 f_0'),$$

where we have used the abbreviations $f_0 = f(x_0)$, $f_0' = f'(x_0)$, and so on. For this choice of c and d, the function

$$u(x) = h(x) - cf(x) - dg(x)$$

satisfies the given homogeneous DE by the Superposition Principle and the initial conditions $u(x_0) = u'(x_0) = 0$. Hence, by the Uniqueness Theorem, $u(x)$ is the trivial solution, $u(x) \equiv 0$, of the given homogeneous DE. Hence $h = cf + dg$.

Two solutions, f and g, of a homogeneous linear second-order DE (8) with the property that every other solution can be expressed as a linear combination of them are said to be a *basis of solutions* of the DE.

3   The Wronskian

The question of whether two solutions of a homogeneous linear DE form a basis of solutions is easily settled by examining their Wronskian, a concept which we now define.

■ DEFINITION.   *The* Wronskian *of any two differentiable functions $f(x)$ and $g(x)$ is*

$$W(f, g; x) = f(x)g'(x) - g(x)f'(x) = \begin{vmatrix} f(x) & f'(x) \\ g(x) & g'(x) \end{vmatrix}. \qquad (9)$$

■ THEOREM 3.   *The Wronskian* (9) *of any two solutions of* (8) *satisfies the identity*

$$W(f, g; x) = W(f, g; a)e^{-\int_a^x p(t)dt}. \qquad (10)$$

Proof — Differentiating (9), then writing $W(f, g; x) = W(x)$ for short, a direct computation gives $W' = fg'' - gf''$. Substituting for g'' and f'' from (8) and cancelling, we have the linear homogeneous first-order DE

$$W'(x) + p(x)W(x) = 0. \qquad (11)$$

Equation (10) follows from the first-order homogeneous linear DE (11) by Theorem 3 of Chapter 1, § 5.

■ COROLLARY.   *The Wronskian of any two solutions of the homogeneous linear DE* (8) *is identically positive, identically negative, or identically zero.*

We now relate the Wronskian of two functions to the concept of linear independence. In general, a collection of functions $f_1, f_2, \ldots, f_n$ is called *linearly independent* on the interval $a \leq x \leq b$ when no linear combination $c_1 f_1(x) + c_2 f_2(x) + \cdots + c_n f_n(x)$ of the functions gives the identically zero function for $a \leq x \leq b$ except the trivial linear combination where all coefficients vanish. Functions that are not linearly independent are called linearly dependent. If f and g are any two linearly dependent functions, then $cf + dg = 0$ for suitable constants c and d, not both zero. Hence $g = -(c/d)f$ or $f = -(d/c)g$: the functions f and g are proportional.

■ **LEMMA.** *If f and g are linearly dependent differentiable functions, then their Wronskian vanishes identically.*

Proof — Suppose that f and g are linearly dependent. Then there are two constants c and d, not both zero, which satisfy the *two* linear equations

$$cf(x) + dg(x) = 0, \qquad cf'(x) + dg'(x) = 0,$$

identically on the interval of interest. Therefore, the determinant of the two equations, which is the Wronskian $W(f, g; x)$, vanishes identically.

The interesting fact is that when f and g are both solutions of a second-order linear DE, the *converse* of this lemma is also true.

■ **THEOREM 4.** *If f and g are two linearly independent solutions of the second-order linear* DE (8), *then their Wronskian never vanishes.*

Proof — Suppose that the Wronskian $W(f, g; x)$ vanished at some point x_1. Then the vectors $(f(x_1), f'(x_1))$ and $(g(x_1), g'(x_1))$ would be linearly dependent and, therefore, proportional: $g(x_1) = kf(x_1)$ and $g'(x_1) = kf'(x_1)$ for some constant k. Consider now the function $h(x) = g(x) - kf(x)$. This function is a solution of the DE (8), since it is a linear combination of solutions. It also satisfies the initial conditions $h(x_1) = h'(x_1) = 0$. By the Uniqueness Theorem, this function must vanish identically. Therefore $g(x) = kf(x)$ for all x, contradicting the hypothesis of linear independence of f and g.

[CAUTION. The functions x^3 and $|x|^3$ are linearly independent on $-1 < x < 1$, yet their Wronskian vanishes identically. Hence, it is not true for functions in general that the vanishing of the Wronskian implies linear dependence. It is true for analytic functions, however.]

If *one* solution $f(x)$ of the homogeneous linear DE (8) is known, the Wronskian can be used to construct a second, linearly independent solution, as follows. By Theorem 3, this unknown solution satisfies the first-order DE

$$f(x)g'(x) - f'(x)g(x) = W(x) = W(a)e^{-\int_a^x p(t)\,dt}. \tag{12}$$

This *first-order* linear DE in $g(x)$ can be solved by using the integrating factor $1/f^2(x)$, as in Chapter 1, Theorem 3, in any interval where f is nonvanishing. The general solution (in terms of quadratures) is

$$g(x) = f(x)\left\{ C + \int_a^x [W(a)e^{-\int_a^s p(t)\,dt}/f^2(s)]\,ds \right\}, \tag{13}$$

where a is any point in the interval of x considered and C is an arbitrary constant of integration (say $C = 0$).

In particular, let f be any nontrivial solution of $u'' + q(x)u = 0$. Then a second, linearly independent solution is given in any interval where f is nonvanishing by the formula

$$g(x) = f(x) \int \frac{dx}{f^2(x)} \tag{13'}$$

for any indefinite integral of $1/f^2(x)$.

Riccati equation. The homogeneous linear second-order DE (8) can also be reduced to a first-order, *nonlinear* DE by another simple algebraic substitution. Namely, the ratio $v = u'/u$ of the first derivative of any solution of the linear DE (8) to the solution, satisfies the quadratic first-order DE

$$v' + v^2 + p(x)v + q(x) = 0. \tag{14}$$

This is called the Riccati equation associated with (8); its solutions form a one-parameter family. Conversely, if $v(x)$ is any solution of the Riccati equation (14) and if $u' = v(x)u$, then u satisfies (8). Hence, every solution $u(x)$ of (8) can be written, in any interval where u does not vanish, in the form

$$u(x) = C \exp \int v(x) \, dx,$$

where $v(x)$ is some solution of the associated Riccati equation (14).

The Riccati substitution $v = u'/u$ thus reduces the problem of solving (8) to the integration of a first-order quadratic DE and a quadrature. For instance the Riccati equation associated with the trigonometric equation $u'' + k^2u = 0$ is $v' + v^2 + k^2 = 0$, whose general solution is $v = k \tan k(x_1 - x)$.

EXERCISES A

1. Show that all solutions of (8) have continuous second-order derivatives. Show that this is not true for (1).
2. Find a formula expressing the fourth derivative u^{iv} of any solution u of (8) in terms of u, u', and the derivatives of p and q. What differentiability conditions must be assumed on the coefficients of (8) to justify this formula?

For the solution pairs of the DE's specified in Exercises 3–5 to follow, (a) calculate the Wronskian, and (b) solve the initial-value problem for the DE specified with each of the initial conditions $u(0) = 2$, $u'(0) = 1$, and with $u(0) = 1$, $u'(0) = -1$ (or explain why there is no solution).
3. $f(x) = \cos x$, $g(x) = \sin x$ (solutions of $u'' + u = 0$).
4. $f(x) = e^{-x}$, $g(x) = e^{-3x}$ (solutions of $u'' + 4u' + 3u = 0$).

5. $f(x) = x$, $g(x) = e^x$ (solutions of $u'' + \dfrac{x}{1-x} u' - \dfrac{1}{1-x} u = 0$.)

6. Let $f(x)$, $g(x)$, and $h(x)$ be any three solutions of (8). Show that

$$\begin{vmatrix} f & f' & f'' \\ g & g' & g'' \\ h & h' & h'' \end{vmatrix} \equiv 0.$$

7. What is wrong with the following "proof" of Theorem 3: "Let $w(x) = \log W(x)$; then $w'(x) = -p(x)$. Hence $w(x) = w(a) - \int_a^x p(x)\, dx$, from which (10) follows."

8. Show that, in the linear homogeneous DE (8), the coefficient functions $p(x)$ and $q(x)$ are determined by any basis of solutions through the formulas

$$p = -\frac{fg'' - gf''}{W(f,g)}, \qquad q = \frac{f'g'' - g'f''}{W(f,g)}.$$

9. Construct second-order linear homogeneous DE's having the following bases of solutions; you may assume the result of Exercise 8:
    (a) $x, \sin x$,   (b) x^m, x^n,   (c) $\sinh x, \sin x$,   (d) $\tan x, \cot x$.
In each case determine the singular points and possible domains of definition of the DE in normal form.

10. (a) Show that if $p, q \in \mathscr{C}^n$, then every solution of (8) is of class $\mathscr{C}^{n+2}$.
    (b) Show that if every solution of (8) is of class $\mathscr{C}^{n+2}$, then $p \in \mathscr{C}^n$ and $q \in \mathscr{C}^n$.

11. The *generalized Riccati* DE is $y' + P(x)y + Q(x)y^2 = R(x)$.
    (a) Show that the substitution $y = u'/Qu$ transforms this DE into

$$u'' + [P - (Q'/Q)]u' - QRu = 0.$$

    (b) Show that the substitution $y = Ru/u'$ transforms this DE into

$$u'' - [P + (R'/R)]u' - QRu = 0.$$

12. (a) Show that the substitution $y = z/a(x)$ transforms the DE

$$y' + a(x)y^2 + b(x)y + c(x) = 0$$

into the Riccati DE (14), with $p(x) = b - a'/a$ and $q(x) = a(x)c(x)$.
    (b) Show that, if y is a solution of $y' + a(x)y^2 + b(x)y = c(x)$, then $z = 1/y$ is a solution of $z' + c(x)z^2 - b(x)z = a(x)$.

13. Let $f(x)$, $g(x)$, $h(x)$ be three solutions of the linear third-order DE

$$y''' + p_1(x)y'' + p_2(x)y' + p_3(x)y = 0.$$

Derive a first-order DE satisfied by the determinant

$$w(x) = \begin{vmatrix} f & f' & f'' \\ g & g' & g'' \\ h & h' & h'' \end{vmatrix}.$$

14*. Let $y'' + q(x)y = 0$, where $q(x)$ is "piecewise continuous" (i.e., continuous and bounded except for isolated discontinuities). Define a "solution" of the above DE as a function $y = f(x) \in \mathscr{C}^1$ which satisfies the DE at all points where $q(x)$ is continuous.

(a) Describe explicitly a basis of solutions for the DE $y'' + q(x)y = 0$, where

$$q(x) = \begin{cases} +1 & \text{when} \quad x > 0 \\ -1 & \text{when} \quad x < 0. \end{cases}$$

(N.B. The preceding function $q(x)$ is commonly denoted sgn x.)

(b) Prove an existence and uniqueness theorem for the initial-value problem, and discuss the associated Wronskian.

15*. In Exercise 14, show that the solution has second left- and right-derivatives at every point of discontinuity.

4   Separation and comparison theorems

The Wronskian can also be used to derive some properties of the graphs of solutions of the DE (8). The following result, the celebrated Sturm Separation Theorem, describes the relative position of the zeros of solutions. (A *zero* of a function is a point where its graph crosses the x-axis.)

■ THEOREM 5.   *If $f(x)$ and $g(x)$ are linearly independent solutions of the DE (8), then $f(x)$ must vanish at one point between any two successive zeros of $g(x)$. In other words, the zeros of $f(x)$ and $g(x)$ occur alternately.*

Proof — If $g(x)$ vanishes at $x = x_i$, then the Wronskian

$$W(f, g; x_i) = f(x_i)g'(x_i) \neq 0,$$

since f and g are linearly independent; hence $f(x_i) \neq 0$ and $g'(x_i) \neq 0$ if $g(x_i) = 0$. If x_1 and x_2 are two successive zeros of $g(x)$, then $g'(x_1)$, $g'(x_2)$, $f(x_1)$, and $f(x_2)$ are all nonzero; moreover, the nonzero numbers $g'(x_1)$ and $g'(x_2)$ cannot have the same sign, because if the function is increasing at $x = x_1$, then it must be decreasing at $x = x_2$, and vice-versa. Since $W(f, g; x)$ has constant sign by the Corollary of Theorem 3, it follows that $f(x_1)$ and $f(x_2)$ must also have opposite signs. Therefore $f(x)$ must vanish somewhere between x_1 and x_2.

For instance, applied to the trigonometric DE $u'' + k^2u = 0$, the Sturm Separation Theorem shows that the zeros of sin kx and cos kx must alternate, simply because these functions are two linearly independent solutions of the same linear homogeneous DE.

A slight refinement of the same reasoning can be used to prove an even more useful Comparison Theorem, also due to Sturm.

■ THEOREM 6.   *Let $f(x)$ and $g(x)$ be nontrivial solutions of the DE's $u'' + p(x)u = 0$ and $v'' + q(x)v = 0$, respectively, where $p(x) \geqq q(x)$. Then $f(x)$ vanishes at least once between any two zeros of $g(x)$, unless $p(x) \equiv q(x)$ and f is a constant multiple of g.*

Proof — Let x_1 and x_2 be two successive zeros of $g(x)$, so that $g(x_1) = g(x_2) = 0$. Suppose that $f(x)$ failed to vanish in $x_1 < x < x_2$. Replacing f and/or g by their negative, if necessary, we could find solutions f and g positive on $x_1 < x < x_2$. This would make

$$W(f, g; x_1) = f(x_1)g'(x_1) \geq 0 \quad \text{and} \quad W(f, g; x_2) = f(x_2)g'(x_2) \leq 0.$$

On the other hand, since $f > 0$, $g > 0$, and $p \geq q$ on $x_1 < x < x_2$, we have

$$\frac{d}{dx}[W(f, g; x)] = fg'' - gf'' = (p - q)fg \geq 0 \quad \text{on} \quad x_1 < x < x_2.$$

Hence, W is nondecreasing, giving a contradiction unless

$$p - q \equiv W(f, g; x) \equiv 0.$$

In this event, $f \equiv kg$ for some constant k by Theorem 4, completing the proof.

■ COROLLARY 1.   *If $q(x) \leq 0$, then no nontrivial solution of the* DE $u'' + q(x)u = 0$ *can have more than one zero.*

The proof is by contradiction. By the Sturm Comparison Theorem, the solution $v \equiv 1$ of the DE $v'' = 0$ would have to vanish at least once between any two zeros of any nontrivial solution of the DE $u'' + q(x)u = 0$.

The preceding results show that the oscillations of the solutions of $u'' + q(x)u = 0$ are largely determined by the sign and magnitude of $q(x)$. When $q(x) \leq 0$, oscillations are impossible: no solution can change sign more than once. On the other hand, if $q(x) \geq k^2 > 0$, then any solution of $u'' + q(x)u = 0$ must vanish between any two successive zeros of any given solution $A \cos k(x - x_1)$ of the trigonometric DE $u'' + k^2 u = 0$, hence in any interval of length π/k.

This result can be applied to solutions of the Bessel DE (5) (e.g., to the Bessel function of order n; see Chapter 3, § 4). Substituting $u = v/\sqrt{x}$ into (5), we obtain the equivalent DE

$$v'' + \left[1 - \frac{4n^2 - 1}{4x^2}\right]v = 0, \tag{15}$$

whose solutions vanish when u does (for $x \neq 0$). Applying the Comparison Theorem to (15) and $u'' + u = 0$, we obtain the following.

■ COROLLARY 2.   *Each interval of length π of the positive x-axis contains at least one zero of any solution of the Bessel* DE *of order zero and, at most, one zero of any nontrivial solution of the Bessel* DE *of order n if $n > \frac{1}{2}$.*

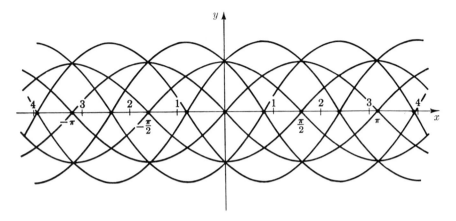

FIGURE 2.1   Solution curves of $u'' + u = 0$.

The fact that the oscillations of the solutions of $u'' + q(x)u = 0$ depend on the sign of $q(x)$ is illustrated by Figures 2.1 and 2.2, which depict sample solution curves for the cases $q(x) = 1$ and $q(x) = -1$, respectively.

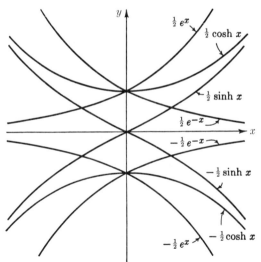

FIGURE 2.2   Solution curves of $u'' - u = 0$.

5* Poincaré phase plane

For any solution $u(x)$ of the normal second-order DE (8), the vector-valued function $v(x) = (u(x), u'(x))$ describes a path in the uu'-plane, called the *Poincaré phase plane* of (8). Conversely, a parametrically defined path $(u(x), u'(x))$ in the uu'-plane represents a solution of (8) if and only if

$$du/dx = u', \qquad du'/dx = -p(x)u' - q(x)u. \tag{16}$$

Such representations of solutions of (8) in the Poincaré phase plane are suggestive geometrically and physically.

We shall now take a fresh look at the theorems of §§2–4 in the Poincaré phase plane, setting

$$u' = r(x) \cos \theta(x), \qquad u(x) = r(x) \sin \theta(x). \tag{17}$$

Thus, we introduce clockwise polar coordinates in the Poincaré phase plane, interchanging the role of u' and u.

Differentiating $r^2(x) = u^2(x) + u'^2(x)$, we obtain, as in the proof of Theorem 1 (where $\sigma(x) = r^2(x)$),

$$rr' = uu' + u'u'' = u'(u - pu' - qu)$$
$$= r^2 \cos \theta[(1 - q(x)) \sin \theta - p(x) \cos \theta].$$

Dividing through by r^2 and simplifying, we obtain

$$dr/r\,dx = -p(x) \cos^2 \theta + (1 - q(x)) \cos \theta \sin \theta. \tag{18}$$

As in Theorem 1, it follows that the magnitude $|d(\ln r)/dx|$ of the logarithmic derivative of $r(x)$ is bounded by $|p|_{\max} + (1 + |q|_{\max})/2$.

We can get a new understanding of Sturm's theorems similarly by differentiating the relation $\cot \theta = u'/u$. This gives, by elementary formulas

$$-(\csc^2 \theta)\theta' = (u''/u) - (u'/u)^2 = -p(u'/u) - q - (u'/u)^2$$
$$= -p \cot \theta - q - \cot^2 \theta.$$

If we multiply through by $-\sin^2 \theta$, this equation gives

$$d\theta/dx = \cos^2 \theta + p(x) \cos \theta \sin \theta + q(x) \sin^2 \theta. \tag{19}$$

This *first*-order DE gives much information about the oscillations of u.

Now, consider the graph of the multiple-valued function $\theta(x)$ in the $x\theta$-plane. Since $\cot \theta$ is periodic with period π, the graph at $\theta = $ arc $\cot(u'/u)$ for any solution of (8) consists of an infinite family of parallel curves, all obtained from any one by vertical translation through integral multiples of π. The curves which form the graphs of $\theta_1(x)$ and $\theta_2(x)$, for any two linearly independent solutions u_1, u_2 of (8), occur alternately. Moreover, by the uniqueness theorem of Chapter 1, they can never cross.

Clearly, $u = 0$ precisely when $\sin \theta = 0$, that is, when $\theta \equiv 0 \pmod{\pi}$. Inspecting (19), we also see that

When $\theta \equiv 0 \pmod{\pi}$,   that is, $u = 0$,   then $d\theta/dx > 0$.   (20a)

When $\theta \equiv \pi/2 \pmod{\pi}$, $d\theta/dx$ has the sign of q.   (20b)

From (20a) it follows that, after the graph of any $\theta(x)$ has crossed the line $\theta = n\pi$, it can never recross it, but must cross the line $\theta = (n + 1)\pi$ where $u(x)$ next vanishes. Therefore, successive zeros of $u(x)$ occur precisely where θ increases from one integral multiple of π to the next!

Sturm's Oscillation Theorem follows: given two linearly independent solutions, we can normalize the associated polar angles so that $\theta_1(x) < \theta_2(x) < \theta_1(x) + \pi$. After verifying that the right side of (19) satisfies a Lipschitz condition, we see that this inequality can never cease to hold; hence, in any interval where $\theta_1(x)$ increases from $n\pi$ to $n\pi + \pi$, $\theta_2(x)$ must cross the line $\theta = n\pi + \pi$ and so u_2 must vanish there. Sturm's Comparison Theorem follows similarly: if $q(x)$ is increased and $p(x)$ is left constant, we can apply the Comparison Theorem of Chapter 1.

When $q(x) > p^2(x)/4$, the quadratic form on the right side of (19) is *positive definite*; hence $d\theta/dx$ is identically positive. Under the circumstances, the DE (8) may be said to be of *oscillatory type*.

When $q(x) < 0$, the DE (8) is said to be of *positive* type. One can say more: by (20a)–(20b), once $\theta(x)$ has entered the first or third quadrant, it can never escape from this quadrant; it is trapped in it. Therefore, a given solution $u(x)$ of (8) can have at most one zero if $q(x) < 0$; solutions are *nonoscillatory*. Moreover, since $uu' > 0$ in the first and third quadrants, $u^2(x)$ and hence $u(x)$ are perpetually *increasing* after a solution has been trapped in one of these quadrants. Finally, since changing x to $-x$ just reverses the sign of $p(x)$ in (8) without affecting $q(x)$, the existence of a solution $v(x)$ of (8) having everywhere-*decreasing* magnitude follows similarly.

6 Adjoint operators

The concepts of integrating factor and exact differential, defined for first-order DE's in Chapter 1, §5, can be extended to equations of higher order. We extend them now to second-order *linear* DE's.

■ DEFINITION.   *The second-order homogeneous linear* DE

$$L[u] = p_0(x)u''(x) + p_1(x)u'(x) + p_2(x)u(x) = 0 \qquad (21)$$

is said to be exact *if and only if, for all functions* $u \in \mathscr{C}^2$,

$$p_0(x)u'' + p_1(x)u' + p_2(x)u = \frac{d}{dx}[A(x)u' + B(x)u] \qquad (21')$$

for some $A(x)$, $B(x) \in \mathscr{C}^1$. *An* integrating factor *for the* DE $(21')$ *is a function* $v(x)$ *such that* $vL[u] = 0$ *is exact.*

If an integrating factor v can be found, then clearly

$$v(x)[p_0(x)u'' + p_1(x)u' + p_2(x)u] = \frac{d}{dx}[A(x)u' + B(x)u]. \qquad (22)$$

Hence, the solutions of the homogeneous DE (21) are those of the first-order inhomogeneous linear DE

$$A(x)u' + B(x)u = C, \qquad (23)$$

where C is an arbitrary constant. Also, the solutions of the inhomogeneous DE $L[u] = r(x)$ are those of the first-order DE

$$A(x)u' + B(x)u = \int v(x)r(x)dx + C. \qquad (23')$$

The DE's (23) and $(23')$ can be solved by a quadrature (Chapter 1, § 6). Hence, if an integrating factor of (21) can be found, we can reduce the solution of $L[u] = r(x)$ to a sequence of quadratures.

Evidently, $L[u] = 0$ is exact if and only if $p_0 = A$, $p_1 = A' + B$, $p_2 = B'$. Hence it is exact if and only if

$$p_2 = B' = (p_1 - A')' = p_1' - (p_0')'.$$

This simple calculation proves the following result.

■ LEMMA.   *The* DE (21) *is exact if and only if its coefficient functions satisfy* $p_0'' - p_1' + p_2 = 0$.

■ COROLLARY.   *A function* $v \in \mathscr{C}^2$ *is an integrating factor for the* DE (21) *if and only if it is a solution of the second order-homogeneous linear* DE

$$M[v] = [p_0(x)v]'' - [p_1(x)v]' + p_2(x)v(x) = 0. \qquad (24)$$

The operator M is called the *adjoint* of the linear operator L. Equation (24) can be expanded to give

$$p_0v'' + (2p_0' - p_1)v' + (p_0'' - p_1' + p_2)v = 0. \qquad (24')$$

This DE is called the *adjoint equation* of the DE (21).

Thus, whenever a nontrivial solution of the adjoint DE (24) of a given second-order linear DE (21) is known, every solution of the DE $L[u] = r(x)$ can be obtained by quadratures.

7   Lagrange identity

The concept of the adjoint of a linear operator, which originated historically in the search for integrating factors, owes its major importance to the role which it plays in the theory of orthogonal and biorthogonal expansions. We now lay the foundations for this theory.

Substituting into (24), we find that the adjoint of the adjoint of a given second-order linear DE (21) is again the original DE (21). Another consequence of (24) is the identity

$$vL[u] - uM[v] = (vp_0)u'' - u(p_0v)'' + (vp_1)u' + u(p_1v)'.$$

This can be simplified to give the *Lagrange identity*

$$vL[u] - uM[v] = \frac{d}{dx}[p_0vu' - (p_0v)'u + p_1uv], \tag{25}$$

or

$$\int_a^b \{vL[u] - uM[v]\}\, dx = [p_0vu' - (p_0v)'u + p_1uv]_{x=a}^{x=b}. \tag{25'}$$

The integrand in (25) is thus an exact differential, the differential of a homogeneous bilinear expression in u, v, and their derivatives.

Self-adjoint equations. Homogeneous linear DE's which coincide with their adjoint are of great importance; they are called *self-adjoint*. For instance, the Legendre DE (6) is self-adjoint. The condition for the second-order DE (21) to be self-adjoint is easily derived. It is necessary by (24') that $2p_0' - p_1 = p_1$, that is, $p_0' = p_1$. Since this relation implies $p_0'' - p_1' = 0$, it is also sufficient. This proves the first statement of the following theorem.

■ THEOREM 7. *The second-order linear* DE (21) *is* self-adjoint *if and only if it has the form*

$$\frac{d}{dx}\left[p(x)\frac{du}{dx}\right] + q(x)u = 0. \tag{26}$$

The DE (21) *can be made self-adjoint by multiplying through by*

$$h(x) = [\exp \int (p_1/p_0)dx]/p_0. \tag{26'}$$

To prove the second statement, first reduce (21) to normal form by dividing through by p_0, and then observe that the DE

$$hu'' + (ph)u' + (qh)u = 0$$

is self-adjoint if and only if $h' = ph$, or $h = \exp(\int p\, dx)$.

For example, the self-adjoint form of the Bessel DE (5) is

$$(xu')' + [x - (n^2/x)]u = 0.$$

EXERCISES B

1. Show that if $u(x)$ and $v(x)$ are solutions of the self-adjoint DE

$$(pu')' + q(x)u = 0,$$

then $p(x)[uv' - vu']$ is a constant (Abel's identity).

2. Reduce the following DE's to self-adjoint form:
   (a) $x^2 u'' + xu' + u = 0$,   (b) $u'' + u' \tan x = 0$.

3. For each of the following DE's, $y = x^3$ is one solution; find a second, linearly independence solution by quadratures.
   (a) $x^2 y'' - 4xy' + 6y = 0$,   (b) $xy'' + (x - 2)y' - 3y = 0$.

4. Show that the substitution $y = e^{\int p \, dx/2} u$ replaces (8) by

$$y'' + I(x)y = 0, \qquad I(x) = q - p^2/4 - p'/2.$$

5*. Show that two DE's of the form (8) can be transformed into each other by a change of dependent variable of the form $y = v(x)u$ if and only if the function $I(x) = q(x) - p^2(x)/4 - p'(x)/2$ is the same for both DE's ($I(x)$ is called the *invariant* of the DE).

6. Reduce the self-adjoint DE $(pu')' + qu = 0$ to normal form, and show that, in the notation of Exercise 5, $I(x) = (p'^2 - 2pp'' + 4pq)/4p^2$.

7. (a) Show that, for the normal form of the Legendre DE $[(1 - x^2)u']' + \lambda u = 0$,

$$I(x) = (1 + \lambda - \lambda x^2)/(1 - x^2)^2. \quad \text{(Use Exercise 6.)}$$

   (b) Show that, if $\lambda = n(n + 1)$, then every solution of the Legendre equation has at least $(2n + 1)/\pi$ zeros on $(-1, 1)$.

8. Let $u(x)$ be a solution of $u'' = q(x)u$, $q(x) > 0$ such that $u(0)$ and $u'(0)$ are positive. Show that uu' and $u(x)$ are increasing for $x > 0$.

9. Let $h(x)$ be a nonnegative function of class $\mathscr{C}^1$. Show that the change of independent variable $t = \int_a^x h(s) \, ds$, $u(x) = v(t)$, transforms DE (8) into $v'' + p_1(t)v' + q_1(t)v = 0$, where $p_1(t) = [p(x)h(x) + h'(x)]/h(x)^2$ and $q_1(t) = q(x)/h(x)^2$.

10. (a) Show that a change of independent variable $t = \pm \int |q(x)|^{1/2} \, dx$, $q \neq 0$, changes the DE (8) into one whose normal form is

$$\frac{d^2 u}{dt^2} + \left(\frac{q' + 2pq}{2|q|^{3/2}}\right)\frac{du}{dt} \pm u = 0. \tag{*}$$

   (b) Show that no other change of independent variable makes $|q| = 1$.

11*. Using Exercise 10, show that DE (8) is equivalent to a DE with constant coefficients under a change of independent variable if and only if $(q' + 2pq)/q^{3/2}$ is a constant.

12*. By a suitable change of independent variable, find the general solution of the DE $(x^3 - x)u'' + u' + n^2 x^3 u = 0$.

8   Green's functions

The *inhomogeneous* linear second-order DE in normal form,

$$L[u] = \frac{d^2 u}{dx^2} + p(x)\frac{du}{dx} + q(x)u = r(x), \tag{27}$$

differs from the homogeneous linear DE

$$L[u] = \frac{d^2u}{dx^2} + p(x)\frac{du}{dx} + q(x)u = 0 \qquad (27')$$

by the nonzero function $r(x)$ on the right side. In applications to electrical and dynamical systems, the function $r(x)$ is called the *forcing term*. By the Uniqueness Theorem of § 2 and Lemma 2 of § 1, it is clear that the solution $u(x)$ of $L[u] = r(x)$ for given homogeneous initial conditions such as $u(0) = u'(0) = 0$ depends linearly on the forcing term. We will now determine the exact nature of this linear dependence.

Given the inhomogeneous linear DE (27), we will show that there exists an integral operator G,

$$G[r] = \int_a^x G(x, \xi)\, r(\xi)\, d\xi, \qquad (28)$$

such that $G[r] = u$. In fact, one can find a function G which makes $G[r]$ satisfy given homogeneous boundary conditions, provided that the latter define a well-set problem.

The kernel $G(x, \xi)$ of Equation (28) is then called the Green's function associated with the given boundary value problem. In operator notation, it is defined by the identity $L[G[r]] = r$ (G is a "right-inverse" of the linear operator L) and the given boundary conditions. For initial value problems, the preceding ideas can be generalized to nth order equations as follows.

■ DEFINITION. *Let*

$$L[u] = \frac{d^nu}{dx^n} + p_1(x)\frac{d^{n-1}u}{dx^{n-1}} + \cdots + p_n(x)u$$

be an nth-order homogeneous linear differential operator. By the Green's *function of $L[u]$ for the initial value problem at $x = a$ is meant a function $G(x, \xi)$ such that the function $u(x)$ defined by (28) satisfies $L[u] = r(x)$ for any continuous $r(x)$, and satisfies the initial conditions $u(a) = \cdots = u^{(n-1)}(a) = 0$.*

To provide an intuitive basis for the concept of a Green's function, two examples will be described first. In these examples, the independent variable will be denoted by t and should be thought of as representing time.

EXAMPLE 5. Suppose that money is deposited continuously in a bank account, at a continuously varying rate $r(t)$, and that interest is compounded continuously at a constant rate p $(=100p\%$ per annum). As a function of time, the amount $u(t)$ in the account satisfies the DE

$$du/dt = pu + r(t).$$

If the account is opened when $t = 0$ and initially has no money: $u(0) = 0$, then one can calculate $u(T)$ at any later time $T > 0$ as follows. Each infinitesimal deposit $r(t)\,dt$, made in the time interval $(t, t + dt)$, increases through compound interest accrued during the time interval from t to T by a factor $e^{p(T-t)}$ to the amount $e^{p(T-t)}r(t)\,dt$. Hence the account should amount, at time T, to the integral (limit of sums)

$$u(T) = \int_0^T e^{p(T\,-t)}r(t)\ dt = e^{pT}\int_0^T e^{-pt}r(t)\ dt. \tag{29}$$

This plausible argument is easily shown to be correct. It is obvious that $u(0) = 0$ in (29). Differentiating the product in the final expression of (24), we obtain

$$u'(T) = pe^{pT}\int_0^T e^{-pt}r(t)\ dt + e^{pT}e^{-pT}r(T) = pu(T) + r(T),$$

where the derivative of the integral is evaluated by the Fundamental Theorem of the Calculus.

EXAMPLE 6.   Consider again the motion of a mass m on a spring, as in Example 4. We have the DE (8) with constant coefficients p and q. Suppose that the mass is at rest up to time t_0, and is then given an impulsive (that is, instantaneous) velocity v_0 at time t_0.

The function f describing the position of the mass m as a function of time under such conditions is continuous, but its derivative f' is not defined at t_0, because of the sudden jump in the velocity. However, the left-hand derivative of f at the point t_0 exists and is equal to zero, and the right-hand derivative also exists and is equal to v_0, the impulsive velocity. For $t > t_0$, the function f is obtained by solving the constant-coefficient DE $u'' + pu' + qu = 0$. If $q > p^2/4$, the roots of the characteristic equation are complex conjugate, and we obtain an oscillatory solution

$$u(t) = \begin{cases} 0, & t < t_0, \\ (v_0/v)e^{-\mu(t\,-t_0)}\sin\nu(t - t_0), & t \geq t_0, \end{cases}$$

where $\mu = p/2$ and $\nu = \sqrt{q - p^2/4}$.

Now suppose the mass is given a sequence of small velocity impulses $\Delta v_k = r(t_k)\Delta t$, at successive instants t_0, $t_1 = t_0 + \Delta t, \ldots, t_k = t_0 + k\Delta t$, $\cdots$. Summing the effects of these over the time interval $0 \leq t \leq T$, and passing to the limit as $\Delta t \to 0$, we are led to conjecture the formula

$$u(T) = \int_0^T \frac{1}{\nu} e^{-\mu(T-t)} \sin \nu(T-t) r(t) \, dt. \qquad (30)$$

This represents the *forced* oscillation associated with the DE

$$u'' + pu' + qu = r(t), \qquad q > p^2/4, \qquad (31)$$

having the forcing term $r(t)$.

9 Variation of parameters

The preceding conjecture can be verified as a special case of the following general result, valid for second-order linear DE's with variable coefficients.

■ THEOREM 8.   *Let the function $G(t, \tau)$ be defined as follows:*
(i)   *$G(t, \tau) = 0$, for $a \leq t \leq \tau$,*
(ii)   *for each fixed $\tau \geq a$ and all $t > \tau$, $G(t, \tau)$ is the solution of the DE $L[G] = G_{tt} + p(t)G_t + q(t)G = 0$ which satisfies the initial conditions $G = 0$ and $G_t = 1$ at $t = \tau$.*
Then G is the Green's function of the operator L for the initial value problem on $t \geq a$.

Proof — We must prove that, for any continuous function r, the definite integral

$$u(t) = \int_a^t G(t, \tau) r(\tau) \, d\tau = \int_a^\infty G(t, \tau) r(\tau) \, d\tau \qquad \text{(by (i))} \qquad (32)$$

is a solution of the second-order inhomogeneous linear DE (27), which satisfies the initial conditions $u(a) = u'(a) = 0$.

The proof is based on Leibniz' Rule for differentiating definite integrals.† This rule is: For any continuous function $g(t, \tau)$ whose derivative $\partial g/\partial t$ is piecewise continuous, we have

$$\frac{d}{dt} \int_a^t g(t, \tau) \, d\tau = g(t, t) + \int_a^t \frac{\partial g}{\partial t}(t, \tau) \, d\tau.$$

Applying this rule twice to the right side of formula (32), we obtain successively

$$u'(t) = G(t, t) r(t) + \int_a^t G_t(t, \tau) r(\tau) \, d\tau = \int_a^t G_t(t, \tau) r(\tau) \, d\tau,$$

$$u''(t) = G_t(t, t) r(t) + \int_a^t G_{tt}(t, \tau) r(\tau) \, d\tau.$$

---

† Kaplan, *Advanced Calculus*, p. 219. In our applications, $\partial g/\partial t$ has, at worst, a simple jump across $t = \tau$.

By assumption (ii), the last equation simplifies to

$$u''(t) = r(t) + \int_a^t G_{tt}(t, \tau) r(\tau) \, d\tau.$$

Here the subscripts indicate partial differentiation with respect to t. Thus

$$L[u] = u''(t) + p(t)u'(t) + q(t)u(t)$$
$$= r(t) + \int_a^t [G_{tt}(t, \tau) + p(t)G_t(t, \tau) + q(t)G(t, \tau)] r(\tau) \, d\tau = r(t),$$

completing the proof.

The reader can easily verify that the function $\nu^{-1} e^{-\mu(t - \tau)} \sin \nu(t - \tau)$ in (30) satisfies the conditions of Theorem 8, in the special case of Example 6.

To construct the Green's function $G(t, \tau)$ of Theorem 8 explicitly, it suffices to know two linearly independent solutions $f(t)$ and $g(t)$ of the reduced equation $L[u] = 0$. Namely, to compute $G(t, \tau)$ for $t \geq \tau$, write $G(t, \tau) = c(\tau)f(t) + d(\tau)g(t)$, by Theorem 2. Solving the simultaneous linear equations $G = 0$, $G_t = 1$, at $t = \tau$ specified in condition (ii) of Theorem 8:

$$c(\tau)f(\tau) + d(\tau)g(\tau) = 0, \qquad c(\tau)f'(\tau) + d(\tau)g'(\tau) = 1,$$

we get the formulas

$$c(\tau) = -g(\tau)/W(f, g; \tau), \qquad d(\tau) = f(\tau)/W(f, g; \tau),$$

where $W(f, g; \tau) = f(\tau)g'(\tau) - g(\tau)f'(\tau)$ is the Wronskian. This gives for the Green's function the formula

$$G(t, \tau) = [f(\tau)g(t) - g(\tau)f(t)]/[f(\tau)g'(\tau) - g(\tau)f'(\tau)].$$

Substituting into (32), we obtain our final result.

■ COROLLARY.   *The solution of* (27) *for the initial conditions* $u(a) = u'(a) = 0$ *is*

$$u(t) = \int_a^t \frac{f(\tau)g(t) - g(\tau)f(t)}{f(\tau)g'(\tau) - g(\tau)f'(\tau)} r(\tau) \, d\tau. \tag{33}$$

In textbooks on the elementary theory of DE's, formula (33) is often derived formally by posing the question: What must $c(\tau)$ and $d(\tau)$ be in order that the function

$$G(t, \tau) = c(\tau)f(t) + d(\tau)g(t),$$

when substituted into (28), will give a solution of the inhomogeneous DE $L[u] = r(t)$? Since $c(\tau)$ and $d(\tau)$ may be regarded as "variable parameters'' which vary with τ, formula (33) is said to be obtained by the method of *variation of parameters*.

EXERCISES C

1. Integrate the following DE's by the method of variation of parameters:
   (a) $y'' - y = x^n$,   (b) $y'' + y = e^x$,
   (c) $y'' - qy' + y = 2xe^x$,   (d) $y'' + 10y' + 25y = \sin x$.
2. Show that the general solution of the inhomogeneous DE $y'' + k^2 y = R(x)$ is given by $y = (1/k) \int_a^x \sin k(x - t) R(t)\, dt + c_1 \sin kx + c_2 \cos kx$.
3. Solve $y'' + 3y' + 2y = x^3$ for the initial conditions $y(0) = y'(0) = (0)$.
4. Show that any second-order inhomogeneous linear DE which is satisfied by both x^2 and $\sin^2 x$ must have a singular point at the origin.
5. Construct Green's functions for the initial-value problem, for the following DE's:
   (a) $u'' = 0$,   (b) $u'' = u$,   (c) $u'' + u = 0$,

   (d) $u'' + \dfrac{x}{1 + x} u' - \dfrac{1}{1 + x} u = 0$.   [HINT: x is a solution.]

6. Find the general solutions of the following inhomogeneous Euler DE's:
   (a) $x^2 y'' - 2xy' + 2y = x^2 + px + q$,   (b) $x^2 y'' + 3xy' + y = R(x)$.
[HINT: Any homogeneous Euler DE has a solution of the form x^ν.]
7. (a) Construct a Green's function for the inhomogeneous first-order DE

$$du/dt = p(t)u + r(t).$$

   (b) Interpret in terms of compound interest (cf. Example 5).
   (c) Relate to formula (10) of Chapter 1.
8. Show that, if $q(t) < 0$, then the Green's function $G(t, \tau)$ of $u_{tt} + q(t)u = 0$ for the initial-value problem is positive and convex upward for $t > \tau$.

10* Two-endpoint problems

So far, we have considered only boundary conditions of the ''initial value'' type. That is, in considering solutions of second-order DE's such as $y'' = -p(x)y' - q(x)y$, we have supposed y and y' both given at the same point a. This is natural in many dynamical problems. One is given the initial position and velocity, and a general law relating the acceleration to the instantaneous position and velocity, and then one wishes to determine the subsequent motion from these data, as in Example 4.

In other problems, *two-endpoint* conditions, at points $x = a$ and $x = b$, are more natural. For instance, the DE $y'' = 0$ characterizes straight lines in the plane, and one may be interested in determining the straight line joining two given points (a, c) and (b, d). That is, the problem is to find the solution $y = f(x)$ of the DE $y'' = 0$ which satisfies the *two* end-point conditions $f(a) = c$ and $f(b) = d$.

Many two-endpoint problems for second-order DE's arise in the calculus of variations; the following example leads to a linear DE.

EXAMPLE 7.   For given p, q, $r \in \mathscr{C}^1$, find the curve which minimizes the integral

$$\int_a^b \tfrac{1}{2}[p(x)y'^2 + 2q(x)yy' + r(x)y^2]\,dx = \int_a^b F(x, y, y')\,dx \qquad (34)$$

among all curves joining two given endpoints (a, c) and (b, d). By a classical result of Euler,† the line integral (34) is an extremum (maximum, minimum, or minimax), relative to all curves $y = f(x)$ satisfying $f(a) = c$ and $f(b) = d$, if and only if $f(x)$ satisfies the self-adjoint second-order linear DE

$$\frac{d}{dx}\left(\frac{\partial F}{\partial y'}\right) - \left(\frac{\partial F}{\partial y}\right) = (py')' + (q' - r)y = 0. \qquad (35)$$

It is natural to ask: under what circumstances does a second-order DE have a unique solution, assuming given values $f(a) = c$ and $f(b) = d$ at two given endpoints a and $b > a$? When this is so, the resulting two-endpoint problem is called *well-set*; the class of such problems obviously includes the case $p = r = 1$, $q = 0$ of $y'' = 0$. The following result provides a partial answer to this question.

THEOREM 9.   *Let the second-order linear homogeneous* DE

$$p_0(x)u'' + p_1(x)u' + p_2(x)u = 0, \qquad p_0(x) \neq 0, \qquad (36)$$

with continuous coefficient-functions have two linearly independent solutions.‡ Then the two-endpoint problem defined by (36) and the endpoint conditions $u(a) = c$, $u(b) = d$ is well-set if and only if no nontrivial solution satisfies the endpoint conditions

$$u(a) = u(b) = 0. \qquad (36')$$

Proof — By Theorem 2, the general solution of the DE (36) is the function $u = \alpha f(x) + \beta g(x)$, where f and g are a basis of solutions of the DE (35), and α, β are arbitrary constants. By the elementary theory of linear equations, the equations

$$\alpha f(a) + \beta g(a) = c, \qquad \alpha f(b) + \beta g(b) = d$$

have one and only one solution vector (α, β) if and only if the determinant $f(a)g(b) - g(a)f(b) \neq 0$. The alternative $f(a)g(b) = f(b)g(a)$ is, however, the condition that the *homogeneous* simultaneous linear equations

---

† See for example Courant, Vol. 1, Chapter 7. We will recur to (34) later, in Chapter 10.

‡ In Chapter 6, it will be shown that this hypothesis is unnecessary; a basis of solutions always exists for continuous $p_i(x)$.

$$\alpha f(a) + \beta g(a) = \alpha f(b) + \beta g(b) = 0 \qquad (37)$$

have a nontrivial solution $(\alpha, \beta) \neq (0, 0)$. This proves Theorem 9.

When the DE (36) has a nontrivial solution satisfying the homogeneous endpoint conditions $\phi(a) = \phi(b) = 0$, the point $(b, 0)$ on the x-axis is called a *conjugate point* of the point $(a, 0)$ for the given homogeneous linear DE (36) or for a variational problem leading to this DE. In general, such conjugate points exist for DE's whose solutions *oscillate* but not for those of nonoscillatory type, such as $u'' = q(x)u$, $q(x) > 0$.

Thus, in Example 7, let $p = 1$, $q = 0$, and $r = -k^2 < 0$. Then the general solution of (36) for the initial condition $u(a) = 0$ is $u = A \sin [k(x - a)]$. For $u(b) = 0$ to be compatible with $A \neq 0$, it is necessary and sufficient that $b = a + (n\pi/k)$. The conjugate points of a are spaced periodically. On the other hand, the DE $y'' - \lambda y = 0$, corresponding to the choice $p = 1$, $q = 0$, $r = \lambda$ in Example 7, admits no conjugate points if $\lambda = r$ is positive.

11* Green's functions

We now show that, except in the case that a and b are conjugate points for the reduced equation $L[u] = 0$, the inhomogeneous linear DE (22) can be solved for the boundary conditions $u(a) = u(b) = 0$ by constructing an appropriate Green's function $G(x, \xi)$ on the square $a \leq x$, $\xi \leq b$ and setting

$$u(x) = \int_a^b G(x, \xi) r(\xi) \, d\xi = G[r]. \qquad (38)$$

Note that G is an *integral operator* whose kernel is the Green's function $G(x, \xi)$.

The existence of a Green's function for a typical two-endpoint problem is suggested by simple physical considerations, as follows.

EXAMPLE 8.   Consider a nearly horizontal taut string under constant tension T, supporting a continuously distributed load $w(x)$ per unit length. If $y(x)$ denotes the vertical displacement of the string, then the load $w(x) \, \Delta x$ supported by the string in the interval $(x_0, x_0 + \Delta x)$ is in equilibrium with the net vertical component of tension forces, which is

$$T \{ y'(x_0 + \Delta x) - y'(x_0) \}$$

in the nearly horizontal ("small amplitude") approximation.† Dividing through by Δx and letting $\Delta x \downarrow 0$, we get $Ty''(x) = w(x)$.

---

† For a more thorough discussion, see J. L. Synge and B. A. Griffith, *Principles of Mechanics*, McGraw-Hill, 1949, p. 99.

The displacement $y(x)$ depends linearly on the load, by Lemma 2 of § 1. This suggests that we consider the load as the sum of point-concentrated loads $w_i = w(\xi_i)\Delta\xi_i$ at isolated points. For each such concentrated load, the taut string consists of two straight segments, the slope jumping by w_i/T at ξ_i. Thus, if the string extends from 0 to 1, the vertical displacement is

$$w_i\, G(x,\, \xi_i) = \begin{cases} \epsilon_i(\xi_i - 1)x, & 0 < x \leq \xi_i, \\ \epsilon_i\, \xi_i(x - 1), & \xi_i \leq x \leq 1, \end{cases}$$

where ϵ_i is set equal to w_i/T in order to give a jump in slope of w_i/T at the point $x = \xi_i$. Passing to the limit as the $\Delta\xi_i \downarrow 0$, we are led to guess that

$$y(x) = \int_0^1 G(x,\, \xi)\, w(\xi)\, d\xi,$$

where

$$G\,(x,\, \xi) = \begin{cases} (\xi - 1)x/T, & 0 \leq x \leq \xi, \\ \xi(x - 1)/T, & \xi \leq x \leq 1. \end{cases}$$

These heuristic considerations suggest that the Green's function $G\,(x,\, \xi)$ is determined by the following conditions: it satisfies $L[G] = 0$ for each fixed ξ in the intervals $a \leq x \leq \xi$ and $\xi \leq x \leq b$; it is continuous across the principal diagonal $x = \xi$ of the square $a \leq x,\, \xi \leq b$ over which G is defined; its derivative $\partial G/\partial x$ jumps by $1/p_0(x)$ across this diagonal. That is, let $f(x)$ and $g(x)$ be any nontrivial solutions of $L[u] = 0$ which satisfy $f(a) = 0$, $g(b) = 0$, respectively. The conjecture is that

$$G(x,\, \xi) = \begin{cases} \epsilon(\xi)f(x)g(\xi), & a \leq x \leq \xi, \\ \epsilon(\xi)f(\xi)g(x), & \xi \leq x \leq b, \end{cases}$$

where the factor $\epsilon(\xi)$ above is chosen to give $\partial G/\partial x$ a jump of $1/p_0(x)$ across $x = \xi$:

$$\frac{\partial G}{\partial x}\, (\xi^+,\, \xi) - \frac{\partial G}{\partial x}\, (\xi^-,\, \xi) = \epsilon(\xi)\{f(\xi)g'(\xi) - g(\xi)f'(\xi)\} = 1/p_0(\xi).$$

We are therefore led to try the kernel

$$G\,(x,\, \xi) = \begin{cases} f(x)g(\xi)/p_0(\xi)W(\xi), & a \leq x \leq \xi, \\ f(\xi)g(x)/p_0(\xi)W(\xi), & \xi \leq x \leq b, \end{cases} \tag{39}$$

where $W = fg' - gf'$ is the Wronskian of f and g.

■ THEOREM 10.   *For any continuous function $r(x)$ on $[a, b]$, the function $u(x)$ defined by (38) and (39) is the solution of $p_0u'' + p_1u' + p_2u = r$ which* *satisfies the boundary conditions* $u(a) = u(b) = 0$, *provided that there is no nontrivial solution of* (36) *satisfying the same boundary conditions.*

The proof is similar to that of Theorem 8; the existence of two linearly independent solutions of (27′) is again assumed. Rewriting (38) in the form

$$u(x) = \int_a^x G(x, \xi) r(\xi)\, d\xi + \int_x^b G(x, \xi) r(\xi)\, d\xi$$

and differentiating by Leibniz' Rule, we have

$$u'(x) = \int_a^x G_x(x, \xi) r(\xi)\, d\xi + \int_x^b G_x(x, \xi) r(\xi)\, d\xi.$$

The endpoint contributions cancel since $G(x, \xi)$ is continuous for $x = \xi$. Differentiating again, we obtain

$$u''(x) = \int_a^x G_{xx}(x, \xi) r(\xi)\, d\xi + G_x(x, x^-) r(x^-)$$

$$+ \int_x^b G_{xx}(x, \xi) r(\xi)\, d\xi - G_x(x, x^+) r(x^+),$$

where $f(x^+)$ signifies the limit of $f(\xi)$ as ξ approaches x from above, and $f(x^-)$ the limit as ξ approaches x from below. The two terms corresponding to the contributions from the endpoints come from the sides $\xi < x$ and $\xi > x$ of the diagonal; since r is continuous, $r(x^-) = r(x^+)$, and hence their difference is $[G_x(x^+, x) - G_x(x^-, x)] r(x)$, which equals $r(x)/p_0(x)$ by (39). Simplifying, we obtain

$$u''(x) = \int_a^b G_{xx}(x, \xi)\, r(\xi)\, d\xi + r(x)/p_0(x).$$

From this identity, we can calculate $L[u]$. It is

$$L[u] = \int_a^b L[G(x, \xi)]\, r(\xi)\, d\xi + r(x) = r(x)$$

since $L[G(x, \xi)] = 0$ except at $x \equiv \xi$. Here the operator L acts on the variable x in $G(x, \xi)$; though G is not in $\mathscr{C}^2$, the expression $L[G]$ is meaningful for one-sided derivatives and the above can be justified. This gives the identity (38).

Since $G(x, \xi)$, as a function of x, satisfies the boundary conditions $u(a) = u(b) = 0$, it follows from (38), by differentiating under the integral sign, that u satisfies the same boundary conditions. This completes the proof of the theorem.

Delta-function interpretation. The ideas underlying the intuitive discussion of Examples 6 and 7 can be given the following heuristic interpretation. Let the symbolic function $\delta(x)$ stand for the limit of nonnegative "density" functions $\rho(x)$ concentrated in a narrow interval $(-\epsilon, \epsilon)$ near $x = 0$, with total mass $\int_{-\epsilon}^{\epsilon} \rho(x)\, dx = 1$, as $\epsilon \downarrow 0$. Then $\delta(x - \xi)$ will stand for a unit "point mass" concentrated at $x = \xi$.

This definition gives, passing to the limit,

$$\int_a^b \delta(x - \xi) f(x)\, dx = f(\xi), \qquad \xi \in (a, b). \tag{40}$$

In particular, setting $f(x)$ equal to one, we get

$$\int_a^b \delta(x - \xi)\, dx = \begin{cases} 1 & \text{if} \quad \xi \in (a, b), \\ 0 & \text{if} \quad \xi \notin [a, b]. \end{cases} \tag{41}$$

The Green's function of a differential operator L and given *homogeneous* linear initial or boundary conditions satisfies the symbolic equation

$$L_x G(x, \xi) = \delta(x - \xi) \tag{42}$$

and the same initial or boundary conditions (in x). Now consider the function

$$u(x) = \int G(x, \xi) r(\xi)\, d\xi. \tag{43}$$

Extending heuristically the Superposition Principle of §1 to integrals (considered as limits of sums), we are led to the good guess that $u(x)$ satisfies the same initial (resp. boundary) conditions and also

$$L[u] = L_x \left[\int G(x, \xi) r(\xi)\, d\xi \right] = \int \delta(x - \xi) r(\xi)\, d\xi = r(x). \tag{44}$$

EXERCISES D

In Exercises 1–3, (a) construct Green's functions for the two-endpoint problem defined by the DE specified and the boundary conditions $u(0) = u(1) = 0$, and (b) solve for $r(x) = x^2$:

1. $u'' - u = r(x)$.
2. $u'' + 4u = r(x)$.
3. $u'' - \dfrac{4x}{2x - 1} u' + \dfrac{4}{2x - 1} u = r(x)$.

In Exercises 4 through 6, find the conjugate points nearest to $x = 0$ for the DE specified.

4. $u'' + 2u' + 10u = 0$.
5. $(x^2 - x + 1)u'' + (1 - 2x)u' + 2u = 0$. [HINT: Look for polynomial solutions.]
6*. $u_{tt} - u_t + e^{2t}u = 0$. [HINT: Use Exercise B10.]
7. (a) Show that, for two-endpoint problems containing no pairs of conjugate points, Green's function is always negative.

(b) Show that, if $q(x) < 0$, then the Green's function for $u'' + q(x)u = 0$ in the two-endpoint problem is always negative and convex (concave downward), with negative slope where $x < \xi$ and positive slope where $x > \xi$.

ADDITIONAL EXERCISES

1. Show that the ratio $v = f/g$ of any two linearly independent solutions of the
DE $u'' + q(x)u = 0$ is a solution of the third-order nonlinear DE

$$S[v] = \frac{v'''}{v'} - \frac{3}{2}\left(\frac{v''}{v'}\right)^2 = 2q(x). \qquad (*)$$

2. The *Schwarzian* $S[v]$ of a function $v(x)$ being defined by the middle term of
(*), show that $S[(av + b)/(cv + d)] = S[v]$ for any four constants, a, b, c, d with
$ad \neq bc$.

3*. Prove that, if v_0, v_1, v_2, v_3 are any four distinct solutions of the Riccati DE,
their cross ratio is constant: $(v_0 - v_1)(v_3 - v_2)/(v_0 - v_2)(v_3 - v_1) = c$.

4. Find the general solutions of the following inhomogeneous Euler DE's:
    (a) $x^2y'' - 2xy' + 2y = x^2 + px + q$,   (b) $x^2y'' + 3xy' + y = R(x)$.

5. (a) Show that, if f and g satisfy $u'' + q(x)u = 0$, the product $fg = y$ satisfies
$2yy'' = (y')^2 - 4y^2q(x) + c$ for some constant c.

    (b)* Express the general solution of the latter DE for given c, in terms of f
and g, assuming $W(f, g) \neq 0$.

    (c) As an application, solve $2yy'' = (y')^2 - (x + 1)^{-2}y^2 + 1$.

6. Show that, if u is the general solution of the DE (1) of the text, and $W_{ij} = p_i p_j' - p_i' p_j$, then $v = u'$ is the general solution of

$$p_0 p_2 v'' + (p_1 p_2 - W_{02})v' + (p_2^2 - W_{12})v = W_{23}.$$

7. (a) Show that the Riccati equation $y' = 1 + x^2 + y^2$ has no solution on the
interval $(0, \pi)$.

    (b) Show that the Riccati equation $y' = 1 + y^2 - x^2$ has a solution on the
interval $(-\infty, +\infty)$.

8. In $u''(x) = p(x)u'(x) + q(x)u(x)$, let $p(x) > p_0$ and $q(x) > q_0$, where p_0, q_0 are
positive constants. Prove that, if $u(0) > 0$ and $u'(0) > 0$, there exists a positive
A such that $u(x) > A \exp(p_0 x)$ for all $x > 0$. [HINT: Apply the Comparison Theorem of Chapter 1 to the Riccati equation.]

9. For the DE $u'' + (B/x^2)u = 0$, show that every solution has infinitely many
zeros on $(1, +\infty)$ if $B > \frac{1}{4}$, and a finite number if $B < \frac{1}{4}$. [HINT: The DE is
an Euler DE.]

10. For the DE $u'' + q(x)u = 0$, show that every solution has a finite number of
zeros on $(1, +\infty)$ if $q(x) < 1/4x^2$, and infinitely many if $q(x) > B/x^2$, $B > \frac{1}{4}$.

11*. For the DE $u'' + q(x)u = 0$, show that every solution has infinitely many
zeros on $(1, +\infty)$ if

$$\int_1^\infty \left[xq(x) - \frac{1}{4x}\right] dx = +\infty.$$

12*. Show that, if p, $q \in \mathscr{C}^2$ and $I(0) \neq 0$, we can transform DE (8) to the form
$d^2z/d\xi^2 = 0$ in some neighborhood of the y-axis by transformations of the form
$z = f(x)y$ and $d\xi = h(x) dx$. [HINT: Use Exs. B4, B5, B10 to transform a basis of
solutions to $y_1 = 1$, $y_2 = \xi$.]

3   *Power Series Solutions*

I   Introduction

In Chapters 1 and 2, we showed how to construct solutions of various special types of DE's, using the Fundamental Theorem of the Calculus—that is, how to reduce the integration of these DE's to one or more quadratures. The devices used lead to formulas expressing the general solution explicitly, in terms of the integration symbol $\int$. However, a much more fundamental approach is to think of the solutions of a given DE as *defined* by this DE and appropriate initial conditions or other boundary conditions.

Even in the integral calculus, many functions "cannot be integrated" in terms of elementary functions. Thus, such expressions as

$$\int \frac{\sin x}{x} \, dx, \quad \int \frac{e^{-x}}{x} \, dx, \quad \text{and} \quad \int \frac{dx}{\sqrt{(1 - x^2)(1 - k^2 x^2)}} \tag{1}$$

are conspicuously missing from Tables of Integrals. The Fundamental Theorem of the Calculus, which guarantees the existence and uniqueness of integrals of continuous functions, provides a way out of the difficulty (cf. Chapter 1, § 2). We simply *define* such higher transcendental functions by the formulas

$$\mathrm{SI}(x) = \int_x^\infty \frac{\sin \xi}{\xi} \, d\xi, \qquad \mathrm{EI}(x) = \int_x^\infty \frac{e^{-\xi}}{\xi} \, d\xi,$$

$$\int_0^x \frac{d\xi}{\sqrt{(1 - \xi^2)(1 - k^2 \xi^2)}} = F(k, \arcsin x). \tag{2}$$

By the Fundamental Theorem of the Calculus, these formulas define differentiable functions whose values can be computed (though inefficiently, see Chapters 7 and 8) as limits of Riemann sums.

This is also a good way to treat the logarithmic function.† One can define $\log_e x = \ln x$ as the definite integral (limit of Riemann sums):

$$\ln x = \int_1^x \frac{dt}{t} = \lim_{n \to \infty} \sum_{k=1}^n \frac{x-1}{n + k(x-1)}. \tag{3}$$

From this definition, using the Fundamental Theorem of the Calculus, one can derive all the properties of logarithms.

Just as $\ln x$ can be defined as the solution of the DE $y' = 1/x$ which satisfies $y(1) = 0$, so the inverse function e^x can be defined as the solution of the DE $y' = y$ satisfying the initial condition $y(0) = 1$, and its fundamental properties can be derived from this definition.

Moreover, many oscillation and nonoscillation properties of functions can be deduced simply by looking at the DE's which they satisfy, and using the results of Chapter 2, §§ 4, 5.

From now on, we will tend more and more to regard the solutions of a DE as *defined* by the DE and appropriate initial conditions or boundary conditions. The validity of this approach depends, of course, on theorems of existence, uniqueness, and continuity, which we have so far proved only in special cases.

In the present chapter, we will first show how various *analytic* functions can be effectively defined as solutions of second-order linear homogeneous DE's

$$u'' + p(x)u' + q(x)u = 0, \tag{4}$$

with *analytic* coefficient-functions

$$p(x) = p_0 + p_1 x + p_2 x^2 + \cdots, \qquad q(x) = q_0 + q_1 x + q_2 x^2 + \cdots. \tag{5}$$

These functions include many of the special functions most commonly used in applied mathematics.

We will then give a similar construction for the solutions of normal first-order DE's of the form $y' = F(x, y)$, where

$$F(x, y) = b_{00} + b_{10} x + b_{01} y + b_{20} x^2 + b_{11} xy + b_{02} y^2 + \cdots \tag{5'}$$

is also assumed to be analytic. Finally, we will estimate the radius of convergence of this series.

In summary, restricting our attention to *analytic* functions, we will develop in this chapter the basic idea stated above: that *DE's and appropriate boundary conditions constitute one of the best ways of defining new functions*, and that the properties of these functions can often be best derived directly from a study of the defining DE.

---

† See, for example, Courant and John, pp. 145–55.

2   Method of undetermined coefficients

The class $\mathscr{A}(D)$ of functions *analytic* in a domain D is defined as the class of those functions which can be expanded in a power series around any point of D, which is *convergent* in some neighborhood of that point. By a translation of coordinates, one can reduce the consideration of such power series to power series like (5) and (5') of §1, having the origin as the center of expansion.

Most of the special functions commonly used in applied mathematics have simple power series expansions. This is especially true of functions defined as definite integrals. Thus:

$$\mathrm{SI}(x) = \int_x^\infty \sum_{k=0}^\infty (-1)^k \frac{\xi^{2k}d\xi}{(2k+1)!} = \frac{\pi}{2} - \sum_{k=0}^\infty (-1)^k \frac{x^{2k+1}}{(2k+1)^2(2k)!} ;$$

only the evaluation of the constant term $\pi/2$ poses any difficulty. Expanding the integrand in power series, we obtain the first few terms of the series expansion for the elliptic integral

$$F(k, \sin^{-1} x) = \int_0^x (1 - \xi^2)^{-1/2}(1 - k^2\xi^2)^{-1/2} \, d\xi$$
$$= x + (1 + k^2)x^3/6 + (3 + 2k^2 + 3k^3)x^5/40 - \cdots,$$

with a little more effort.

Likewise, consider the exponential function e^x, defined as the solution of $y' = y$ and the initial condition $y(0) = 1$. Differentiating this DE n times, we get $y^{(n+1)} = y^{(n)}$. Substitution into Taylor's formula then gives the familiar exponential series $e^x = \sum_{k=0}^\infty x^k/(k!)$.

We now give some simple applications of the same principle to some special functions familiar in applied mathematics, defined as solutions of second-order linear homogeneous DE's (4) with analytic coefficient-functions.

To express such solutions in the form of power series, we write the solution in the form of a power series $u = a_0 + a_1 x + a_2 x^2 + \cdots$ with undetermined coefficients a_k, substitute into the DE, differentiate term by term, and equate to zero the coefficients of each power x^k of x. This is called the Method of Undetermined Coefficients.

To apply this method, we must assume that p and q are analytic near the origin. This means that they can be expanded into power series

$$p(x) = p_0 + p_1 x + p_2 x^2 + \cdots, \qquad q(x) = q_0 + q_1 x + q_2 x^2 + \cdots, \qquad (5)$$

convergent for sufficiently small x.

To compute the solution, form the trial series

$$u = a_0 + a_1 x + a_2 x^2 + a_3 x^3 + \cdots = \sum_{k=0}^\infty a_k x^k. \qquad (6)$$

Term-by-term differentiation gives

$$u'' = 2a_2 + 6a_3 x + 12a_4 x^2 + \cdots + (n+1)(n+2)a_{n+2} x^n + \cdots,$$

$$pu' = p_0 a_1 + (2p_0 a_2 + p_1 a_1)x + \cdots + \left[\sum_{k=0}^{n}(n+1-k)p_k\, a_{n+1-k}\right]x^n + \cdots,$$

$$qu = q_0 a_0 + (q_0 a_1 + q_1 a_0)x + \cdots + \left[\sum_{k=0}^{n} q_k\, a_{n-k}\right]x^n + \cdots.$$

Substituting into (4) and equating the coefficients of $1, x, \cdots, x^{n-1}, \cdots$ to zero, we get successively

$$a_2 = -(p_0 a_1 + q_0 a_0)/2, \qquad a_3 = -(2p_0 a_2 + p_1 a_1 + q_0 a_1 + q_1 a_0)/6,$$

and so on. The general equation is

$$a_{n+1} = -\left[\sum_{k=0}^{n-1}(n-k)p_k\, a_{n-k} + \sum_{k=0}^{n-1} q_k\, a_{n-1-k}\right]\Big/ n(n+1), \qquad n \geqq 1. \quad (7)$$

Given $a_0 = f(0)$ and $a_1 = f'(0)$, a unique power series is determined by (7) which formally satisfies the DE (4). We have proved the following theorem.

■ **THEOREM 1.** *Given a linear homogeneous second-order* DE (4) *with analytic coefficient functions* (5), *there exists a unique power series* (6) *which formally satisfies the* DE, *for each choice of a_0 and a_1.*

CAUTION.   We have not stated or proved that the formal power series (6) converges or that it represents a function. To see the need for proving this, consider the DE $x^2 u' = u - x$, which has the everywhere *divergent* formal power series solution

$$x + x^2 + (2!)x^3 + (3!)x^4 + \cdots + (n-1)!\, x^n + \cdots.$$

For *normal* second-order linear DE's (4), the *convergence* of the power series (6) to an *analytic function* will be proved in § 6. First we treat some special cases, in which convergence is easily verified.

EXAMPLE 1.   The Legendre DE (Chapter 2, § 1) is usually written

$$\frac{d}{dx}\left[(1-x^2)\frac{du}{dx}\right] + \lambda u = 0, \qquad (8)$$

where λ is a parameter.

Substituting the series (6) into the linear DE (8), and equating to zero the coefficients of $1 = x^0, x, x^2, \cdots$, we get an infinite system of linear equations

$$0 = 2a_2 + \lambda a_0 = 6a_3 + (\lambda - 2)a_1 = 12a_4 + (\lambda - 6)a_2 = \cdots.$$

The kth equation of this system is the *recurrence relation*

$$a_{k+2} = [k(k+1) - \lambda]a_k/(k+1)(k+2). \tag{8'}$$

This relation defines for each λ two linearly independent solutions, one consisting of *even* powers of x, and the other of *odd* powers of x. These solutions are power series whose *radius of convergence* is unity by the Ratio Test,† unless $\lambda = n(n+1)$ for some nonnegative integer n. In this case there is a polynomial solution which is an even function if n is even and an odd function if n is odd. These polynomial solutions are the *Legendre polynomials* $P_n(x)$.

Graphs of the Legendre polynomials $P_0(x), \ldots, P_4(x)$ are shown in Figure 3.1. Note how the number of their oscillations increases with $\lambda = n(n+1)$, as predicted by the Sturm Comparison Theorem.

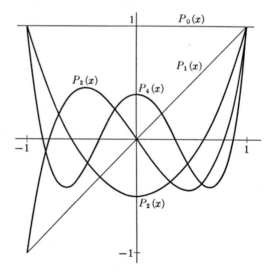

Figure 3.1   Graphs of $P_n(x)$; Legendre polynomials.

EXAMPLE 2.   The Hermite DE is

$$u'' - 2xu' + \lambda u = 0. \tag{9}$$

Applying the Method of Undetermined Coefficients to (9), we obtain the recursion formula

$$a_{k+2} = (2k - \lambda)a_k/(k+1)(k+2), \tag{9'}$$

which again gives, for each λ, one power series in the even powers x^{2k} of x and another in the odd powers x^{2k+1}. These power series are convergent for all x; if $\lambda = 2n$ is a nonnegative even integer, one series is a polynomial of degree n, the *Hermite polynomial* $H_n(x)$.

---

† Courant and John, p. 520; Widder, p. 288.

3* Sine and cosine functions

To emphasize the idea that the properties of solutions of DE's can be derived from the DE's themselves, we now study the *trigonometric DE*

$$y'' + y = 0. \qquad (10)$$

The general solution of this DE is $y = a \cos x + b \sin x$, where a and b are arbitrary constants, and the functions $\cos x$ and $\sin x$ are defined geometrically.

We shall now pretend that we do not know this, and show that all properties of the trigonometric functions $\sin x$ and $\cos x$ can be deduced analytically from the trigonometric DE (10), and the initial conditions which they satisfy. In this spirit, we *define* the functions $C(x)$ and $S(x)$ as the solutions of the DE (10) satisfying the initial conditions $C(0) = 1$, $C'(0) = 0$ and $S(0) = 0$, $S'(0) = 1$, respectively. The Method of Undetermined Coefficients of § 2 gives, for these functions, the familiar power series expansions

$$C(x) = 1 - \frac{x^2}{2!} + \frac{x^4}{4!} - \cdots, \qquad S(x) = x - \frac{x^3}{3!} + \frac{x^5}{5!} - \cdots, \qquad (11)$$

whose convergence for all x follows by the Ratio Test.

Differentiation of (10) gives the DE $y''' + y' = 0$. Therefore, the function $C'(x)$ is also a solution of the DE (10); moreover, since this function satisfies the initial conditions $C'(0) = 0$ and $C''(0) = -C(0) = -1$, it follows from the Uniqueness Theorem (Chapter 2, Theorem 1) that $C'(x) = -S(x)$. This proves the differentiation rule for the cosine function. A similar computation gives $S'(x) = C(x)$.

The Wronskian of the functions $C(x)$ and $S(x)$ can be computed from these two formulas; it is $W(C, S; x) = C(x)^2 + S(x)^2$. From Theorem 3 of Chapter 2, $W(C, S; x) \equiv C(0)^2 + S(0)^2 = 1$ follows. This proves the familiar trigonometric formula $\cos^2 x + \sin^2 x = 1$.

Again, by Theorem 2 of Chapter 2, every solution of the DE (10) is a linear combination of the functions S and C. We now use this fact to derive the addition formula for the sine function:

$$\sin(a + x) = \cos a \sin x + \sin a \cos x.$$

First, by the chain rule for differentiating composite functions, the function $S(a + x)$ is also a solution of DE (10). Therefore (Chapter 2, Theorem 2), this function must be a linear combination of $S(x)$ and $C(x)$:

$$S(a + x) = AS(x) + BC(x).$$

Furthermore, if we write $f(x) = S(a + x)$, then $f(0) = S(a)$ and $f'(0) = C(a)$. But if we differentiate the right side of the equality displayed above, we find that $f(0) = B$ and $f'(0) = A$, and this proves the addition formula. The addition formula for C(x),

$$C(a + x) = C(a)C(x) - S(a)S(x),$$

can be derived similarly.

Finally, the fact that the functions S and C are periodic can be proved from the addition formulas, if one defines $\pi/4$ as the least positive x such that $S(\pi/4) = 1/\sqrt{2}$. Since $S' = C = \sqrt{1 - S^2} \geq 1/\sqrt{2}$ on any interval $[0, b]$ where $S(x) \leq 1/\sqrt{2}$, we see that $S(x)$ is increasing and satisfies $S(x) \geq x/\sqrt{2}$ there. Hence $S(x) \leq 1/\sqrt{2}$ on $[0, 1]$ is impossible, which shows that $\pi/4$ exists in $[0, 1]$. Moreover $\pi/4 = S^{-1}(1/\sqrt{2})$, where S^{-1} is the inverse function of S. Since the derivative of S^{-1} is given by $1/S'(x) = 1/\sqrt{1 - S^2}$, this makes $\pi/4 = \int_0^{1/\sqrt{2}} dt/\sqrt{1 - t^2}$. Moreover, C cannot change sign until $S^2 = 1 - C^2 = 1$. Hence $\cos(\pi/4) = 1/\sqrt{2} = \sin(\pi/4)$. Consequently, by the addition formulas proved above, we have

$$\sin\left(\frac{\pi}{4} + x\right) = \frac{1}{\sqrt{2}}(\sin x + \cos x) = \cos\left(\frac{\pi}{4} - x\right).$$

In particular, $\sin(\pi/2) = (2/\sqrt{2})/\sqrt{2} = 1$ and, therefore, $\cos(\pi/2) = 0$. Using the addition formulas again, we get the formulas $\sin(\pi/2 + x) = \sin(\pi/2 - x)$, $\cos(\pi/2 + x) = -\cos(\pi/2 - x)$, $\sin(\pi + x) = -\sin x$, $\cos(\pi + x) = -\cos x$ and, finally, the periodicity relations $\cos(2\pi + x) = \cos x$, $\sin(2\pi + x) = \sin x$.

EXERCISES A

1. (a) Prove that the Legendre DE has a polynomial solution if and only if $\lambda = n(n + 1)$. (b) Prove that the radius of convergence of every nonpolynomial solution of the Legendre DE is one.
2. Find a recurrence relation like (8′) for the DE $(1 + x^2)y'' = y$, and compute expansions through terms in x^{10} for a basis of solutions.
3. (a) Find power series expansions for a basis of solutions of Airy's DE
   $u'' + xu = 0$.
   (b) Prove that the radius of convergence of both solutions is infinite.
   (c) Show that any solution of Airy's DE vanishes infinitely often on $(0, \infty)$, but at most once on $(-\infty, 0)$.
   (d) Reduce $u'' + (ax + b)u = 0$ to $d^2u/dt^2 + tu = 0$ by a suitable change of independent variable.
4. Define sinh x and cosh x as the solutions of the DE $u'' = u$ which satisfy the initial conditions $u(0) = 0$, $u'(0) = 1$ and $u(0) = 1$, $u'(0) = 0$, respectively. Show that sinh x has only one real zero and cosh x has no real zeros. Relate this to the Sturm Comparison Theorem.
5*. Using methods like those of § 3, establish the following formulas (cf. Ex. 4):
   (a) $\cosh^2 x - \sinh^2 x = 1$,   (b) $\cosh(-x) = \cosh x$,
   (c) $\sinh(-x) = -\sinh x$,   (d) $\sinh(x + y) = \sinh x \cosh y + \cosh x \sinh y$,
   (e) $\sinh^{-1} x = \ln(x + \sqrt{x^2 + 1})$.

6. Show that $u(x)$ satisfies the Hermite DE (9) if and only if $v = e^{-x^2/2}\,u$ satisfies $v'' + (\lambda + 1 - x^2)v = 0$.

7. Show that the DE $(Ax^2 + B)u'' + Cxu' + Du = 0$ has a solution which is a polynomial of degree n if and only if $An^2 + (C - A)n + D = 0$.

8. Show that the change of independent variable $x = \cos\,\theta$ transforms the Legendre DE (8) of the text into $u_{\theta\theta} + (\cot\,\theta)u_\theta + \lambda u = 0$. What is the self-adjoint form of this equation?

9*. Find conditions on the constants $A, \cdots, F$ necessary and sufficient for the DE $(Ax^2 + Bx + C)u'' + (Dx + E)u' + Fu = 0$ to have a solution which is a polynomial of degree n.

10*. (Rodrigues' formula) Show that, for any positive integer n, the polynomial $d^n[(x^2 - 1)^n]/dx^n$ is a solution of the Legendre DE with $\lambda = n(n + 1)$.

4* Bessel functions

The Bessel function of order n can be defined similarly, for $n = 0$, 1, 2, ..., as a solution of the Bessel DE of order n,

$$u'' + \frac{1}{x}\,u' + \left(1 - \frac{n^2}{x^2}\right)u = 0. \tag{12}$$

The coefficients of this DE have a singular point at $x = 0$, but are analytic at all other points (see § 5).

Though the Bessel DE (12) of integral order n has a singular point at the origin, it has a nontrivial analytic solution there. The power series expression for this solution can be computed by the Method of Undetermined Coefficients. For example, when $n = 0$, the DE (12) reduces to

$$(xu')' + xu = 0. \tag{13}$$

Substituting $u = \sum a_k x^k$ into (13), we get the recursion relation $k^2 a_k = -a_{k-2}$. For $a_0 = 1$, $a_1 = 0$, (13) has the analytic solution

$$J_0(x) = 1 - \left(\frac{x}{2}\right)^2 + \left(\frac{x^2}{2\cdot4}\right)^2 - \left(\frac{x^3}{2\cdot4\cdot6}\right)^2 + \cdots$$

$$= 1 - \frac{x^2}{4} + \frac{x^4}{64} - \frac{x^6}{2304} + \cdots + (-1)^r\frac{x^{2r}}{[2^r(r!)]^2} + \cdots. \tag{14}$$

This series is convergent for all x, by the Ratio Test; it defines the Bessel function of order zero

Similar calculations give, for general n, the solution

$$J_n(x) = \left(\frac{x}{2}\right)^n\left\{\frac{1}{n!} - \frac{x^2}{4(n+1)!} + \frac{x^4}{32(n+2)!} - \cdots \right.$$

$$\left. + (-1)^r\left(\frac{x}{2}\right)^{2r}/(r!)(n+r)! + \cdots\right\}, \tag{15}$$

whose coefficients $b_k = a_{k+n}$ satisfy the relation $(n^2 - k^2)b_k = b_{k-2}$. The series (15) is also everywhere convergent. Hence the Bessel function $J_n(x)$ of order n is an *entire* function, analytic for all finite x. Graphs of $J_0(x)$ and $J_1(x)$ are shown as Figure 3.2.

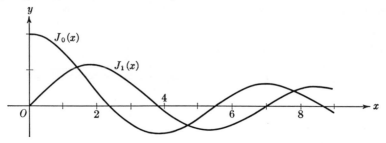

Figure 3.2   Bessel functions $J_0(x)$ and $J_1(x) = -J_0'(x)$.

By comparing coefficients, one can easily verify the relations

$$J_1 = -J_0', \qquad xJ_2 = J_1 - xJ_1' = 2J_1 - xJ_0, \qquad xJ_3 = 2J_2 - xJ_2'.$$

For general n, one can verify, in the same way, the *recursion formula*

$$xJ_{n+1} = nJ_n - xJ_n' = 2nJ_n - xJ_{n-1}. \tag{16}$$

Clearly, formula (16) defines $J_1, J_2, J_3, \ldots$ recursively from J_0.

One can prove all the properties of the Bessel functions of integral order from (12) and the recursion relations (16). For example, one can obtain such useful formulas as

$$\int xJ_0\, dx = xJ_1, \qquad \int xJ_1\, dx = -xJ_0 + \int J_0\, dx,$$

$$\int xJ_0^2\, dx = (x^2/2)(J_0^2 + J_1^2) = (x^2/2)(J_0^2 + J_0'^2).$$

More generally, we can obtain useful expressions representing, in closed form, integrals of arbitrary polynomial functions times Bessel functions and products of Bessel functions. The basic formulas are (16) and

$$\int x^k J_1\, dx = -x^k J_0 + k\int x^{k-1}J_0\, dx, \tag{17a}$$

$$\int x^k J_0\, dx = x^k J_1 - (k-1)\int x^{k-1}J_1\, dx, \tag{17b}$$

$$2\int x^k J_0 J_1\, dx = -x^k J_0^2 + k\int x^{k-1}J_0^2\, dx, \tag{17c}$$

$$\int x^k (J_0^2 - J_1^2)\, dx = x^k J_0 J_1 - (k-1)\int x^{k-1}J_0 J_1\, dx, \tag{17d}$$

$$\int x^k [(k+1)J_0^2 + (k-1)J_1^2]\, dx = x^{k+1}(J_0^2 + J_1^2). \tag{17e}$$

Equation (17a) follows from $J_1 = -J_0'$, integrating by parts. To derive (17b), note that since $(xJ_0')' = -xJ_0$, it follows that

$$(x^k J_1)' = -[x^{k-1}(xJ_0')]' = -(k-1)x^{k-1}J_0' + x^k J_0.$$

To derive (17c)–(17e), differentiate $x^k J_0^2$, $x^k J_0 J_0'$, and $x^{k+1}(J_0^2 + J_0'^2)$, respectively, and use (13) to eliminate J_0''. The integral $\int J_0\, dx$ cannot be reduced further, and so it has been calculated (by numerical integration) and tabulated.†

Important *qualitative* information can also be obtained from a study of DE (12) which the Bessel functions satisfy. Substituting $u = v/\sqrt{x}$ into (12), we obtain the equivalent DE

$$v'' + \left[1 - \frac{4n^2 - 1}{4x^2}\right]v = 0. \tag{18}$$

The oscillatory behavior of nontrivial solutions of the Bessel DE (12), for large x, can now be shown, using the Sturm Comparison Theorem (Chapter 2, § 4). When applied to (18), this result shows that, for large x, the distance between successive zeros of $J_0(x)$ is inferior to π by a small quantity (at most $\pi/8x^2$), while that between successive zeros x_i and x_{i+1} of $J_n(x)$ exceeds π by about $n^2\pi/2x_i^2$ if $n \geq 1$. Also, since $J_1 = -J_0'$, there is a zero of J_1 between any two successive zeros of J_0.

Setting $\sigma(x) = v^2 + v'^2 = x(J_n^2 + J_n'^2) + J_n J_n' + J_n^2/4x$, it also follows from (18) that $\sigma'(x) = (4n^2 - 1)vv'/2x^2$. Since $|2vv'| \leq v^2 + v'^2 = \sigma(x)$, there follows

$$|\sigma'(x)| \leq K_n \sigma(x)/x^2, \qquad K_n = |n^2 - \tfrac{1}{4}|, \qquad \sigma(x) > 0. \tag{18'}$$

Using the Comparison Theorem of Chapter 1, § 11, we get from (18')

$$Ae^{-K_n/x} \leq \sigma(x) = x(J_n^2 + J_n'^2) + J_n J_n' + J_n^2/4x \leq Ae^{K_n/x},$$

where $K_n = |n^2 - 1/4|$. For large x, therefore, $\sigma(x)$ must approach a constant A. Clearly, $A/\sqrt{x}$ is the asymptotic *amplitude* of the oscillations of the Bessel functions for large x, since J_n' vanishes at maxima and minima of $J_n(x)$, so that $\sigma(x) = xJ_n^2(x)$ there. Much more precise results about the oscillations of Bessel functions will be proved in Chapter 10.

The function $Y_0(x)$. The general solution of the Bessel DE of zero order is, by Chapter 2, (13'),

$$Z_0(x) = J_0(x)[A + B\int dx/xJ_0^2(x)]. \tag{19}$$

---

† G. N. Watson, *Bessel Functions*, Chapter 8. Cambridge; A. N. Lowan et al., *J. Math. and Phys.* **22** (1943).

But a straightforward computation with power series gives

$$1/J_0{}^2(x) = 1 + x^2/2 + 5x^4/32 \cdots.$$

From this formula, substituting back into (19) and integrating the resulting series term-by-term, we see that the general solution $Z_0(x)$ of the Bessel DE of zero order is

$$Z_0(x) = J_0(x)[A + B(\ln x + x^2/4 + 5x^4/128 + \cdots). \tag{20}$$

It follows that every solution not linearly dependent on $J_0(x)$ becomes logarithmically infinite as $x{\downarrow}0$, since $B \neq 0$.

Generating functions. Given a sequence $\{a_n\}$ of constants $a_0, a_1, a_2, \cdots$, the power series

$$g(x) = a_0 + a_1 x + a_2 x^2 + \cdots = \sum_{n=0}^{\infty} a_n x^n$$

is called its *generating function.* When the series on the right converges in an interval, this defines a function $g(x)$ there; otherwise, the infinite series is just a formal power series. In many cases, useful information can be obtained about a sequence $\{a_n\}$ merely by recognizing its generating function explicitly. Examples of generating functions can be found in the exercises below.

Likewise given a sequence of functions $F_n(r)$, the function defined by the power series $\sum t^n F_n(r)$ is also called the " generating function " of the sequence. The same phrase is used when the sum is taken over all integers; for example, the Bessel functions of integral order have the generating function

$$\sum_{-\infty}^{\infty} t^n J_n(r) = e^{r(t-t^{-1})/2}; \tag{21}$$

see Exercise 8 below.

EXERCISES B

1. Verify formula (16).
2. Verify the three formulas displayed below (16).

Establish the identities for Bessel functions of integral order in Exs. 3–6.

3. $J_n(-x) = (-1)^n J_n(x)$.   5*. $J_{n-1}(x) + J_{n+1}(x) = 2nx^{-1} J_n(x)$.

4*. $\left(\dfrac{1}{x}\dfrac{d}{dx}\right)^k (x^n J_n(x)) = x^{n-k} J_{n-k}(x)$.   6*. $J_{n-1}(x) - J_{n+1}(x) = 2J'_n(x)$.

7. In polar coordinates, $\nabla^2 u = u_{rr} + r^{-1}u_r + r^{-2}u_{\theta\theta}$. Show that $u = J(r) \sin n\theta$ satisfies $\nabla^2 u + u = 0$ if and only if $J(r)$ satisfies $J_{rr} + r^{-1}J_r + (1 - n^2/r^2)J = 0$.

8*. (a) Show that the real and imaginary parts cos $(r \sin \theta)$ and sin $(r \sin \theta)$ of $e^{iy} = e^{ir \sin \theta}$ satisfy $\nabla^2 u + u = 0$.

(b) Show that $e^{iy} = e^{r(t-t^{-1})/2}$, $t = e^{i\theta}$, $y = r \sin \theta$.

(c) Show that the functions $F_n(r)$ in the Laurent series expansion

$$e^{r(t-t^{-1})/2} = \sum_{-\infty}^{\infty} t^n F_n(r)$$

satisfy the Bessel equation of order n. [Use (a) and (b).]

(d) Comparing the coefficients of $t^n r^n$, prove the identity $e^{r(t-t^{-1})/2} = \sum_{-\infty}^{\infty} t^n J_n(r)$, where $J_{-n}(x) = J_n(-x) = (-)^n J_n(x)$.

9. In spherical coordinates, the Laplacian of a function $F(r, \theta)$ is

$$\nabla^2 F = F_{rr} + \frac{2}{r} F_r + \frac{1}{r^2} [F_{\theta\theta} + (\cot \theta) F_\theta].$$

Show that $F(r, \theta) = r^n P(\cos \theta)$ satisfies $\nabla^2 F = 0$ if and only if $P(x)$ satisfies the Legendre DE with $\lambda = n(n + 1)$.

10. (a) Show that, in spherical coordinates, $U(r, \theta) = (1 - 2r \cos \theta + r^2)^{-1/2}$ satisfies $\nabla^2 U = 0$. [HINT: Consider the potential of a charge at $(1, 0, 0)$.]

(b) Infer that $(1 - 2r \cos \theta + r^2)^{-1/2} = \sum_0^\infty r^n P_n(\cos \theta)$, where $P_n(x)$ is a solution of the Legendre equation (8) with $\lambda = n(n + 1)$.

11*. (a) Show that $u(r, \theta, \alpha) = \cos [r \cos (\theta - \alpha)]$ satisfies $\nabla^2 u + u = 0$ for all α, whence so does its average

$$\frac{1}{2\pi} \int_0^{2\pi} u(r, \theta; \alpha) \, d\alpha = U(r).$$

(b) Prove that

$$J_0(r) = \frac{1}{2\pi} \int_{-\pi}^{\pi} \cos [r \cos \alpha] \, d\alpha = \frac{1}{\pi} \int_0^{\pi} \cos [r \cos \alpha] \, d\alpha.$$

12. (a) Show that Kummer's confluent hypergeometric function

$$M(a, b; x) = 1 + \frac{a}{b} x + \frac{a(a+1)}{b(b+1)} \frac{x^2}{2!} + \cdots + \frac{a(a+1) \cdots (a+n)}{b(b+1) \cdots (b+n)} \frac{x^n}{n!} + \cdots$$

is a solution of the DE $xF'' + (b - x)F' + aF = 0$.

(b) Show that the preceding function is an entire function.

5 Analytic functions

A function is called *analytic* in a domain D, when it can be expanded in a power series at any point of D which is *convergent* in some neighborhood of that point. For instance, a real function $p(x)$ of one real variable is analytic in the open interval (x_1, x_2) when, given any x_0 in this interval (i.e., satisfying $x_1 < x_0 < x_2$), there exist coefficients $p_0, p_1, p_2, \cdots$ and a positive number δ such that

$$p(x) = \sum_{k=0}^{\infty} p_k(x - x_0)^k \qquad \text{if} \quad |x - x_0| < \delta, \quad \delta > 0. \tag{22}$$

The numerical values of the coefficients p_k will, of course, depend on x_0.

Likewise, a real function $F(x, y)$ is analytic in a domain D of the real xy-plane when, given $(x_0, y_0) \in D$, there exist constants b_{jk} $(j, k = 0, 1, 2, \ldots)$ and $\delta > 0$ such that

$$F(x, y) = \sum_{j=0}^{\infty} \sum_{k=0}^{\infty} b_{jk}(x - x_0)^j (y - y_0)^k \qquad \text{if} \quad |x - x_0| + |y - y_0| < \delta.$$

An example of such a series expansion is the double geometric series

$$G(x, y) = M \Big/ \left(1 - \frac{x}{H}\right)\left(1 - \frac{y}{K}\right) = \sum_{j=0}^{\infty} \sum_{k=0}^{\infty} \frac{M}{H^j K^k} x^j y^k.$$

This series converges in the rectangle $|x| < H$, $|y| < K$ and defines an analytic function in this rectangle.

Analytic functions of three and more variables are defined similarly.

For analytic functions of one variable, the key concept is that of the radius of convergence. The *radius of convergence* R of the power series (22) is the largest δ such that the series (22) converges whenever $|x - x_0| < \delta$. The radius of convergence of the series (22) is given in terms of its coefficients by Cauchy's formula

$$1/R = \lim \sup_{n \to \infty} \sqrt[n]{|p_n|} = \lim_{n \to \infty} \{\sup_{k > n} \sqrt[k]{|p_k|}\}. \tag{23}$$

The series then diverges for all x with $|x - x_0| > R$. The *interval of convergence* of (22) is the interval $(x_0 - R, x_0 + R)$.

In the complex plane, the radius of convergence of the series (22) can still be defined by formula (23). The series (22) is convergent in the *circle of convergence* $|x - x_0| < R$ and divergent if $|x - x_0| > R$; it defines a single-valued analytic (or *holomorphic*) complex function inside its circle of *convergence*. When $R = \infty$, the power series (22) defines an analytic function for all x, real or complex; such functions are called *entire* functions.

Power series in two or more complex variables also define analytic functions in their domain of convergence, which is always convex. It is understood that the coefficients b_{jk} (like the p_k in (22)) can be complex or real.

Power series can be added, subtracted, multiplied, differentiated, and integrated term-by-term within their interval (circle) of convergence.†

A property of normal *linear* DE's with analytic coefficient functions is the following. Every solution is analytic, with a radius of convergence

---

† Courant, and John, pp. 542–544, 555; Widder, pp. 303–306 and 318–320. For a more complete discussion, see K. Knopp, *Theory and Application of Infinite Series*, Dover, 1956.

at least as large as the smaller of the radii of convergence of the coefficient-functions. We first establish this result in an important special case.

EXAMPLE 3.   The substitution $\xi = C - x$ reduces the DE

$$u'' + \frac{A}{C - x} u' + \frac{B}{(C - x)^2} u = 0, \qquad C > 0, \tag{24}$$

to *Euler's homogeneous* DE

$$\frac{d^2 u}{d\xi^2} - \frac{A}{\xi} \frac{du}{d\xi} + \frac{B}{\xi^2} u = 0, \tag{25}$$

to be discussed more fully in Chapter 4, § 2, and in Chapter 9.

To solve (25), try the function $u = \xi^\nu = (C - x)^\nu$. This satisfies (25) if and only if ν is a root of the *indicial equation* of (25),

$$\nu(\nu - 1) - A\nu + B = 0.$$

When $B < 0$, this indicial equation has one positive root ν and one negative root $-\mu$. Hence (24) has two linearly independent real solutions, given by the binomial series

$$\left(1 - \frac{x}{C}\right)^\nu = 1 - \nu\left(\frac{x}{C}\right) + \frac{\nu(\nu - 1)}{2}\left(\frac{x}{C}\right)^2 - \cdots, \quad |x| < C, \tag{26}$$

and a like series with ν replaced by $-\mu$. When ν is a nonnegative integer, a polynomial solution is obtained. Otherwise, the radius of convergence of the series is C, the same as that of the power series expansions of the coefficient-functions

$$p(x) = A/(C - x) = (A/C)\left[1 + \sum_{k=1}^{\infty} (x/C)^k\right].$$

and $q(x) = B/(C - x)^2$ of DE (24).

6 Method of majorants

If one keeps in mind the results of § 5, one can show quite easily that the formal power series obtained by the Method of Undetermined Coefficients of § 2 have, for all choices of a_0 and a_1, radii of convergence at least as large as the smaller of the radii of convergence of the coefficient functions. To prove this, one uses an ingenious method due to Cauchy, the so-called Method of Majorants.

A power series $\sum a_k x^k$ is said to be *majorized* by the series $\sum A_k x^k$ if and only if $|a_k| \leqq A_k$ for all $k = 0, 1, 2, 3, \ldots$. By the Comparison Test, the radius of convergence of $\sum a_k x^k$ is then at least as large as that of $\sum A_k x^k$, and all A_k are positive or zero. Therefore, we say that the DE

$$u'' = P(x)u' + Q(x)u, \qquad P(x) = \sum P_k x^k, \qquad Q(x) = \sum Q_k x^k, \quad (27)$$

majorizes the DE (4) if and only if $P_k \geq |p_k|$ and $Q_k \geq |q_k|$, for all k.

In particular, the choice of coefficient-functions

$$P(x) = \sum |p_k| x^k \qquad \text{and} \qquad Q(x) = \sum |q_k| x^k \tag{27'}$$

in (27) gives a DE which majorizes (4). Moreover by (23), the coefficient-functions (27') have the same radius of convergence as $p(x)$ and $q(x)$, respectively.

■ **LEMMA.** *Let the* DE (27) *majorize* DE (4), *and let* $\sum_{k=0}^{\infty} c_k x^k$ *be the formal power series solution of* (27) *whose first two coefficients are* $|a_0|$ *and* $|a_1|$. *Then* $c_k \geq |a_k|$ *for all* k.

This lemma may be thought of as a generalized comparison test.

Proof — For the DE (27), the coefficients of formal power series solutions satisfy, by (7) with $p_k = -P_k$, $q_k = -Q_k$:

$$c_{n+1} = \left[\sum_{k=0}^{n-1} (n-k) P_k c_{n-k} + \sum_{k=0}^{n-1} Q_k c_{n-k-1} \right] / n(n+1), \qquad n \geq 1. \quad (7')$$

Hence, if $c_0 \geq |a_0|$, $c_1 \geq |a_1|$, $\cdots$, $c_n \geq |a_n|$, it follows that $c_{n+1} \geq |a_{n+1}|$, as stated. This is because a_{n+1} is given for $n \geq 1$ by a display (7) like (7') above, with each (positive) term replaced by one having at most as great an absolute value. The lemma follows by induction on n.

Now let x_1 be any number whose absolute value $|x_1| = C$ is less than the smaller of the radii of convergence of the two series (5). Then $p_k x_1^k$ and $q_k x_1^k$ are uniformly bounded† in magnitude for all k by some finite constant M. Hence we have

$$|p_k| \leq MC^{-k}, \qquad |q_k| \leq MC^{-k}, \qquad k = 0, 1, 2, \ldots .$$

This implies that the power series for $p(x)$ and $q(x)$ are both majorized by the geometric series

$$M \sum_{k=0}^{\infty} (x/C)^k = MC/(C-x), \qquad \text{for some} \qquad M > 0, C > 0.$$

This series being majorized in turn by

$$MC^2/(C-x)^2 = M \sum_{k=0}^{\infty} (k+1)(x/C)^k,$$

---

† Because, if a series is convergent, its nth term tends to zero as $n \to \infty$.

the DE (4) is majorized by the DE

$$u'' = \frac{MC}{(C-x)} \, u' + \frac{MC^2}{(C-x)^2} \, u. \tag{28}$$

But, as in Example 3, one solution of this DE is the function

$$\phi(x) = [1 - (x/C)]^{-\mu},$$

where $-\mu$ is the negative root of the quadratic indicial equation of (28). As in Example 3, this equation is

$$\nu(\nu - 1) - MC\nu - MC^2 = 0, \qquad \text{where} \quad -MC^2 < 0.$$

This function $\phi(x)$ has a power series expansion

$$\phi(x) = \left(1 - \frac{x}{C}\right)^{-\mu} = 1 + \frac{\mu x}{C} + \frac{\mu(\mu + 1)x^2}{2C^2} + \cdots \tag{29}$$

convergent for $|x| < C$, as in (26).

Now apply the above lemma. Each solution of (4) is majorized by K times the solution $\phi(x)$ of (28), provided that

$$K = \max \left\{ |a_0|, \, |a_1 C/\mu| \right\}. \tag{29'}$$

But $K\phi(x)$ has the radius of convergence C. Hence, by the preceding lemma, the radius of convergence of the series (6) is at least $C = |x_1|$. This proves the following result.

■ THEOREM 2.   *For any choice of a_0 and a_1, the radius of convergence of any power series solution defined by the recursion formula (7) is at least as large as the smaller of the radii of convergence for the series defining the coefficient functions in (4).*

We now recall (§ 5) that power series can be added, multiplied together, and differentiated term-by-term within their intervals (circles) fo convergence. It follows from Theorem 2 that, when applied to power series defined by (7), the three equations displayed in § 2 between formulas (6) and (7) are identities in the common interval of convergence specified. Hence the power series defined by (7) are solutions of (4), and we have proved the following local existence theorem.

■ THEOREM 3.   *Any initial-value problem defined by a normal second-order linear homogeneous DE (4) with analytic coefficient functions and initial conditions $f(0) = a_0$, $f'(0) = a_1$ has an analytic solution near $x = 0$, given by (7).*

EXERCISES C

1. Let $\Sigma\, a_k x^k$ have the radius of convergence R. Show that, for any $r < R$, the series is majorized by $\Sigma\,(m/r^k)x^k$ for some $m > 0$.
2. Using Exercise 1, prove Cauchy's formula (23).
3. Prove that, unless ν is a nonnegative integer, the radius of convergence of the binomial series (26) is C.
4. Using the symbols A, B, C to denote the series $\Sigma a_k x^k$, $\Sigma b_k x^k$, $\Sigma c_k x^k$, and writing $A \ll B$ to express the statement that series A is majorized by series B, prove the following results:
   (a) $A \ll B$ and $B \ll C$ imply $A \ll C$.
   (b) $A \ll B$ and $B \ll A$ imply $A = B$.
   (c) If $A \ll B$, then the derivative series $A' : \Sigma k a_k x^k$ and $B' : \Sigma k b_k x^k$ satisfy $A' \ll B'$.
   (d) If $A \ll B$ and $C \ll D$, then $A + C \ll B + D$ and $AC \ll BD$.
5. Prove that the radius of convergence of $\Sigma a_k x^k$ is unaffected by term-by-term differentiation or integration.
6. (a) Obtain a recursion relation on the coefficients a_k of power series solutions $\Sigma a_k x^k$ of Pearson's DE $y' = (D + Ex)y/(A + Bx + Cx^2)$, $A \neq 0$.
   (b) What is the radius of convergence of the solution?
   (c) Integrate by quadratures, and compare.
7*. Extend the Method of Majorants of § 6 to prove the convergence of the power series solutions of the inhomogeneous DE $u'' + p(x)u' + q(x)u = r(x)$, when the functions p, q, r are all analytic.
8*. Let the coefficients of $u = \Sigma a_k x^k$ satisfy a recursion relation of the form $a_{k+1}/a_k = P(k)/Q(k+1)$, where P and Q are polynomials without common factors. Show that u must satisfy a DE of the form

$$Q\left(x\,\frac{d}{dx}\right)[u] = x P\left(x\,\frac{d}{dx}\right)[u],$$

and conversely.

7   First-order nonlinear DE's

The Method of Undetermined Coefficients and the Method of Majorants can also be applied to any normal analytic *first-order* DE of the form

$$dy/dx = F(x, y) = \sum_{j=0}^{\infty} \sum_{k=0}^{\infty} b_{jk}\, x^j y^k. \tag{30}$$

The discussion is however more difficult, since *nonlinear* DE's are concerned. We first treat a simple example.

EXAMPLE 4.   The general solution of the DE

$$y' = 1 + y^2 \tag{31}$$

is $y = \tan{(x - c)}$, since (31) implies

$$x = \int dy/(1 + y^2) = c + \arctan y,$$

where c is an arbitrary constant. We therefore *define* the function $\tan x$ as the solution of (31) which satisfies the initial condition $y(0) = 0$, and proceed to derive some of its basic properties from this definition.

Since $1 + y^2$ is positive, $\tan x$ is always increasing. Again, by repeated differentiation, we get the formulas

$$y'' = 2yy' = 2(y + y^3), \qquad y''' = 2(1 + 3y^2)y' = 2(1 + 3y^2)(1 + y^2),$$

and so on. These formulas show that y'' has the same sign as y: the graph of $y = \tan x$ is concave upwards in the upper half-plane; likewise, y''' is always positive.

Again, setting $t = -x$ and $z = -y$, we obtain the formulas

$$dz/dt = dy/dx = 1 + y^2 = 1 + z^2 \qquad \text{and} \qquad z(0) = 0.$$

Hence $z(t)$ satisfies the initial-value problem of Example 4; therefore, by the uniqueness theorem (Chapter 1, Theorem 5) for first-order DE's, $z = \tan t$. This proves that $-\tan(-x) = \tan x$: $\tan x$ is an *odd function*.

Consequently, the Taylor series expansion of $\tan x$ contains only terms of odd order:

$$y = x + a_3 x^3 + a_5 x^5 + a_7 x^7 + a_9 x^9 + \cdots.$$

Substituting into the defining DE (31), we obtain

$$1 + 3a_3 x^2 + 5a_5 x^4 + 7a_7 x^6 + 9a_9 x^8 + \cdots$$
$$= 1 + x^2 + 2a_3 x^4 + (2a_5 + a_3{}^2)x^6 + 2(a_7 + a_3 a_5)x^8 + \cdots.$$

Equating coefficients of like powers of x, we get

$$3a_3 = 1, \qquad 5a_5 = 2a_3, \qquad 7a_7 = 2a_5 + a_3{}^2, \qquad 9a_9 = 2a_7 + 2a_3 a_5,$$

and so on. Solving recursively, we get the first few terms of the power series expansion for $\tan x$,

$$\tan x = x + \frac{x^3}{3} + \frac{2x^5}{15} + \frac{17}{315}x^7 + \frac{62}{2835} x^9 + \cdots. \tag{32}$$

The radius of convergence of this power series is $\pi/2$; this follows from the formula $\tan x = \sin x/\cos x$ and the results of § 3.

8 Undetermined coefficients

The preceding Method of Undetermined Coefficients can be applied to analytic first-order DE's generally. For simplicity, we treat the initial condition $y(0) = 0$, to which any initial condition can be reduced by a translation of coordinates.

Namely, we look for a solution of (30) in the power series form

$$y = f(x) = a_1 x + a_2 x^2 + a_3 x^3 + \cdots; \tag{33}$$

the coefficient a_0 vanishes since it is assumed that $f(0) = 0$. Hence

$$y' = a_1 + 2a_2 x + 3a_3 x^2 + \cdots \tag{33'}$$

in the interval of convergence. The coefficients a_k can be calculated recursively by substituting these power series into the given equation (30), and equating the coefficients of like powers of x in the resulting expression. Carrying out the steps indicated, we obtain in succession

$$a_1 = b_{00}, \qquad 2a_2 = b_{10} + b_{01}a_1,$$
$$3a_3 = b_{01}a_2 + b_{20} + b_{11}a_1 + b_{02}a_1{}^2, \tag{34}$$

and so on. The expression on the right side of each of these equations is a polynomial with positive integral coefficients. Equations (34) can be solved recursively, giving the formulas

$$a_1 = b_{00}, \qquad a_2 = (b_{10} + b_{00}b_{01})/2,$$
$$a_3 = (b_{20} + b_{11}b_{00} + b_{02}b_{00}{}^2)/3 + (b_{10}b_{01} + b_{00}b_{01}{}^2)/6,$$

and so on. When we substitute the series (33) for y into the series (30) for $F(x, y)$, the coefficient of x^h is a sum of products of factors b_{jk} (with $j + k \leq h$) times polynomials of degree k in the a_i obtained by raising the series (33) to the kth power. The coefficient of x^h on the left side of (30) is, however, $(h + 1)a_{h+1}$, by (33′). Equating coefficients of like powers of x, we have, therefore,

$$(h + 1)a_{h+1} = q_h(b_{00}, \ldots, b_{0h}; b_{10}, \ldots, b_{1,h-1}; \ldots; b_{h0}; a_1, \ldots, a_h), \tag{34'}$$

where the coefficients of q_h are positive integers. Substituting for $a_1, \ldots, a_h$ already available formulas, we obtain

$$a_{h+1} = p_h(b_{00}, \ldots, b_{0h}; b_{10}, \ldots, b_{1,h-1}; \ldots; b_{h0}).$$

The *polynomial* functions p_h have *positive, rational* numbers as coefficients. They are the same, no matter which function $F(x, y)$ is used in (30).

Solving the resulting equation at $x = 0$ for $a_{n+1} = y^{(n+1)}/(n + 1)!$, we get the following result.

■ THEOREM 4.   *There exists a power series (33) which formally satisfies any analytic first-order DE (30). The coefficients of this formal power series are polynomial functions of the b_{hk} with positive rational coefficients.*

The preceding formulas can also be obtained in another way. Let $y = f(x)$ be the graph of any solution of the DE $y' = F(x, y)$, and let

$u(x, y)$ be any function analytic in a domain containing this graph. Differentiating with respect to x along the graph, we get the formula

$$\frac{du}{dx} = \frac{\partial u}{\partial x} + \left(\frac{\partial u}{\partial y}\right)\left(\frac{dy}{dx}\right) = \frac{\partial u}{\partial x} + + F\frac{\partial u}{\partial y}.$$

This formula can be differentiated repeatedly, giving the operator identity

$$\frac{d^n}{dx^n} = \left(\frac{\partial}{\partial x} + F(x, y)\frac{\partial}{\partial y}\right)^n. \tag{35}$$

Applying this identity to the function $F(x, y) = y'$, we get, in succession,

$$y'' = F_x + FF_y, \qquad y''' = F_{xx} + 2FF_{xy} + F^2F_{yy} + F_xF_y + FF_y^2,$$

and so on. The general formula is

$$y^{(n+1)} = \frac{d^{n+1}y}{dx^{n+1}} = \left(\frac{\partial}{\partial x} + F\frac{\partial}{\partial y}\right)^n [F(x, y)]. \tag{35'}$$

The right side of (35'), evaluated at $x = y = 0$, is a polynomial in the variables b_{jk} with positive integers as coefficients. This is because the operations used in evaluating this expression are addition, multiplication, and differentiation.

EXERCISES D

In Exercises 1–7, calculate the first four terms of the power series expansion of the solutions of the DE indicated, for the initial value $y(0) = 0$.

1. $y' = x + y$.
2. $y' = 1 + x^2y^2$.
3. $y' = g(x) = \Sigma\, b_k x^k$.
4. $y' = g(y) = \Sigma\, b_k y^k$.
5. $y' = xy^2 + yx^2 + 1$.
6. $y' = 1 + y^n$.
7. $y' = \cos \sqrt{y} + 1$.
8. Calculate explicitly the polynomials p_h of Theorem 4 for $h = 4$.
9. Compute the first five polynomials p_h of Theorem 4 when $F(x, y) = b(x)y + c(x)$ in (30).
10. Same question for the Riccati DE $y' + y^2 = b(x)y + c(x)$.
11. Show that the DE $y' = x^2 + y^2$ has a solution of the form $\sum_1^\infty a_k x^{4k-1}$ with all $a_k > 0$. For $a_1 = 1$, compute a_2, a_3, a_4.
12. (a) From the DE $y' = 1 + y^2$, prove that the coefficient a_{n+1} in the expansion $\tan x = \Sigma\, a_k x^k, a_0 = 0$, satisfies $(n + 1)a_{n+1} = \sum_{k=1}^{n-1} a_k a_{n-1}$.
    [HINT: Differentiate y^2 using the binomial expansion of $(uv)^{(n)}$.]
    (b) Compute the first five nonzero coefficients, and compare with those obtained by solving for y recursively from $x = y - y^3/3 + y^5/5 - \cdots$, the series for $x = \arctan y$.
13. Show that if $y' = F(x, y)$, where $F \in \mathscr{C}^3$, then

$$y^{iv} = F_{xxx} + 3y'F_{xxy} + 3y'^2F_{xyy} + y'^3F_{yyy} + 3y''F_{xy} + 3y'y''F_{yy} + y'''F_y.$$

14. For the DE $y' = 2y/x$ and the initial condition $y(1) = 1$, calculate the first four terms of the Taylor series of the solution.

9*   Radius of convergence

The DE $y' = 1 + y^2$ of Example 4 shows that the radius of convergence of power series solutions of a *nonlinear* DE $y' = F(x, y)$ can be much less than that of the function $F(x, y)$. For, the radius of convergence of the solution $\tan (x + c)$ of the DE $y' = 1 + y^2$ which satisfies $y(0) = \tan c = \gamma$ is only $\pi/2 - c$, the distance to the nearest singular point of the solution. This can be made arbitrarily small by making γ large enough, even though the radius of convergence of $F(x, y) = 1 + y^2$ is infinite.

The preceding situation is typical of nonlinear DE's and shows that we cannot hope to establish an existence theorem for nonlinear DE's as strong as Theorem 3. The contrast with the situation for nonlinear DE's is further illustrated by the Riccati equation of Chapter 2, § 3, (14).

EXAMPLE 5.   The Riccati equation

$$dv/dx = -v^2 - p(x)v - q(x) \tag{36}$$

is satisfied by the ratio $v(x) = u'(x)/u(x)$, if $u(x)$ is any nontrivial solution of the second-order linear DE (4). Conversely, if $v(x)$ is any solution of the Riccati DE (36), then the function $u = \exp (\int v(x)\, dx)$ satisfies the linear DE (4).

Now, let p, q be analytic and a, c given constants. Using Theorem 2 to find a solution u of (4) satisfying the initial conditions $u(a) = 1$ and $u'(a) = c$, we obtain an analytic solution $v = u'/u$ of the Riccati equation (36) which satisfies $v(a) = c$. This gives a local existence theorem for the nonlinear Riccati DE (36).

However, this solution becomes infinite when $u = 0$; hence the radius of convergence of its power series can be made arbitrarily small by choosing c sufficiently large. Also, the location of the singular points of solutions of (36) is variable, depending on the zeros of u.

The Riccati equation also serves to illustrate Theorem 4. A simple computation gives, for $v = \sum_1^\infty a_k x^k$, the formula

$$v^2 = a_1^2 x^2 + 2a_1 a_2 x^3 + (a_2^2 + 2a_1 a_3)x^4 + \cdots + \sum_{i=1}^{h-1} a_i a_{h-i} x^h + \cdots.$$

Substituting back into (36), we get the recursion relation

$$(h + 1)a_{h+1} = -\sum_{i=1}^{h-1} a_i a_{h-i} - \sum_{i=1}^{h} a_i p_{h-i} - q_h.$$

This is, of course, just the special case of formula (34′) corresponding to $F(x, y) = -y^2 - \sum_0^\infty p_k x^k y - \sum_0^\infty q_k x^k$.

We shall now return to the general case. Let F be any function of x

and y analytic in some neighborhood of $(0, 0)$. This means that F can be expanded into a double power series

$$F(x, y) = b_{00} + (b_{10}x + b_{01}y) + (b_{20}x^2 + b_{11}xy + b_{02}y^2) \cdots, \quad (37)$$

where b_{jk} are given real numbers, and the series is convergent for sufficiently small x and y. We will show that the series (33) referred to in Theorem 4, and defined by formula (34′), has a positive radius of convergence.

Analytic functions of two variables. To prove this, we shall need a few facts about analytic functions of two variables and the convergence of double power series like (37). The terms of any absolutely convergent series can be rearranged in any order without destroying the convergence of the series or changing the value of the sum. If we substitute into a double power series like (37) convergent near $(0, 0)$ any power series $y = \sum_{k=0}^{\infty} a_k x^k$ having a positive radius of convergence, we will obtain an analytic function $F(x, f(x))$ which itself has a positive radius of convergence.

Finally, let the double power series (37) be convergent at (H, K), where $H > 0$ and $K > 0$. Then the terms of the series $\sum b_{jk} H^j K^k$ are bounded in magnitude by some finite constant $M = \max |b_{jk}| H^j K^k$. This gives the bound

$$|b_{jk}| \leq M/H^j K^k, \qquad M < +\infty,$$

to the terms of the series (37). Comparing with the double geometric series mentioned in § 5,

$$G(x, y) = M \Big/ \left(1 - \frac{x}{H}\right)\left(1 - \frac{y}{K}\right) = \sum_{j=0}^{\infty} \sum_{k=0}^{\infty} \left(\frac{M}{H^j K^k}\right) x^j y^k, \quad (38)$$

and applying the Comparison Test, we see that the series (37) is absolutely convergent in the open rectangle $|x| < H$, $|y| < K$, and can be differentiated term-by-term there any number of times.

From the preceding remarks, we have the following immediate consequence.

■ COROLLARY. *If the power series (33) of Theorem 4 has a positive radius of convergence, then the function which it defines is a solution of* the DE (30) *for the initial condition* $y(0) = 0$.

10* Method of majorants, II

We will now complete the proof of an existence theorem for analytic first-order DE's by showing that the series (33) has a positive radius of convergence. This is again shown by the Method of Majorants, which we now extend to functions of two variables.

Consider the power series

$$y: \quad a_1 x + a_2 x^2 + a_3 x^3 + \cdots,$$

$$F: \quad b_{00} + b_{10} x + b_{01} y + b_{20} x^2 + b_{11} xy + \cdots,$$

as infinite arrays of real or complex numbers, irrespective of any questions of convergence. Such power series can be added, subtracted, and multiplied algebraically as infinite polynomials, without ever being evaluated as functions of x and y. Such expressions are called *formal power series*. It is possible to substitute one formal power series into another: after rearranging terms, another formal power series is obtained. Two formal power series are considered identical when all their coefficients coincide.

Comparing F with the formal power series

$$G: \quad c_{00} + c_{10} x + c_{01} y + c_{20} x^2 + c_{11} xy + \cdots,$$

one says that the formal power series G *majorizes* the formal power series F when

$$|b_{jk}| \leqq c_{jk} \qquad \text{for all} \quad j, k = 0, 1, 2, \ldots.$$

In symbols,

$$F \ll G. \tag{39}$$

This implies that all coefficients c_{jk} are nonnegative.

The following lemma is immediate.

■ **LEMMA 1.**   *Let F, G, H be any three formal power series. Then $F \ll G$ and $G \ll F$ imply $F = G$, and $F \ll G$ and $G \ll H$ imply $F \ll H$.*

It is not true, however, that $F \ll F$ if F has any negative coefficient.

The relation (39) of majorization between formal power series is useful in estimating the radius of convergence of such series. From the Comparison Test for convergence, we obtain the following directly.

■ **LEMMA 2.**   *If F and G are formal power series and if $F \ll G$, then F converges absolutely at any point (x, y) if G converges at $(|x|, |y|)$.*

The crucial result for the proof of convergence of the formal power series (33), obtained from Theorem 4, is the following.

■ **LEMMA 3.**   *Let $F \ll G$, and let f and g be the formal power series (without constant terms) obtained by solving $y' = F(x, y)$ and $y' = G(x, y)$ formally,* as in Theorem 4, for the initial condition $y(0) = 0$. Then g majorizes f (that is, $f \ll g$).

Proof — The polynomials p_h in Theorem 4 have nonnegative coefficients. It follows that

$$|a_{h+1}| = |p_h(b_{00}, b_{10}, b_{01}, \ldots)| \leq p_h(c_{00}, c_{10}, c_{01}, \ldots)$$

for all h; hence, the absolute value of each coefficient a_h is less than or equal to the corresponding coefficient of the formal power series g, q.e.d.

It is now a straightforward matter to prove our main result.

■ THEOREM 5.   Let $F(x, y)$ be analytic in the closed rectangle $|x| \leq H$, $|y| \leq K$, where H and K are positive. Then the formal power series solution (33) of the DE (30) has a positive radius of convergence.

Proof — The power series for the function F is convergent at (H, K); as in § 9, it follows that for some finite $M = \max |b_{jk} H^j K^k|$,

$$|b_{jk} H^j K^k| \leq M, \qquad \text{whence} \qquad |b_{jk}| \leq \frac{M}{H^j K^k}.$$

That is, the formal power series F is majorized by the double geometric series (38):

$$G(x, y) = M \Big/ \left[\left(1 - \frac{x}{H}\right)\left(1 - \frac{y}{K}\right) \right] = \sum_{j,k=0}^{\infty} \frac{M}{H^j K^k} x^j y^k.$$

This series is the product of two geometric series, each absolutely convergent if $|x| < H$, $|y| < K$. Therefore, it is also absolutely convergent in this rectangular domain, and defines an analytic function there.

Furthermore, the DE $y' = G(x, y)$ can be solved in closed form by separation of variables. The solution satisfying $y(0) = 0$ is

$$y = K[1 - \sqrt{1 + (2MH/K) \ln (1 - (x/H))}], \tag{40}$$

where the principal values of the logarithmic and square root functions are taken, corresponding to the usual expansions of the functions $\sqrt{1 + t}$ and $\ln (1 + t)$ in power series with center at $t = 0$. The radius of convergence is given by the equation $(2MH/K) \ln [1 - x/H] = -1$, or

$$R = H[1 - e^{-K/2MH}] \tag{41}$$

since the binomial series for the radicand in (40) converges so long as $(2MH/K)|\ln [1 - (x/H)]| < 1$. This completes the proof.

By Theorem 5 of Chapter 1, whose hypotheses are satisfied since F is continuously differentiable, the solution satisfying the initial condition $f(0)$ is unique. This proves the following result.

■ COROLLARY.   *Every solution of the analytic DE* (30) *is analytic. The solution satisfying the initial condition* $f(0) = 0$ *is unique, and given by the power series* (33).

11*   Complex solutions

The preceding discussion applies with very minor changes to complex power series. Let

$$dw/dz = F(z, w) = \sum_{j,k} b_{jk} z^j w^k \qquad (42)$$

be any analytic first-order DE, whose right side is a complex analytic function. (For F to be analytic, it is sufficient for the function F to be differentiable, since differentiability implies analyticity in any complex domain.†) Then all the formulas of § 9 remain valid; so do the lemmas about majorants in § 10.

For complex z, w, the domain D: $|z| \leq H$, $|w| \leq K$ of Theorem 5 is not a rectangle, but the four-dimensional product of two discs. Though this domain is harder to visualize than a rectangle, it has the advantage that Cauchy's integral formulas hold on it: the constant M in (41) is given explicitly by‡

$$M = \sup_{(z,w) \in D} |F(z, w)|.$$

These remarks cover the extension of Theorem 5 to complex DE's.

Dependence on initial value.   We now consider the dependence of the solutions of real or complex analytic first-order DE's (30) or (42) on their initial values. This dependence is analytic; it follows that the solutions of any real normal DE form a *normal curve family*.

■ THEOREM 6.   *Let* $f(x, c)$ *be the solution of the first-order analytic DE* $y' = F(x, y)$ *which satisfies the initial condition* $f(a) = c$. *Then* $f(x, c)$ *is a locally analytic function of the two variables* x *and* c *near* $(a, 0)$.

Proof — As before, we can assume that $a = 0$; let $\eta = y - c$, so that $y = c + \eta$. For any fixed c, the function $\eta(x, c) = f(x, c) - c$ is the solution of

$$d\eta/dx = F_1(x, \eta) = F(x, c + \eta) = \sum b_{jk} x^j (c + \eta)^k = \sum \beta_{jk} x^j \eta^k, \quad (43)$$

---

† Ahlfors, pp. 24, 25; Hille, pp. 72, 196.
‡ See for example Picard, Vol. 2, p. 259.

satisfying the initial condition $\eta(0) = 0$. Here each $\beta_{jk} = \beta_{jk}(c)$ is an analytic function of c, the coefficients of whose power series expansion in c are *positive* multiples $\binom{k}{h}b_{jh}$ of some b_{jh}. By Theorems 4 and 5, the solution $\eta(x, c)$ of (43) is $\sum_{n=0}^{\infty} \alpha_n x^n$, where each coefficient $\alpha_n = \alpha_n(c)$ is a polynomial in the β_{jk} with *positive* rational coefficients. Hence, the doubly infinite formal power series

$$\eta(x, c) = \sum \alpha_n(c) x^n = \sum \gamma_{mn} c^m x^n$$

obtained has coefficients γ_{mn} which are polynomials in the b_{jk} with *positive* coefficients. This series formally satisfies (43).

As in the proof of Theorem 5, this series is majorized by the power series solution without constant term of the DE

$$dz/dx = G(x, c + z) = M/[(1 - x/H)(1 - (c + z)/K)].$$

Integrating, we get

$$\left(1 - \frac{c}{K}\right) z - \frac{z^2}{2K} = -MH \ln\left(1 - \frac{x}{H}\right). \qquad (44)$$

Elementary algebraic manipulation now gives

$$[(z + c) - K]^2 = (c - K)^2 + 2MHK \ln\left(1 - \frac{x}{H}\right).$$

The branch of the function $z(x, c)$ which makes $z(0, 0) = 0$ is given by the formula

$$z = K - c - \left\{(c - K)^2 + 2MHK \ln\left(1 - \frac{x}{H}\right)\right\}^{1/2}.$$

The resulting function (as one sees by expanding the functions $\sqrt{1 + u}$ and $\ln[1 - (x/H)]$ into power series) is analytic for x and c sufficiently small. This is, the power series solution of (44), $g(x, c) = \sum \delta_{mn} c^m x^n$ (in which all $\delta_{mn} \geq 0$ as shown above) is also convergent. But this *majorizes* $f(x, c)$, whose power series expansion is therefore also convergent, completing the proof.

EXERCISES E

For the power series expansion of each function defined in Exercises 1–4, determine the domain of convergence:

1. $J_0(x + y)$.   2. $\sqrt{(1 - x)(1 - y)}$.
3. $1/[1 - (x^2 + y^2)]$.   4. $1/[1 + (x^2 + y^2)]$.
5. Show that the solution of $y' = G(x, y)$, where G is the geometric series (38) is the function (40).
6. Find the value of $\sum_{j, k=0}^{\infty} x^j y^k/(H^j K^k)$.
7. Find the value of $\sum_{j,k=0}^{\infty} jk x^j y^k/(H^j K^k)$.

In Exercises 8–11, establish the properties of the relation " $\ll$ " ($P = P(x, y)$, $Q = Q(x, y)$, $p = p(x)$, and $q = q(x)$ are formal power series).

8. If $F \ll G$ and $P \ll Q$, then $F + P \ll G + Q$.

9. If $F \ll G$ and $P \ll Q$, then $FP \ll GQ$.

10. If $F \ll G$ and $p \ll q$, then $F(x, p(x)) \ll G(x, q(x))$.

11. If $F \ll G$, then $\partial F/\partial x \ll \partial G/\partial x$ (interpret the derivatives formally). Is the converse true?

4 Linear Equations with Constant Coefficients

1 The characteristic polynomial

The nth order linear DE with *constant coefficients* is

$$L[u] = u^{(n)} + a_1 u^{(n-1)} + a_2 u^{(n-2)} + \cdots + a_n u = r(x). \qquad (1)$$

Here $u^{(k)}$ stands for the kth derivative $d^k u/dx^k$ of the unknown function $u(x)$; $a_1, \ldots, a_n$ are arbitrary constants, real or complex†; and $r(x)$ is any continuous function.

As in Chapter 2, § 1, the letter L stands for the *operator* defined by (1). This transforms functions of class $\mathscr{C}^n$ into functions of class $\mathscr{C}$. The operator L is *linear*. That is, $L[au + bv] = aL[u] + bL[v]$ for any functions u and v of class $\mathscr{C}^n$ and constants a and b.

We first consider the *homogeneous* case $r(x) = 0$:

$$L[u] = u^{(n)} + a_1 u^{(n-1)} + a_2 u^{(n-2)} + \cdots + a_n u = 0. \qquad (2)$$

If one thinks of x as representing time, the DE (2) represents the most general *time-independent* linear DE. This gives DE's of the form (2) a special importance, which will be discussed further in Chapter 5.

Solutions of (2) can be found by trying the *exponential substitution* $u = e^{\lambda x}$, where λ is a real or complex number to be determined later. Since $d^n(e^{\lambda x})/dx^n = \lambda^n e^{\lambda x}$, this substitution reduces (2) to the identity

$$L[e^{\lambda x}] = (\lambda^n + a_1 \lambda^{n-1} + a_2 \lambda^{n-2} + \cdots + a_n)e^{\lambda x} = 0.$$

---

† Familiarity with complex polynomials and the complex exponential function will be assumed in this chapter.

This is satisfied if and only if λ is a (real or complex) root of the *characteristic polynomial* of the DE (1), defined as

$$p(\lambda) = p_L(\lambda) = \lambda^n + a_1\lambda^{n-1} + \cdots + a_{n-1}\lambda + a_n. \tag{3}$$

The Fundamental Theorem of Algebra† states that the characteristic polynomial p can be factored into linear factors

$$p(\lambda) = (\lambda - \lambda_1)^{k_1}(\lambda - \lambda_2)^{k_2}\cdots(\lambda - \lambda_m)^{k_m}, \tag{4}$$

where the λ_i are all distinct, $k_i > 0$, and $k_1 + \cdots + k_m = n$. The root λ_j is said to be of *multiplicity* k_j.

If the characteristic polynomial has n distinct real or complex roots, the DE (2) has n solutions $e^{\lambda_j x}$, $j = 1, 2, \ldots, n$.

Now, recall that if $\lambda = \mu + i\nu$, where μ, ν are real, then we have

$$e^{\lambda x} = e^{\mu x + i\nu x} = e^{\mu x}(\cos \nu x + i \sin \nu x). \tag{5}$$

Since $|e^{i\nu x}| = 1$ for all real ν, x, it follows that, where $e^{\lambda x}$ is considered as a *complex*-valued function of the *real* independent variable x,

$$|e^{\lambda x}| = e^{\mu x}, \qquad \arg\{e^{\lambda x}\} = \nu, \qquad \lambda = \mu + i\nu. \tag{5'}$$

Operational calculus. The case of multiple roots can be treated similarly by using the operator notation more extensively. Denoting the operator d/dx by the letter D, we obtain the identity

$$L = p(D) = D^n + a_1 D^{n-1} + \cdots + a_n.$$

This formula means that $L[u] = p(D)[u]$ for any function $u \in \mathscr{C}^n$. Observe that since the coefficient-functions $a_1, \ldots, a_n$ are *constants*, the terms of L are all permutable with each other, that is,

$$D[a_k u] = a_k D[u] \qquad \text{for} \quad k = 1, \ldots, n.$$

Generally, we have the identity

$$p(D)[q(D)[f]] = q(D)[p(D)[f]] = r(D)[f], \qquad r(D) = p(D)q(D)$$

for any polynomials p and q with constant coefficients.

The operational calculus is less simple for linear DE's with variable coefficients. Thus, since

$$Dxf = (xf)' = xf' + f = (xD + 1)f \qquad \text{for} \quad f \in \mathscr{C}^1[a, b],$$

we have $Dx = xD + 1$. This shows that the differentiation operator D is not permutable with the operator "multiply by x."

Using the operational calculus, it is easy to prove the following result.

---

† Birkhoff and MacLane, p. 101.

■ THEOREM 1. *If λ is a root of multiplicity k of the characteristic polynomial* (3), *then the functions $x^r e^{\lambda x}$ $(r = 0, \ldots, k-1)$ are solutions of the linear* DE (2).

Proof — The result stated follows directly from the identity

$$(D - \lambda)[x^r e^{\lambda x}] = r x^{r-1} e^{\lambda x}.$$

Iterating this identity, an easy computation gives

$$(D - \lambda)^k [x^r e^{\lambda x}] = 0 \qquad \text{if} \quad k > r.$$

The operators $(D - \lambda_i)^{k_i}$ being permutable, we can write, for any i,

$$L[u] = q_i(D)(D - \lambda_i)^{k_i}[u], \qquad q_i(D) = \prod_{j \neq i}(D - \lambda_j)^{k_j},$$

where $q_i(D)$ is the product of the $(D - \lambda_j)^{k_j}$ for $j \neq i$. But for $r < k_i$, $(D - \lambda_i)^{k_i}[x^r e^{\lambda_i x}] = 0$, as above. Substituting in the preceding identity, we obtain $L[x^r e^{\lambda_i x}] = q_i(D)[0] = 0$, completing the proof.

2 Real and complex solutions

The preceding theorem holds whether the coefficients a_k of the DE (2) are real or complex.

If all the coefficients a_k are real numbers, then more detailed information can be obtained about the solutions, as follows.

■ LEMMA. *Let the complex-valued function $w(x) = u(x) + iv(x)$ satisfy a homogeneous linear* DE (1) *with real coefficients. Then the functions $u(x)$ and $v(x)$ (the real and imaginary parts of $w(x)$) both satisfy the* DE.

Proof — The complex conjugate† $w^*(x) = u(x) - iv(x)$ of $w(x)$ satisfies the complex conjugate of the given DE (2), obtained by replacing every coefficient a_k by its complex conjugate a_k^*, because $L[w^*] = \{L[w]\}^* = 0$. If the a_k are real, then $a_k^* = a_k$, and so $w^*(x)$ also satisfies (2). Hence, the linear combinations

$$u(x) = [w(x) + w^*(x)]/2 \qquad \text{and} \qquad v(x) = [w(x) - w^*(x)]/2i$$

also satisfy (2), as stated.

This result is also valid for DE's with variable coefficients $a_k(x)$.

■ COROLLARY 1. *If the* DE (2) *has* real *coefficients and $e^{\lambda x}$ satisfies* (2),

---

† The complex conjugate w^* of a complex number $w = u + iv$ is $u - iv$. Some authors use $\bar{w}$ instead of w^* to denote the complex conjugate of w.

then so does $e^{\lambda^* x}$. The nonreal roots of the characteristic polynomial (3) *occur in conjugate pairs $\lambda_j = \mu_j \pm i \nu_j$, having the same multiplicity k_j.*

Now, using formula (5), we obtain the following.

■ COROLLARY 2.   *Each pair of complex conjugate roots λ_j, λ_j^* of* (3) *of multiplicity k_j gives real solutions of* (2) *of the form*

$$x^r e^{\mu_j x} \cos \nu_j x, \quad x^r e^{\mu_j x} \sin \nu_j x, \qquad r = 0, \ldots, k_j - 1. \tag{6}$$

These solutions differ from the solutions $e^{\lambda x}$ with real λ in that they have infinitely many zeros in any infinite interval of the real axis; that is, they are *oscillatory* (see Chapter 2, §4). This proves the following result.

■ THEOREM 2.   *If the characteristic polynomial* (3) *with real coefficients has $2r$ nonreal roots, then the* DE (2) *has $2r$ linearly independent oscillatory real solutions of the form* (6).

Euler's homogeneous DE.   The homogeneous linear DE

$$x^n u^{(n)} + b_1 x^{n-1} u^{(n-1)} + b_2 x^{n-2} u^{(n-2)} + \cdots + b_n u = 0 \tag{7}$$

is called Euler's homogeneous differential equation. Particular solutions of (7) can be found by substituting x^λ for u. This substitution yields an equation of the form $I(\lambda) x^\lambda = 0$, where $I(\lambda)$ is a polynomial of degree n, called the indicial equation. Any λ for which $I(\lambda) = 0$ gives a solution x^λ of (7).

For example, when $n = 2$, Euler's homogeneous DE is

$$x^2 u'' + pxu' + qu = 0, \qquad p, q \quad \text{real constants.} \tag{8}$$

Trying $u = x^\lambda$, we get the *indicial equation* of (8):

$$\lambda(\lambda - 1) + p\lambda + q = 0. \tag{8'}$$

Alternatively, making the change of variable $x = e^t$, we get

$$\frac{d^2 u}{dt^2} + (p - 1)\frac{du}{dt} + qu = 0, \qquad t = \ln x \tag{8''}$$

since $\dfrac{d^2}{dt^2} = x\dfrac{d}{dx}\left(x\dfrac{d}{dx}\right) = x^2\dfrac{d^2}{dx^2} + x\dfrac{d}{dx}.$

If $(p - 1)^2 > 4q$, the indicial equation has two distinct real roots $\lambda = \alpha$ and $\lambda = \beta$, and so the DE (8) has the two linearly independent *real* solutions x^α and x^β, defined for *positive* x. For positive *or* negative x, we have the solutions $|x|^\alpha$ and $|x|^\beta$ since the substitution of $-x$ for x

does not affect (8). Note that the DE (8) has a singular point at $x = 0$ and that $|x|$ has discontinuous slope there.

When the discriminant $(p - 1)^2 - 4q$ is negative, the indicial equation has two conjugate complex roots $\lambda = \mu \pm i\nu$, where $\mu = (1 - p)/2$ and $\nu = [4q - (p - 1)^2]^{1/2}/2$. A basis of real solutions of (8″) is then $e^{\mu t} \cos \nu t$ and $e^{\mu t} \sin \nu t$; the corresponding solutions of the second-order Euler homogeneous DE (8) are $x^{\mu} \cos (\nu \ln x)$ and $x^{\mu} \sin (\nu \ln x)$. These are, for $x > 0$, the real and imaginary parts of the *complex power* function

$$x^{\lambda} = x^{\mu \pm i\nu} = e^{(\mu \pm i\nu) \ln x} = x^{\mu}[\cos (\nu \ln x) \pm i \sin (\nu \ln x)],$$

as follows from the above lemma. For $x < 0$, we can get real solutions by using $|x|$ in place of x. But for $x < 0$ the resulting real solutions of (8) are no longer the real and imaginary parts of x^{λ}, because $\ln (-x) = \ln x \pm i\pi$; cf. Chapter 9, §1.

There remains the *exceptional case* $(p - 1)^2 = 4q$, where $\lambda = (1 - p)/2$ is a double root of the indicial equation (8′). In this case, the functions x^{λ} and $x^{\lambda} \ln x$ form a basis of solutions of (8) for $x > 0$, while $|x|^{\lambda}$ and $|x|^{\lambda} \ln |x|$ satisfy (8) for all real $x \neq 0$.

General case. The general nth-order case can be treated in the same way. We can again make the change of independent variable

$$x = e^t, \qquad t = \ln x, \qquad xd/dx = d/dt.$$

This reduces (7) to a DE of the form (2), whose solutions $t^r e^{\lambda t}$ give a basis of solutions for (7) of the form $(\ln x)^r x^{\lambda}$.

EXERCISES A

In Exercises 1–4, find a basis of real solutions of the DE specified.

1. $u'' + 5u' + 4u = 0$.   2. $u''' + 6u'' + 12u' + 8u = 0$.
3. $u^{\text{vi}} = u$.   4. $u^{\text{vi}} = -u$.

In Exercises 5–6, find a basis of complex solutions of the DE specified.
5. $u'' + 2iu' + 3u = 0$.   6. $u''' + 6u'' + 12u' + (8 + i)u = 0$.
7. Prove that the DE's of Exercises 5–6 have no nontrivial real solution.

In Exercises 8–9, find a basis of solutions for the Euler DE.
8. $x^2 u'' + 5xu' + 4u = 0$.   9. $x^2 u'' + 2ixu'a - 3u = 0$.
10. Describe the behavior of the function z^i of the complex variable $z = x + iy$ as z traces the unit circle $z = e^{i\theta}$ around the origin.
11. Do the same as in Exercise 10 for the function $z^i e^{iz}$.
12. State an analog of Theorem 1 for Euler's DE, and give it a direct proof.

3 Linearly independent solutions

As in Chapter 2, § 3, a set of n real or complex functions $f_1, f_2, \ldots, f_n$ defined on an interval (a, b) is said to be *linearly independent* when no linear combination with constant coefficients of the functions is identically zero; that is, when $\sum_{k=1}^{n} c_k f_k(x) \equiv 0$ implies $c_1 = c_2 = \cdots = c_n = 0$. A set which is not linearly independent is said to be *linearly dependent*.†

There are two notions of linear independence, according as we allow the coefficients c_k to assume only *real values*, or also *complex* values. In the first case, one says that the functions are linearly independent over the *real field*; in the second case, that they are linearly independent over the *complex field*.

■ **Lemma 1.** *A set of real-valued functions on an interval* (a, b) *is linearly independent over the complex field if and only if it is linearly independent over the real field.*

Proof — Linear dependence over the real field implies linear dependence over the complex field, *a fortiori*. Conversely, the $f_j(x)$ being real, suppose that $\sum c_j f_j(x) \equiv 0$ for $a < x < b$. Then $[\sum c_j f_j(x)]^* \equiv 0$, hence $\sum c_j^* f_j(x) \equiv 0$. Subtracting, we obtain $\sum [(c_j - c_j^*)/i] f_j(x) \equiv 0$. If all c_j are real, there is nothing to prove. If some c_j is not real, some real number $(c_j - c_j^*)/i$ will not vanish, and we still have a vanishing linear combination with real coefficients.

A set of functions which is linearly dependent on a given domain may become linearly independent when the functions are extended to a larger domain. However, a linearly independent set of functions clearly remains linearly independent when the functions are extended to a larger domain.

■ **Lemma 2.** *Any set of functions of the form*

$$f_{rj}(x) = x^r e^{\lambda_j x}, \qquad j = 1, \ldots, n, \tag{9}$$

where the r are nonnegative integers and the λ_j *complex numbers, is linearly independent over the complex field on any nonvoid open interval, unless two or more of the functions are identical.*

Proof — Suppose that $\sum c_{ri} f_{ri}(x) \equiv 0$. For any given λ_j, choose R to be the largest r such that $c_{rj} \neq 0$. Form the operator

$$q(D) = (D - \lambda_j)^R \prod_{i \neq j} (D - \lambda_i)^{k_i + 1},$$

where k_i is the largest k such that $x^k e^{\lambda_i x}$ is a member of the set (9). It

---

† For the facts about linear independence and vectors assumed here, see Birkhoff and MacLane, pp. 149–58.

follows that $q(D)[f_{ri}] = 0$ unless $i = j$, and that $q(D)[f_{rj}] = 0$ for $r < R$. Hence, we have

$$q(D)[\sum c_{ri} f_{ri}(x)] = c_{Rj} q(D)[x^R e^{\lambda_j x}].$$

On the other hand, as in the proof of Theorem 1, we see that

$$q(D)[x^R e^{\lambda_j x}] = (R!) \prod_{i \neq j} (\lambda_j - \lambda_i)^{k_i + 1} e^{\lambda_j x} \neq 0.$$

Therefore, substituting back, we find that $c_{Rj} = 0$. Since we assumed that $c_{Rj} \neq 0$, this gives a contradiction unless all $c_{rj} = 0$, proving linear independence.

From Theorem 1 we obtain the following corollary.

■ COROLLARY 1.   *The* DE (2) *has* at least *n solutions of the form* $x^r e^{\lambda x}$ *which are linearly independent over the complex field.*

The analogous result for *real* solutions of DE of the form of (2) with *real* coefficients can be proved as follows. For any two conjugate complex roots $\lambda = \mu + i\nu$ and $\lambda^* = \mu - i\nu$ of the characteristic equation of (2), the real solutions $x^r e^{\mu x} \cos \nu x$ and $x^r e^{\mu x} \sin \nu x$ are complex linear combinations of $x^r e^{\lambda x}$ and $x^r e^{\lambda^* x}$, and conversely. Hence, they can be substituted for $x^r e^{\lambda x}$ and $x^r e^{\lambda^* x}$ in any set of solutions without affecting their linear independence. Since linear independence over the complex field implies linear independence over the real field, this proves the following.

■ COROLLARY 2.   *A linear* DE (2) *with constant* real *coefficients* a_k *has a set of n solutions of the form* $x^r e^{\mu x}$ *or* (6) *which is linearly independent over the* real *field in any nonvoid interval.*

4   Solution bases

We can show that *all* solutions of the real homogeneous linear DE (2) are linear combinations of the special solutions described in Corollary 2 above.† To this end, we consider more generally the homogeneous linear

$$L[u] = u^{(n)} + p_1(x)u^{(n-1)} + \cdots + p_n(x)u = 0 \tag{10}$$

DE with real continuous coefficient-functions $p_k(x)$.

As in Chapter 2, a *basis* of solutions of the linear DE (10) is a set of n solutions $u_1(x), \cdots, u_n(x)$ such that the general solution of (10) can be

---

† The result is valid also for linear DE's with constant complex coefficients, by the uniqueness theorem of Chapter 6.

uniquely expressed as a linear combination $c_1u_1(x) + \cdots + c_n u_n(x)$, the c_k being arbitrary constants. We now show that any n linearly independent solutions of (10) form a basis of solutions.

■ **THEOREM 3.**   *Let $u_1, \ldots, u_n$ be n linearly independent real solutions of the nth order linear homogeneous DE* (10) *with real coefficient-functions. Then, given arbitrary real numbers $a, u_0, u_0', \ldots, u_0^{(n-1)}$, there exist unique constants $c_1, \ldots, c_n$ such that $u(x) = \sum c_k u_k(x)$ is a solution of* (10) *satisfying*

$$u(a) = u_0, \; u'(a) = u_0', \; \ldots, \; u^{(n-1)}(a) = u_0^{(n-1)}. \tag{11}$$

The functions $u_k(x)$ are a basis of solutions of (10).

The key to the proof of Theorem 3 is given by the following Lemma, which is also a special case of the much more general uniqueness theorem of Chapter 6, § 3.

■ **LEMMA.**   *Let $f(x)$ be a real or complex solution of the nth order homogeneous linear DE* (10) *with continuous real coefficient-functions in the closed interval $[a, b]$. If $f(a) = f'(a) = \cdots = f^{(n-1)}(a) = 0$, then $f(x) \equiv 0$ on $[a, b]$.*

Proof — We first suppose $f(x)$ *real*. The function

$$\sigma(x) = f(x)^2 + f'(x)^2 + \cdots + f^{(n-1)}(x)^2 \geqq 0$$

satisfies the initial condition $\sigma(a) = 0$. Differentiating $\sigma(x)$, we find, since $\sigma(x)$ is real, that

$$\sigma'(x) = 2[f(x)f'(x) + f'(x)f''(x) + \cdots + f^{(n-1)}(x)f^{(n)}(x)].$$

Using the inequality $|2\alpha\beta| \leqq \alpha^2 + \beta^2$ repeatedly $n - 1$ times, we have

$$\sigma'(x) \leqq (f^2 + f'^2) + (f'^2 + f''^2) + \cdots$$
$$+ ([f^{(n-2)}]^2 + [f^{(n-1)}]^2) + 2f^{(n-1)}f^{(n)}.$$

Since $L[f] = 0$, it follows that $f^{(n)} = -\sum_{k=1}^{n} p_k f^{(n-k)}$. Hence, the last term can be rewritten in the form

$$f^{(n-1)}f^{(n)} = -\sum_{k=1}^{n} p_k f^{(n-1)}f^{(n-k)}.$$

Applying the inequality $|2\alpha\beta| \leqq \alpha^2 + \beta^2$ again, we obtain

$$2|f^{(n-1)}f^{(n)}| \leqq \sum_{k=1}^{n} |p_k|([f^{(n-k)}]^2 + [f^{(n-1)}]^2).$$

Substituting and rearranging terms, we obtain

$$\sigma'(x) \leq (1 + |p_n|)f^2 + (2 + |p_{n-1}|)f'^2 + (2 + |p_{n-2}|)f''^2 + \cdots$$

$$+ (2 + |p_2|)[f^{(n-2)}]^2 + (1 + |p_1| + \sum_{k=1}^{n} |p_k|)[f^{(n-1)}]^2.$$

Now let $K = 2 + \max |p_1(x)| + \max_{a \leq x \leq b} \sum_{k=1}^{n} |p_k(x)|$. Then it follows
from the last inequality that $\sigma'(x) \leq K\sigma(x)$. From this inequality and
the initial condition $\sigma(a) = 0$, the identity $\sigma(x) \equiv 0$ follow by Lemma 2
of Chapter 1, §11. Hence, we have $f(x) \equiv 0$.

If $h(x) = f(x) + ig(x)$ (f, g real) is a *complex* solution of (10), then $f(x)$
and $g(x)$ satisfy (10) by the lemma of §2. Moreover, $h(a) = h'(a) = \cdots = h^{(n-1)}(a) = 0$ implies the corresponding equalities on f and g.
Hence, by the preceding paragraph, we have $h = f + ig \equiv 0 + 0 = 0$,
completing the proof.

We are now ready to prove Theorem 3. Suppose that, for some a, u_0,
u_0', $\cdots$, $u_0^{(n-1)}$, there were no linear combination $\Sigma c_k u_k(x)$ satisfying
the given initial conditions (11). That is, suppose the n vectors

$$(u_k(a), u_k'(a), \ldots, u_k^{(n-1)}(a)), \quad k = 1, \ldots, n,$$

were *linearly dependent*. Then† there would exist constants $\gamma_1, \ldots, \gamma_n$,
not all zero, such that

$$\sum_{k=1}^{n} \gamma_k u_k(a) = 0, \quad \sum_{k=1}^{n} \gamma_k u_k'(a) = 0, \ldots, \sum_{k=1}^{n} \gamma_k u^{(n-1)}(a) = 0.$$

That is, the function $\phi(x) = \gamma_1 u_1(x) + \cdots + \gamma_n u_n(x)$ would satisfy

$$\phi(a) = \phi'(a) = \cdots = \phi^{(n-1)}(a) = 0.$$

From this it would follow, from the lemma, that $\phi(x) \equiv 0$.

Recapitulating, we can find either $c_1, \ldots, c_n$ not all zero such that

$$u(x) = c_1 u_1(x) + \cdots + c_n u_n(x)$$

satisfies (11), or $\gamma_1, \ldots, \gamma_n$ not all zero such that

$$\phi(x) = \gamma_1 u_1(x) + \cdots + \gamma_n u_n(x) \equiv 0.$$

The second alternative contradicts the hypothesis of linear independence
in Theorem 3, which proves the first conclusion there.

To prove the second conclusion, let $v(x)$ be *any* solution of (10). By
the first conclusion, constants $c_1, \ldots, c_n$ can be found such that

$$u(x) = c_1 u_1(x) + \cdots + c_n u_n(x)$$

---

† Birkhoff and MacLane, p. 156.

satisfies $u(a) = v(a)$, $u'(a) = v'(a)$, $\ldots$, $u^{(n-1)}(a) = v^{(n-1)}(a)$. Hence the difference $f(x) = u(x) - v(x)$ satisfies the hypotheses of the lemma above. Using the lemma, we obtain $u(x) \equiv v(x)$ and $v(x) = \sum c_k u_k(x)$, proving the second conclusion of Theorem 3.

■ COROLLARY 1. *Let* $\lambda_1, \ldots, \lambda_m$ *be the roots of the characteristic polynomial of the real†* DE (2) *with multiplicities* $k_1, \ldots, k_m$. *Then the functions* $x^r e^{\lambda_j x}$, $r = 0, \ldots, k_j - 1$, *are a basis of solutions of* (2).

Referring to Theorem 2, we have also the following.

■ COROLLARY 2. *If the coefficients of the* DE (2) *are real, then it has a basis of real solutions of the form* $x^r e^{\lambda x}$, $x^r e^{\mu x} \cos \nu x$, *and* $x^r e^{\mu x} \sin \nu x$, *where* λ, μ, *and* ν *are real constants.*

EXERCISES B

1. Solve the following initial-value problems:
   (a) $u^{\mathrm{iv}} - u = 0$, $u(0) = u'(0) = u'''(0) = 0$, $u''(0) = 1$,
   (b) $u^{\mathrm{iv}} + u'' = 0$, $u(0) = u''(0) = u'''(0) = 0$, $u'(0) = 1$,
   (c) $u^{\mathrm{iv}} = 0$, $u'(0) = u''(0) = u'''(0) = 0$, $u(0) = 1$.
2. Knowing a basis of solutions of DE (2) with constant coefficients, find a basis of solutions of the DE of order $2n$, $L[L[u]] = 0$.
3. Let $L_1[u] = 0$ and $L_2[u] = 0$ be two DE's of the form (2). Prove by induction that the DE's $L_1[L_2[u]] = 0$ and $L_2[L_1[u]] = 0$ coincide.
4. Knowing bases of solutions of $L_1[u] = 0$ and $L_2[u] = 0$ of the form given by Theorem 1, find a basis of solutions of $L_1[L_2[u]] = 0$.
5. Knowing a basis of solutions of (1) of the form given by Theorem 1, find a basis of solutions of $L^k[u] = 0$. $(L^k[u] = L[L^{k-1}[u]])$.
6. Extend Lemma 2 of § 3 to the case where the r are arbitrary complex numbers.
7*. State an analog of Corollary 2 of § 3 for Euler's DE, and prove this statement without assuming Corollary 2.

5 Stability

An important physical concept is that of the stability of equilibrium. An equilibrium state of a physical system is said to be *stable* when small departures from equilibrium remain small with the lapse of time, and *unstable* when arbitrarily small initial deviations from equilibrium can ultimately become quite large.

In considering the stability of equilibrium, it is suggestive to think of the independent variable as standing for the time t. Accordingly, one rewrites the DE (2) as

$$\frac{d^n u}{dt^n} + a_1 \frac{d^{n-1} u}{dt^{n-1}} + a_2 \frac{d^{n-2} u}{dt^{n-2}} + \cdots + a_{n-1} \frac{du}{dt} + a_n u = 0. \qquad (12)$$

---

† The preceding result can be proved more generally for linear DE's with constant complex coefficients, by similar methods, See Chapter 6, § 10.

For such homogeneous *linear* DE's, the trivial solution $u \equiv 0$ represents an equilibrium state, and the possibilities for stable and unstable behavior are relatively few. They are adequately described by the following definition (cf. Chapter 5, § 7 for the nonlinear case).

■ DEFINITION. The homogeneous linear DE (12) is *strictly stable* when every solution tends to zero as $t \to \infty$; it is *stable* when every solution remains bounded as $t \to \infty$; when not stable, it is called *unstable*.

Evidently, a homogeneous linear DE is strictly stable if and only if it has a finite *basis* of solutions tending to zero, and stable if and only if it has a basis of bounded solutions. The reason for this is that every finite linear combination of bounded functions is bounded, as is easily shown. Hence Theorem 3, Corollary 2 gives algebraic tests for stability and strict stability of the DE (12). Take a basis of solutions of the form $t^r e^{\mu t}$, $t^r e^{\mu t} \sin \nu t$, $t^r e^{\mu t} \cos \nu t$. Such a solution tends to zero if and only if $\mu < 0$, and it remains bounded as $t \to \infty$ if and only if $\mu < 0$ or $\mu = r = 0$. This gives the following result.

■ THEOREM 4. *A given* DE (12) *is* stable *if and only if no root* λ_j *of its characteristic polynomial has a positive real part, and all multiple roots (with* $k_j > 1$ *in* (4)) *have negative real parts; it is* strictly stable *if and only if every root of its characteristic polynomial has a negative real part.*

Polynomials all of whose roots have negative real parts are said to be of *stable type*.† There are algebraic inequalities, called the *Routh-Hurwitz conditions*, on the coefficients of a real polynomial, which are necessary and sufficient for it to be of stable type. Thus, consider the quadratic characteristic polynomial of the DE of the mass-spring system of Example 4, Chapter 2, §2. It is easily verified that the real DE

$$\ddot{u} + a_1 \dot{u} + a_2 u = 0, \qquad \ddot{u} = d^2 u/dt^2, \qquad \dot{u} = du/dt,$$

is strictly stable if and only if a_1 and a_2 are both positive (positive damping and positive restoring force). That is, when $n = 2$, the Routh-Hurwitz conditions are $a_1 > 0$ and $a_2 > 0$.

In the case of a third-order DE ($n = 3$), the test for strict stability is provided by the inequalities $a_j > 0$ ($j = 1, 2, 3$) and $a_1 a_2 > a_3$. When $n = 4$, the conditions for strict stability are $a_j > 0$ ($j = 1, 2, 3, 4$), $a_1 a_2 > a_3$, and $a_1 a_2 a_3 > a_1^2 a_4 + a_3^2$.

Second-order linear DE's with constant coefficients, of the form $\ddot{u} + p\dot{u} + qu = 0$, have so many applications that it is convenient to

---

† See Birkhoff and Mac Lane, p. 108. For polynomials of stable type of higher degree, see F. R. Gantmacher, *Applications of the Theory of Matrices*, Interscience, New York, 1959.

summarize their properties in a diagram. We have just seen that they are strictly stable if and only if $p > 0$ and $q > 0$. Again, their solutions are oscillatory if and only if $p^2 < 4q$, because this is the condition that $\lambda^2 + p\lambda + q$ have complex roots. Figure 4.1 indicates these properties,

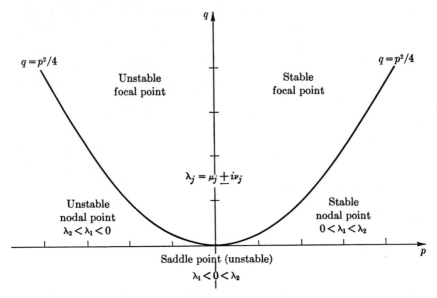

FIGURE 4.1   Stability Diagram for $\ddot{u} + p\dot{u} + qu = 0$.

and others to be derived in Chapter 5, by showing the loci in the pq-plane corresponding to different types of roots of the characteristic equation. Thus, the first quadrant is the locus Re $\{\lambda_j\} > 0$, $j = 1, 2$.

6   Inhomogeneous equations

We now return to the nth order *inhomogeneous* linear DE with constant coefficients,

$$L[u] = \frac{d^n u}{dt^n} + a_1 \frac{d^{n-1} u}{dt^{n-1}} + \cdots + a_{n-1} \frac{du}{dt} + a_n u = r(t), \qquad (13)$$

already introduced in §1. We first describe a simple method for solving DE (13) in closed form, in the special case that $r(t) = \sum p_k(t)e^{\lambda_k t}$ is a linear combination of polynomials and exponentials.

In the operational notation of §1, one easily verifies the identity for all $f \in \mathscr{C}^1$:

$$(D - \lambda)[e^{\lambda t} f(t)] = e^{\lambda t} f'(t).$$

As a corollary, since every polynomial of degree s is the derivative $r(t) = f'(t)$ of a suitable polynomial of degree $s + 1$, we obtain the following result.

■ **LEMMA 1.**   *If $r(t)$ is a polynomial of degree s, then $(D - \lambda)[u] = e^{\lambda t} r(t)$ has a solution of the form $u = e^{\lambda t} q(t)$, where $q(t)$ is a polynomial of degree $s + 1$.*

More generally, one easily verifies the identity

$$(D - \lambda_1)[e^{\lambda t} f(t)] = e^{\lambda t}[(\lambda - \lambda_1)f(t) + f'(t)].$$

If $\lambda \neq \lambda_1$, and $f(t)$ is a polynomial of degree s, then the right side of the preceding identity is a polynomial of degree s times $e^{\lambda t}$. This proves another useful algebraic fact.

■ **LEMMA 2.**   *If $r(t)$ is a polynomial of degree s and $\lambda \neq \lambda_1$, then*

$$(D - \lambda_1)[u] = e^{\lambda t} r(t)$$

has a solution of the form $u = e^{\lambda t} q(t)$, where $q(t)$ is a polynomial of degree s.

Applying the two preceding lemmas repeatedly to the factors of the operator

$$L = p_L(D) = (D - \lambda_1)^{k_1}(D - \lambda_2)^{k_2} \cdots (D - \lambda_m)^{k_m},$$

we get the following result.

■ **THEOREM 5.**   *The DE $L[u] = e^{\lambda t} r(t)$, where $r(t)$ is a polynomial, has a particular solution of the form $e^{\lambda t} q(t)$, where $q(t)$ is also a polynomial. The degree of $q(t)$ equals that of $r(t)$ unless $\lambda = \lambda_j$ is a root of the characteristic polynomial $p_L(\lambda) = \prod (\lambda - \lambda_j)^{k_j}$ of L. If $\lambda = \lambda_j$ is a k-fold root of $p_L(\lambda)$, then the degree of $q(t)$ exceeds that of $r(t)$ by k.*

Knowing the form of the answer, we can solve for the coefficients b_k of the unknown polynomial $q(t) = \sum b_k t^k$ by the method of undetermined coefficients. Namely, applying $p(D)$ to $u(t) = e^{\lambda t}(\sum b_k t^k)$, one can compute the numbers P_{kl} in the formula

$$p(D)[u] = e^{\lambda t} \sum (P_{kl} b_l) t^k,$$

using formulas for differentiating elementary functions. One does not need to factor p_L. The simultaneous linear equations $\sum P_{kl} b_l = c_k$ can then be solved for the b_k, given $r(t) = \sum c_k t^k$, by elementary algebra. Theorem 5 simply states how many unknowns b_k must be used to get a compatible system of linear equations.

7   The transfer function

Inhomogeneous linear DE's (13) are widely used to represent electric and acoustic networks or *filters*. Such a filter may be thought of as a "black box" into which a current or a sound wave is fed as an *input* $r(t)$ and out of which comes a resulting *output* $u(t)$.

Mathematically, this amounts to considering an *operator* transforming the function r into a function u which is the solution of the inhomogeneous linear DE (13). Writing this operator as $u = F[r]$, we easily see that $L[F[r]] = r$. Thus, such an input–output operator is a right-*inverse* of the operator L.

Since there are many solutions of the inhomogeneous DE (13) for a given input $r(t)$, the preceding definition of F is incomplete: the above equations do not define $F = L^{-1}$ unambiguously. This difficulty can often be resolved by insisting that $F[r]$ be in the class $B(-\infty, +\infty)$ of *bounded* functions; in §§ 7–8, we will make this restriction. For, in this case, for any two solutions u_1 and u_2 of the inhomogeneous DE $L[u] = r$, the difference $v = u_1 - u_2$ would have to satisfy $L[v] = 0$. Unless the characteristic polynomial $p_L(\lambda) = 0$ has pure imaginary roots, this implies $u = v$. Hence, in particular, the DE $L[u] = r$ has at most one bounded solution if the DE $L[u] = 0$ is *strictly stable*, an assumption which corresponds in electrical engineering to a passive electrical network with dissipation. Moreover, the effect of initial conditions is "transient": it dies out exponentially.

In §§ 9–10, we will define F by restricting its values to functions that satisfy $u(0) = u'(0) = \cdots = u^{(n-1)}(0) = 0$; this also defines F unambiguously, by Theorem 3.

We now consider bounded solutions of (13) for some input functions, without necessarily assuming that the homogeneous DE is strictly stable.

Sinusoidal input functions are of the greatest importance; they represent alternating currents and simple musical notes of constant pitch. These are functions of the form

$$A \cos (kt + \alpha) = \operatorname{Re} \{ce^{ikt}\}, \qquad A = |c|, \qquad \alpha = \arg c;$$

A is called the *amplitude*, $k/2\pi$ the *frequency*, and α the *phase constant*. The frequency $k/2\pi$ is the reciprocal of the *period* $2\pi/k$.

One can find a particular solution of the DE (13) for the sinusoidal input $r(t) = ce^{ikt}$ by making the substitution $u = C(k)ce^{ikt}$, where $C(k)$ is to be determined. Substituting into the inhomogeneous DE (13), we see that $L[C(k)ce^{ikt}] = ce^{ikt}$ if and only if

$$C(k) = 1/p_L(ik), \qquad p_L(ik) \neq 0, \tag{14}$$

where $p_L(\lambda)$ is the characteristic polynomial defined by (3).

■ DEFINITION. *The complex-valued function $C(k)$ of the real variable k defined by* (14) *is called the* transfer function *associated with the linear, time-independent operator L. If $C(k) = \rho(k)e^{i\gamma(k)}$, then $\rho = |C(k)|$ is the* gain function, *and $\gamma(k) = \arg C(k)$ is the* phase lag *associated with k.*

The reason for this terminology lies in the relationship between the real part of $u(t)$ and that of the input $r(t)$. Clearly,

$$\operatorname{Re}\{u(t)\} = \operatorname{Re}\{C(k)ce^{ikt}\} = |C(k)| \cdot |c| \cos (kt + \alpha - \gamma).$$

This shows that the amplitude of the output is $\rho(k)$ times the amplitude of the input, and the phase of the output lags $\gamma = -\arg C$ behind that of the input.

In the *strictly stable* case, the particular solution of the inhomogeneous linear DE $L[u] = ce^{ikt}$ found by the preceding method is the only bounded solution; hence $F[ce^{ikt}] = C(k)ce^{ikt}$ describes the effect of the input–output operator F on sinusoidal inputs. Furthermore, since every solution of the homogeneous DE (12) tends to zero as $t \to +\infty$, every solution of $L[u] = ce^{ikt}$ approaches $C(k)ce^{ikt}$ exponentially.

Resonance. The preceding method fails when the characteristic polynomial $p_L(\lambda)$ has one or more purely imaginary roots $\lambda = ik_j$ (in electrical engineering, this occurs in a " lossless passive network ").

Thus, suppose that ik is a root of the equation $p_L(\lambda) = 0$ and that we wish to solve the inhomogeneous DE $L[u] = e^{ikt}$. From the identity (cf. § 6)

$$L[te^{\lambda t}] = L\left[\frac{\partial}{\partial \lambda} e^{\lambda t}\right] = \frac{\partial}{\partial \lambda} L[e^{\lambda t}] = \frac{\partial}{\partial \lambda} [p_L(\lambda)e^{\lambda t}] = p'_L(\lambda)e^{\lambda t} + p_L(\lambda)te^{\lambda t},$$

we obtain, setting $\lambda = ik$,

$$L[te^{ikt}] = p'_L(ik)e^{ikt}.$$

If ik is a simple root of the characteristic equation, then $p'_L(ik) \neq 0$. Hence a solution of $L[u] = e^{ikt}$ is $u(t) = (1/p'_L(ik))te^{ikt}$. The amplitude of this solution is $(1/|p'_L(ik)|)t$, and it increases to infinity as $t \to \infty$. This is the phenomenon of *resonance*, which arises when a nondissipative physical system $\sum$ is excited by a force whose period equals one of the periods of free vibration of $\sum$.

A similar computation can be made when ik is a root of multiplicity n of the characteristic polynomial, using the identity $L[t^n e^{ikt}] = p_L^{(n)}(ik)e^{ikt}$, which is proved in much the same way. In this case the amplitude of the solution again increases to infinity.

Periodic inputs. The transfer function gives a simple way to find the outputs for periodic input functions $r(t)$ in (13). Changing the time unit, we can then write $r(t + 2\pi) = r(t)$. For $r \in \mathscr{C}'$, we can then expand $r(t)$ in Fourier series, getting

$$L[u] = \frac{a_0}{2} + \sum_{k=1}^{\infty} (a_k \cos kt + b_k \sin kt) \tag{15}$$

or, in complex form,

$$2L[u] = \sum_{k=-\infty}^{\infty} c_k e^{ikt}; \qquad c_0 = a_0, \qquad c_k = c^*_{-k} = a_k - ib_k \tag{15'}$$

for positive integers k.

Applying the superposition principle to the Fourier components $c_k e^{ikt}$ of $r(t)$ in (15'), we obtain, provided that no $p_L(ik)$ vanishes,

$$u(t) = \sum_{k=-\infty}^{\infty} [c_k/p_L(ik)]e^{ikt} \tag{16}$$

as at least a formal solution. The series (16) is absolutely and uniformly convergent, since $p_L(ik) = O(k^{-n})$ for an nth-order DE. We leave to the reader the proof and the determination of sufficient conditions for term-by-term differentiability.

8*   The Nyquist diagram

The transfer function $C(k) = 1/p_L(ik)$ of a linear differential equation with constant coefficients $L[u] = 0$ is of great help in the study of the inhomogeneous DE (13). To visualize the transfer function, one graphs the logarithmic gain $\ln \rho(k)$ and phase lag $\gamma(k)$ as functions of the frequency $k/2\pi$. If $\lambda_1, \ldots, \lambda_n$ are the roots of the characteristic polynomial, we have

$$\ln \rho(k) = -\sum_{j=1}^{n} \ln |ik - \lambda_j| = -\tfrac{1}{2} \sum \ln [(k - \nu_j)^2 + \mu_j^2], \tag{17a}$$

$$\gamma(k) = \sum_{j=1}^{n} \arg (ik - \lambda_j) = \sum \arctan [(k - \nu_j)/\mu_j], \tag{17b}$$

from which these graphs are easily plotted. Figure 4.2(a) depicts the gain function and phase lag of the DE

$$u^{\mathrm{iv}} + 0.8u''' + 5.22u'' + 1.424u' + 4.1309u = 0,$$

whose characteristic polynomial has the roots $\lambda_j = -0.1 \pm i, -0.3 \pm 2i$.

We now compute how the phase lag $\gamma(k)$ changes as the frequency $k/2\pi$ increases from $-\infty$ to $+\infty$. By (17b), it suffices to add the changes in the functions $\arg (ik - \lambda_j)$ for each λ_j. If Re $\{\lambda_j\}$ is negative, then the vertical straight line $ik - \lambda_j$ $(-\infty < k < \infty)$ lies in the right

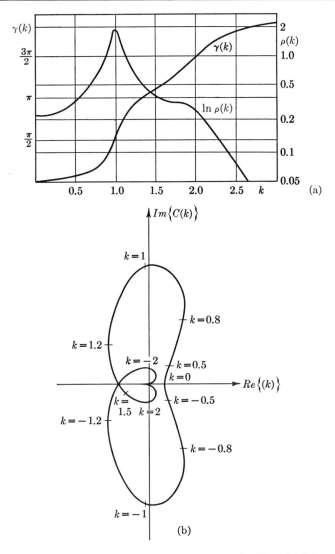

FIGURE 4.2.   (a) Phase-lag and gain functions, (b) Nyquist Diagram.

half of the complex plane; hence $\arg(ik - \lambda_j)$ increases by π as k increases from $-\infty$ to $+\infty$. If $\operatorname{Re}\{\lambda_j\}$ is positive, then $\arg(ik - \lambda_j)$ decreases by π for a similar reason. Hence, if there are no roots with zero real part, the change in $\gamma(k)$ is $(m - p)\pi$, where m is the number of λ_j with negative real part, and p is the number with positive real part.†

---

† For purely imaginary roots, the change of argument of λ is undefined (it could be π or $-\pi$). In this case, we make the convention that the change in the argument is zero. The following theorem is true with the proviso that, whenever the argument is undefined, the change is taken to be zero.

If there are no purely imaginary roots, then $m + p = n$, and we obtain a useful test for strict stability.

THEOREM 6.   *The DE* $L[u] = r(t)$ *of degree* n *is strictly stable if and only if the phase lag* $\gamma = -\arg C(k)$ *increases by* $n\pi$ *as* k *increases from* $-\infty$ *to* $+\infty$. *In this case, the phase lag increases monotonically with* k.

If the differential operator L has *real* coefficients, then $\gamma(-k) = -\gamma(k)$ and $\rho(-k) = \rho(k)$, since the complex roots λ_j occur in conjugate pairs $\mu_j \pm i\nu_j$. In particular, we have $\gamma(0) = 0$, and the change in $\gamma(k)$ as k increases from 0 to ∞ is $(m - p)\pi/2$. This proves the following specialization of Theorem 6.

■ **COROLLARY 1.**   *A linear* DE *of order* n *with constant* real *coefficients is strictly stable if and only if the phase lag increases from* 0 *to* $n\pi/2$ *as* k *increases from* 0 *to* ∞.

If all roots λ_j of the characteristic polynomial are real, then one easily verifies that all $\ln |ik - \lambda_j|$ increase monotonically as k increases from 0 to ∞. Hence, in this case, the gain $\rho(k)$ is a monotonically decreasing function of the frequency. In the case of complex roots $\lambda_j = \mu_j \pm i\nu_j$ with μ_j very small, the gain function $\rho(k)$ is very large near $k = \nu_j$; this is due to near *resonance*.

Another useful way to visualize the transfer function is to plot the curve $z = C(k)$ in the *complex plane* as k ranges through all real values. The curve thus obtained is called the *Nyquist diagram* of DE (13). Figure 4.2(b) depicts the Nyquist diagram of the DE below (17b).

Since $C(k)$ is the inverse of a polynomial, it tends to the origin as $k \to \pm\infty$, that is, it "starts" and "ends" at the origin. It is a continuous curve except when the characteristic equation has one or more imaginary roots $\lambda_j = ik_j$. From Theorem 6 we obtain the following *Nyquist Stability Criterion*.

■ **COROLLARY 2.**   *The equation* $L[u] = 0$ *is strictly stable if and only if the Nyquist diagram for* $C(k)$ *turns through* $-n\pi$ *radians as* k *increases from* $-\infty$ *to* $+\infty$.

If L is real, then $C(-k) = C^*(k)$, and it suffices to plot half of the Nyquist diagram. The operator L is strictly stable if and only if the Nyquist diagram turns through $n\pi/2$ radians as k increases from 0 to ∞.

EXERCISES C

In Exercises 1–4, test the DE specified for stability and strict stability.

1. $u'' + 5u' + 4 = 0$.   2. $u''' + 6u'' + 12u' + 8u = 0$.
3. $u''' + 6u'' + 11u' + 6u = 0$.   4. $u^{\mathrm{iv}} + 4u''' + 4u'' = 0$.

5. For which n is the DE $u^{(n)} + u = 0$ stable?

   In Exercises 6–9, find a particular solution of the DE specified. In Exercises 6–8, find the solutions satisfying $u(0) = 0$; $u'(0) = 1$, and vice versa.

6. $u'' = te^t$.   7. $u'' + u = te^t$.
8. $u'' - u = te^t$.   9. $u^{iv} = t^5 e^t$.

In Exercises 10–13, plot the gain and transfer functions of the operator specified (I denotes the identity operator):

10. $D^2 + 4D + 4I$.   11. $D^3 + 6D^2 + 12D + 8I$.
12. $D^2 + 2D + 101I$.   13. $D^4 - I$.

14. For a strictly stable $L[u] = u'' + au' + bu = r(t)$ calculate the outputs (the *responses*) to the inputs $r(t) = 1$ and $r(t) = t$ for $a^2 > 4b$ and $a^2 < 4b$.
15. Do the same as in Exercise 14 for the step-function

$$h(t) = \begin{cases} 1 & \text{on} \quad (0, 1), \\ 0 & \text{elsewhere.} \end{cases}$$

16. For $u'' + au' + bu = ce^{ikt}$, make graphs of the gain function versus the dimensionless frequency $k/\sqrt{b}$ for the values $\eta = 0$, $\eta = 1/2$, $\eta = 1/\sqrt{2}, \eta = 2$ of the parameter $\eta = a/2\sqrt{b}$ $(b > 0)$.
17. Show that, if $p_L(ik) = p'_L(ik) = \cdots = p_L^{n-1}(ik) = 0$ but $p_L^{(n)}(ik) \neq 0$, then a solution of $L[u] = e^{ikt}$ is $u(t) = (1/p_L^{(n)}(ik))t^n e^{ikt}$.
18. A DE (12) is stable at $t \to -\infty$ when all solutions of the DE remain bounded as $t \to -\infty$. Find necessary and sufficient conditions for stability at $-\infty$.
19. In Exercise 18, find necessary and sufficient conditions for strict stability at $-\infty$.
20. Show that no DE (12) can be strictly stable at both ∞ and $-\infty$.
21. Show that a DE (12) is stable at both ∞ and $-\infty$ if and only if every root of the characteristic equation is simple and a purely imaginary number.

9   The Green's function

The concept of the Green's function was introduced in Chapter 2, §8. For the inhomogeneous linear DE $L[u] = r(t)$, it is a function $G(t, \tau)$ such that

$$u = f(t) = \int_a^t G(t, \tau) r(\tau) \, d\tau \tag{18}$$

satisfies $L[u] = r(t)$ if $t \geqq a$, for any continuous function r. We now state a generalization of Theorem 8 of Chapter 2, §9, which describes the Green's function of a linear operator of arbitrary order.

■ THEOREM 7.   The Green's function for the initial value problem *of the* nth *order real linear differential operator with continuous coefficients*

$$L = \frac{d^n}{dt^n} + p_1(t)\frac{d^{n-1}}{dt^{n-1}} + \cdots + p_{n-1}(t)\frac{d}{dt} + p_n(t), \qquad a \leqq t \leqq b, \tag{19}$$

is zero if $t < \tau$. For $t \geqq \tau$, it is that solution of the DE (for fixed τ and *variable t)* $L[G] = 0$ *which satisfies the initial conditions*

$$G = \partial G/\partial t = \cdots = \partial^{n-2}G/\partial t^{n-2} = 0, \qquad \partial^{n-1}G/\partial t^{n-1} = 1 \quad for \quad t = \tau.$$

In the case $p_i(t) = a_i$ of linear DE's with constant real coefficients, the existence of such a solution follows from the results of §3. Green's function is easily computed as a sum of polynomials times exponentials. Thus, if (19) is $u''' + 3u'' + 3u' + u$, the Green's function is

$$G(t, \tau) = \begin{cases} 0 & \text{if } t < \tau, \\ (t - \tau)^2 e^{\tau - t}/2 & \text{if } t \geq \tau. \end{cases}$$

For variable coefficient-functions, existence will follow from the results of the next chapter.

We omit the proof of Theorem 7. It follows exactly the proof for second-order differential operators, given in Chapter 2, §9. This can be easily extended to the present case: one simply applies the rule for differentiation under the integral sign n times instead of twice.

The computation of Green's functions for linear DE's with constant coefficients is most easily performed and its significance best understood by using the following result.

■ THEOREM 8.   *The Green's function for the initial value problem of any linear differential operator with constant coefficients is a function $G(t, \tau) = \Gamma(t - \tau)$ depending only on the difference $t - \tau$.*

Proof — Let $\Gamma(t) = G(t, 0)$; then $\Gamma(t) = 0$ if $t < 0$. If $t \geq 0$, the function $\Gamma(t)$ is the solution of the DE $L[\Gamma] = 0$ which satisfies the initial conditions

$$\Gamma(0) = \Gamma'(0) = \cdots = \Gamma^{(n-2)}(0) = 0, \qquad \Gamma^{(n-1)}(0) = 1.$$

We now remark that, if $u(t)$ is a solution of the DE $L[u] = 0$, for each fixed τ the function $u(t + \tau)$ of the variable t is also a solution of the DE. It follows that the function $F(t) = G(t + \tau, \tau)$ (for fixed τ) is a solution of the DE. This function satisfies the same initial conditions as the function Γ, because of the way in which Green's function is defined. By the uniqueness theorem (Theorem 3), it follows that $\Gamma(t) = G(t + \tau, \tau)$. Hence, setting $s = t + \tau$, we obtain $\Gamma(s - \tau) = G(s, \tau)$, q.e.d.

Referring to Theorems 1 and 3, we obtain the next corollary,

■ COROLLARY 1.   *In Theorem 8, the function $\Gamma(t - \tau)$ is of class $\mathscr{C}^{n-2}$. It satisfies $\Gamma(s) = 0$ for $s < 0$, while $\Gamma(s)$ is a linear combination of functions $s^r e^{\lambda_j s}$ for $s > 0$.†*

---

† The function $\Gamma(s)$ is, of course, *also* expressible for $s > 0$ as a *real* linear combination of functions of the form (6).

Changing variables in (18), we have also

■ COROLLARY 2.   *If r(t) vanishes for t < a, and is bounded and continuous for a ≤ t, then the function*

$$f(t) = \int_{-\infty}^{\infty} \Gamma(t-\tau)r(\tau)\,d\tau = \int_{-\infty}^{\infty} \Gamma(s)r(t-s)\,ds \qquad (19a)$$

is a solution of the inhomogeneous linear DE *with constant coefficients* (13) *on* [a, ∞], *which satisfies* $f(a) = f'(a) = \cdots = f^{(n-1)}(a) = 0$. *(Note that, unless* r(0) = 0, $f^{(n)}(a)$ *does not exist.)*

Indeed, since $r(\tau)$ vanishes for $\tau < a$ and $\Gamma(t-\tau)$ vanishes for $\tau > t$, the integral (19a) can be written as

$$f(t) = \int_a^t \Gamma(t-\tau)r(\tau)\,d\tau \qquad (19b)$$

and is equal to (18), by Theorem 8.

■ THEOREM 9.   *If L is strictly stable, formulas* (19a) *remain valid for any bounded continuous function r(t) defined for* $-\infty < t < \infty$; *for such a function,* f(t) *is the only solution of the* DE (13) *which is bounded for* $-\infty < t < \infty$.

Proof — By Corollary 1 above, $\Gamma(s)$ is equal, for $s \geq 0$, to a linear combination of the form

$$\Gamma(s) = \sum_{j=1}^{n} c_j s^{r_j} e^{\lambda_j s}, \qquad s \geq 0.$$

If the equation $L[u] = 0$ is strictly stable, then the real parts of all λ_j are negative. Let $-m$ be the largest of these real parts. Then $-m < 0$, and

$$\left| e^{ms/2}\,\Gamma(s) \right| \leq \sum_{j=1}^{n} \left| c_j s^{r_j} e^{(\lambda_j + (m/2))s} \right|.$$

Since Re $\{\lambda_j\} + (m/2) < 0$ for $1 \leq j \leq m$, the right side remains bounded for $0 \leq s \leq \infty$. Let M be an upper bound for the right side. Then we obtain

$$|\Gamma(s)| \leq Me^{-ms/2}, \qquad 0 \leq s < \infty.$$

We next show that the integrals in (19a) are well-defined for any bounded continuous function r. The first integral can be rewritten in the form

$$\int_{-\infty}^{t} \Gamma(t-\tau)r(\tau)\,d\tau$$

since $\Gamma(t-\tau)=0$ for $t<\tau$. Using the above estimate for $\Gamma(s)$, and letting R be an upper bound for $|r(\tau)|$ on $-\infty<\tau<\infty$, we obtain

$$\left|\int_{-\infty}^{t}\Gamma(t-\tau)r(\tau)\,d\tau\right|\leqq\int_{-\infty}^{t}\left|\Gamma(t-\tau)\right|\left|r(\tau)\right|d\tau$$

$$\leqq RM\int_{-\infty}^{t}e^{-m(t-\tau)/2}\,d\tau=\frac{2RM}{m}<+\infty$$

for all t. Hence the integral is well-defined and defines a bounded function $f(t)$. To show that f is a solution of the DE, we can argue as in Theorem 8 of Chapter 2, provided we can carry out the differentiation under the integral sign. This can indeed be justified†; instead, however, we shall give a direct argument.

Consider the sequence of functions $r_k(t)$ defined by the formulas

$$r_k(t)=\begin{cases}r(t) & \text{if}\quad t\geqq-k,\\0 & \text{if}\quad t<-k,\quad k=1,2,\dots.\end{cases}$$

Then the functions

$$f_k(t)=\int_{-k}^{t}\Gamma(t-\tau)r_k(\tau)\,d\tau=\int_{-\infty}^{\infty}\Gamma(t-\tau)r_k(\tau)\,d\tau$$

are solutions of the DE (13). We shall show that, for t ranging over any interval $a\leqq t\leqq b$, the functions $f_k(t)$, as well as their derivatives of orders up to n, converge uniformly to the derivatives of the function $f(t)$. This will also prove that $f(t)$ is a solution of the DE (13).

From the expression of $\Gamma(s)$ as a linear combination of functions of the form $s^{r_j}e^{\lambda_j s}$, we see that all derivatives of $\Gamma(s)$ are also linear combinations of functions of the same form, for different r_j, but with the same sequence of exponents λ_j. That is, for the derivative of order ℓ, we have

$$\Gamma^{(\ell)}(s)=\sum_{j=1}^{n}p_j(s)e^{\lambda_j s},$$

where the p_j are polynomials in the variable s, depending on the order of differentiation ℓ.‡ It follows, as before, that

$$|\Gamma^{(\ell)}(s)|\leqq M_\ell e^{-ms/2},\qquad\ell=1,2,\dots.$$

Now, from the expression

$$f_k^{(\ell)}(t)=\int_{-k}^{t}\Gamma^{(\ell)}(t-\tau)r_k(\tau)\,d\tau$$

---

† Courant, Vol. 2, p. 312.
‡ This can be easily seen by applying Leibniz's rule; cf. Courant and John, p. 203.

we find, for sufficiently large k and j, where $k \geqq j$,

$$|f_k^{(\ell)}(t) - f_j^{(\ell)}(t)| \leqq \int_{-k}^{-j} |\Gamma^{(\ell)}(t - \tau)| \, |r_k(\tau) - r_j(\tau)| \, d\tau$$

$$\leqq \int_{-k}^{-j} |\Gamma^{(\ell)}(t - \tau)| \, |r_k(\tau)| \, d\tau$$

$$\leqq RM_\ell \int_{-k}^{-j} e^{-m(t-\tau)/2} \, d\tau,$$

and the last integral clearly tends to zero as j, $k \to \infty$, uniformly for $a \leqq t \leqq b$. Therefore, $|f_k^{(\ell)}(t) - f_j^{(\ell)}(t)| < \epsilon$ for sufficiently large k, j, uniformly for $a \leqq t \leqq b$. This completes the proof of the fact that f is a solution of the DE.

Lastly, one can easily see, by the following argument, that f thus defined is the only bounded solution. If f_1 were another bounded solution, then $f - f_1$ would be a bounded solution of the homogeneous DE. But, since the DE is *strictly* stable as $t \to \infty$, no nontrivial solution of the homogeneous DE can remain bounded as $t \to -\infty$ (cf. Theorem 4). Hence, $f - f_1 \equiv 0$, and the proof is complete.

EXERCISES D

In Exercises 1–6, construct the Green's function for the initial value problem of the DE indicated.

1. $d^3u/dt^3 = r(t)$.
2. $d^n u/dt^n = r(t)$.
3. $u^{\mathrm{iv}} - u = r(t)$.
4. $u''' + u = r(t)$.
5. $u^{\mathrm{iv}} + u = r(t)$.
6*. $u^{\mathrm{iv}} - u = r(t)$.

7. Find Green's function of the DE $d^n u/dt^n = r(t)$.
8. Carry out in detail the proof of Theorem 7 for $n = 3$, performing all differentiations under the integral sign explicitly.
9*. Show that, if (18) is defined for all t and the Green's function $G(t, \tau) = \Gamma(t - \tau)$, then all coefficients $p_k(t)$ are constant.
10*. Show that, if $u(t + \tau)$ is a solution of (18) with $r(t) = 0$ whenever $u(t)$ is, then the coefficients $p_k(t)$ are all constants.

10* Laplace transforms

An effective technique for solving inhomogeneous linear DE's with constant coefficients is the Laplace transform. It is especially well-suited to solving initial value problems.

■ DEFINITION. *The* Laplace transform $\phi = \mathscr{L}[f]$ *of an integrable function* $f(t)$, $0 \leqq t < \infty$, *is the function* ϕ *defined by the equation*

$$\phi(s) = \int_0^\infty e^{-st} f(t) \, dt. \tag{20}$$

It is well-defined for all real $s > M$, provided that $|f(t)| \leq K e^{Mt}$ for some finite K; the least real s_c such that (20) *is defined for all $s > s_c$ is called the* abscissa of convergence.†

The variable s is allowed to take real or complex values. We shall consider it as a real variable in this section.

The Laplace transform is a linear operator:

$$\mathscr{L}[c_1 f_1 + c_2 f_2] = c_1 \mathscr{L}[f_1] + c_2 \mathscr{L}[f_2],$$

for any constants c_1, c_2 and functions f_1, f_2.

Some common Laplace transforms are the following‡:

$$\mathscr{L}[1] = 1/s. \tag{21-1}$$

$$\mathscr{L}[t^r] = \Gamma(r + 1)/s^{r+1}. \tag{21-2}$$

$$\mathscr{L}[e^{at}] = 1/(s - a). \tag{21-3}$$

$$\mathscr{L}[t^r e^{at}] = \Gamma(r + 1)/(s - a)^{r+1}. \tag{21-4}$$

$$\mathscr{L}[\cos bt] = s/(s^2 + b^2). \tag{21-5}$$

$$\mathscr{L}[\log t] = [\Gamma'(1) - \ln s]/s. \tag{21-6}$$

$$\mathscr{L}[(\sin t)/t] = \arctan s^{-1}. \tag{21-7}$$

$$\mathscr{L}[J_0(t)] = 1/\sqrt{s^2 + 1}. \tag{21-8}$$

The abscissas of convergence are $s = 0$ or (for functions containing the factor e^{at}) $s = a$.

Not every function can be represented as a Laplace transform; Laplace transforms tend to zero as $s \to +\infty$. But functions whose Laplace transforms coincide (for sufficiently large s) are identical, by virtue of the following theorem.

■ LERCH'S THEOREM.§   *If $f(t)$ and $g(t)$ have the same Laplace transform $\mathscr{L}[f] = \mathscr{L}[g]$ for an infinite set of numbers $s = s_0 + nh$ [$h > 0, n = 1, 2, 3, \ldots$] in an arithmetic progression, then $f(t) = g(t)$ for all positive t.*

The Laplace transform of the derivative of a function is easily computed. Integrating by parts, we obtain

$$\int_0^\infty e^{-st} f'(t)\, dt = \lim_{T \to \infty} \left\{ [e^{-st} f(t)]_0^T + s \int_0^T e^{-st} f(t)\, dt \right\}$$

$$= -f(0) + s \int_0^\infty e^{-st} f(t)\, dt,$$

---

† Widder, Chapter 13, where Lerch's Theorem is proved, p. 460, and the Laplace transforms (21) are given, p. 473.
‡ Here, Γ is the gamma function, and $\Gamma'(1)$ is the Euler constant $\gamma = 0.577257 \cdots$.
§ Cf. Widder, Chapter 14; R. V. Churchill, *Operational Mathematics*, 2d. ed., McGraw-Hill, 1958.

where the passage to the limit is easily justified if $f'(t)$ is bounded by Me^{Kt} for some $M > 0$ and $K < s$. By the definition of the Laplace transform, this asserts that

$$\mathscr{L}[f'] = s\mathscr{L}[f] - f(0). \tag{22}$$

From this rule, by induction on n, we can obtain the rule for taking the Laplace transform of the nth derivative of a given function. This rule is as follows.

■ LEMMA. *If u is of class $\mathscr{C}^k$, and $|u^{(k)}(t)| \leq Ke^{Mt}$ for some finite K and M, then*

$$\mathscr{L}[u^{(k)}] = s^k\mathscr{L}[u] - [s^{k-1}u(0) + s^{k-2}u'(0) + \cdots + u^{(k-1)}(0)]. \tag{23}$$

The Laplace transform can be applied to the inhomogeneous linear DE (13) with constant coefficients

$$L[u] = u^{(n)} + a_1 u^{(n-1)} + a_2 u^{(n-2)} + \cdots + a_n u = r(t),$$

subject to the initial conditions of Theorem 7,

$$u = u' = u'' = \cdots = u^{(n-1)} = 0 \qquad \text{when} \quad t = 0. \tag{24}$$

Taking the Laplace transform of both sides, we get

$$\int_0^\infty e^{-st}u^{(n)}\,dt + a_1\int_0^\infty e^{-st}u^{(n-1)}\,dt + \cdots + a_n\int_0^\infty e^{-st}u\,dt = \int_0^\infty e^{-st}r(t)\,dt.$$

The following theorem is also needed.

■ THEOREM 10. *Let u be the solution of $L[u] = r$ satisfying the initial conditions $u(0) = u'(0) = \cdots = u^{(n-1)}(0) = 0$. Then, for sufficiently large s,*

$$p_L(s)\mathscr{L}[u] = \mathscr{L}[r] \qquad or \qquad \mathscr{L}[u] = \mathscr{L}[r]/p_L(s), \tag{25}$$

provided that $|r(t)| \leq Ke^{Mt}$ for some finite K and M. Here $p_L(s)$ is the characteristic polynomial of the operator L.

Proof — The solution u is given by the formula (19b) for $f = u$ and $a = 0$. By Theorem 9, $|\Gamma(t)| \leq ce^{mt}$ as $s \to \infty$ for some constants c and m. Hence we have, for $t > 0$,

$$|u(t)| \leq \int_0^t ce^{m(t-\tau)}Ke^{M\tau}\,d\tau \leq Qe^{qt}$$

for some constants Q and q. Therefore, $\mathscr{L}[u]$ is defined for sufficiently large s.

Since the terms in square brackets in (23) vanish, formula (25) follows immediately.

Using Theorem 10, we can solve the initial value problem for $L[u] = r$ with the initial conditions (24), provided that we can find the function whose Laplace transform is $\mathcal{L}[r]/p_L(s)$. To find such a function, it is best to decompose $p_L(s)$ into *partial fractions* and then to consult a table of Laplace transforms for the different terms obtained.

When the roots $\lambda_1, \ldots, \lambda_n$ of a polynomial $p(s)$ are distinct, the reciprocal $1/p(s)$ has a particularly simple decomposition into partial fractions. We can determine the coefficients b_k in the expression

$$1/p(s) = b_1/(s - \lambda_1) + \cdots + b_n/(s - \lambda_n)$$

from the relation $b_k = \lim_{s \to \lambda_k} (s - \lambda_k)/p(s)$, which implies that $b_k = 1/p'(\lambda_k)$. Hence

$$\frac{1}{p_L(s)} = \frac{b_1}{s - \lambda_1} + \frac{b_2}{s - \lambda_2} + \cdots + \frac{b_n}{s - \lambda_n}, \qquad b_k = \frac{1}{p'_L(\lambda_k)}. \qquad (26)$$

As an application of the Laplace transform, we compute the formula for the Green's function $\Gamma(t)$ for the initial value problem. This is the solution of the DE $L[u] = 0$ for $t \geq 0$ which satisfies the initial conditions $\Gamma(0) = \Gamma'(0) = \cdots = \Gamma^{(n-2)}(0) = 0$, $\Gamma^{(n-1)}(0) = 1$. Using the preceding theorem, we obtain another result.

■ THEOREM. 11.   *The Laplace transform of the Green's function for the initial value problem of any linear differential operator L with constant coefficients is the function $1/p_L(s)$.*

Comparing with formula (14), we have

■ COROLLARY 1.   *The Laplace transform $\mathcal{L}[\Gamma_L]$ of Green's function of L is $C(-is)$, where $C(k)$ is the transfer function of L.*

The function $b_k/(s - \lambda_k)$ is the Laplace transform of the function $b_k e^{\lambda_k t}$ (cf. formula (21)). Hence we have also

■ COROLLARY 2.   *If the characteristic equation $p_L(s) = 0$ has n distinct roots $\lambda_1, \lambda_2, \ldots, \lambda_n$, then the Green's function for the initial value problem for $L[u] = r$ is the function $\Gamma(t - \tau)$, defined for $s > 0$ by*

$$\Gamma(s) = b_1 e^{\lambda_1 s} + \cdots + b_n e^{\lambda_n s}, \qquad b_k = 1/p'_L(\lambda_k), \qquad (26')$$

and by $\Gamma(s) = 0$ for $s < 0$.

The Laplace transform is a continuous analog of a generating function, as defined in Chapter 3, § 4. One replaces the discrete variable n by a continuous nonnegative real variable t; this replaces the sequence a_n by a function $a(t)$. Replacing the sum by the analogous integral, we obtain the formula $g(x) = \int a(t)x^t \, dt$. On setting $x = e^{-s}$, we obtain the Laplace transform of the function $a(t)$, as in formula (20) above.

11* Convolution

An important property of the Laplace transform is related to the operation of convolution of two functions. Let $f(t)$ and $g(t)$ be functions defined for all real t. Their convolution is defined by the formula

$$h(x) = \int_{-\infty}^{\infty} f(x-t)g(t)\, dt \qquad (27)$$

whenever the integral is finite. If the functions f and g are identically zero for $t < 0$, this formula simplifies to

$$h(x) = f * g(x) = \int_{0}^{x} f(t)g(x-t)\, dt. \qquad (27')$$

In many ways this operation is analogous to the multiplication of two infinite series. It is commutative and associative, as can be easily seen. The relevant property of convolution is expressed by the formula $\mathscr{L}[f * g] = \mathscr{L}[f]\mathscr{L}[g]$; in other words, the Laplace transform of the convolution of two functions is the product of the single Laplace transforms. This property can be verified by a change in the order of integration, as follows:

$$\mathscr{L}[f * g] = \int_{0}^{\infty} e^{-sx} \int_{0}^{x} f(t)g(x-t)\, dt\, dx = \int_{0}^{\infty} f(t) \int_{t}^{\infty} e^{-sx} g(x-t)\, dx\, dt$$

$$= \int_{0}^{\infty} f(t)e^{-ts}\, dt \int_{0}^{\infty} g(v)e^{-vs}\, dv = \mathscr{L}[f]\mathscr{L}[g], \qquad v = x - t.$$

For example, let 1 denote the function equal to one for $0 \leq x < \infty$ and to zero for $x < 0$. Then $1 * 1 = x$, $1 * 1 * \cdots * 1 = [1/(n-1)!]x^{n-1}$. As an application, we obtain *Liouville's formula* for iterated integrals:

$$1 * f = \int_{0}^{x} f(t)\, dt,$$

$$\underbrace{1 * 1 * \cdots * 1}_{n \text{ terms}} * f = \int_{0}^{x} \int_{0}^{t_n} \cdots \int_{0}^{t_2} f(t_1)\, dt_1 \cdots dt_n$$

$$= \frac{1}{\Gamma(n)} \int_{0}^{x} (x-t)^{n-1} f(t)\, dt.$$

The Laplace transform of $1 * f$ is $(1/s)\hat{f}(s)$, $\hat{f} = \mathscr{L}[f]$. Therefore, the Laplace transform of the indefinite integral $\int_{0}^{x} f(t)\, dt$ is $(1/s)\hat{f}(s)$. More generally, the Laplace transform of $[1/\Gamma(n)] \int_{0}^{x} (x-t)^{n-1} f(t)\, dt$ is $s^{-n}\hat{f}(s)$.

As another application, we reinterpret Corollary 2 of Theorem 8. It states that the solution of the DE $L[u] = r(t)$ for the initial conditions

$u(0) = u'(0) = \cdots = u^{(n-1)}(0) = 0$ is the convolution $r * \Gamma$ of r and the displaced Green function Γ for the same initial conditions, provided that $r \equiv 0$ for $t < 0$.

Theorem 9 can also be interpreted in terms of the convolution operation. It asserts that, for strictly stable L, the solution of the "input–output" problem $L[u] = r(t)$ is $r * \Gamma$ for any uniformly bounded "input" $r(t)$.

EXERCISES E

1 ———8. Derive formulas (21-1) through (21-8), respectively.
9. Show that, if the Laplace transform of $f(t)$ is $\hat{f}(s)$, then that of (a) $f(at)$ is $a^{-1}\hat{f}(sa^{-1})$, (b) $e^{-bt}f(t)$ is $\hat{f}(s+b)$, (c) $a^{-1}f(ta^{-1})$ is $\hat{f}(as)$.

In Exercises 10–11, find the solution of the DE specified which satisfies the initial condition $u(0) = u'(0) = 0$; (a) by using formula (23), (b) by the Method of Undetermined Coefficients.

10. $u'' - u = t.$ 11. $u'' - 3u' + 2u = te^t.$

In Exercises 12–13, do the same for the initial conditions

$$u(0) = u'(0) = u''(0) = u'''(0) = 0.$$

12. $u^{iv} - u = t^2.$ 13. $u^{iv} = t^2.$

14*. Let $f(t) \in \mathscr{C}^n$ satisfy $|f(t)| \leqq A + Bt^n$ for some finite A, B, on $0 \leqq t < +\infty$. Show that the Laplace transform of $f(t)$ has an abscissa of convergence $s_c \leqq 0$ and satisfies $\phi = O(1/s^r)$ for large s, where $f^{(r)}$ is the first derivative of $f(t)$ which does *not* vanish at $t = 0$. [HINT Use (22).]
15. Show that $\mathscr{L}[SI(kt)] = s^{-1} \arctan(k/s).$
16. Prove that, if $\phi(s)$ is a Laplace transform, then $e^{Ls}\phi(s) \to 0$ as $s \to 0$ for some $L > 0$.
17. Verify that convolution is a commutative and associative operation.
18*. Show that the Laplace transform of $e^{-t^2/4}$ is $\sqrt{\pi} \, e^{s^2} \operatorname{erfc} s.$

ADDITIONAL EXERCISES

1*. Prove Theorem 2 directly, using the factorization of a real polynomial into linear and quadratic real polynomials.
2. Plot the function $x^\mu \cos(\nu \log x)$ for $x > 0$, for $\mu = 1$ and $\nu = 2$.
3. For the DE $x^2u'' + Axu' + Bu = 0$, A, B real, find necessary and sufficient conditions that every solution vanish infinitely often on $(-\infty, +\infty)$.
4*. Suppose that $p_L[\lambda] = (\lambda - \lambda_1)^k \phi(\lambda)$, where $\phi(\lambda_1) \neq 0$. Show that the DE $L[u] = e^{\lambda_1 t}q(t)$ has a solution of the form $e^{\lambda_1 t}Q_1(t)$, where the degree of the polynomial $Q_1(t)$ exceeds that of $q(t)$ by k.
5. Consider the system of linear DE's with constant coefficients $L[u] = v$, $M[v] = r(t)$. Show that the resulting DE $M[L[u]] = r(t)$ is stable if and only if both L and M are stable.
6. The system $L[u] = v$, $M[v] = u$ is said to have *feedback*. If L and M have constant coefficients, show that this system is strictly stable if and only if $\arg\{p_L(ik)p_M(ik) - 1\}$ decreases by $n\pi$, where n is the sum of the orders of L and M.

7. Let L in (19) be defined for $-\infty < t < \infty$, and let, for fixed τ,

$$L_\tau[u] = \sum_{k=0}^{n} p_{n-k}(t + \tau)u^{(k)}, \qquad p_0(t) \equiv 1.$$

Express the Green's function of L_τ in terms of Green's function for L.

8. If $\Gamma(t)$ is the Green's function of a DE (13) with constant coefficients, show that

$$\Gamma^{(n)}(0) + a_1 = 0, \qquad \Gamma^{(n+1)}(0) + a_1\Gamma^{(n)}(0) + a_2 = 0,$$

$$\Gamma^{(n+2)}(0) + a_1\Gamma^{(n+1)}(0) + a_2\Gamma^{(n)}(0) + a_3 = 0, \qquad \text{etc.}$$

9*. (a) For $0 \leqq j \leqq n - 1$, let

$$U_j(t) = \Gamma^{(n-j-1)}(t) + a_1\Gamma^{(n-j-2)}(t) + \cdots + a_{n-j-1}\Gamma(t).$$

Show that $U_j^{(k)}(0) = 0$ for $0 \leqq k \leqq n - 1$, $k \neq j$ and $U_j^{(j)}(0) = 1$. [HINT Use Exercise 8.]

(b) Show that every solution of $L[u] = 0$ is given by the formula

$$u(t) = \sum_{k=0}^{n+1} u^{(k)}(0)U_k(t).$$

10*. Show that the convolution of two bounded integrable functions on $0 \leqq t < \infty$ is a continuous function, even though the functions are discontinuous.

5 *Plane Autonomous Systems*

1 Autonomous systems

One of the basic notions of analysis is that of a *system* of n first-order ordinary DE's in normal form:

$$dx_1/dt = X_1(x_1, \ldots, x_n; t),$$
$$\cdot \quad \cdot \quad \cdot \quad \cdot \quad \cdot \quad \cdot \quad \cdot \qquad (1)$$
$$dx_n/dt = X_n(x_1, \ldots, x_n; t).$$

The X_i are given functions of the $n + 1$ real variables $x_1, \ldots, x_n, t$. We want to find *solutions* of (1), that is, sets of n functions $x_1(t), \ldots, x_n(t)$, of class $\mathscr{C}^1$, which satisfy (1).

We shall assume the functions X_i to be continuous and real-valued in a given region R of the $(n + 1)$-dimensional space of the independent variables $x_1, x_2, \ldots, x_n, t$. A solution of a normal system (1) can be visualized as a curve in R defined by the functions $x_1(t), \ldots, x_n(t)$; when $n = 1$, this specializes to the concept of a solution curve defined in Chapter 1. For this reason, the curve in R defined by any solution of (1) is called a *solution curve* of (1).

The simplicity of the concept of a first-order normal system becomes apparent when (1) is written in vector notation. A *vector* is an n-tuple $\mathbf{x} = (x_1, \ldots, x_n)$ of real (or complex) numbers. Thus, the functions $X_i(x_1, \ldots, x_n; t) = X_i(\mathbf{x}, t)$, in (1) define $\mathbf{X} = (X_1, \ldots, X_n)$ as a *vector-valued* function of the vector variable $\mathbf{x}$ and the real variable t.

In vector notation, the system (1) assumes the very concise form

$$d\mathbf{x}/dt = \mathbf{X}(\mathbf{x}, t). \qquad (2)$$

A *solution* of (2) is a vector-valued function $\mathbf{x}(t)$ of a real (scalar) variable t, such that $\mathbf{x}'(t) = \mathbf{X}(\mathbf{x}(t), t)$. The analogy between (2) and the normal first-order DE $y' = F(x, y)$ studied in Chapter 1 is apparent; the difference is that the dependent variable in (2) is a vector and not a number (or "scalar"). Hence, one can call (2) a *normal first-order vector DE*.

Chapter 6 will contain proofs of existence, uniqueness, continuity, and differentiability theorems for solutions of first-order systems (1). In the present chapter, attention will be confined to *autonomous* first-order systems. By definition, these are systems of the form

$$dx_i/dt = X_i(x_1, \ldots, x_n), \qquad i = 1, \ldots, n. \tag{3}$$

The characteristic property of autonomous sytems is the fact that the functions X_i do not depend on the independent variable t. When this variable is thought of as representing time, autonomous systems are thus *time-independent* or *stationary*.

In vector notation, the autonomous system (1) reduces to

$$d\mathbf{x}/dt = \mathbf{X}(\mathbf{x}). \tag{3'}$$

Each first-order autonomous system is characterized by its *vector field*†: To every system (3) there corresponds a unique vector field $\mathbf{X}(\mathbf{x})$ in Euclidean n-space, and conversely. Throughout this chapter, we will consider only vector fields which are of class $\mathscr{C}^1$ and, hence, satisfy a Lipschitz condition in every compact domain. As will be shown in Chapter 6, this implies that one and only one solution $\mathbf{x}(t, \mathbf{c})$ of the autonomous system (3) satisfies the initial condition $\mathbf{x}(0) = \mathbf{c}$, and that this solution depends continuously on $\mathbf{c}$.

When $n = 3$, the autonomous system (3) can be imagined as representing the steady flow of a fluid in space: To each point $\mathbf{x}$ in a region of space, there is associated a vector $\mathbf{X}(\mathbf{x})$ which describes the velocity of the fluid at that point in magnitude and direction. The flow is called *steady* because its velocity depends only on position and does not vary with time. The solution $\mathbf{x}(t, \mathbf{c})$ of the autonomous system (3) then has a simple physical interpretation: it is the *streamline* (*path*, *orbit*, or *trajectory*) of a moving fluid particle, whose position is given as a function of the time t.

When the preceding path $\mathbf{x}(t, \mathbf{c})$ is considered as a set of points (that is, as a geometric curve), without reference to its parametric representation, it is also called an *integral curve* of the autonomous system (3), or of the associated vector field $\mathbf{X}(\mathbf{x})$. If $\mathbf{x}(t, \mathbf{c})$ is a solution of the autonomous system (3), then so is $\mathbf{x}(t + a, \mathbf{c})$ for any constant a; this can be interpreted as the path of a particle which passes through the point $\mathbf{c}$ at time $t = -a$. Thus, there is always a one-parameter family of *solutions* of (3) describing the same integral curve in Euclidean n-space.

---

† For the concept of a vector field, see Courant, Vol. 2, p. 82.

EXAMPLE 1.   The solutions of the autonomous system

$$dx/dt = mx, \qquad dy/dt = ny \tag{4}$$

are evidently $x = c_1 e^{mt}$, $y = c_2 e^{nt}$ where c_1, c_2 are arbitrary constants. The corresponding integral curves are the loci $y^m = kx^n$. Figure 5.1 depicts sample curves for the case $m = 2$, $n = 3$.

In Figure 5.1, the origin $(0, 0)$ is evidently a very special point: integral curves emanate from it both horizontally and vertically. This

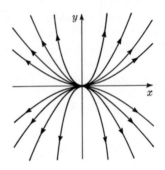

FIGURE 5.1   Integral curves of $\dot{x} = 2x$, $\dot{y} = 3y$.

is possible only because the vector field (mx, ny) defined there reduces to the null vector $\mathbf{0} = (0, 0)$, whose direction is indeterminate. Such points are of particular importance for the study of autonomous systems; they are called critical points.

■ DEFINITION.   *A point* $\mathbf{x} = (x_1, \ldots, x_n)$ *where all the functions* X_i *are equal to zero is called a* critical point *of the autonomous system* (3) *and of the associated vector field* $\mathbf{X}(\mathbf{x})$.

If $\mathbf{x} = \mathbf{c}$ is a critical point of (3), then the functions $x_i(t) \equiv c_i$ define a trivial solution $\mathbf{x}(t) = \mathbf{c}$ of (3), which describes not a curve but just a point. In the terminology of hydrodynamics, $\mathbf{c}$ is called a *stagnation point* of the velocity field $\mathbf{X}(\mathbf{x})$.

Every normal system (1) of $(n - 1)$ first-order DE's

$$dx_i/dt = X_i(x_1, \ldots, x_{n-1}; t), \qquad i = 1, \ldots, n - 1$$

is equivalent to an autonomous system in n variables. To see this, introduce an additional variable $x_n = t$, and rewrite (1) as

$$dx_i/dt = X_i(x_1, \ldots, x_n), \qquad i = 1, \ldots, n - 1, \qquad dx_n/dt = 1$$

Evidently, the system so constructed has no critical points.

2 Plane autonomous systems

When $n = 2$ in (3), it is convenient to write (3) in the form

$$\frac{dx}{dt} = X(x, y), \qquad \frac{dy}{dt} = Y(x, y); \tag{5}$$

we then speak of a *plane* autonomous system. The plane autonomous system (5) evidently has the solutions of the first-order DE

$$\frac{dy}{dx} = \frac{Y(x, y)}{X(x, y)} \tag{5'}$$

for integral curves; hence, (5) can be thought of as a generalization of the first-order normal DE $y' = F(x, y)$. The main advantage of this generalization is that points $X(x, y) = 0$ of vertical tangency of the solutions of the DE (5') are no longer singular points of the corresponding plane autonomous system (5).

This advantage is apparent in the following example, already treated in Chapter 1, §2.

EXAMPLE 2.   Consider the autonomous system

$$\frac{dx}{dt} = -y, \qquad \frac{dy}{dt} = x, \tag{6}$$

whose solutions are the function-pairs $x = r \cos (t + c)$, $y = r \sin (t + c)$, where r and c are arbitrary constants. The graphs of these solutions are concentric circles, with center at the origin. The solutions of the corresponding first-order DE

$$\frac{dy}{dx} = -\frac{x}{y} \tag{6'}$$

are the functions $y = \pm\sqrt{r^2 - x^2}$, which are defined only for $|x| < |r|$. Whereas the function $-x/y$ is undefined where $y = 0$, the functions $X(x, y) = -y$ and $Y(x, y) = x$ in the system (6) are defined throughout the plane. This gives an obvious advantage to the system (6) over the DE (6').

Referring to the definition of Chapter 1, §3, we see that the circles $x^2 + y^2 = r^2$ form a regular† curve family in the " punctured " xy-plane, the critical point of (6) at the origin $(0, 0)$ being deleted. In Chapter 6, §11, it will be shown that this is true of plane autonomous systems in general.

---

† Note that this regular curve family is not normal, whereas the graphs of the functions $y = \sqrt{r^2 - x^2}$ form a normal curve family in the domain $y > 0$.

Plane autonomous systems have the following interesting relation to contour lines (cf. Chapter 1, §4).

■ THEOREM 1.   *For any continuously differentiable function* $V(x, y)$, *each integral curve of the plane autonomous system*

$$\frac{dx}{dt} = \frac{\partial V}{\partial y}(x, y), \qquad \frac{dy}{dt} = -\frac{\partial V}{\partial x}(x, y) \tag{7}$$

lies on some contour line $V(x, y) = $ *constant.*

The proof is immediate: along any integral curve we have

$$\frac{dV}{dt} = \frac{\partial V}{\partial x} \cdot \frac{dx}{dt} + \frac{\partial V}{\partial y} \cdot \frac{dy}{dt} = \frac{\partial V}{\partial x} \cdot \frac{\partial V}{\partial y} - \frac{\partial V}{\partial y} \cdot \frac{\partial V}{\partial x} = 0$$

and so $V(x(t), y(t)) = $ constant.   Observe that the associated steady flow is divergence-free or *area conserving*:

$$\operatorname{div}(\partial V/\partial y, -\partial V/\partial x) = \partial^2 V/\partial x\,\partial y - \partial^2 V/\partial y\,\partial x = 0.$$

In fluid mechanics, such a steady flow (7) is called *incompressible*, and V is called its *stream function*.

The advantage of the representation (7) over the DE

$$dy/dx = -(\partial V/\partial x)/(\partial V/\partial y) \tag{7'}$$

considered in Chapter 1, §4, is the following.   Whereas the integral curves of (7') terminate wherever $\partial V/\partial y$ vanishes, those of (7) terminate only where the function V has a *critical point* (maximum, minimum, or saddle-point) in the sense that grad $V = 0$.   This happens exactly where the autonomous system (7) has critical points.

If we set $V = -(x^2 + y^2)/2$ in Theorem 1, we get the system (6) of Example 2, having circular streamlines.   If $\mu(x, y)$ is nonvanishing, then the system $dx/dt = -y\mu$, $dy/dt = x\mu$ also has circles for integral curves, and we can construct a wide variety of autonomous systems having the same integral curves in this way, as has been noted before.

Another illustration of Theorem 1 is obtained by setting

$$V(x, y) = (x^3 + y^3)/xy = r(\cos^3 \theta + \sin^3 \theta)/\cos \theta \sin \theta$$

and letting $\mu(x, y) = x^2 y^2$.   Evaluating (7), we get the following example.

EXAMPLE 3.   The plane autonomous system

$$dx/dt = x(2y^3 - x^3), \qquad dy/dt = -y(2x^3 - y^3) \tag{8}$$

has as integral curves the curves $x^3 + y^3 - 3cxy = 0$, where c is an arbitrary constant.   Each such integral curve is a folium of Descartes, as in Figure 5.2. The coordinate axes are also integral curves. The origin is the only critical point of (8); correspondingly, the folia of

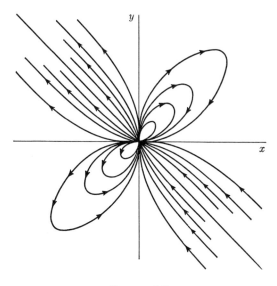

FIGURE 5.2

Descartes in Figure 5.2 form with the axes a curve family that is regular except at the origin.

Note that the trajectories of any autonomous system are endowed with a natural sense or *orientation*, namely, the direction of increasing t. This orientation is indicated in drawings of integral curves by arrows pointing in this direction. Note also that the curves of Figure 5.2 form a family of *similar curves*, all similar to $x^3 + y^3 = 3xy$ under a transformation $x \to cx,\ y \to cy,\ t \to t/c^3$, where c is a constant. The reason is that the DE

$$dy/dx = -y(2x^3 - y^3)/x(2y^3 - x^3)$$

is homogeneous of degree zero (see the end of Chapter 1, §8).

3 Poincaré phase plane

An important class of plane autonomous systems (5) is obtained from *dynamical systems* with one degree of freedom. Let a particle be constrained to move on a straight line (or other curve) and let its acceleration $\ddot{x}$ be determined by Newton's Second Law of Motion as a function of its instantaneous position x and velocity $\dot{x}$. Then

$$\ddot{x} = F(x, \dot{x}), \tag{9}$$

where we have adopted Newton's notation, representing time-derivatives by dots placed over the variable differentiated.

It is usual to denote $\dot{x} = dx/dt$ by the letter v, and to call the xv-plane the *Poincaré phase plane*. Since the variables x and mv are conjugate position and momentum variables, the Poincaré phase plane is a special instance of the concept of phase space in classical dynamics.

Since (9) is time-independent, it is called an *autonomous* second-order DE. In the xv-plane, the second-order autonomous DE (9) is equivalent to the first-order plane autonomous system

$$dx/dt = v, \qquad dv/dt = v \, dv/dx = F(x, v). \tag{9'}$$

The integral curves of this autonomous system in the Poincaré phase-plane depict graphically the types of motions determined by the DE (9).

EXAMPLE 4.   Consider the *damped linear oscillator* defined by the second-order linear DE with constant coefficients:

$$\ddot{x} + p\dot{x} + qx = 0, \qquad p, q \text{ constant}, \tag{10}$$

discussed in Chapter 2, §2. The associated autonomous system in the Poincaré phase plane is

$$dx/dt = v, \qquad dv/dt = -pv - qx. \tag{10'}$$

The direction field of this system is easily plotted for any p, q.

For example, let $p = -1$, $q = 1$. The resulting DE $\ddot{x} - \dot{x} + x = 0$ describes the free oscillations of a negatively damped particle in an attractive force-field   Sample solution curves in the Poincaré phase plane are sketched in Figure 5.3.

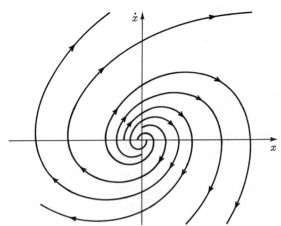

FIGURE 5.3

EXAMPLE 5.   The DE of a simple pendulum of length ℓ is

$$\frac{d^2\theta}{dt^2} = -k^2 \sin \theta, \qquad k^2 = g/\ell, \tag{11}$$

where θ is the angle of deflection. The corresponding autonomous system in the Poincaré phase plane is

$$\dot\theta = v, \qquad \dot v = -k^2 \sin \theta. \tag{11'}$$

Since the function $\sin \theta$ is periodic, the integral curves form a periodic pattern in the sense that, if $(\theta(t), v(t))$ is a solution, so is $(\theta(t) + 2\pi, v(t))$. They are sketched in Figure 5.4. There are infinitely many critical

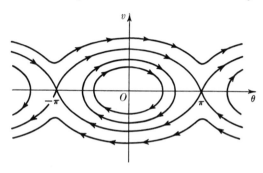

FIGURE 5.4

points at $v = 0$ and $\theta = \pm n\pi$, $n = 0, 1, 2, \ldots$. The integral curves of $(11')$ are given by $v = \pm(2k^2 \cos \theta + c)^{1/2}$, $-2k^2 \leq c < +\infty$. The closed ovals inside the "separatrices" $v = \pm 2k \cos (\theta/2)$ passing through the unstable critical points $((2n + 1)\pi, 0)$ correspond to periodic oscillations; the wavy lines outside these separatrix curves correspond to whirling motions of the pendulum, which are also periodic.

EXERCISES A

1. Find and describe geometrically the integral curves of the following vector fields: (a) (x, y, z),   (b) (ax, by, cz),   (c) $(y, -x, 1)$,   (d) (y, z, x).
2. Show that the integral curves of the autonomous system

$$dx/dt = e^x - 1, \qquad dy/dt = ye^x,$$

are the curves $y = c(e^x - 1)$, and the y-axis $x = 0$.
3. Show that the functions xyz and $x^2 + y^2$ are integrals of the system

$$dx/dt = xy^2, \qquad dy/dt = -x^2y, \qquad dz/dt = z(x^2 - y^2).$$

Describe the loci $xyz = $ constant, and sketch typical integral curves.
    The *gradient field* of a scalar function $V(\mathbf{x})$ is defined as the vector field

$$\text{grad } V = (\partial V/\partial x_1, \ldots, \partial V/\partial x_n).$$

In Exercises 4–6, find the integral curves of the gradient fields of the following functions:

4. $V = xy$.   5. $V = x^2 + y^2 - 2z^2$.   6. $V = \ln{[(x - a)^2 + y^2/[(x + a)^2 + y^2]]}$.

7. Is the following statement true or false? If $f \in \mathscr{C}^1$, the integral curves of the gradient field of the function $f(V)$ coincide with those of V. Prove the statement, or construct a counterexample.

8. Show that a function $\phi(x_1, \ldots, x_n)$ of class $\mathscr{C}^1$ is an integral of the system (3) if and only if it satisfies the partial DE $X_1\, \partial\phi/\partial x_1 + \cdots + X_n\, \partial\phi/\partial x_n = 0$.

9. Show that if $\partial X/\partial x = \partial Y/\partial y$ and $\partial X/\partial y = -\partial Y/\partial x$, the plane autonomous system (5) is the real form of a single first-order *complex* analytic DE, and conversely.

10*. Let $e_1, \ldots, e_n$ and $a_1, \ldots, a_n$ be real constants, and let

$$r_j = [(x - a_j)^2 + y^2 + z^2]^{1/2}.$$

Show that, if $V = \Sigma\, e_j/r_j$, the functions

$$\psi = \Sigma\, e_j \arccos \alpha_j, \qquad \alpha_j = (x - a_j)/r_j, \qquad \text{and} \qquad \theta = \arctan{(z/y)}$$

are integrals of $\dot{x} = \partial V/\partial x$, $\dot{y} = \partial V/\partial y$, $\dot{z} = \partial V/\partial z$. Express the integral curves as intersections of the surfaces defined by the preceding equations.

11. Determine the integral curves of $\ddot{x} = -x^3$ in the Poincaré phase plane, and sketch typical curves.

12*. Prove that, if $X_n \neq 0$, the nth order autonomous system (3) is equivalent to a normal $(n - 1)$st order system, with x_n as the independent variable.

4   Linear autonomous systems

An autonomous system (3) is, by definition, *linear* if and only if all the functions X_i are linear homogeneous functions of the x_k, so that

$$dx_i/dt = a_{i1}x_1 + \cdots + a_{in}x_n, \qquad i = 1, \ldots, n. \tag{12}$$

Hence a linear autonomous system is just a (homogeneous) linear system of DE's with constant coefficients. Such a system is determined by the square *matrix* $A = \|a_{ij}\|$ of its coefficients, and its vector field satisfies $\mathbf{X}(\mathbf{x}) = A\mathbf{x}$.

We now discuss in detail the case $n = 2$ of linear *plane* autonomous systems. Any such system has the form

$$dx/dt = ax + by, \qquad dy/dt = cx + dy, \tag{13}$$

where a, b, c, d are constants. The coefficient matrix $A = \begin{pmatrix} a & b \\ c & d \end{pmatrix}$ of constants is nonsingular unless its determinant is $ad - bc = 0$. The origin $(0, 0)$ is always a critical point of the system (13). Since the simultaneous linear equations $ax + by = cx + dy = 0$ have no solution except $x = y = 0$ unless A is singular, we see that the origin is the only critical point of the system (13), unless $ad = bc$ (the *degenerate* case $|A| = 0$).

Applying the construction of §2 to (13), we get the linear fractional DE

$$dy/dx = (cx + dy)/(ax + by), \tag{13'}$$

studied in Chapter 1, §6. The integral curves of (13') form a regular curve family if $ad \neq bc$, except near the origin; the types of such curve families will be described in §8.

For any p, q, the Poincaré phase-plane representation (10') of the damped linear oscillator (10) defines a plane linear autonomous system,

$$d\mathbf{x}/dt = A\mathbf{x}, \qquad A = \begin{pmatrix} 0 & 1 \\ -q & -p \end{pmatrix}.$$

Conversely, it can be shown (Theorem 5) that almost every linear plane autonomous system is equivalent to one obtained in this way. To show this, one needs to introduce a new concept.

■ DEFINITION. *The* secular equation *of* (13) *is*

$$\ddot{u} - (a + d)\dot{u} + (ad - bc)u = 0. \tag{14}$$

■ THEOREM 2. *If $(x(t), y(t))$ is any solution of the plane autonomous system* (13), *then $x(t)$ and $y(t)$ are solutions of the secular equation* (14) *of* (13).

Proof — We shall prove that $x(t)$ is a solution of (14); the proof for $y(t)$ is the same, replacing a with d and b with c. The first equation of (13) implies $by = \dot{x} - ax$, whence we have $\ddot{x} - a\dot{x} = b\dot{y}$. From the second equation, it follows that

$$\ddot{x} - a\dot{x} = bcx + bdy = bcx + d(\dot{x} - ax).$$

Transposing, we see that $x(t)$ satisfies (14).

The secular equation (14) of (13) has many interesting properties. Thus, referring to Chapter 4, §1, we see that the *characteristic polynomial* of (14) is

$$\lambda^2 - (a + d)\lambda + (ad - bc) = \begin{vmatrix} a - \lambda & b \\ c & d - \lambda \end{vmatrix} = |A - \lambda I|; \tag{14'}$$

it is (apart from the sign of λ) the characteristic polynomial† of the co-efficient-matrix of (13). But its most important property is the *equivalence* of most autonomous systems having the same secular equation, in a sense that will be made precise in the next section.

---

† For the characteristic polynomial of a matrix and its properties, including the Caylye-Hamilton theorem, see Birkhoff and Mac Lane, Chapter 10.

Systems in n variables. One can generalize Theorem 2 as follows. Define the "secular equation" of the linear autonomous system (12) to be the DE

$$L[u] = c_0 u + c_1 u' + \cdots + u^{(n)} = p_A(D)[u] = 0, \qquad (15)$$

where $p_A(\lambda) = |A - \lambda I| = c_0 + c_1 \lambda + \cdots \pm \lambda^n$ is the characteristic polynomial of the matrix A, and $D = d/dt$. We then have the following.

■ THEOREM 3.   *If $\mathbf{x}(t)$ is any solution of* (12), *then every component $x_i(t)$ of $\mathbf{x}(t)$ satisfies the secular equation* (15) *of* (12).

Proof — Since $\mathbf{x}(t)$ satisfies (12), $D\mathbf{x} = A\mathbf{x}$. Hence $p_A(D)\mathbf{x} = p_A(A)\mathbf{x}$. On the other hand, by the Cayley-Hamilton Theorem, $p_A(A)$ is the null matrix 0 and, trivially, $0\mathbf{x} = 0$. Therefore, $p_A(D)\mathbf{x} = \mathbf{0}$, as claimed.

Clearly, the origin $\mathbf{0} = (0, \ldots, 0)$ is always a critical point for the system (12); unless the matrix A is singular, so that $A\mathbf{x} = \mathbf{0}$ for some $\mathbf{x} \neq \mathbf{0}$, the system has no other critical point. Conversely, in the neighborhood of any critical point $\mathbf{c}$ of any analytic autonomous system (3), Taylor's Theorem implies that

$$d\xi_i/dt = \sum a_{ij} \xi_j + R_i(\xi), \qquad i, j = 1, \ldots, n, \qquad \xi_i = x_i - c_i, \quad (16)$$

where the R_i are infinitesimals of the second order in the ξ_i (that is, $|R_i(\xi)| \leq M |\xi|^2$ for small $|\xi|$).

The preceding observation suggests that the behavior of the solutions of any analytic autonomous system such as (16) near any critical point is approximately like that of the solutions of the associated *linearized* autonomous system (12). Much of the importance of the study of linear autonomous systems is due to the fact that this is usually (though not always) true.

The matrix notation has many other uses. For example, it yields a simple formula for the solution of (12), which has the initial-value vector $\mathbf{x}(0) = \mathbf{c}$; this solution is

$$\mathbf{x}(t) = e^{tA}\mathbf{c}, \qquad e^{tA} = I + tA + t^2 A^2/2! + t^3 A^3/3! + \cdots. \quad (17)$$

Note also that the determinant $|e^{tA}|$ of the matrix e^{tA} is $e^{t \operatorname{Tr} A}$, where $\operatorname{Tr} A = \sum_{i=1}^{n} a_{ii}$ is the trace of A (the sum of its diagonal entries). See Appendix.

5 Equivalent systems

One can often simplify the form of a DE or system of DE's by an appropriate transformation of coordinates. For instance, consider the

system

$$dx/dt = (3x^4 - 12x^2y^2 + y^4)/(x^2 + y^2)^{3/2},$$
$$dy/dt = (6x^3y - 10xy^3)/(x^2 + y^2)^{3/2}. \tag{18}$$

In polar coordinates $r = (x^2 + y^2)^{1/2}$, $\theta = \arctan(y/x)$ with inverse functions $x = r\cos\theta$, $y = r\sin\theta$, this system reduces to

$$dr/dt = 3r\cos 3\theta, \qquad d\theta/dt = \sin 3\theta. \tag{18'}$$

In this form, one sees at a glance that the rays $\theta = n\pi/3$ are integral curves, for $n = 0, \ldots, 5$. Other integral curves are sketched in Figure 5.5.

FIGURE 5.5

We shall study below how far we can simplify *linear* autonomous systems by such coordinate transformations. Our study will be based on a general concept of *equivalence by transformation*, which we now define precisely. Let

$$u_i = f_i(x_1, \ldots, x_n), \qquad i = 1, \ldots, n, \tag{19}$$

be continuously differentiable functions with inverse functions

$$x_j = g_j(u_1, \ldots, u_n), \qquad j = 1, \ldots, n, \tag{19'}$$

so that $\mathbf{f}(\mathbf{g}(\mathbf{u})) = \mathbf{u}$ and $\mathbf{g}(\mathbf{f}(\mathbf{x})) = \mathbf{x}$. For such inverse functions to exist locally and be continuously differentiable, it is necessary and sufficient (by the Implicit Function Theorem†) that the Jacobian of (19) be nonvanishing: that $|\partial f_i/\partial x_j| \neq 0$.

If $\mathbf{x}(t)$ is any solution of the autonomous system

$$dx_j/dt = X_j(x_1, \ldots, x_n), \qquad j = 1, \ldots, n, \tag{20}$$

then the functions

$$u_i(t) = f_i(x_1(t), \ldots, x_n(t)), \qquad i = 1, \ldots, n, \tag{21}$$

---

† See Chapter 1, §2. The Jacobian of (14) is the determinant of the square matrix $\|\partial f_i/\partial x_j\|$ of first partial derivatives. See Widder, p. 28 ff. Transformations with the properties stated are called "diffeomorphisms."

satisfy the autonomous system

$$\frac{du_i}{dt} = U_i(\mathbf{u}), \qquad U_i = \sum_{j=1}^{n} \frac{\partial f_i}{\partial x_j} \frac{dx_j}{dt} = \sum_{j=1}^{n} \frac{\partial f_i}{\partial x_j} (\mathbf{g}(\mathbf{u})) X_j(\mathbf{g}(\mathbf{u})), \quad (22)$$

and conversely. In this sense, the autonomous systems (20) and (22) are *equivalent*. We formalize the preceding discussion in a definition.

■ DEFINITION.   *Let* $dx/dt = \mathbf{X}(\mathbf{x})$ *and* $du/dt = \mathbf{U}(\mathbf{u})$ *be autonomous systems, defined in regions* R *and* R' *of* n-*dimensional space, respectively. The two systems are* equivalent *if and only if there exists a one-one transformation* $\mathbf{u} = \mathbf{f}(\mathbf{x})$ *of coordinates, of class* $\mathscr{C}^1$ *and with nonvanishing Jacobian, which maps* R *onto* R' *and carries* $dx/dt = \mathbf{X}(\mathbf{x})$ *into* $du/dt = \mathbf{U}(\mathbf{u})$.

Under these circumstances, the inverse transformation is also of class $\mathscr{C}^1$ with nonvanishing Jacobian; the relation of equivalence is symmetric, reflexive, and transitive: it is an equivalence relation.† It follows from the preceding discussion that equivalent autonomous systems have integral curves obtainable from each other by a coordinate transformation. If the systems (20) and (22) are equivalent under the change of coordinates (21), and if $V(\mathbf{u})$ is an integral of (21), then $V(\mathbf{f}(\mathbf{x}))$ is an integral of (20).

However, two autonomous systems may have the same integral curves without being equivalent. Thus the integral curves of

$$\dot{x} = (x^2 + y^2)y, \qquad \dot{y} = -(x^2 + y^2)x \tag{23}$$

are concentric circles, as in Example 2 ($\dot{x} = -y$, $\dot{y} = x$). Yet the two systems are not equivalent: all solutions of $\dot{x} = -y$, $\dot{y} = x$ are periodic with period 2π, whereas those of (23) have variable periods.

6 Linear equivalence

In dealing with linear autonomous systems, it is natural to consider equivalence under *linear* transformations of coordinates

$$u_i = k_{i1}x_1 + \cdots + k_{in}x_n, \qquad i = 1, \dots, n. \tag{24}$$

Two systems which are equivalent under a homogeneous linear transformation of the form (24) are called *linearly equivalent*. Writing $\mathbf{u} = K\mathbf{x}$ in vector notation, the inverse transformation is then just $\mathbf{x} = K^{-1}\mathbf{u}$, where K^{-1} is the inverse of the square matrix K. Note that $K = \|\partial u_i / \partial x_j\|$, so that the Jacobian of the transformation is just the determinant $|K|$ of K.

---

† Birkhoff and Mac Lane, p. 30.

Also, if $\mathbf{x}(t)$ is a solution of the linear autonomous system $d\mathbf{x}/dt = A\mathbf{x}$ and $\mathbf{u} = K\mathbf{x}$ is given by (24), then

$$d\mathbf{u}/dt = K d\mathbf{x}/dt = KA\mathbf{x} = (KAK^{-1})\mathbf{u}. \tag{25}$$

In algebraic language, linearly equivalent linear autonomous systems are associated with *similar*† matrices A and KAK^{-1}. Therefore, the reduction of linear autonomous systems to a standard simplified (or "canonical") form amounts to reducing matrices to canonical form. The simplified forms usually preferred are diagonal, companion matrix or (for complex matrices) Jordan canonical form. This problem will be treated here only for 2×2 matrices—i.e., for linear plane autonomous systems:

$$dx/dt = ax + by, \qquad dy/dt = cx + dy. \tag{26}$$

Its solution enables us to classify critical points of plane autonomous systems. We first prove a useful lemma.

■ LEMMA.   *Linearly equivalent linear plane autonomous systems have the same secular equation.*

Proof — This result follows immediately from (14′), (25), and general identities of linear algebra. If $B = KAK^{-1}$, we know that

$$|B - \lambda I| = |KAK^{-1} - \lambda I| = |K(A - \lambda I)K^{-1}|$$
$$= |K| \cdot |A - \lambda I| \cdot |K^{-1}| = |A - \lambda I|.$$

(The lemma is also a corollary of Theorem 3 unless there are two linearly independent equations $\ddot{u} + p\dot{u} + qu = 0$ satisfied by both components of all solutions of $d\mathbf{x}/dt = A\mathbf{x}$.)

■ THEOREM 4.   *Unless $a = d$ and $b = c = 0$, the linear plane autonomous system (26) is linearly equivalent to the Poincaré phase-plane representation*

$$du/dt = v, \qquad dv/dt = -qu - pv, \qquad p = -(a + d), \qquad q = (ad - bc) \tag{27}$$

of its secular equation (14).

Proof — If $b \neq 0$, let $u = x$, $v = ax + by$; that is, let $K = \begin{pmatrix} 1 & 0 \\ a & b \end{pmatrix}$.

Then (26) reduces to

$$\dot{u} = v, \qquad \dot{v} = a\dot{x} + b\dot{y} = (a^2 + bc)x + (ab + bd)y. \tag{28}$$

---

† Birkhoff and Mac Lane, p. 232. For reduction to diagonal form and Jordan canonical form, see *ibid.*, pp. 259, 311. For the companion matrix form $\begin{pmatrix} 0 & 1 \\ -p & -q \end{pmatrix}$, see *ibid.*, p. 297.

The last expression in (28) is equal to

$$(a^2 + ad)x + (ab + bd)y - (ad - bc)x = (a + d)v - (ad - bc)u$$

by definition of u, v; hence (26) is equivalent to

$$\dot{u} = v, \qquad \dot{v} = (a + d)v - (ad - bc)u = -pv - qu,$$

that is, to (27). This shows, in particular, that

$$KAK^{-1} = \begin{pmatrix} 0 & 1 \\ -q & -p \end{pmatrix}$$

is the *companion matrix* of the secular equation of (26).

This proves Theorem 4 for the case $b \neq 0$. The case $c \neq 0$ can be treated in the same way, letting $u = y$ and $v = cx + dy$.

When $b = c = 0$, let $u = x + y$, $v = ax + dy$; if $a \neq d$, we can set $x = (du - v)/(d - a)$, $y = (au - v)/(a - d)$. By (26), with $b = c = 0$, we have $\dot{u} = \dot{x} + \dot{y} = ax + dy = v$. Likewise,

$$\dot{v} = a\dot{x} + d\dot{y} = a^2x + d^2y.$$

Comparing this with the expression

$$(a + d)v - (ad)u = [(a^2 + ad)x + (ad + d^2)y - adx - ady],$$

we verify (27) also in this case.

Exceptional case. The case $a = d$, $b = c = 0$ of

$$\dot{x} = ax, \qquad \dot{y} = ay \tag{29}$$

is genuinely exceptional. The secular equation of (29) is $\ddot{x} - 2a\dot{x} + a^2x = 0$, just as it is for the system

$$\dot{x} = ax, \qquad \dot{y} = x + ay, \tag{29'}$$

but (29) and (29') are not linearly equivalent. Every component of every solution of (29) satisfies $\dot{u} = au$, but this is not true of the solution (e^{at}, te^{at}) of (29').

The exceptional case arises when the characteristic polynomial of the secular equation (14) has equal roots, that is, when its *discriminant* $\Delta = p^2 - 4q = (a - d)^2 + 4bc$ vanishes. This gives us the following corollary of Theorem 4.

■ COROLLARY. *Unless the discriminant $(a - d)^2 + 4bc$ vanishes, two linear plane autonomous systems are linearly equivalent if and only if they have the same secular equation.*

EXERCISES B

1. (a) Show that the characteristic equation of the system

$$\dot{x} = \mu x - \nu y, \qquad \dot{y} = \nu x + \mu y \qquad (*)$$

has the complex roots $\lambda = \mu \pm i\nu$.
   (b) Infer that any linear plane autonomous system (13) with discriminant $\Delta < 0$ is linearly equivalent to (*), for some μ, ν.
   (c) Show that, in polar coordinates, the system (*) defines the flow $r \to e^{\mu t} r$, $\theta \to \theta + \nu t$.
   (d) Show that (*) is the real form of the first-order complex linear DE $\dot{z} = \lambda z$, $z = x + iy$.
2. Consider the system $dx/dt = \alpha x$, $dy/dt = \beta y$ for $\alpha \neq 0$.
   (a) Show that its integral curves are $y = C|x|^p$, $p = \beta/\alpha$.
   (b) Prove that any linear plane autonomous system (13) with positive discriminant is linearly equivalent to a DE of the above form under a suitable change of basis.
   (c)* Show that, in the punctured plane $x^2 + y^2 > 0$, the systems $dx/dt = \alpha x$, $dy/dt = \beta y$ and $dx/dt = k\alpha x$, $dy/dt = k\beta y$ are equivalent if $k \neq 0$, but that they are not equivalent in any domain which contains the origin unless $k = 1$.
3. Show that any linear plane autonomous system (13) with zero discriminant is equivalent to $dx/dt = ax$, $dy/dt = ay$, or to $dx/dt = ax$, $dy/dt = x + ay$. Describe the associated flows geometrically.
4. (a) Show that, if $ad \neq bc$, the linear fractional DE

$$dy/dx = (cx + dy + f)/(ax + by + e)$$

is equivalent by an (affine) transformation to one of the canonical forms of Exercises 1–3.
   (b) Derive a set of canonical forms for the exceptional case $ad = bc$.
5. The *elliptic functions* $u = \operatorname{sn} t$, $v = \operatorname{cn} t$, $w = \operatorname{dn} t$, may be defined (cf. Chapter 3, § 1) as the solutions of the system

$$du/dt = vw, \qquad dv/dt = -wu, \qquad dw/dt = -k^2 uv, \qquad (*)$$

having the initial values $u(0) = 0$, $v(0) = w(0) = 1$.
   (a) Establish the identities $(\operatorname{sn} t)^2 + (\operatorname{cn} t)^2 = 1$, $k^2(\operatorname{sn} t)^2 + (\operatorname{dn} t)^2 = 1$.
   (b) Using (a), show that the three functions specified are defined and analytic for all real t.
   (c) Expand the solutions in power series through terms in t^5.
6. (a) Show that, in Exercise 5, if $k^2 < 1$, the function cn t vanishes at

$$t = K = \int_0^1 dx/\sqrt{(1 - x^2)(1 - k^2 x^2)}.$$

   (b) Prove the addition formulas, valid with $k' = \sqrt{1 - k^2}$.

sn $(t + K) = \operatorname{cn} t/\operatorname{dn} t$,   cn $(t + K) = -k' \operatorname{sn} t/\operatorname{dn} t$,
dn $(t + K) = k'/\operatorname{dn} t$,

[HINT: Show that the vector-valued function $(v/w, -k'u/w, k'/w)$ satisfies (*) and that this vector reduces at $t = K$ to $(1, 0, k')$.]
   (c) Prove that sn $(-t) = -\operatorname{sn} t$, cn $(-t) = \operatorname{cn} t$, sn $(t + 2K) = -\operatorname{sn} t$,

cn $(t + 2K) = -\operatorname{cn} t$,   dn $(t + 2K) = \operatorname{dn} t$.

(d) Show that sn t and cn t have infinitely many zeros and that the zeros of sn t separate those of cn t.

7. Show that the system $dx/dt = -x + y$, $dy/dt = -x - y$ goes into

$$dx/dt = (y - x)/2, \qquad dy/dt = (-x - y)/2$$

under the transformation $r \to r^2$, $\theta \to 2\theta$ of polar coordinates. In what domain are the two systems "equivalent"?

8. Prove that, in the exceptional case (29) of $a = d$ and $b = c = 0$,

$$|\mathbf{x}(t)| = e^{at}|\mathbf{x}(0)|.$$

7   Stability

The concepts of stability and strict stability, already defined for linear DE's with constant coefficients in Chapter 4, § 5, apply to the critical points of any autonomous system. Loosely speaking, a critical point P is stable when the solution curves originating near P stay uniformly near it at all later times; P is strictly stable if, in addition, each such individual solution curve gets and stays arbitrarily near P as t increases without limit. In vector notation, the precise definition is as follows.

■ DEFINITION.   *Let* **a** *be a critical point of the autonomous system* $\mathbf{x}'(t) = \mathbf{X}(\mathbf{x})$, *so that* $\mathbf{X}(\mathbf{a}) = \mathbf{0}$. *The critical point* **a** *is called*
   (i) stable *when, given* $\epsilon > 0$, *there exists a* $\delta > 0$ *so small that, if* $|\mathbf{x}(0) - \mathbf{a}| < \delta$, *then* $|\mathbf{x}(t) - \mathbf{a}| < \epsilon$ *for all* $t > 0$;
   (ii) asymptotically stable *when, for some* $\delta > 0$,

$$|\mathbf{x}(0) - \mathbf{a}| < \delta \qquad implies \qquad \lim_{t \to \infty} |\mathbf{x}(t) - \mathbf{a}| = 0; \qquad (30)$$

   (iii) strictly stable *when it is stable and asymptotically stable.*
   A stable critical point which is not asymptotically stable is called neutrally *stable; a critical point which is not stable is called* unstable.

Evidently, the preceding definitions are invariant under diffeomorphisms (§ 5); thus, they describe important qualitative distinctions between the kinds of critical points. For first-order autonomous DE's, asymptotic stability has a simple interpretation.

■ THEOREM 5.   *The critical point* 0 *of the first-order autonomous* DE $x'(t) = X(x)$ *is asymptotically stable if and only if*
   (ii') *For some* $\delta > 0$, $0 < |x| < \delta$ *implies* $xX(x) < 0$.
In this case, the DE *is strictly stable.*

Proof — If $X(x_1) = 0$ for some x_1 with $0 < |x_1| < \delta$, then $x(t) = x_1$ is a solution, violating (ii) above. Likewise, if $x_1X(x_1) > 0$ (that is, if

x_1 and $X(x_1)$ have the same sign), then the solution with initial value $x(0) = (x_1 + \delta \operatorname{sgn} x_1)/2$ could never cross x_1; hence it would also violate (ii). Therefore, condition (ii) is necessary for asymptotic stability. It is sufficient since, if $0 < x(0) < \delta$, then $\sup_{[\delta_1, x(0)]} X(x) = -a_1 < 0$ for any $\delta_1 \in (0, x(0))$. Hence, we have $0 < x(t) < \delta_1$ for all $t \geq x_1/a_1$, proving (30); we omit the details. A similar argument covers the case $-\delta < x(0) < 0$.

In both cases, stability is immediate; indeed, stability follows if O is a limit point of x with $xX(x) < O$.

Asymptotic stability also implies strict stability for *linear* autonomous systems, that is, for linear DE's with constant coefficients. We now prove this important result, which is due to Lagrange.

■ THEOREM 5′.   *The critical point* **0** *of the constant-coefficient linear autonomous system* $\mathbf{x}'(t) = A\mathbf{x}$ *is asymptotically stable if and only if every eigenvalue of* A *has negative real part. In this case, the system is also strictly stable.*

Proof — If some eigenvalue λ of A has a nonnegative real part, then (12) has a solution of the form $\mathbf{x}(t) = e^{\lambda t}\mathbf{f}$ (an "eigensolution" or "normal mode"), where the initial eigenvector $\mathbf{x}(0) = \mathbf{f}$ can have arbitrarily small length. Conversely, note that, by Theorem 3, every component $x_i(t)$ of every solution $\mathbf{x}(t)$ of (12) satisfies the secular equation $P_A(D)x_i(t) = 0$, where the roots of the polynomial equation $P_A(\lambda) = 0$ are just the eigenvalues λ_j of A. From Theorem 4 of Chapter 4, we know that every $x_i(t) \to 0$ if these λ_i all have negative real parts, which implies (30). This proves the first statement of Theorem 5′.

To prove the second statement, we extend the concept of solution basis introduced in Chapter 4, §4, to vector DE's with constant coefficients. If $\mathbf{x}(0) = \mathbf{0}$ and $\mathbf{x}'(t) = A\mathbf{x}$, then by repeated differentiations, we have $\mathbf{x}^{(n)}(0) = 0$ for all n Hence, in Theorem 3, every $x_i^{(k)}(0) = 0$ and, by the crucial Lemma of Chapter 4, § 4, every $x_i(t) \equiv 0$. It follows from this that (12) can have, at most, n linearly independent solutions (it will be proved in Chapter 6 that it has exactly n of them). Calling them $\mathbf{u}^1(t), \ldots, \mathbf{u}^n(t)$, we see that the general solution of (12), is $\mathbf{x}(t) = \sum c_l \mathbf{u}^l(t) \to 0$, where $|\mathbf{x}(t)| < \epsilon$ for all sufficiently large t, *uniformly*, provided only that $\sum c_l < \delta$, some sufficiently small number. The stability condition (i) above follows.

It follows from Chapter 4, § 5, that the conditions for strict stability of the second-order system $dx/dt = ax + by$, $dy/dt = cx + dy$, are $p = -(a + d) > 0$, $q = ad - bc > 0$, or $a + d < 0$, $ad > bc$.

CAUTION.   One should not conclude from Theorems 5 and 5′ that asymptotic stability implies strict stability for all autonomous systems.

We now construct an unstable nonlinear plane autonomous system which is asymptotically stable†. Figure 5.6 depicts sample solution curves.

FIGURE 5.6   Unstable critical point.

EXAMPLE 6.   Let D_1 be the lower half-plane $y \leq 0$; let D_2 be the locus $x^2 + y^2 \leq 2|x|$, consisting of the discs $(x \pm 1)^2 + y^2 \leq 1$; let D_3 be the half-strip $|x| \leq 2$, $y > 0$, exterior to D_2; let D_4 be the locus $|x| > 2$, $y > 0$, all as in Figure 5.6. The system

$$\dot{x} = \begin{cases} 2xy & \text{on} \quad D_1 \cup D_2 \cup D_3, \\ 2xy/[3 - (4|x|)] & \text{on} \quad D_4; \end{cases}$$

$$\dot{y} = \begin{cases} y^2 - x^2 & \text{on} \quad D_1 \cup D_2, \\ 4|x| - y^2 - 3x^2 & \text{on} \quad D_3, \\ (4|x| - y^2 - 3x^2)/[3 - 4/|x|] & \text{on} \quad D_4 \end{cases}$$

is unstable, yet $\lim_{t \to \infty} |\mathbf{x}(t)| = 0$ for all orbits $\mathbf{x}(t)$.

Dynamical systems.   If the DE's for an autonomous dynamical system are written in normal form, as

$$d^2 q_i/dt^2 = F_i(\mathbf{q}, d\mathbf{q}/dt) = F_i(\mathbf{q}, \mathbf{p}), \qquad i = 1, \ldots, m, \qquad (31)$$

and conjugate velocity variables $p_i = dq_i/dt$ are introduced, then (31) defines an autonomous system of first-order DE's

$$dq_i/dt = p_i, \qquad dp_i/dt = F_i(\mathbf{q}, \mathbf{p}), \qquad (31')$$

---

† The authors are indebted to Dr. Thomas Brown for constructing Example 6.

in an associated $2m$-dimensional *phase space*. A given point $(\mathbf{q}, \mathbf{p})$ of phase space is a *critical* point for the system (31′) if and only if $\mathbf{p} = \mathbf{0}$ and $\mathbf{F}(\mathbf{q}, \mathbf{0}) = \mathbf{0}$, so that $\mathbf{q}$ is an *equilibrium* point of the dynamical system (31).

The dynamical system (31) is called *conservative* when $F_i(\mathbf{q}, \dot{\mathbf{q}}) = -\partial V/\partial q_i$ for a suitable *potential energy* function $V(\mathbf{q})$. For any conservative system, the total energy function $E(\mathbf{q}, \mathbf{p}) = (\sum m_i p_i^2/2) + V(\mathbf{q})$ is an integral of the system (31). Moreover, the point $(\mathbf{a}, \mathbf{0})$ is a critical point of (31′) if and only if the gradient $\nabla V(\mathbf{a}) = \mathbf{0}$, so that the potential energy function has a stationary value.† The point is neutrally stable if the potential energy has a (strict) local minimum at $\mathbf{q} = \mathbf{a}$; it is never strictly stable.

Thus, consider the simple pendulum of Example 5, § 3, with $k = 1$. For $c = -2$, the "integral curve" reduces to a set of isolated critical points $v = 0$, $\theta = \pm 2n\pi$. If $|c| < 2$, then $|\theta - 2n\pi| < \theta_0$, where $\theta_0 < \pi$ is the smallest positive angle such that $\cos \theta_0 = -c/2$. Therefore, the integral curves for $-2 < c < 2$ are closed curves (loops) surrounding the origin or any one of the critical points for $\theta = \pm 2n\pi$. As $c \to -2$, these loops tend to the origin. Therefore, the origin and its translates $\theta = \pm 2n\pi$, $v = 0$ are neutrally *stable*. For $c = 2$, we have the separatrix curve defined by $v = \pm 2 \cos(\theta/2)$. From the first of equations (11′), it is seen that the direction of the motion is from $-\pi$ to π for $v > 0$ and from π to $-\pi$ for $v < 0$. Therefore, the critical points $v = 0$, $\theta = \pm(2n + 1)\pi$ are *unstable*. These unstable critical points occur when the pendulum is balanced vertically above the point of support.

8 Focal, nodal, and saddle points

The results of §§ 6–7 lead to a complete classification of linear plane autonomous systems (26). This classification is based on a study of the possible root-pairs λ_1, λ_2 of the characteristic equation (cf. (14′))

$$\lambda^2 - (a + d)\lambda + (ad - bc) = \lambda^2 + p\lambda + q = 0 \qquad (32)$$

of (26). By Theorem 4, unless $a = d$, $b = c = 0$, it suffices to display one autonomous system for each such root pair. We now enumerate the different possibilities, which depend largely on the sign of the *discriminant*

$$\Delta = p^2 - 4q = (a - d)^2 + 4bc \qquad (33)$$

of the characteristic equation (32). We begin with the case $\Delta \neq 0$, $q \neq 0$ of distinct nonzero roots $\lambda_1 \neq \lambda_2$.

---

† Courant, Vol. 2, p. 186. Points where the value of a function is stationary are also often called "critical points."

A. *Focal points.* Suppose $\Delta < 0$, so that the characteristic equation (32) has distinct *complex* roots $\lambda_j = \mu \pm i\nu$ $(\nu \neq 0)$. This is the case $q = (\mu^2 + \nu^2) > 0$ and $0 \leq p^2 = 4\mu^2 < 4q$ of a harmonic oscillator. We choose the canonical form (see the Corollary of Theorem 4 and Exercises B1–B3)

$$dx/dt = \mu x - \nu y, \qquad dy/dt = \nu x + \mu y \qquad (34a)$$

for (26), whose solutions are the equiangular *spirals* $r = \rho e^{\mu t}$, $\theta = \nu t + \tau$ in polar coordinates, where $\rho \geq 0$ and τ are arbitrary constants. When $p > 0$, the spirals approach the origin (*stable* focal point); when $p < 0$, they diverge from it (*unstable* focal point); when $p = 0$, they are closed curves representing periodic oscillations (neutrally stable *vortex* points). See Figures 5.7a and 5.7b.

B. *Nodal points.* Suppose that $\Delta > 0$ and $q > 0$, so that the roots $\lambda = \mu_1$, μ_2 of the characteristic equation (32) are real, distinct, and of the same sign. We choose, as the linearly equivalent canonical form,

$$dx/dt = \mu_1 x, \qquad dy/dt = \mu_2 y, \qquad 0 < |\mu_1| < |\mu_2|, \qquad (34b)$$

whose general solution is $(ae^{\mu_1 t}, be^{\mu_2 t})$. The system is stable when μ_1 and μ_2 are negative and unstable when they are positive (the two subcases are related by the transformation $t \to -t$ of time reversal). Geometrically, the integral curves $y = cx^{\mu_2/\mu_1}$ look like a sheaf of parabolas, tangent at the origin, as in Figure 5.7c.

C. *Saddle-points.* Suppose that $\Delta > 0$ but $q < 0$, so that the roots of the characteristic equation (32) are real and of opposite sign. We again have the canonical form (34b). But since μ_1 and μ_2 have opposite signs, the integral curves $x^m y = c$, $m = -\mu_2/\mu_1 > 0$ look like a family of similar hyperbolas having given asymptotes, as in Figure 5.7d. A saddle-point is always *unstable*.

There remain various degenerate cases and subcases, in which $\Delta = 0$ or $q = 0$. The simplest such case is the exceptional case (29), in which $\Delta = 0$, $q = a^2 > 0$. The integral curves consist of the straight lines through the origin, and the configuration formed by them is called a *star*, as in Figure 5.7e. In the nonexceptional subcase, we have the canonical form of (29')

$$dx/dt = ax, \qquad dy/dt = x + ay, \qquad (34c)$$

whose integral curves have the appearance of Figure 5.7f. Such a point is also called a *nodal* point, and it is stable or unstable according as $a < 0$ or $a > 0$.

The case $q = 0$, $\Delta \neq 0$ corresponds to the Poincaré phase-plane representation of the second-order DE $\ddot{x} + p\dot{x} = 0$, $p \neq 0$. This corresponds to a rowboat "coasting" on a lake, with no wind and its oars shipped.

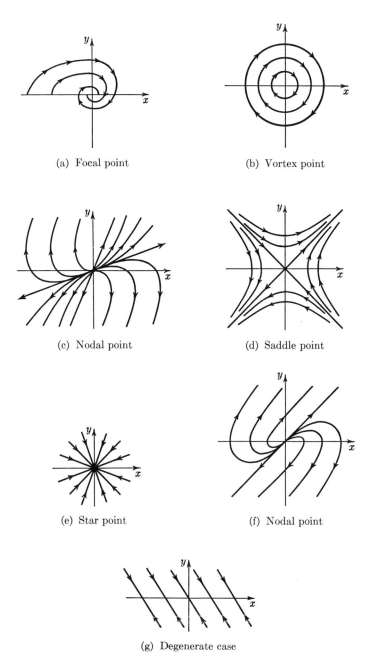

(a) Focal point

(b) Vortex point

(c) Nodal point

(d) Saddle point

(e) Star point

(f) Nodal point

(g) Degenerate case

FIGURE 5.7

The boat comes to rest in a finite distance, in infinite time. The integral curves form a family of parallel straight lines $\dot{x} + px =$ constant, as in Figure 5.7g. The origin is a stable (but not strictly stable) critical point if $p > 0$, unstable if $p < 0$.

Finally, the case $q = \Delta = 0$ reduces to $\dot{x} = \dot{y} = 0$ in the exceptional case (29), and to the Poincaré phase-plane representation of $\ddot{x} = 0$ otherwise. The former case is (neutrally) stable: the latter case is unstable.

EXERCISES C

1. For the following DE's, determine the stability and type of the solution curves in the Poincaré phase plane, sketching typical curves in each case:
    (a) $\ddot{u} + u = 0$,   (b) $\ddot{u} + \dot{u} + u = 0$,   (c) $\ddot{u} - \dot{u} + u = 0$,
    (d) $\ddot{u} + \dot{u} - u = 0$,   (e) $\ddot{u} + 2\dot{u} + u = 0$,   (f) $\ddot{u} + 4\dot{u} + u = 0$.
2. For which of the following is $x = 0$ a stable critical point:
$$\dot{x} = x^2, \qquad \dot{x} = -x^2, \qquad \dot{x} = x^3, \qquad \dot{x} = -x^3?$$

3. Determine conditions on the coefficients a, b, c, d of (13) necessary and sufficient for neutral stability.
4. Show that $\dot{x} = X(x)$ has a strictly stable critical point at $x = 0$ if $X(0) = 0$ and $X'(0) < 0$.
5. Show that the plane autonomous system $\dot{x} = x - y$, $\dot{y} = 4x^2 + 2y^2 - 6$ has critical points at $(1, 1)$ and $(-1, -1)$, both of them unstable.
6. Show that the system $dx/dt = \ln(1 + x + 2y)$, $dy/dt = (x/2) - y + (x^2/2)$ has an unstable critical point at the origin.
7*. Is the system (*) of Exercise B5 strictly stable, neutrally stable, or unstable at $(0, 0, 0)$?
8. Show that the autonomous system
$$dx/dt = (1/2)e^{2x}\sin 3y + 2\sin x \cos x + e^z - 1,$$
$$dy/dt = \sin(2x + 3y), \qquad dz/dt = \tan(2x + z),$$
has an unstable critical point at $x = y = z = 0$.
9. Show that the DE $\ddot{x} + x\sin(1/x) = 0$ is neutrally stable at $x = 0$.
10*. Let $S = S(\mathbf{x})$ be a function of class $\mathscr{C}^1$ in some neighborhood of the origin, such that $S(\mathbf{0}) = 0$, while $S(\mathbf{x}) > 0$ if $0 < |\mathbf{x}| < \epsilon$ for some $\epsilon > 0$.
    (a) Prove that the system $d\mathbf{x}/dt = \mathbf{X}(\mathbf{x})$ is *unstable* at the origin if $\Sigma X_i \partial S/\partial x_i > 0$ there and is strictly stable if $\Sigma X_i \partial S/\partial x_i < 0$ there.
    (b) Derive from (a) a stability criterion for the autonomous nth order DE
$$d^n x/dt^n = \Phi(x, dx/dt, \ldots, d^{n-1}x/dt^{n-1}).$$

11. Show that the integral curves in Example 6 are the semicircles
$$x^2 + y^2 = \pm 2ax \quad \text{in} \quad D_1 \cup D_2,$$
and of the form $x(x^2 - 2|x| + y^2) =$ constant in $D_3 \cup D_4$.

9   Method of Liapunov

Formula (16) of §4 shows that a first approximation to autonomous systems generally, near critical points, is provided by homogeneous linear systems. But it does not show how closely the *solutions* of an autonomous system, near a critical point, resemble those of the associated linear system obtained by omitting higher-order terms. We now show that, so far as the *strict stability* of critical points is concerned, the linear terms are decisive.

■ THEOREM 6. *If the critical point* $(0, 0)$ *of the linear plane autonomous system* (13) *is strictly stable, then so is that of the perturbed system*

$$\dot{x} = ax + by + \xi(x, y), \qquad \dot{y} = cx + dy + \eta(x, y), \tag{35}$$

provided† that $|\xi(x, y)| + |\eta(x, y)| = O(x^2 + y^2)$.

Idea of proof — The proof is based on a simple geometrical idea due to Liapunov. Let $E(x, y)$ be any function having a strict local minimum at the origin. For small positive C, the level curves $E(x, y) = E(0, 0) + C$ constitute a family of small concentric loops, roughly elliptical in shape, enclosing the origin. Now, examine the direction of the vector field defined by (35) on these small loops. Intuition suggests that the critical point will be strictly stable whenever, for all small enough loops, the vector field points inward. For this implies that any trajectory which once crosses a loop is forever trapped inside it, because, to get outside, the trajectory would have to cross the loop in an outward direction. At such a crossing point, the vector could not point inward, giving a contradiction.

To make the preceding intuitive argument precise, we define a *Liapunov function* for a critical point **a** of an autonomous system $\mathbf{x}'(t) = \mathbf{X}(\mathbf{x})$ to be a function $E(\mathbf{x})$ which assumes its minimum value at **a** and satisfies

$$\sum X_i(\mathbf{x}) \, \partial E / \partial x_i < 0 \qquad \text{for all} \quad \mathbf{x} \neq \mathbf{a}.$$

Since $\dot{E} = dE/dt = \sum x_i'(t) \, \partial E / \partial x_i$ for any solution $\mathbf{x}(t)$, this implies that E is decreasing along any trajectory $\mathbf{x}(t)$.

To construct a Liapunov function for the critical point $(0, 0)$ under the hypotheses of Theorem 6, we consider, in turn, each of the three canonical forms (34a) through (34c) derived in §8. Since the definition of stability is invariant under linear transformations of coordinates, it suffices to consider these three cases.

For the linear terms in (35), the necessary calculations are simple. The Liapunov function can be taken as a positive definite quadratic function $E = \alpha x^2 + 2\beta xy + \gamma y^2$, $\alpha > 0$, $\alpha\gamma > \beta^2$, whose level curves

---

† The symbol $O(x^2 + y^2)$ stands for a function bounded by $M(x^2 + y^2)$ for some constant M and all sufficiently small x, y.

are a family of concentric coaxial ellipses. We will show, by considering cases separately, that $\dot{E} \leq -kE$ for some positive constant k.

In (34a), the Liapunov function $E = x^2 + y^2$ satisfies

$$\dot{E} = 2(x\dot{x} + y\dot{y}) = 2\mu E.$$

In the strictly stable case, $\mu < 0$. In (34b), the same Liapunov function satisfies $\dot{E} = 2(x\dot{x} + y\dot{y}) = 2\mu_1 x^2 + 2\mu_2 y^2 \leq 2\mu_1 E$, in the strictly stable case $0 > \mu_1 \geq \mu_2$. (By allowing equality, we take care also of the exceptional case of a star point.) In (34c), the Liapunov function $E = x^2 + a^2 y^2$ satisfies, in the strictly stable case $a < 0$,

$$\dot{E} = 2(x\dot{x} + a^2 y\dot{y}) = 2(ax^2 + a^2 xy + a^3 y^2) = aE + a(x + ay)^2 \leq aE.$$

Hence, in the three possible cases of strict linear stability, we have $\dot{E} = 2\mu E$, $\dot{E} \leq 2\mu_1 E$, or $\dot{E} \leq aE$, where the coefficient on the right side is negative. It follows that $\dot{E} \leq -kE$ for some $k > 0$, in every case. Since the quadratic function $E(x, y)$ is positive definite, we conclude that $E(x, y) \geq K(x^2 + y^2)$ for some constant $K > 0$.

We now consider the nonlinear system (35). Since $E_x = \partial E/\partial x$ and $E_y = \partial E/\partial y$ are linear functions of x and y, we have

$$|E_x \xi + E_y \eta| = O(|x| + |y|)(x^2 + y^2).$$

Hence, for some $\epsilon > 0$, $E(x, y) \leq \epsilon$ implies $|E_x \xi + E_y \eta| \leq kE(x, y)/2$.

Now let $(x(t), y(t))$ be a trajectory of (35) such that $E(x(t_0), y(t_0)) \leq \epsilon$. Along this trajectory, for $t \geq t_0$, $E(t) = E(x(t), y(t))$ will satisfy

$$\dot{E}(t) \leq -kE + |E_x \xi + E_y \eta| \leq -kE(t)/2.$$

By Theorem 8 of Chapter 1, it follows that $E(t) \leq E(t_0)e^{-k(t-t_0)/2}$. Hence, $E(t)$ approaches zero exponentially. Since $E(x, y) \geq K(x^2 + y^2)$, it follows at once that the trajectory tends to the origin.

Using similar arguments, we can prove the following classic generalization of Theorem 6, which we state without proof.

■ POINCARÉ-LIAPUNOV THEOREM.   *If the critical point* **0** *of the linear autonomous system* $\mathbf{x}'(t) = A\mathbf{x}$ *is strictly stable, then so is that of the perturbed system*

$$x_i'(t) = \sum a_{ij} x_j + \boldsymbol{\xi}(\mathbf{x}),$$

provided that $|\boldsymbol{\xi}(\mathbf{x})| = O(|\mathbf{x}|^2)$.

10   Undamped nonlinear oscillations

The classification made in § 8 covers linear oscillators near equilibrium points, which correspond to critical points in the Poincaré phase plane.

We will now study the nonlinear oscillations of a particle with one degree of freedom, about a position of stable equilibrium. The case of undamped (i.e., frictionless) oscillations will be treated first. This case is described by the second-order DE

$$\ddot{x} + q(x) = 0. \tag{36}$$

In the Poincaré phase plane, this corresponds to the plane autonomous system

$$dx/dt = v, \qquad dv/dt = -q(x). \tag{37}$$

By a translation of coordinates, we can move any position of equilibrium to $x = 0$; hence we can let $q(0) = 0$. If equilibrium is stable, then the "restoring force" $q(x)$ must act in a direction opposite to the displacement x, at least for small displacements. Therefore we assume that $xq(x) > 0$ for $x \neq 0$ sufficiently small. This will make the system (37) have an isolated critical point at $x = v = 0$, as in the case of the simple pendulum (Example 5, § 3).

The key to the analysis of systems (36) is the *potential energy* integral

$$V(x) = \int_0^x q(\xi)\, d\xi. \tag{38}$$

Since $xq(x) > 0$, the function $V(x)$ is increasing when x is positive and decreasing when x is negative; it has a local minimum $V(0) = 0$ at $x = 0$. Differentiating the *total energy*

$$E(x, v) = v^2/2 + V(x) \tag{39}$$

with respect to t, we get $\dot{E} = \dot{x}[\ddot{x} + q(x)] = 0$; hence, $E(x, v)$ is a constant along any trajectory in the Poincaré phase plane. We also note that $E(x, v)$ has a strict local minimum at $(0, 0)$.

■ THEOREM 7. *If $q \in \mathscr{C}^1$ and if $xq(x) > 0$ for small nonzero x, then the critical point $(0, 0)$ of the system* (36) *is a vortex point*†.

Proof — For any given positive constant E, the locus $v^2/2 + V(x) = E$ is an integral curve, where $V(0) = 0$ and $V(x)$ increases with $|x|$, on both sides of $x = 0$. These curves are symmetric under reflection $(x, v) \to (x, -v)$ in the x-axis; they slope down with slope $-q(x)/v$ in the first and third quadrants and up in the second and fourth quadrants. For any given small value of E, the function $E - V(x)$ has a maximum at $x = 0$ and decreases monotonically on both sides, crossing zero at

---

† As in the linear case, a critical point of a plane autonomous system is called a *vortex point* when nearby solution curves are concentric simple closed curves.

points $x = -B$ and $x = A$, where B and A are small and positive. Hence each locus $v^2 = 2[E - V(x)]$ is a simple closed curve, symmetric about the x-axis.

As the energy parameter E decreases, so does $|v| = \sqrt{2[E - V(x)]}$; thus, the simple closed curves defined by the trajectories of (38) shrink monotonically toward the origin as $E \downarrow 0$. In fact, consider the new coordinates (u, v), defined by $u = \pm\sqrt{2V(x)}$, according as x is positive or negative. The transformation $(x, v) \to (u, v)$ is of class $\mathscr{C}^1$ with a nonvanishing Jacobian, near $(0, 0)$, if $q'(0)$ exists and is positive. Hence the integral curves of (37) resemble a distorted family of circles $u^2 + v^2 = 2E$.

11   Soft and hard springs

The most familiar special case of (36) is the undamped linear oscillator

$$\ddot{x} + qx = 0, \qquad q = k^2 > 0, \tag{40}$$

for which $q(x) = k^2 x$. The general solution of (40) is the function $x = A \cos[k(t - t_0)]$, representing an *oscillation* of *amplitude* A, *frequency* $k/2\pi$ (period $2\pi/k$), and *phase* t_0.

In other cases, DE (36) can be imagined as determining the motion of a unit mass, attached to an *elastic spring* which resists a displacement x by a force $q(x)$, independent of the velocity $\dot{x}$. The ratio $h(x) = q(x)/x$ is called the *stiffness* of the spring; it is bounded for bounded x if $q \in \mathscr{C}^1$ and $q(0) = 0$. The case (40) of a linear spring is the case of constant stiffness (Hooke's Law). For linear springs, the formulas of the last paragraph show that the frequency $f = k/2\pi$ increases as the square root of the stiffness k^2 and is independent of the amplitude. We will now show that, for *nonlinear* springs, the frequency f still increases with the stiffness but is amplitude-dependent in general.

Indeed, the force law (36) implies that $\dot{x} = v = \sqrt{2[E - V(x)]}$. Hence, if the limits of oscillation (i.e., the smallest negative and positive roots of the equation $V(x) = E$) are $x = -B$ and $x = A$, the period T of the complete oscillation is

$$T = 2 \int_{-B}^{A} \frac{dx}{\sqrt{2[E - V(x)]}}. \tag{41}$$

The integral (41) is improper, but it converges, provided that $q(x)$ does not vanish at $-B$ or A; hence it converges for all sufficiently small amplitudes if $q \in \mathscr{C}^1$ in the stable case $h(0) > 0$.

We now compare the periods T and T_1 of the oscillation of two springs, having stiffness $h(x)$ and $h_1(x) \geq h(x)$, and the same limits of oscillation

$-B$ and A. By (39), $E = \int_0^A q(u)\, du = V(A)$; hence, $E - V(x) = \int_x^A q(u)\, du$. From the stiffness inequality assumed above, therefore, we obtain,

$$E - V(x) = \int_x^A q(u)\, du \leqq \int_x^A q_1(u)\, du = E - V_1(x), \qquad 0 \leqq x \leqq A.$$

Reversing the sign of x, we get the same inequality for $-B \leqq x \leqq 0$. Substituting into (41), we obtain $T \geqq T_1$. We thus get the following comparison theorem.

■ THEOREM 8.   *For any two oscillations having the same span* $[-B, A]$, *the period becomes shorter and the frequency greater as the stiffness* $q(x)/x$ *increases in* (36).

Springs for which $h(x) = h(-x)$ are called symmetric; this makes $q(-x) = -q(x)$ and $V(-x) = V(x)$, so that $B = A$ in the preceding formulas: symmetric springs oscillate symmetrically about their equilibrium position. Hence, for symmetric springs, the phrase "span $[-B, A]$" in Theorem 8 can be replaced by "amplitude A."

For any symmetric spring, $h'(0) = 0$; if $h''(0)$ is positive, so that $h(x)$ increases with $|x|$, the spring is said to be "hard"; if $h''(0)$ is negative, so that $h(x)$ decreases as $|x|$ increases, it is said to be "soft." Thus the simple pendulum of Example 5, § 3, acts as a "soft" spring. We now show that the period of oscillation is amplitude-dependent, at least for symmetric hard and soft springs.

■ THEOREM 9.   *The period of a hard symmetric spring decreases as the span of oscillation increases; the period of a soft symmetric spring increases with the span.*

Proof — The period is given by (41); it suffices to compare the periods of quarter-oscillations, say from 0 to A and from 0 to A_1, with $A_1 > A$. We write $A_1 = cA$, with $c > 1$. To study the period p_1 of the quarter-oscillation from 0 to $cA = A_1$, we let $x = cy$ in (36). The equivalent DE for y is

$$d^2 y/dt^2 + yh(cy) = 0, \qquad (42)$$

where $h(x) = q(x)/x$ The oscillation of amplitude cA for (36) corresponds to the oscillation of amplitude A for (42); and, since the independent variable t is unchanged, the periods of oscillation are the same for both. Therefore, it suffices to compare the quarter periods p and p_1 for amplitude A for the two springs (36) and (42), respectively. Using Theorem 8, we find that, for $y > 0$, if $yh(cy) \geqq q(y) = yh(y)$, that is, if $h(cy) \geqq h(y)$

for $c > 1$ (hard spring), then we have $p_1 \leqq p$, that is, the period decreases as the amplitude increases. Soft springs can be treated similarly.

EXERCISES D

1. (a) Show that the integral curves of $\ddot{x} - x + x^3 = 0$ in the Poincaré phase plane are the curves $v^2 - x^2 + x^4/2 = C$.
    (b) Sketch the curves.
    (c) Show that the autonomous system defining these curves has a saddle point at $(0, 0)$ and vortex points at $(0, \pm 1)$.

2. Duffing's equation without forcing term is $\ddot{x} + qx + rx^3 = 0$. Show that, for oscillations of small but finite half-amplitude L, the period T is

$$T = 4\sqrt{2} \int_0^{\pi/2} \frac{d\theta}{\sqrt{2q + rL^2(1 + \sin^2 \theta)}}.$$

Verify Theorem 9 in this special case as a corollary.

3. (a) From the assumptions of Exercise B5, show that the function $u = \operatorname{sn} t$ satisfies the second-order DE

$$\ddot{u} + (1 + k^2)u - 2k^2u^3 = 0. \tag{**}$$

    (b) Infer from (**) that $\dot{u}^2 + (1 + k^2)u^2 - k^2u^4 = \text{constant}$.
    (c) Sketch the integral curves of DE (**) in the Poincaré phase plane, marking the special curve ($\operatorname{sn} t$, $\operatorname{cn} t$, $\operatorname{dn} t$) and any critical points.
    (d) Determine the nature of the other critical points, if any.

4*. (a) Show that a one-parameter family of solutions of $\ddot{\theta} + k^2 \sin \theta = 0$ is given by $\sin (\theta/2) = \sin (\alpha/2) \operatorname{sn} [k(t - t_0)]$, where α is the amplitude of oscillation.
    (b) Show that $\dot{\theta} = 2k \sin (\alpha/2) \operatorname{cn} [k(t - t_0)]$.

5. The Weierstrass p-function satisfies the DE $d^2p/dx^2 = 6p^2 - g_2/2$, g_2 a constant. What are its critical points in the pp'-plane, that is, the Poincaré phase plane, and what are their types?

6. The equation of a falling stone in air satisfies approximately the DE

$$\ddot{x} = g - \dot{x}^2/v^2,$$

where v is the "terminal velocity." Sketch the integral curves of this DE in the Poincaré phase plane, and interpret them physically.

7*. A stone thrown through the air satisfies approximately the system of DE's

$$dv/dt = -g[(v/V)^2 + \sin \theta], \qquad d\theta/dt = (g \cos \theta)/v.$$

where θ is the angle with the horizontal and V is the terminal velocity. Sketch the integral curves in the (v, θ)-*cylinder*. [N.B. The variable θ is periodic modulo 2π.]

8. Show that the origin is a stable critical point of the system

$$\dot{x} = ax + by + \epsilon_1(x, y), \qquad \dot{y} = cx + dy + \epsilon_2(x, y),$$

if $a + d < 0$, $ad > bc$, and $|\epsilon_1(x, y)| + |\epsilon_2(x, y)| = O(x^2 + y^2)$.

9. Discuss the dependence on the sign of the constant μ, of the critical point at the origin of the system

$$\dot{u} = -v + \mu u^3, \qquad \dot{v} = u + \mu v^3.$$

10. (a) Show that the trajectories of $\ddot{x} + q(x) = 0$ in the Poincaré phase plane are convex closed curves if $q(x)$ is an increasing function with $q(0) = 0$.
    (b) Is the converse true?

11. Show that, if $\dot{x} = ax + by$, $\dot{y} = cx + dy$ is unstable at the origin, and

$$X(x, y) = ax + by + O(x^2 + y^2), \qquad Y(x, y) = cx + dy + O(x^2 + y^2),$$

where $ad \neq bc$ and $\Delta \neq 0$, then the system $\dot{x} = X(x, y)$, $\dot{y} = Y(x, y)$ is unstable there.

12. Show that the plane autonomous system $\dot{x} = y - x^3$, $\dot{y} = -x^3$ is stable, though its linearization is unstable. [HINT: Show that $x^4 + 2y^2$ is a Liapunov function.]

13*. Show that for the analytic plane autonomous system

$$\dot{x} = 2x^3 y, \qquad \dot{y} = x^2 y^2 - x^4 - y^{11}$$

the origin is an unstable critical point which is asymptotically stable. [HINT: Study Example 6. To prove instability, show that the ellipse $4y^2 = x - x^2$ cannot be crossed from the left in the first quadrant.]

12   Damped nonlinear oscillations

The equation of motion for a particle of mass m having an equilibrium point at $x = 0$, in the presence of a restoring force $mq(x)$ and a friction force $f(x, v) = mvp(x, v)$, is

$$\ddot{x} + p(x, \dot{x})\dot{x} + q(x) = 0, \qquad q(x) = xh(x), \qquad p \in \mathscr{C}^2, \quad h \in \mathscr{C}^1 \quad (43)$$

When $h(0)$ is positive, the equilibrium point is called *statically stable*, because the restoring force tends to restore equilibrium under static conditions (when $v = 0$). The conservative system (36) obtained from any statically stable system (43) by omitting the friction term $\dot{x}p(x, \dot{x})$, is neutrally stable by Theorem 7.

The differential equation (43) has a very simple interpretation in the Poincaré phase plane, as

$$dx/dt = v, \qquad dv/dt = -vp(x, v) - q(x). \qquad (44)$$

The critical points of the system (44) are all on the x-axis, where $\dot{x} = v = 0$; they are the equilibrium points $(x, 0)$ where $q(x) = 0$ in (43). Since $q(0) = 0h(0) = 0$ in (43), the origin is always a critical point of (44); unless $h(0)$ changes sign, there is no other.

We shall consider below only the case $h(x) > 0$ of static stability in the large, which is the case of greatest interest for applications. For simplicity, we will also assume that $p(0, 0) \neq 0$.

Under these assumptions, the origin is the only critical point of (44). Moreover the direction field, whose slope is

$$dv/dx = \tau(x, v) = -p(x, v) - q(x)/v,$$

points to the right in the upper half-plane, where $\dot{x} = v > 0$, and to the left in the lower half-plane. On the x-axis, the solution curves have finite curvature $q(x)$; they cut it vertically downward on the positive x-axis and vertically upward on the negative x-axis thus, the solution curves have a general clockwise orientation.

Conversely, any continuous oriented direction field with the properties specified represents a DE of the form (43) in the Poincaré phase plane. From this it is clear that the behavior of the solutions of the DE's of the form (43) can be extremely varied in the large (see § 13). However, the local possibilities are limited.

■ THEOREM 10.   *If p and h are of class $\mathscr{C}^1$ in (43), and if $p(0, 0)$ and $h(0)$ are positive, then the origin is a strictly stable critical point of (44).*

Proof — Under the hypotheses of Theorem 10, we have that $p > 0$ near the critical point $(0, 0)$, and we can write (44) as

$$dx/dt = v, \qquad dv/dt = -h(0)x - p_0 v + O(x^2 + v^2).$$

An easy computation shows that the linearization of the system (44) has the secular equation $\lambda^2 + p_0\lambda + h(0) = 0$. Since this quadratic polynomial has positive coefficients, it is of stable type (Chapter 4, § 5). Hence, by Theorem 6, the origin is a strictly stable critical point of (43) when the *damping* factor $p(0, 0)$ is *positive*. The equilibrium point $x = 0$ of (43) is then said to be *dynamically stable*: the solution curves tend to the origin in the vicinity of the origin.

When $p(0, 0)$ is negative, the system is said to be *negatively damped*, and the equilibrium point to be *dynamically unstable*. Since (43) can be rewritten as

$$\frac{d^2x}{d(-t)^2} + p\left(x, \frac{-dx}{d(-t)}\right)\frac{-dx}{d(-t)} + xh(x) = 0, \tag{45}$$

we see that the substitutions $t \to -t$, $x \to x$, $v \to -v$, of time reversal, reverse the sign of $p(x, \dot{x})$ but do not affect (43) otherwise. Hence, if $p(0, 0) < 0$, all solution curves of (44) tend outward near the origin.

13* Limit cycles

We now come to a major difference between nonlinear oscillations and linear oscillations. When a linear oscillator is negatively damped, the amplitude of oscillation always increases exponentially without limit. In contrast the amplitude of oscillation of a negatively damped, statically stable, nonlinear oscillator commonly tends to a finite limit. The limiting periodic oscillation of finite amplitude so approached is called a *limit cycle*.

The simplest DE which gives rise to a limit cycle is the *Rayleigh equation*,

$$\ddot{x} - \mu(1 - \dot{x}^2)\dot{x} + x = 0, \qquad \mu > 0. \tag{46}$$

The characteristic feature of this DE is the fact that the damping is negative for small $\dot{x}$ and positive for large $\dot{x}$. Hence it tends to increase the amplitude of small oscillations and to decrease the amplitude of large oscillations. In between these two types of motions, there is an oscillation of constant amplitude, a limit cycle.

If we differentiate the Rayleigh equation (46) and set $y = \dot{x}\sqrt{3}$, we obtain the *van der Pol equation*

$$\ddot{y} - \mu(1 - y^2)\dot{y} + y = 0, \qquad \mu > 0. \tag{47}$$

This DE arises in the study of vacuum tubes. The sign of the damping term depends on the magnitude of the displacement y. The remarks about the Rayleigh equation made above apply also to the van der Pol equation.

As stated in §12, negatively damped nonlinear oscillators can give rise to a great variety of qualitatively different solution curve configurations in the Poincaré phase plane. For any particular DE (43), such as the Rayleigh or van der Pol equation with given μ, one can determine the behavior of solutions by integrating the DE

$$[v + p(x, v)]\, dv + q(x)\, dx = dE + p(x, v)\, dv$$

graphically (Chapter 1, § 7). Figure 5.8 depicts sample integral curves

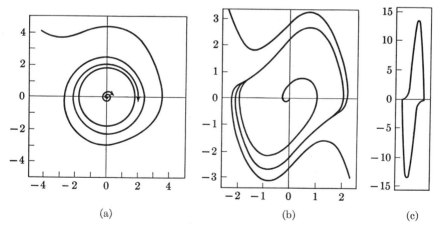

(a)   (b)   (c)

FIGURE 5.8   van der Pol Equation.

for the van der Pol equation with $\mu = 0.1$, $\mu = 1$, and $\mu = 10$ so obtained. More accurate results can be had by use of numerical integration.

With modern computing machines, using the techniques to be described in Chapter 8, it is a routine operation to obtain such families of integral curves.

Liénard equation. General criteria are also available which determine the qualitative behavior of the oscillations directly from that of the coefficient-functions. Such criteria are especially useful for DE's depending on parameters, because graphical integration then becomes very tedious. They are available for DE's of the form

$$\ddot{x} + f(x)\dot{x} + q(x) = 0 \qquad \text{(Liénard equation).} \tag{48}$$

The van der Pol equation is a Liénard equation; moreover, it is *symmetric* in the sense that $-x(t)$ is a solution if $x(t)$ is a solution. This holds whenever $q(-x) = -q(x)$ is odd and $f(-x) = f(x)$ is even.

One can prove the *existence* of limit cycles for a wide class of Liénard equations; we can even prove that *every* nontrivial solution is either a limit cycle, or a spiral which tends toward a limit cycle as $t \to +\infty$. This is true if: (i) $xq(x) > 0$ for $x \neq 0$, (ii) $f(x)$ in (48) is negative in an interval $a < x < b$ containing the origin and positive outside this interval, and

$$\int_0^\infty f(x)\,dx = \int_{-\infty}^0 f(x)\,dx = +\infty. \tag{49}$$

We sketch the proof†.

In the xv-plane, solution curves satisfy

$$dv/dx + f(x) + q(x)/v = 0 \qquad \text{if} \qquad v \neq 0. \tag{50}$$

It follows, since $xq(x) > 0$, that they can cross the x-axis only downward if $x > 0$, and upward if $x < 0$. Also by (50), between successive crossings of the x-axis, $v(x)$ is a bounded single-valued function, decreasing in magnitude if $x > b$ in the upper half-plane, and if $x < a$ in the lower half-plane.

Now, consider the *Liénard function*

$$E(x, v) = \tfrac{1}{2}[v + F(x)]^2 + U(x) \qquad F(x) = \int_0^x f(x)\,dx,$$

$$U(x) = \int_0^x q(x)\,dx \geqq 0. \tag{51}$$

A straightforward calculation gives $dE/dt = -q(x)F(x)$, where, by (49), $F(x)$ becomes positively infinite as $|x| \to \infty$. For sufficiently large $|x|$, since $xq(x) > 0$, dE/dt is identically negative. Since the set of all (x, v) for which $E(x, v) \leqq E_0$, any finite constant, is contained in the bounded

---

† For a complete proof, see Lefschetz, p. 247, or Stoker, Appendices III and IV.

strip $x + F(x) \leq 2E_0$, it also follows that solution curves can stay in one half-plane ($v > 0$ or $v < 0$) for only a finite distance (and time): if non-trivial, they must cut the x-axis infinitely often.

Let $x_0, x_1, x_2, \ldots$ be successive zero-crossings; we can assume that $x_{2n} > 0$ and $x_{2n+1} < 0$ without loss of generality. If $x_2 = x_0$, then (by uniqueness) $x_{2n} = x_0$ and $x_{2n+1} = x_1$ for all $n > 0$; the solution curve is a limit cycle. Likewise, if $x_2 > x_0$, then we find that $x_{2n} > x_{2n-2}$ and $x_{2n+1} < x_{2n-1}$ for all $n > 0$ and the solution curve spirals outward as t increases. Similarly, if $x_2 < x_0$, then the solution curve must spiral inward.

Finally, since $f(0) < 0$, Theorem 6 applies if $f, g \in \mathscr{C}^1$: solution curves near the origin must spiral outward. Also, we know that

$$E(x_{2n}, 0) - E(x_{2n-1}, 0) = - \int_{x_{2n-1}}^{x_{2n}} q(x) F(x) \, dx,$$

and the definite integral is negative for sufficiently large oscillations since $xq(x) > 0$ and $F(\pm\infty) = +\infty$, by (49). Hence, every solution curve sufficiently far from the origin must spiral inward. Therefore, every oscillation of sufficiently large initial amplitude must spiral inward toward a limit cycle of maximum amplitude. Likewise, every oscillation of sufficiently small initial amplitude must spiral outward to a smallest limit cycle.

For the Rayleigh and van der Pol equations, these limit cycles are the same. Therefore, every nontrivial solution tends to a unique limit cycle, which is stable. The preceding result holds under much more general conditions. We quote one set of such conditions without proof.

■ LEVINSON–SMITH THEOREM.   *In* (48), *let* $q(x) = xh(x)$, *where* $h(x) > 0$ *and let* $f(x)$ *be negative in an interval* (a, b) *containing the origin and positive outside this interval. Let* $q(-x) = -q(x), f(-x) = f(x)$, *and let* (49) *hold. Then* (48) *has a unique stable limit cycle in the Poincaré phase plane, toward which every nontrivial integral curve tends.*

EXERCISES E

1. Show that any DE

$$\ddot{x} + (px^2 - q)\dot{x} + rx = 0,$$

where q and r are positive constants, can be reduced to the van der Pol DE by a change of dependent and independent variables.

2. (a) Show that the autonomous plane system

$$\dot{u} = u - v - u^3 - uv^2, \qquad \dot{v} = u + v - v^3 - u^2 v$$

has a unique critical point, which is unstable, and a unique limit cycle.

(b) Discuss the stability of the related system

$$\dot{u} = -u - v + u^3 + uv^2, \qquad \dot{v} = u - v + v^3 + u^2v$$

with special reference to oscillations of very small and very large amplitude.

3. In the DE $\ddot{x} + q(x) = 0$, let $V(x) = \int_0^x q(u)\, du$, and let q be a continuous function satisfying a Lipschitz condition. Show that, if $V(x_1) = V(x_2)$ and $V(x) < V(x_1)$ for $x_1 < x < x_2$, the equivalent autonomous system (44) has a periodic solution passing through the points $(x_1, 0)$ and $(x_2, 0)$.

4. Show that the plane autonomous system.

$$\dot{r} = (r^3 - r)/100, \qquad \dot{\theta} = 1 \qquad \text{(polar coordinates)}$$

has just one limit cycle.

5. Discuss the limit cycles of the system

$$\dot{r} = (r/100) \sin (1/r), \qquad \dot{\theta} = 1.$$

6. Prove in detail that, for $\mu = 1$ and the initial condition $x(0) = 10$, $\dot{x}(0) = 0$, the amplitude of successive oscillations decreases in the Rayleigh DE (46).

7. Same question for the van der Pol DE, if $y(0) = 10$, $\dot{y}(0) = 0$.

8. Sketch the integral curves of the van der Pol DE in the Poincaré phase plane for $\mu = 100$. [HINT: Most of the time, the integral curves are "relaxation oscillations," near $\dot{y} = 0$ or $y = 1$.]

9. Same question for the Rayleigh DE.

ADDITIONAL EXERCISES

1. Locate the critical points of the DE $\dot{x} = x(1 - x)(a - x)$, and discuss how their stability or instability varies with a.

2. Same question for $\dot{x} = x(1 - x)(x - a)$.

3. Show that, in the complex domain, every system $\dot{x} = ax + by$, $\dot{y} = cx + dy$ is linearly equivalent to either $\dot{x} = \lambda x$, $\dot{y} = \mu y$ or $\dot{x} = \lambda x$, $\dot{y} = \lambda y + x$, for suitable λ, μ.

4. Show that, in the *punctured* plane $x^2 + y^2 > 0$, two linear systems (13) are equivalent, provided that their discriminants Δ, Δ' are not zero, and they both have either (a) stable focal points, (b) unstable focal points, (c) vortex points, (d) stable nodal points, (e) unstable nodal points, or (f) saddle-points.

5. Consider the linear autonomous system

$$\dot{x} = a_1 x + a_2 y + a_3 z, \qquad \dot{y} = b_1 x + b_2 y + b_3 z, \qquad \dot{z} = c_1 x + c_2 y + c_3 z.$$

(a) Show that the x-component of any solution satisfies

$$\frac{d^3 x}{dt^3} = p_1 \ddot{x} - p_2 \dot{x} + p_3 x, \qquad \text{where} \qquad p_1 = a_1 + b_2 + c_3, \qquad (\sigma)$$

$$p_2 = a_1 b_2 - a_2 b_1 + b_2 c_3 - b_3 c_2 + c_3 a_1 - c_1 a_3, \qquad p_3 = \begin{vmatrix} a_1 & a_2 & a_3 \\ b_1 & b_2 & b_3 \\ c_1 & c_2 & c_3 \end{vmatrix}.$$

(b) Show that the *secular equation* (σ) is invariant under any nonsingular linear transformation of the variables x, y, z.

(c) Conversely, show that, if the polynomial $\lambda^3 = p_1 \lambda^2 - p_2 \lambda + p_3$ has distinct real roots λ_1, λ_2, λ_3, then the given DE is linearly equivalent to $\dot{\xi}_j = \lambda_j \xi_j$ $(j = 1, 2, 3)$.

(d*) Work out a set of real canonical forms for the given DE, with respect to linear equivalence, in the general case.

6. Let $\nabla U = \mathbf{X}$, $U = U(x, \sqrt{y^2 + z^2})$ be any axially symmetric gradient field of class $\mathscr{C}^1$. Show that the DE $\dot{x} = \nabla U$ admits as an integral the "stream function" $V = \int r[(\partial U/\partial x)\, dr + (\partial U/\partial r)\, dx]$, the integral being independent of the path.

7. Sketch the integral curves in the Poincaré phase plane for

(a) $\ddot{x} + x + \dfrac{A}{x - a} = 0$,   (b) $\ddot{x} + \dot{x}/|\dot{x}| = 0$ (Coulomb friction),

(c) $\ddot{x} + \dot{x}|\dot{x}| + k \sin x = 0$.

8. Let $q(x)$ be an increasing function, with $q(0) = 0$ and $q(-L) = -q(L)$; let $Q(x) = [q(x) - q(-x)]/2$. Show that the period of oscillation of half-amplitude L for $\ddot{x} + Q(x) = 0$ is less than that for $\ddot{x} + q(x) = 0$ unless $q(-x) = -q(x)$ for all $x \in [0, L]$.

9. Show that the DE's $\dot{x} = 2x + \sin x$ and $\dot{x} = 2x$ are equivalent on $(-\infty, +\infty)$ but that $\dot{x} = x + x^3$ is not equivalent to $\dot{x} = x$. [HINT: Consider the escape time.]

10. Show that, if $a_1 < a_2 < \cdots < a_n$ and $b_1 < b_2 < \cdots < b_n$, the DE's $\dot{x} = \Pi(x - a_i)$ and $\dot{x} = \Pi(x - b_i)$ are equivalent.

6 Existence and Uniqueness Theorems

1 Introduction

We now resume the study of general normal systems of first-order DE's, of the form

$$dx_1/dt = X_1(x_1, \ldots, x_n; t),$$
$$\cdot \quad \cdot \quad \cdot \quad \cdot \quad \cdot \quad \cdot \quad \cdot \quad \cdot \quad \cdot \qquad (1)$$
$$dx_n/dt = X_n(x_1, \ldots, x_n; t).$$

Our main concern in this chapter is to prove general theorems about the existence, uniqueness, continuity, and differentiability of solution of such systems for given fixed and variable initial conditions. These theorems will generalize results proved in Chapter 1 for the special case $n = 1$. In Chapters 7 and 8, we shall describe limiting processes for constructing and even computing such solutions.

We continue to make the assumptions of Chapter 5, § 1: that the X_i are continuous, real-valued functions of the independent variables $x_1, x_2, \ldots, x_n, t$ in some region $\mathscr{R}$ of interest in $(x_1, \ldots, x_n, t)$-space. We shall also use the vector notation introduced there, rewriting (1) as

$$d\mathbf{x}/dt = \mathbf{X}(\mathbf{x}, t) \qquad \text{or} \qquad \mathbf{x}'(t) = \mathbf{X}(\mathbf{x}, t). \qquad (2)$$

The curve $\mathbf{x}(t)$ in $\mathscr{R}$ defined by any solution of (1) will be called a *solution curve* of the system (1).

Note that we can trivially inflate *any* normal system (1) of n first-order DE's to a normal *autonomous* system of $n + 1$ DE's by the simple device of writing $t = x_{n+1}$. This gives the equivalent system

$$dx_j/dt = X_j(x_1, \ldots, x_n; x_{n+1}), \qquad j = 1, \ldots, n + 1,$$

where X_{n+1} is the function 1. However, this does not help to prove the theorems of major interest.

A nonconstant function $U(x_1, \ldots, x_n; t)$ which is defined in $\mathscr{R}$ and of class $\mathscr{C}^1$ there is called an *integral* of (1) when $U(x_1(t), \ldots, x_n(t); t)$ is constant for every solution of (1). This means that each solution curve of (1) stays on a single level surface $U(x_1, \ldots, x_n; t) = C$ of the function U in $(x_1, \ldots, x_n; t)$-space ("space-time") and, thus, generalizes the definition of "integral" in Chapter 1, § 3.

EXAMPLE 1. Consider the system

$$dx/dt = tx/(x^2 - y^2), \qquad dy/dt = ty/(y^2 - x^2).$$

It is easy to verify that, when $x = x(t)$ and $y = y(t)$ are solutions, the two functions

$$V(x, y, t) = xy \qquad \text{and} \qquad W(x, y, t) = x^2 + y^2 - t^2$$

satisfy $dV/dt = x\,dy/dt + y\,dx/dt = 0$ and $dW/dt = 0$. Therefore, V and W are integrals of the system. The intersection of two surfaces $V = c_1$ and $W = c_2$ is a solution curve of the system. Thus, every solution curve lies on the intersection of a hyperbolic cylinder $xy = c_1$ and a hyperboloid (or cone) $x^2 + y^2 - t^2 = c_2$.

First-order systems of DE's (1) provide a standard form to which *all* normal ordinary DE's and systems of DE's can be reduced. Using (1), we can thus give a unified theory for the existence and uniqueness of solutions of DE's and systems of DE's of all orders, as we shall see in this chapter.

For example, one can reduce the solution of a normal nth order DE to the solution of a system of n first-order DE's as follows. Let $u(t)$ be any solution of the given nth order DE,

$$d^n u/dt^n = F(u, du/dt, d^2u/dt^2, \ldots, d^{n-1}u/dt^{n-1}; t).$$

Then the n functions $x_1(t) = u$, $x_2(t) = du/dt$, $\ldots$, $x_n(t) = d^{n-1}u/dt^{n-1}$ satisfy the normal first-order system

$$dx_k/dt = x_{k+1}, \qquad k = 1, \ldots, n-1; \qquad dx_n/dt = F(x_1, x_2, \ldots, x_n; t).$$

Conversely, given any solution of the preceding first-order system, the first component $x_1(t)$ will have the other components $x_2, \ldots, x_n$ as its derivatives of orders $1, \ldots, n-1$. Hence, substituting back, $x_1(t)$ will satisfy the given nth order equation.

2 Lipschitz condition

In order to make use of vector notation for systems of DE's, we recall a few facts about vectors in n-dimensional Euclidean spaces. Addition of two vectors and multiplication of vectors by scalars are defined component-wise, as in the plane and in space.† The *length* of a vector $\mathbf{x} = (x_1, x_2, \ldots, x_n)$ is defined as

$$|\mathbf{x}| = (x_1^2 + \cdots + x_n^2)^{1/2}.$$

Length satisfies the triangle inequality

$$|\mathbf{x} + \mathbf{y}| \leq |\mathbf{x}| + |\mathbf{y}|.$$

The dot product or *inner product* of two vectors is defined as

$$\mathbf{x} \cdot \mathbf{y} = x_1 y_1 + \cdots + x_n y_n$$

and satisfies the Schwarz inequality $|\mathbf{x} \cdot \mathbf{y}| \leq |\mathbf{x}| \cdot |\mathbf{y}|$.

We shall integrate, differentiate, and take limits of vector functions $\mathbf{x}(t)$ of a scalar (real) variable t. All these operations can be carried out component by component, as in vector addition.

For example, the derivative of a vector function

$$\mathbf{x}(t) = (x_1(t), x_2(t), \ldots, x_n(t))$$

is the vector function $\mathbf{x}'(t) = (x_1'(t), x_2'(t), \ldots, x_n'(t))$. The integral $\int_a^b \mathbf{x}(t)\, dt$ is the vector with components $\int_a^b x_1(t)\, dt$, $\int_a^b x_2(t)\, dt$, $\ldots$, $\int_a^b x_n(t)\, dt$. We shall often make use of the fundamental inequality‡

$$\left| \int_a^b \mathbf{x}(t)\, dt \right| \leq \int_a^b |\mathbf{x}(t)|\, dt. \tag{3}$$

A vector function $\mathbf{X}(\mathbf{x})$ of a vector variable is said to be *continuous* when each component X_i of $\mathbf{X}$ is a continuous function of the n variables $x_1, \ldots, x_n$, the components of the vector independent variable $\mathbf{x}$. This is equivalent to the following statement: The function $\mathbf{X}(\mathbf{x})$ is continuous at the point (vector) $\mathbf{c}$ whenever, given $\epsilon > 0$, there exists $\delta > 0$ such that, if $|\mathbf{x} - \mathbf{c}| < \delta$, then $|\mathbf{X}(\mathbf{x}) - \mathbf{X}(\mathbf{c})| < \epsilon$. We leave it as an exercise to verify that these definitions are equivalent.

Note that there is no such thing as " the " derivative of a function $\mathbf{X}(\mathbf{x})$ of a *vector* independent variable, but only a matrix of *partial* derivatives $\partial X_i / \partial x_j$ relative to the different components $x_1, \ldots, x_n$.

The reader who is not accustomed to working with functions of vectors should familiarize himself with the differences between the following types of functions: vector-valued functions of a scalar variable

---

† Birkhoff and Mac Lane, Chapter 7. The three-dimensional case is treated in Courant, Vol. 2, Chapter 2; Widder, Chapter 2, and in most other texts on the advanced calculus.
‡ This inequality is the continuous analog of the triangle inequality

$$|\mathbf{x}^{(1)} + \mathbf{x}^{(2)} + \cdots + \mathbf{x}^{(n)}|| \leq |\mathbf{x}^{(1)}| + |\mathbf{x}^{(2)}| + \cdots + |\mathbf{x}^{(n)}|.$$

It can be obtained from this inequality by recalling the definition of the integral $\int_a^b \mathbf{x}(t)\, dt$ as a limit of Riemann sums, using the triangle inequality for each of the Riemann sums, and passing to the limit on both sides.

(such as $\mathbf{x}(t) = (x_1(t), x_2(t), \ldots, x_n(t)))$, scalar-valued functions of a vector variable (such as $|\mathbf{x}| = \sqrt{x_1^2 + \cdots + x_n^2}$), vector-valued functions of a vector variable such as

$$\mathbf{X}(\mathbf{x}) = (X_1(x_1, x_2, \ldots, x_n), X_2(x_1 \ldots, x_n), \ldots, X_m(x_1, \ldots, x_n)),$$

vector-valued function of a vector variable $\mathbf{x}$ and a parameter t (such as $\mathbf{X}(\mathbf{x}, t)$).

A vector-valued function $\mathbf{X}(\mathbf{x})$ of a vector variable is said to be of class $\mathscr{C}^n$ in a given region when each of the component functions $X_i(x_1, \ldots, x_n)$ is of class $\mathscr{C}^n$ there.

One can also easily extend the definition of a Lipschitz condition to vector-valued functions; as we shall see, this provides a simple sufficient condition for the uniqueness and existence of solutions for normal systems.

■ DEFINITION. *A vector-valued function* $\mathbf{X}(\mathbf{x}, t)$ *satisfies a* Lipschitz condition *in a region* $\mathscr{R}$ *of* $\mathbf{x}t$-*space if and only if, for some Lipschitz constant* L,

$$|\mathbf{X}(\mathbf{x}, t) - \mathbf{X}(\mathbf{y}, t)| \leqq L|\mathbf{x} - \mathbf{y}| \qquad if \quad (\mathbf{x}, t) \in \mathscr{R}, \quad (\mathbf{y}, t) \in \mathscr{R}. \qquad (4)$$

Note that both terms on the left side of (4) involve the same value of t.

■ LEMMA. *If* $\mathbf{X}(\mathbf{x}, t)$ *is of class* $\mathscr{C}^1$ *in a bounded closed* ("*compact*") *convex*† *domain* D, *then it satisfies a Lipschitz condition there.*

Proof — Let M be the maximum of all partial derivatives $|\partial X_i / \partial x_j|$ in the closed domain D. For each component X_i we have, for fixed $\mathbf{x}, \mathbf{y}, t$ and for variable s,

$$\frac{d}{ds}[X_i(\mathbf{x} + s\mathbf{y}, t)] = \sum_{k=1}^{n} \frac{\partial X_i}{\partial x_k}(\mathbf{x} + s\mathbf{y}, t)y_k.$$

Hence, by the mean-value theorem applied to the function $X_i(\mathbf{x} + s\mathbf{y}, t)$ of the variable s on the interval $0 \leqq s \leqq 1$, we have

$$X_i(\mathbf{x} + \mathbf{y}, t) - X_i(\mathbf{x}, t) = \sum_{k=1}^{n} \frac{\partial X_i}{\partial x_k}(\mathbf{x} + \sigma_i\mathbf{y}, t)y_k,$$

for some σ_i between 0 and 1. Squaring, and applying the Schwarz

---

† A set S in n-space is *convex* when the segment joining any two points of the set S lies entirely within S. This definition applies both to closed domains D and open regions $\mathscr{R}$.

inequality to the right side, we get

$$|X_i(\mathbf{x} + \mathbf{y}, t) - X_i(\mathbf{x}, t)|^2 \leq \left(\sum_{k=1}^{n} \left| \frac{\partial X_i}{\partial x_k} \right|^2 \right) \left(\sum_{k=1}^{n} |y_k|^2 \right) \leq nM^2|\mathbf{y}|^2.$$

Hence, summing over all components i, we obtain

$$|\mathbf{X}(\mathbf{x} + \mathbf{y}, t) - \mathbf{X}(\mathbf{x}, t)|^2 \leq n^2M^2|\mathbf{y}|^2.$$

Taking square roots, the Lipschitz condition follows with Lipschitz constant nM.

3   Well-set problems

For DE's to be useful in predicting the future behavior of a physical system from its present state, their solutions must exist, be unique, and depend continuously on their initial values. As stated in Chapter 1, § 9, an initial-value problem is said to be *well-set* when these conditions are satisfied. We now show that, if $\mathbf{X}$ satisfies a Lipschitz condition, the vector DE (2) defines a well-set initial-value problem.

We begin by proving uniqueness. As in the special case $n = 1$ of Chapter 1, §10, uniqueness does not follow from the continuity of $\mathbf{X}(\mathbf{x}, t)$ alone.

■ THEOREM 1 (Uniqueness Theorem).   *If the function* $\mathbf{X}(\mathbf{x}, t)$ *satisfies a Lipschitz condition* (4) *in a domain* $\mathscr{R}$, *there is at most one solution* $\mathbf{x}(t)$ *of the vector DE* (2) *which satisfies a given initial condition* $\mathbf{x}(a) = \mathbf{c}$ *in* $\mathscr{R}$.

The proof of this theorem parallels that of Theorem 5 of Chapter 1. We show that, if $\mathbf{x}(t)$ and $\mathbf{y}(t)$ are both solutions of (2) and if they are equal for one value of t, say $t = a$, it follows that $\mathbf{x}(t) \equiv \mathbf{y}(t)$ in any domain in which a Lipschitz condition is satisfied.

Consider the square of the n-dimensional distance between the two vectors $\mathbf{x}(t)$ and $\mathbf{y}(t)$. By definition, this is

$$\sigma(t) = \sum [x_k(t) - y_k(t)]^2 = |\mathbf{x}(t) - \mathbf{y}(t)|^2 \geq 0.$$

Differentiating $\sigma(t)$, and using the fact that $\mathbf{x}$ and $\mathbf{y}$ are solutions of the normal system (2), we get

$$\sigma'(t) = 2\sum [x_k(t) - y_k(t)][X_k(\mathbf{x}(t), t) - X_k(\mathbf{y}(t), t)]$$
$$= 2(\mathbf{x}(t) - \mathbf{y}(t)) \cdot [\mathbf{X}(\mathbf{x}(t), t) - \mathbf{X}(\mathbf{y}(t), t)].$$

By the Schwarz inequality, therefore, we have

$$\sigma'(t) \leq |\sigma'(t)| = 2|(\mathbf{x} - \mathbf{y}) \cdot (\mathbf{X}(\mathbf{x}, t) - \mathbf{X}(\mathbf{y}, t))|$$
$$\leq 2|\mathbf{x} - \mathbf{y}| \cdot |\mathbf{X}(\mathbf{x}, t) - \mathbf{X}(\mathbf{y}, t)| \leq 2L|\mathbf{x} - \mathbf{y}|^2 = 2L\sigma(t).$$

By the Corollary of Lemma 2 of Chapter 1, §10, it follows that if $\mathbf{x}(a) = \mathbf{y}(a)$, that is, if $\sigma(a) = 0$, then $\sigma(t) \equiv 0$ (that is, $|\mathbf{x}(t) - \mathbf{y}(t)|^2 \equiv 0$) for all $t \geq a$.

A similar argument works for $t < a$: replacing t by $-t$, we obtain

$$d\sigma/d(-t) \leq |\sigma'(t)| \leq 2L\sigma(t),$$

again using the preceding inequality.

We shall prove next that the solutions of a normal first-order system (2) depend continuously on their initial values.

■ Theorem 2 (Continuity Theorem).   *Let* $\mathbf{x}(t)$ *and* $\mathbf{y}(t)$ *be any two solutions of the vector* DE (2), *where* $\mathbf{X}(\mathbf{x}, t)$ *is continuous and satisfies the Lipschitz condition* (4). *Then*

$$|\mathbf{x}(a + h) - \mathbf{y}(a + h)| \leq e^{L|h|} |\mathbf{x}(a) - \mathbf{y}(a)|. \tag{5}$$

Proof — Replacing $a + t$ by $a - t$, we can always reduce to the case $h \geq 0$. Consider again $\sigma(t) = |\mathbf{x}(t) - \mathbf{y}(t)|^2$. As in the proof of Theorem 1,

$$\sigma'(t) = 2[\mathbf{x}(t) - \mathbf{y}(t)] \cdot [\mathbf{X}(\mathbf{x}(t) - \mathbf{X}(\mathbf{y}(t)] \leq 2L |\mathbf{x} - \mathbf{y}|^2 = 2L\sigma(t).$$

Applying Lemma 2 of Chapter 1, § 10 to $\sigma(t)$, we get $\sigma(a + h) \leq \sigma(a)e^{2Lh}$. Taking the square root of both sides, we get the desired result.

From Theorem 2 we can easily infer the following important property of the solutions of the DE (2).

■ Corollary.   *Let* $\mathbf{x}(t, \mathbf{c})$ *be the solution of the* DE (2) *satisfying the initial condition* $\mathbf{x}(a, \mathbf{c}) = \mathbf{c}$. *Let the hypotheses of Theorem 2 be satisfied, and let the functions* $\mathbf{x}(t, \mathbf{c})$ *be defined for* $|\mathbf{c} - \mathbf{c}^0| \leq K$ *and* $|t - a| \leq T$. *Then:*

   (a) $\mathbf{x}(t, \mathbf{c})$ *is a continuous function of both variables;*
   (b) *if* $\mathbf{c} \to \mathbf{c}^0$, *then* $\mathbf{x}(t, \mathbf{c}) \to \mathbf{x}(t, \mathbf{c}^0)$ *uniformly for* $|t - a| \leq T$.

Both properties follow from the inequality (5).

In view of the preceding results, it remains only to prove an *existence* theorem, in order to show that the initial value problem is well-set for normal first-order systems (1). This will be done in Theorems 6–8 below.

EXERCISES A

1. Show that $u = x + y + z$ and $v = x^2 + y^2 + z^2$ are integrals of the linear system $dx/dt = y - z$, $dy/dt = z - x$, $dz/dt = x - y$. Interpret geometrically.
2. Reduce each of the following DE's to an equivalent first-order system, and determine in which domain or domains (e.g., entire plane, any bounded region, a half-plane, etc.) the resulting system satisfies a Lipschitz condition:

   (a) $d^3x/dt^3 + x^2 = 1$,   (b) $d^2x/dt^2 = x^{-1/2}$,   (c) $d^3x/dt^3 = (1 + (d^2x/dt^2)^2)^{1/2}$.

3. Reduce the following system to normal form, and determine in which domains a Lipschitz condition is satisfied:

$$du/dt + dv/dt = u^2 + v^2, \qquad 2du/dt + 3dv/dt = 2uv.$$

4. Show that the vector-valued function $(t + be^{at}, -e^{-at}/ab)$ satisfies the DE (2) with $\mathbf{X} = (1 - (1/x_2), 1/(x_1 - t))$, for any nonzero constants a, b.

5. State and prove a uniqueness theorem for the DE $y'' = F(x, y, y')$, with $F \in \mathscr{C}^1$. [HINT: Reduce to a first-order system, and use Theorem 1.]

6. (a) Show that any solution of the linear system $dx/dt = y$, $dy/dt = z$, $dz/dt = x$ satisfies the vector DE $d^3\mathbf{x}/dt^3 = \mathbf{x}$, where $\mathbf{x} = (x, y, z)$.

   (b) Show that every solution of the preceding system can be written $\mathbf{x} = e^t\mathbf{a} + e^{-t/2}[\mathbf{b} \cos \sqrt{3}\,t/2 + \mathbf{c} \sin \sqrt{3}\,t/2]$, for suitable constant vectors $\mathbf{a}$, $\mathbf{b}$ and $\mathbf{c}$.

   (c) Express $\mathbf{a}$, $\mathbf{b}$ and $\mathbf{c}$ in terms of $\mathbf{x}(0)$, $\mathbf{x}'(0)$ and $\mathbf{x}''(0)$.

7. Show that the general solution of the system $dx/dt = x^2/y$, $dy/dt = x/2$ is $x = 1/(at + b)^2$, $y = -1/[2a(at + b)]$.

8. Show that the curves defined parametrically as solutions $dx/dt = \partial F/\partial x$, $dy/dt = \partial F/\partial y$, $dz/dt = \partial F/\partial z$ are orthogonal to the surfaces $F(x, y, z) = $ constant. What differentiability condition on F must be assumed to make the above system satisfy a Lipschitz condition?

9. (a) Find a system of first-order DE's satisfied by all curves orthogonal to the spheres $x^2 + y^2 + z^2 = 2ax - a^2$.

   (b) By integrating the preceding system, find the orthogonal trajectories in question. Describe the solution curves geometrically.

10. (a) In what sense is the following statement inexact? "The general solution of the DE $cy'' = (1 + y'^2)^{3/2}$ is the circle $(x - a)^2 + (y - b)^2 = c^2$, where a and b are arbitrary constants."

    (b) Correct the preceding statement, distinguishing carefully between explicit, implicit, and multiple-valued functions.

11. (a) Given $\dot{x} = a(t)x + b(t)y$ and $\dot{y} = c(t)x + d(t)y$, prove that, if $b \neq 0$,

$$\ddot{x} - [(a + d) + \dot{b}/b)]\dot{x} + [(ad - bc) - \dot{a} + (a\dot{b}/b)]x = 0.$$

    (b) Given that $\ddot{x} + p(t)\dot{x} + q(t)x = r(t)$, prove that, if $q \neq 0$, $v = \dot{x}$ satisfies

$$\ddot{v} + [p - (\dot{q}/q)]\dot{v} + [\dot{p} + q - (\dot{q}p/q)]v = \dot{r} - r\dot{q}/q.$$

12. For which values of a, β does the function $x^a y^\beta$ satisfy a Lipschitz condition: (a) in the open square $0 < x, y < 1$, (b) in the quadrant $0 < x, y < +\infty$, (c) in the part of the quadrant of (b) exterior to the square of (a)?

13. For each of the following scalar-valued functions of a vector $\mathbf{x}$ and each of the following domains, state whether a Lipschitz condition is satisfied or not: (a) $x_1 + x_2 + \cdots + x_n$, (b) $x_1x_2 \cdots x_n$, (c) $y/(x^2 + y^2)$, (d) $|\mathbf{x}|$, in (i) $|\mathbf{x}| < 1$, (ii) $-\infty < x_k < \infty$, (iii) $-\infty < x_1 < \infty$, $|x_k| < 1$, $k \geqq 2$.

14. Let $\mathbf{X}(\mathbf{x}, t) = (X_1(\mathbf{x}, t), \ldots, X_n(\mathbf{x}, t))$ be a vector-valued function. Show that $\mathbf{X}$ satisfies a Lipschitz condition if and only if each scalar-valued component X_i satisfies a Lipschitz condition, and relate the Lipschitz constant of $\mathbf{X}$ to those of the X_i.

4   Continuity

We shall now prove a much stronger continuity property of the solutions of systems of DE's, namely that the solutions of (2) vary continuously when the function **X** varies continuously. Loosely speaking, the solution of a DE depends continuously upon the DE for given initial values.

■ THEOREM 3.   *Let* **x**(*t*) *and* **y**(*t*) *satisfy the* DE's

$$d\mathbf{x}/dt = \mathbf{X}(\mathbf{x}, t) \qquad and \qquad d\mathbf{y}/dt = \mathbf{Y}(\mathbf{y}, t),$$

respectively, on $a \le t \le b$. *Further, let the functions* **X** *and* **Y** *be defined and continuous in a common domain* D, *and let*

$$|\mathbf{X}(\mathbf{z}, t) - \mathbf{Y}(\mathbf{z}, t)| \le \epsilon, \qquad a \le t \le b, \quad \mathbf{z} \in D. \tag{6}$$

Finally, let **X**(**x**, *t*) *satisfy the Lipschitz condition* (4). *Then*

$$|\mathbf{x}(t) - \mathbf{y}(t)| \le |\mathbf{x}(a) - \mathbf{y}(a)| \, e^{L|t-a|} + \frac{\epsilon}{L} [e^{L|t-a|} - 1]. \tag{7}$$

The function **Y** is not required to satisfy a Lipschitz condition.

Proof — Consider the real-valued function $\sigma(t)$, defined for $a \le t \le b$ by

$$\sigma(t) = |\mathbf{x}(t) - \mathbf{y}(t)|^2 = \sum_{k=1}^{n} [x_k(t) - y_k(t)]^2.$$

From the last expression we see that σ is differentiable. Its derivative can be written in the form

$$\sigma'(t) = 2[\mathbf{X}(\mathbf{x}(t), t) - \mathbf{Y}(\mathbf{y}(t), t)] \cdot [\mathbf{x}(t) - \mathbf{y}(t)]$$
$$= 2\{[\mathbf{X}(\mathbf{x}(t), t) - \mathbf{X}(\mathbf{y}(t), t)] \cdot [\mathbf{x}(t) - \mathbf{y}(t)]\}$$
$$+ 2\{[\mathbf{X}(\mathbf{y}(t), t) - \mathbf{Y}(\mathbf{y}(t), t)] \cdot [\mathbf{x}(t) - \mathbf{y}(t)]\}.$$

We now apply the triangle inequality to the right side, and then the Schwarz inequality to each of the two terms of the last expression. This gives the inequality

$$|\sigma'(t)| \le 2|\mathbf{X}(\mathbf{x}(t), t) - \mathbf{X}(\mathbf{y}(t), t)| \, |\mathbf{x}(t) - \mathbf{y}(t)|$$
$$+ 2|\mathbf{X}(\mathbf{y}(t), t) - \mathbf{Y}(\mathbf{y}(t), t)| \, |\mathbf{x}(t) - \mathbf{y}(t)|.$$

To the first term on the right side we now apply the Lipschitz condition which **X** satisfies; to the second term, we apply (6). This gives the following differential inequality for σ:

$$\sigma'(t) \le 2L\sigma(t) + 2\epsilon\sqrt{\sigma(t)}. \tag{8}$$

The theorem is now an immediate consequence of the following

■ **Lemma.**   *Let $\sigma(t) \geq 0$, $a \leq t \leq b$ be a differentiable function satisfying the differential inequality* (8). *Then*

$$\sigma(t) \leq [\sqrt{\sigma(a)}\, e^{L(t-a)} + \frac{\epsilon}{L}(e^{L(t-a)} - 1)]^2, \qquad a \leq t \leq b. \qquad (9)$$

Proof — We shall apply Theorem 7 of Chapter 1 on differential inequalities to (8). The right side of (8), the function $F(\sigma, t) = 2L\sigma + 2\epsilon\sqrt{\sigma}$, satisfies a Lipschitz condition in any half plane $\sigma \geq \sigma_0$ which does not include the line $\sigma = 0$. Therefore, Theorem 7 of Chapter 1 applies when $\sigma(a) > 0$. For, if $\sigma(a) > 0$, then the solution of the DE

$$du/dt = 2\epsilon\sqrt{u} + 2Lu, \qquad u \geq 0, \qquad (9')$$

which satisfies the initial condition $u(a) = \sigma(a)$, will have a nonnegative derivative, and therefore will remain, for $t > a$, within the half-plane $u \geq \sigma(a)$.

The DE $(9')$ is a Bernoulli DE (Chapter 1, Exercise B2). To find the solution satisfying $u(a) = \sigma(a)$, make the substitution $v(t) = \sqrt{u(t)}$. (The square root is well-defined because $u(t) \geq \sigma(a) > 0$.) This gives the equivalent DE

$$2vv' = 2\epsilon v + 2Lv^2.$$

If $u(a) > 0$, it follows that $u(t) > 0$ for all later t, since the derivative of u is positive. This gives $v(t) > 0$, and so we can divide both sides of this DE by v. The resulting DE is $v' - Lv = \epsilon$, an inhomogeneous linear DE (Chapter 1, § 5, Example 2), whose solution satisfying the initial condition $v(a) = \sqrt{u(a)}$ is the function

$$\sqrt{u(t)} = v(t) = \sqrt{u(a)}\, e^{L(t-a)} + (\epsilon/L)(e^{L(t-a)} - 1).$$

On applying Theorem 7 of Chapter 1, we obtain the inequality (9).

We must now consider the case $\sigma(a) = 0$ when Theorem 7 of Chapter 1 does not apply directly. In this case, we consider the solution $u_n(t)$ of the differential equation $(9')$ which satisfies the initial condition $u_n(a) = 1/n$. Since the right side of $(9')$ is positive, $u_n(t)$ is an increasing function of t. We shall prove that $u_n(t) \geq \sigma(t)$. Suppose that at some point $t_1 > a$ we had $u_n(t_1) < \sigma(t_1)$. Then among all numbers t with $a < t < t_1$ such that $u_n(t) \geq \sigma(t)$ there would be a largest, say t_0. Hence, we would have $u_n(t_0) = \sigma(t_0) > 0$ and $u_n(t) < \sigma(t)$ for $t_0 < t \leq t_1$. But this is impossible by what we have already proved, since in the interval $t_0 \leq t \leq t_1$ the functions $u(t)$ and $\sigma(t)$ stay away from 0, and therefore a Lipschitz condition is satisfied for $(9')$. We infer that

$$\sigma(t) \leq [n^{-1/2}e^{L|t-a|} + (\epsilon/L)(e^{L|t-a|} - 1)]^2$$

for all $n > 0$. Letting $n \to \infty$, we obtain the inequality (9) also in this case.

The following corollary follows immediately from Theorem 3.

■ COROLLARY. *Let* $\mathbf{X}(\mathbf{x}, t; \epsilon)$ *be a set of continuous functions of* $\mathbf{x}$ *and* t, *defined in the domain* D: $|t - a| \leq T$, $|\mathbf{x} - \mathbf{c}| \leq K$ *for all sufficiently small values of a parameter* ϵ. *Suppose that, as* $\epsilon \to 0$, *the functions converge uniformly in* D *to a function* $\mathbf{X}(\mathbf{x}, t)$ *which satisfies a Lipschitz condition. For each* $\epsilon > 0$, *let* $\mathbf{x}(t; \epsilon)$ *be a solution of* $d\mathbf{x}/dt = \mathbf{X}(\mathbf{x}, t; \epsilon)$ *satisfying the initial condition* $\mathbf{x}(a; \epsilon) = \mathbf{c}$. *Then the* $\mathbf{x}(t; \epsilon)$ *converge to the solution of* $d\mathbf{x}/dt = \mathbf{X}(\mathbf{x}, y)$ *satisfying* $\mathbf{x}(a) = \mathbf{c}$, *uniformly in any closed subinterval* $|t - a| \leq T_1 \leq T$ *where all functions are defined.*

EXERCISES B

1. Let $\mathbf{X}$ and $\mathbf{Y}$ be as in Theorem 3, and let $\mathbf{x}(a) = \mathbf{y}(a)$. Show that $|\mathbf{x}(t) - \mathbf{y}(t)|/|t - a|$ remains bounded as $t \to a$.

2. Let $f(x)$ and $g(x)$ be respective solutions of $y' = xy$ and $y' = y \sin x$ such that $f(0) = g(0)$. Show that $|f(x) - g(x)| < \frac{1}{640}$ for $|x| < \frac{1}{2}$.

Bound the differences between solutions having the same initial value $y(0) = c$, for the pairs of DE's in Exercises 3 through 5.

3. $y' = \sin xy$ and $y' = xy - \dfrac{x^3 y^3}{3!} + \dfrac{x^5 y^5}{5!} + \cdots + (-1)^n \dfrac{(xy)^{2n+1}}{(2n+1)!}$.

4. $y' = e^y$ and $y' = 1 + y + \cdots + \dfrac{y^n}{n!}$.

5. $d^2\theta/dt^2 = -\theta$ and $d^2\theta/dt^2 = -\sin\theta$.

6. To what explicit formulas does formula (7) specialize for the system $d\mathbf{x}/dt = \mathbf{X}(t)$? For the DE $dx/dt = ax + b$?

7*. Show that the conclusion of Theorem 3 holds if only a one-sided Lipschitz condition $(\mathbf{x} - \mathbf{y}) \cdot (\mathbf{X}(\mathbf{x}, t) - \mathbf{X}(\mathbf{y}, t)) \leq L |\mathbf{x} - \mathbf{y}|^2$ is assumed for $\mathbf{X}$.

8. Let $\mathbf{X}(\mathbf{x}, t, s)$ be continuous for $|\mathbf{x} - \mathbf{c}| \leq K$, $|t - a| \leq T$, and $|s - s_0| \leq S$, and let it satisfy $|\mathbf{X}(\mathbf{x}, t, s) - \mathbf{X}(\mathbf{y}, t, s))| \leq L |\mathbf{x} - \mathbf{y}|$. Show that the solution $\mathbf{x}(t, s)$ of $\mathbf{x}' = \mathbf{X}(\mathbf{x}, t, s)$ satisfying $\mathbf{x}(a, s) = \mathbf{c}$ is a continuous function of s.

5* Normal systems

Many important mathematical problems have normal systems of DE's of order $m > 1$ as their natural formulation. We now give two examples, and show how to reduce every normal system of ordinary DE's to a first-order system.

■ DEFINITION. *A* normal system *of ordinary* DE's *for the unknown functions* $\xi_1(t), \xi_2(t), \ldots, \xi_m(t)$ *is any system of the form*

$$\frac{d^{n(k)}\xi_k}{dt^{n(k)}} = F_k\left(\xi_1, \frac{d\xi_1}{dt}, \ldots; \xi_2, \frac{d\xi_2}{dt}, \ldots; \xi_m, \frac{d\xi_m}{dt}, \ldots; t\right), \qquad (10)$$

$k = 1, \ldots, m$, in which for each k only derivatives $d^p \xi_j / dt^p$ of any ξ_j of orders $p < n(j)$ occur on the right side.

In other words, the requirement is that the derivative $d^{n(k)} \xi_k / dt^{n(k)}$ of highest order of each ξ_k constitutes the left-hand side of one equation and occurs nowhere else.

■ THEOREM 4.   *Each normal system* (10) *of ordinary* DE's *is equivalent to a first-order normal system* (1) (*with* $n \geq m$).

Proof — Each function F_k appearing on the right side of (10) is a function of several real variables. Denote these variables by $x_1, x_2, \ldots, x_n, t$, where $n = n_1 + \cdots + n_m$. We now construct a system for $x_1, \ldots, x_n$ by replacing each derivative $d^p \xi_j / dt^p$ of ξ_j of order $p < n(j)$ by a new variable, that is, by setting

$$x_1 = \xi_1, \ x_2 = d\xi_1/dt, \ x_3 = d^2\xi_1/dt^2, \ \ldots, x_{n_1} = d^{n_1-1}\xi_1/dt^{n_1-1},$$

$$x_{n_1+1} = \xi_2, \ x_{n_1+2} = d\xi_2/dt, \ \ldots, \ x_{n_1+n_2} = d^{n_2-1}\xi_2/dt^{n_1-1}, \text{ etc.}$$

The equivalent system for the x_k is then the system
$$dx_1/dt = x_2, \ dx_2/dt = x_3, \ \ldots, \ dx_{n_1-1}/dt = x_{n_1}, \ dx_{n_1}/dt = F_1(x_1, \ldots, x_n),$$

$$dx_{n_1+1}/dt = x_{n_1+2}, \ \ldots, \ dx_{n_1+n_2}/dt = F_2(x_1, \ldots, x_n, t), \text{ etc.}$$

It is clear that this system satisfies the requirements of the theorem.

The *initial value problem* for the normal system (10) is the problem of finding a solution for which the variables

$$\xi_1, d\xi_1/dt, \ldots, d^{n_1-1}\xi_1/dt^{n_2-1}, \ldots, d^{n_m-1}\xi_m/dt^{n_m-1}$$

assume given values at $t = a$.

It is easily seen from the proof of Theorem 4 that, if the functions F_k, considered as functions of the vector variable $\mathbf{x} = (x_1, \ldots, x_n)$ and t, satisfy Lipschitz conditions, then so do the functions $X_k(\mathbf{x}, t)$ in the associated first-order systems (1). This gives the following.

■ COROLLARY.   *If the functions* F_k *of the normal system* (10) *satisfy Lipschitz conditions in a domain* D, *then the system has at most one solution in* D *satisfying given initial conditions.*

EXAMPLE 2   (the n-body problem).   Let n mass points with masses m_j attract each other according to an inverse αth power law of attraction. Then, in suitable units, their position coordinates satisfy a normal system of $3n$ second-order differential equations of the form

$$d^2x_i/dt^2 = \sum_{j \neq i} m_j(x_j - x_i)/r_{ij}^{\alpha+1}.$$

and the same is true for d^2y_i/dt^2 and d^2z_i/dt^2, where

$$r_{ij} = [(x_i - x_j)^2 + (y_i - y_j)^2 + (z_i - z_j)^2]^{1/2} = r_{ji}.$$

Then Theorem 1 asserts that the initial positions $(x_i(0), y_i(0), z_i(0))$ and velocities $(x_i'(0), y_i'(0), z_i'(0))$ of the mass points *uniquely* determine their subsequent motion (if any such motion is possible). That is, the uniqueness theorem asserts the *determinacy of the n-body problem.* This theorem, taken with the continuity theorem, and Theorem 8 to follow, asserts that the n-body problem is well-set.

To see this, let $\xi = (\xi_1, \ldots, \xi_{6n})$ be the vector with components defined as follows, for $k = 1, \ldots, n$.

$$\xi_k = x_k, \quad \xi_{n+k} = y_k, \quad \xi_{2n+k} = z_k,$$

$$\xi_{3n+k} = x_k', \quad \xi_{4n+k} = y_k', \quad \xi_{5n+k} = z_k'.$$

In this notation, the system (10) is equivalent to a first-order normal system of the form (1):

$$\frac{d\xi_h}{dt} = F_h(\xi) = \begin{cases} \xi_{h+3n}, & h = 1, \ldots, 3n, \\ \sum_j m_j(\xi_{j-3n} - \xi_{h-3n})/r_{hk(j)}^{\alpha+1}, & h = 3n + 1, \ldots, 6n, \end{cases}$$

where $k(j)$ is the remainder of j when divided by n, and summation is extended to those $n - 1$ values of j such that $(h - 1)/n$ and $(j - 1)/n$ are distinct and have the same integral part. So long as no $r_{hj} = 0$, that is, so long as there are *no collisions,* a Lipschitz condition is evidently satisfied by the functions F_h. When one or more r_{hj} vanish, however, some of the functions F_h become *singular* (they are undefined) and Theorem 1 is inapplicable.

EXAMPLE 3. The *Frenet-Serret formulas*† comprise the following normal system of first-order DE's:

$$\frac{d\alpha}{ds} = \frac{\beta}{R(s)}, \quad \frac{d\beta}{ds} = -\frac{\alpha}{R(s)} + \frac{\gamma}{T(s)}, \quad \frac{d\gamma}{ds} = -\frac{\beta}{T(s)},$$

where α, β and $\gamma = \alpha \times \beta$ are three-dimensional‡ vectors: the unit tangent, normal, and binormal vectors to a space curve. The curvature $\kappa(s) = 1/R(s)$ and torsion $\tau(s) = 1/T(s)$ are functions of the arc length s; $\alpha = d\mathbf{x}/ds$ is the derivative of vector position with respect to arc length.

---

† Widder, p. 101.
‡ $\alpha \times \beta$ denotes the cross product of the vectors α and β.

If we let $\boldsymbol{\eta}(s)$ be the nine-dimensional vector $(\alpha_1, \alpha_2, \alpha_3, \beta_1, \beta_2, \beta_3,$ $\gamma_1, \gamma_2, \gamma_3)$, the system can be written as the first-order vector DE

$$d\boldsymbol{\eta}/ds = \mathbf{Y}(\boldsymbol{\eta}; s).$$

Here $\mathbf{Y}(\boldsymbol{\eta}; s)$ is obtained by setting

$$Y_h(\eta; s) = \begin{cases} \kappa(s)\eta_{h+3}, & h = 1, 2, 3, \\ -\kappa(s)\eta_{h-3} + \tau(s)\eta_{h+3}, & h = 4, 5, 6, \\ -\tau(s)\eta_{h-3}, & h = 7, 8, 9. \end{cases}$$

If $\kappa(s)$ and $\tau(s)$ are bounded, the function $\mathbf{Y}(\boldsymbol{\eta}; s)$ satisfies a Lipschitz condition (4) with $L = \sup\{|\kappa(s)| + |\tau(s)|\}$; hence, for given initial tangent direction $\boldsymbol{\alpha}(0)$, normal direction $\boldsymbol{\beta}(0)$ perpendicular to $\boldsymbol{\alpha}(0)$, and binormal direction $\boldsymbol{\gamma}(0) = \boldsymbol{\alpha}(0) \times \boldsymbol{\beta}(0)$, there is only one set of directions satisfying the Frenet-Serret formulas. This proves that *a curve is determined up to a rigid motion by its curvature and torsion.*†

EXERCISES C

1. Find all solutions of the system

$$x\frac{d^2x}{dt^2} - y\frac{d^2y}{dt^2} = 0, \qquad \frac{d^2x}{dt^2} + \frac{d^2y}{dt^2} + x + y = 0.$$

2. Show that, if $a_{ihk} = -a_{khi}$, then Σx_i^2 is an integral of the system

$$dx_i/dt = \Sigma\, a_{ihk}\, x_h\, x_k\,.$$

3. The *one-body* problem is defined in space by the system

$$\ddot{x} = -xf(r), \qquad \ddot{y} = -yf(r), \qquad \ddot{z} = -zf(r), \qquad r^2 = x^2 + y^2 + z^2.$$

  (a) Show that the components $L = y\dot{z} - z\dot{y}$, $M = z\dot{x} - x\dot{z}$, and $N = x\dot{y} - y\dot{x}$ of the angular momentum vector (L, M, N) are integrals of this system.
  (b) Show that any solution of the system lies in a plane $Ax + By + Cz = 0$.
  (c) Construct an energy integral for the system.
4. Let $\alpha = 2$ in the n-body problem (Newton's law of gravitation), and define the potential energy as $V = -\sum_{i<j} m_i m_j / r_{ij}$.
  (a) Show that the n-body problem is defined by the system

$$m_i\, d^2x_i/dt^2 = -\partial V/\partial x_i\,.$$

  (b) Show that the total energy $\Sigma\, m_i \dot{x}_i^2/2 + V(\mathbf{x})$ is an integral of the system.
  (c) Show that the components $\Sigma\, m_i \dot{x}_i$, etc., of linear momentum are integrals.
  (d) Do the same as in (c) for the components $\Sigma\, m_i(y_i\dot{z} - z_i\dot{y}_i)$, etc., of angular momentum.
5. Show that the general solution of the vector DE $d^3\mathbf{x}/dt^3 = d\mathbf{x}/dt$ is $\mathbf{a} + \mathbf{b}e^t + \mathbf{c}e^{-t}$, where $\mathbf{a}, \mathbf{b}, \mathbf{c}$ are arbitrary vectors.

---

† This theorem of differential geometry can fail when $\kappa(s)$ is zero, because $\boldsymbol{\beta} = x''(s)/|x''(s)|$ is then geometrically undefined, so that the Frenet-Serret formulas do not necessarily hold.

Exercises 6–9 refer to the Frenet-Serret formulas.

6. Show that, if $\boldsymbol{\alpha}(s)$, $\boldsymbol{\beta}(s)$, $\boldsymbol{\gamma}(s)$ are orthogonal vectors of length one when $s = 0$, this is true for all s, provided they satisfy the Frenet-Serret formulas.

7. Show that if $1/T(s) \equiv 0$, and $d\mathbf{x}/ds = \boldsymbol{\alpha}$, the curve $\mathbf{x}(s)$ lies in a plane. [HINT: Consider the dot product $\boldsymbol{\gamma} \cdot \mathbf{x}$.]

8*. Show that, if $T = kR$ (k constant), the curve $\mathbf{x}(s)$ lies on a cylinder.

9*. Show that, if $R/T + (TR')' = 0$, the curve $\mathbf{x}(s)$ lies on a sphere.

6 Equivalent integral equation

We now establish the *existence* of a solution of a normal first-order system of DE's for arbitrary initial values. To this end, it is convenient to reduce the problem to an equivalent one where integrals take the place of derivatives. One reason why this restatement of the problem makes it easier to treat is that we do not have to deal with differentiable functions directly, but only with continuous functions and their integrals. Every continuous function has an integral, while many continuous functions are not differentiable.

■ THEOREM 5. *Let $\mathbf{X}(\mathbf{x}; t)$ be a continuous vector function of the variables $\mathbf{x}$ and t. Then any solution $\mathbf{x}(t)$ of the vector integral equation*

$$\mathbf{x}(t) = \mathbf{c} + \int_a^t \mathbf{X}(\mathbf{x}(s), s) \, ds \qquad (11)$$

is a solution of the vector DE (2) which satisfies the initial condition $\mathbf{x}(a) = \mathbf{c}$, and conversely.

The vector integral equation (11) is a system of integral equations for r unknown scalar functions $x_1(t), \ldots, x_r(t)$, the components of the vector function $\mathbf{x}(t)$. That is,

$$x_k(t) = c_k + \int_a^t X_k(x_1(s), x_2(s), \ldots, x_r(s), s) \, ds, \qquad 1 \leq k \leq r.$$

(In §§ 6-7, we will deal with r-dimensional vectors.)

Proof — If $\mathbf{x}(t)$ satisfies the integral equation (11), then $\mathbf{x}(a) = \mathbf{c}$ and, by the Fundamental Theorem of the Calculus, $x_k'(t) = X_k(\mathbf{x}(t); t)$ for $k = 1, \ldots, r$, so that $\mathbf{x}(t)$ also satisfies the system (2). Conversely, the Fundamental Theorem of the Calculus shows that $x_k(t) = x_k(a) + \int_a^t x_k'(s) \, ds$ for all continuously differentiable functions $\mathbf{x}(t)$. If $\mathbf{x}(t)$ satisfies the normal system of DE's (2), then $\mathbf{x}(t) = \mathbf{x}(a) + \int_a^t \mathbf{X}(\mathbf{x}(s); s) \, ds$; if, in addition, $\mathbf{x}(a) = \mathbf{c}$, the integral equation (11) is obtained, q.e.d.

EXAMPLE 4. Consider the DE $dx/dt = e^x$ for the initial condition $x(0) = 0$. Separating variables, we see that this initial-value problem has the (unique) solution $1 - e^{-x} = t$, $x = -\ln (1 - t)$. Theorem 5 shows that it is equivalent to the integral equation $x(t) = \int_0^t e^{x(s)} \, ds$, which therefore has the same (unique) solution. Since the solution is defined only in the interval $-\infty < t < 1$, we see again that only a *local* existence theorem can be proved.

Operator interpretation. The problem of finding a solution to the integral equation (11) can be rephrased in terms of operators on vector functions as follows. We define an operator $\mathbf{y} = U[\mathbf{x}] = U\mathbf{x}$, transforming vector functions $\mathbf{x}$ into vector functions $\mathbf{y}$ by the identity

$$\mathbf{y}(t) = U[\mathbf{x}(t)] = \mathbf{c} + \int_a^t \mathbf{X}(\mathbf{x}(s), s) \, ds. \tag{12}$$

If $\mathbf{X}(\mathbf{x}, t)$ is defined for all $\mathbf{x}$ in the slab $|t - a| \leq T$ and is continuous, the domain of this operator can be taken to be the family of continuous vector functions defined in the interval $|t - a| \leq T$; its range consists of all continuously differentiable vector functions defined in this interval, satisfying $\mathbf{y}(a) = \mathbf{c}$. In this case, Theorem 5 has the following.

■ COROLLARY.   *The* DE *(2) has a solution satisfying* $\mathbf{x}(a) = \mathbf{c}$ *if and only if the mapping* U *of* (12) *has a fixpoint in* $\mathscr{C}[a, b]$.

However, if $\mathbf{X}(\mathbf{x}, t)$ is not defined for all $\mathbf{x}$, the domain of the operator U has to be determined with care. This is done in Theorem 8 below.

7   Successive approximation

Picard had the idea of iterating the integral operator U defined by (12), and proving that, for any initial trial function $\mathbf{x}^0$, the successive integral transforms (Picard approximations)

$$\mathbf{x}^0, \mathbf{x}^1 = U\mathbf{x}_0, \qquad \mathbf{x}^2 = U^2[\mathbf{x}^0] = U[\mathbf{x}^1], \qquad \mathbf{x}^3 = U[\mathbf{x}^2], \ldots$$

converge to a solution. This idea works under various sets of hypotheses; one such set is the following.

■ THEOREM 6.   *Let the vector function* $\mathbf{X}(\mathbf{x}; t)$ *be continuous and satisfy the Lipschitz condition (4) on the interval* $|t - a| \leq T$ *for all* $\mathbf{x}, \mathbf{y}$. *Then, for any constant vector* $\mathbf{c}$, *the vector* DE $\mathbf{x}'(t) = \mathbf{X}(\mathbf{x}; t)$ *has a solution defined on the interval* $|t - a| \leq T$, *which satisfies the initial condition* $\mathbf{x}(a) = \mathbf{c}$.

Proof — As remarked at the end of the preceding section, the operator U is defined by (12) for all functions $\mathbf{x}(t)$ continuous for $|t - a| \leq T$. In particular, since $U\mathbf{x}$ is again a continuous function on $|t - a| \leq T$, the function $\mathbf{x}^2 = U^2[\mathbf{x}] = U^2\mathbf{x}$ is well-defined. Similarly, the *iterates* $U^3\mathbf{x}$, $U^4\mathbf{x}$, etc., are well-defined. These iterates will always converge; a typical case is depicted in Figure 6.1.

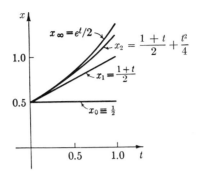

FIGURE 6.1   Picard Approximation for $dx/dt = x$, $x(0) = 1/2$.

■ LEMMA.   *If* $\mathbf{x}^0(t) \equiv \mathbf{c}$, *the sequence of functions defined recursively by*
$$\mathbf{x}^1 = U[\mathbf{x}^0], \quad \mathbf{x}^2 = U[\mathbf{x}^1] = U^2[\mathbf{x}^0], \quad \ldots, \quad \mathbf{x}^n = U[\mathbf{x}^{n-1}] = U^n[\mathbf{x}^0], \ldots$$
converges uniformly for $|t - a| \leq T$.

Proof — Let $M = \sup_{|t-a| \leq T} |\mathbf{X}(\mathbf{c}; t)|$; the number M is finite because continuous functions are bounded on a closed interval. Without loss of generality we can assume that $a = 0$ and $t \geq a$, that is, that the interval is $0 \leq t \leq T$; the proof for general a and for $t < a$ can be deduced from this case by the substitutions $t \to t + a$ and $t \to a - t$.

By the basic inequality (3) for vector-valued functions, the function $\mathbf{x}^1(t)$ satisfies the inequality

$$|\mathbf{x}^1(t) - \mathbf{x}^0(t)| = \left| \int_0^t \mathbf{X}(\mathbf{x}^0(s), s) \, ds \right| \leq \int_0^t |\mathbf{X}(\mathbf{x}^0, s)| \, ds \leq M \int_0^t ds = Mt. \quad (13)$$

Again, by (3), the function $\mathbf{x}^2 = U[\mathbf{x}^1]$ satisfies the inequality

$$|\mathbf{x}^2(t) - \mathbf{x}^1(t)| = \left| \int_0^t [\mathbf{X}(\mathbf{x}^1(s), s) - \mathbf{X}(\mathbf{x}^0(s), s)] \, ds \right|$$
$$\leq \int_0^t |\mathbf{X}(\mathbf{x}^1(s), s) - \mathbf{X}(\mathbf{x}^0(s), s)| \, ds.$$

We now use the assumption that the function $\mathbf{X}$ satisfies a Lipschitz condition with Lipschitz constant L. This gives, by (13), the inequality

$$|\mathbf{x}^2(t) - \mathbf{x}^1(t)| \leq \int_0^t |\mathbf{X}(\mathbf{x}^1(s), s) - \mathbf{X}(\mathbf{x}^0(s), s)| \, ds$$
$$\leq \int_0^t L|\mathbf{x}^1(s) - \mathbf{x}^0(s)| \, ds \leq L \int_0^t Ms \, ds = LMt^2/2.$$

Similarly, for any $n = 1, 2, 3, \ldots,$

$$|\mathbf{x}^{n+1}(t) - \mathbf{x}^n(t)| \leqq \int_0^t |\mathbf{X}(\mathbf{x}^n(s), s) - \mathbf{X}(\mathbf{x}^{n-1}(s), s)| \, ds$$

$$\leqq L \int_0^t |\mathbf{x}^n(s) - \mathbf{x}^{n-1}(s)| \, ds.$$

We now proceed by induction. Assuming that

$$|\mathbf{x}^n(t) - \mathbf{x}^{n-1}(t)| \leqq (M/L)(Lt)^n/n!,$$

we infer that

$$|\mathbf{x}^{n+1}(t) - \mathbf{x}^n(t)| \leqq L\left(\frac{M}{L}\right) \int_0^t \frac{(Ls)^n}{n!} \, ds = M(Lt)^{n+1}/L(n+1)! \quad (14)$$

Next, we show that the sequence of functions $\mathbf{x}^n(t)$ $(n = 0, 1, 2, \ldots)$ is uniformly convergent for $0 \leqq t \leqq T$. Indeed, the infinite series

$$(M/L) \sum_{n=0}^{\infty} (Lt)^{n+1}/(n+1)!$$

of positive terms is convergent to $(M/L)(e^{Lt} - 1)$, and uniformly convergent for $0 \leqq t \leqq T$. Hence, by the Comparison Test,[†] the series $x^0(t) + \sum_{k=0}^{\infty} [\mathbf{x}^{k+1}(t) - \mathbf{x}^k(t)]$ is uniformly convergent for $0 \leqq t \leqq T$. The nth partial sum of this series is the function $\mathbf{x}^n(t)$. It follows that the sequence of functions $\mathbf{x}^n(t)$ is uniformly convergent. This completes the proof of the lemma.

To complete the proof of Theorem 6, let $\mathbf{x}^\infty(t)$ denote the limit function of the sequence $\mathbf{x}^n(t)$; it suffices by Theorem 5 to show that $\mathbf{x}^\infty(t)$ is a solution of the integral equation (11). To this end, we consider the limit of the equations $\mathbf{x}^{n+1} = U[\mathbf{x}^n]$, namely the equations

$$\mathbf{x}^{n+1}(t) = \mathbf{c} + \int_0^t \mathbf{X}(\mathbf{x}^n(s), s) \, ds.$$

The left side converges uniformly, by the preceding lemma. By the Lipschitz condition, $|\mathbf{X}(\mathbf{x}^m(s), s) - \mathbf{X}(\mathbf{x}^n(s), s)| \leqq L|\mathbf{x}^m(s) - \mathbf{x}^n(s)|$, and so the integrand on the right side also converges uniformly. Since the integrands on the right side form a uniformly convergent sequence, their indefinite integrals are also uniformly convergent[‡]; hence, passing to the limit, we have

$$\mathbf{x}^\infty(t) = \mathbf{c} + \int_0^t \mathbf{X}(\mathbf{x}^\infty(s), s) \, ds.$$

This demonstrates (11) and completes the proof of Theorem 6.

---

† Courant and John, p. 535; see also Widder, p. 285.
‡ Courant and John, p. 537; Widder, p. 304.

EXERCISES D

In Exercises 1 through 5, solve the integral equations specified.

1. $u(t) = 1 + \int_0^t su(s)\,ds.$ 2. $u(t) = 1 + \int_0^t su^2(s)\,ds.$
3. $u(t) + e^t = \int_0^t su(s)\,ds.$ 4. $u(t) = 1 - \int_0^t u(s)\tan s\,ds.$
5. $u(t) = \int_0^t [u(s) + v(s)]\,ds,$ $v(t) = 1 - \int_0^t u(s)\,ds.$

6. Show that the nth iterate for the solution of $y' = yx$ such that $y(0) = 1$ is the sum of the first $n + 1$ terms of the power series expansion of $e^{x^2/2}$.

For the initial value problems in Exercises 7 through 10, obtain an expression for the nth function of the sequence of Picard approximations $\mathbf{x}^n = U^n[\mathbf{x}^0]$ to the exact solutions.

7. $dx/dt = x,$ $x(0) = 1.$ 9. $dx/dt = tx,$ $x(0) = 1.$
8. $dx/dt = y,$ $dy/dt = -4x.$ 10. $dx/dt = ty,$ $dy/dt = -tx.$
    $x(0) = 0,$ $y(0) = 1.$ $x(0) = 0,$ $y(0) = 1.$

For the initial value problems of Exercises 11–13, compute the functions x^1, x^2, x^3 of the sequence of Picard approximations.

11. $dx/dt = x^2 + t^2,$ $x(0) = 0.$
12. $dx/dt = y^2 + t^2,$ $dy/dt = x^2 + t^2,$ $x(0) = y(0) = 0.$
13. $dx/dt = x(1 - 2t),$ $x(0) = 1.$
14*. Show that, in Ex. 13, the sequence of Picard approximations converges for all t, but that this is not so in Ex. 11. In Ex. 13, is the convergence uniform?
15. Let $\mathbf{X}(\mathbf{x}, t) = A\mathbf{x}$, where A is a constant matrix. Show that each component of the nth Picard approximation to any solution is a polynomial function of degree at most n.
16. Establish the following inequalities for the sequence of Picard approximations.

$$|\mathbf{x}^n(t) - \mathbf{x}^{n-1}(t)| \leq \frac{M}{L}\left(\frac{(L\,|t - a|)^n}{n!}\right), \qquad |\mathbf{x}^n(t) - \mathbf{x}^\infty(t)| \leq \frac{M}{L}\sum_{k=n+1}^\infty \frac{(L\,|t - a|)^k}{k!}.$$

8   Linear systems

A first-order system of DE's (1) is said to be *linear* when it is of the form

$$dx_i/dt = \sum_{j=1}^n a_{ij}(t)x_j(t) + b_i(t), \qquad 1 \leq i \leq n. \tag{15}$$

In this case, we have $X_i(\mathbf{x}, t) = \sum_{j=1}^n a_{ij}(t)x_j + b_i(t)$. In vector notation, the linear system (15) is written in the form

$$d\mathbf{x}/dt = A(t)\,\mathbf{x} + \mathbf{b}(t), \tag{16}$$

where $A(t)\,\mathbf{x}$ stands† for the matrix $\|a_{ij}(t)\|$ applied to the vector $\mathbf{x}$, and $\mathbf{b}$ stands for the vector $(b_1, \ldots, b_n)$.

---

† For the definition and elementary properties of matrices, see Birkhoff and Mac Lane, Chapters 8, 10.

When $\mathbf{b}(t) \equiv 0$, the system (16) is said to be *homogeneous*. Otherwise, it is called *inhomogeneous*. The homogeneous system obtained from a given inhomogeneous system (15) by setting the b_j equal to zero is called the *reduced* system associated with (15).

A basic property of a linear system of DE's (16) is that the difference $\mathbf{x} - \mathbf{y}$ of any two solutions of (16) is a solution of the reduced system. It can be immediately verified that any linear combination $a\mathbf{x}(t) + b\mathbf{y}(t)$ of solutions $\mathbf{x}(t)$ and $\mathbf{y}(t)$ of a homogeneous linear system is again a solution.

We shall now establish the existence of solutions of linear systems and describe the set of all solutions.

■ **LEMMA.** *Any linear system* (15) *with continuous coefficient functions on a closed interval I satisfies a Lipschitz condition* (4) *with*

$$L = \sum_{i,j} \sup_{t \in I} |a_{ij}(t)|. \tag{17}$$

Proof — Since $\mathbf{X}(\mathbf{x}, t) - \mathbf{X}(\mathbf{y}, t)$ is the vector sum of n^2 vectors $\mathbf{z}_{ij}$, with ith component $a_{ij}(x_j - y_j)$ and other components zero, repeated use of the triangle inequality gives

$$|\mathbf{X}(\mathbf{x}, t) - \mathbf{X}(\mathbf{y}, t)| \leq \sum_{i,j} |\mathbf{z}_{ij}| \leq \sum_{i,j} |a_{ij}(t)| \cdot |x_j - y_j|$$

$$\leq \sum_{i,j} \sup_{t \in I} |a_{ij}(t)| \cdot |\mathbf{x} - \mathbf{y}|.$$

The functions $a_{ij}(t)$, being continuous on a closed interval, are bounded.† Hence, the Lipschitz constant L of (17) is finite. This completes the proof of the lemma.

We can now state the existence theorem for linear systems.

■ **THEOREM 7.** *A linear system* (15), *with the $a_{ij}(t)$ and $b_i(t)$ defined and continuous for* $|t - a| \leq T$, *has a unique solution on* $|t - a| \leq T$ *satisfying any given initial condition* $\mathbf{x}(a) = \mathbf{c}$.

Proof — The preceding lemma shows that such a system satisfies the hypotheses of Theorem 6. This gives the existence of the solution. The uniqueness follows from Theorem 1, again by the preceding lemma.

For *homogeneous* systems, we can construct a basis of solutions, as follows.

■ **COROLLARY 1.** *Let* $\mathbf{x}^i(t)$ *be the solution of a homogeneous linear system* $d\mathbf{x}/dt = A(t)\mathbf{x}$ *which satisfies the initial condition* $x_k^i(a) = 0$, $i \neq k$, $x_i^i(a) = 1$.

† Courant and John, p. 101.

Then the solution satisfying the initial condition $\mathbf{x}(a) = \mathbf{c} = (c_1, \ldots, c_n)$
is equal to the linear combination $\mathbf{x}(t) = c_1\mathbf{x}^1(t) + c_2\,\mathbf{x}^2(t) + \cdots + c_n\mathbf{x}^n(t)$.

Proof — The vector-valued function $\mathbf{y}(t) = \mathbf{x}(t) - \sum_{j=1}^{n} c_j\mathbf{x}^j(t)$ is a
solution of the linear system, since it is a linear combination of solutions.
This function satisfies the initial condition $\mathbf{y}(a) = (0, 0, \ldots, 0)$ because
of the way in which the initial conditions for the solutions $\mathbf{x}^i$ have been
chosen. Since the identically zero function is also a solution of the
linear system, it follows from the uniqueness in Theorem 7 that $\mathbf{y}(t) \equiv 0$,
q.e.d.†

The reduction of an nth order normal DE to a first-order system
sketched in § 1, when applied to a linear nth order DE in normal form

$$\frac{d^n u}{dt^n} = p_1(t)\,\frac{d^{n-1}u}{dt^{n-1}} + p_2(t)\,\frac{d^{n-2}u}{dt^{n-2}} + \cdots + p_{n-1}(t)\,\frac{du}{dt} + p_n(t)u,$$

transforms the DE into a homogeneous linear system $d\mathbf{x}/dt = A(t)\mathbf{x}$,
where the matrix $\|a_{ij}(t)\| = A(t)$ is defined as follows: $a_{ij}(t) = 0$ if
$1 \leq i \leq n - 1$ and $j \neq i + 1$; $a_{i,\,i+1}(t) = 1$ if $1 \leq i \leq n - 1$; $a_{nj}(t) = p_{n-j+1}(t)$.

We therefore obtain the following result.

■ COROLLARY 2.   *An nth order* DE *in normal form, with coefficients* $p_j(t)$
continuous for $|t - a| \leq T$, *has a basis of solutions* $u_j(t)$ $(1 \leq j \leq n)$
satisfying the initial‡ conditions $u_j^{(i)}(0) = \delta_j^{i+1}$, $0 \leq i \leq n - 1$.

More results about solutions of linear systems of DE's will be derived
in the Appendix.

9   Local existence theorem

In Theorem 6, it was assumed that $\mathbf{X}(\mathbf{x}, t)$ was defined for all $\mathbf{x}$ and
that a Lipschitz condition held for all $\mathbf{x}, \mathbf{y}$. But often this is not the
case. For instance, this assumption does not hold for the DE $dx/dt = e^x$
of Example 4. The ratio

$$|X(x, t) - X(0, t)|/|x - 0| = (e^x - 1)/x$$

is unbounded if the domain of e^x is unrestricted††.

---

† In algebraic terms, Corollary 1 states that the solutions of a homogeneous linear system
of dimension n form an n-dimensional vector space of functions. Therefore, any $n + 1$
solutions of such a system are always linearly dependent.
‡ δ_j^i is the Kronecker delta function: $\delta_j^i = 0$ if $i \neq j$ and $\delta_i^i = 1$. For the concept of a
basis of solutions of nth order DE'S, see Chapter 4, § 4.
†† The same complications arise with the DE $y' = 1 + y^2$, as has already been shown in
Chapter 3, § 9.

Correspondingly, the conclusion of Theorem 6 fails for this DE: the solution which takes the value c at $t = 0$ is the function $x(t) = -\ln(e^{-c} - t)$, and this function is defined only in the interval $-\infty < t < e^{-c}$. Hence, there is *no* $\epsilon > 0$ such that the DE $dx/dt = e^x$ has a solution defined on all of $|t| < \epsilon$ for every initial value: the interval of definition of a solution changes with the initial value.

To take care of this situation, and also of cases where the function $\mathbf{X}$ is defined only in a small region of $(x_1, \ldots, x_n)$-space, we now prove a *local* existence theorem, whose assumptions and conclusions refer only to neighborhoods of a given point.

■ THEOREM 8.   *Suppose that the function* $\mathbf{X}(\mathbf{x}, t)$ *in* (2) *is defined and continuous in the closed domain* $|\mathbf{x} - \mathbf{c}| \leq K$, $|t - a| \leq T$ *and satisfies a Lipschitz condition* (4) *there. Let* $M = \sup|\mathbf{X}(\mathbf{x}, t)|$ *in this domain. Then the* DE (2) *has a unique solution satisfying* $\mathbf{x}(a) = \mathbf{c}$ *and defined on the interval* $|t - a| \leq \min(T, K/M)$.

Proof — All steps in the proof of Theorem 6 can be carried out, provided we know that the functions $\mathbf{x}^n(t)$ referred to there take their values within the domain D_1: $|\mathbf{x} - \mathbf{c}| \leq K$, $|t - a| \leq \min(T, K/M)$, in which $\mathbf{x}(t)$ is surely defined. In particular, note that since $D_1 \subset D$, the bound M and Lipschitz constant L of Theorem 6 can be used in D_1. Therefore, the proof is a corollary of the following

■ LEMMA.   *Under the hypotheses of Theorem* 8, *the operator* U *defined by* (12) *carries functions* $\mathbf{x}(t)$ *satisfying the conditions* (i) $\mathbf{x}(t)$ *is defined and continuous on* $|t - a| \leq \min(T, K/M)$, (ii) $\mathbf{x}(a) = \mathbf{c}$, (iii) $|\mathbf{x}(t) - \mathbf{c}| \leq K$ *on the interval* $|t - a| \leq \min(T, K/M)$, *into functions satisfying the same conditions.*

Proof — In (12), suppose that $\mathbf{x}(s)$ satisfies conditions (i), (ii), (iii). We must show that $\mathbf{y}(t)$ satisfies the same conditions. Clearly (i) and (ii) are satisfied by $\mathbf{y}(t)$. By the inequality (3) we have (taking again $t \geq a$ for simplicity)

$$|\mathbf{y}(t) - \mathbf{c}| = \left| \int_a^t \mathbf{X}(\mathbf{x}(s), s)\, ds \right| \leq \int_a^t |\mathbf{X}(\mathbf{x}(s), s)|\, ds.$$

If M is the maximum of $\mathbf{X}$ and if $|t - a| \leq K/M$, this gives

$$|\mathbf{y}(t) - \mathbf{c}| \leq MK/M = K.$$

Therefore, (iii) is satisfied and $\mathbf{y}(t)$ is defined for $|t - a| \leq \min(T, K/M)$, completing the proof.

Using the reduction of § 1, taking an nth-order normal DE

$$u^{(n)} = F(u, u', u'', \ldots, u^{(n-1)}, t) \qquad (18)$$

into an equivalent first-order normal system (1), we obtain the

■ COROLLARY. *Let the function* $F(x_1, x_2, \ldots, x_n, t)$ *be continuous in the cylinder* $|t - a| \leq T$, $|\mathbf{x} - \mathbf{c}| \leq K$. *Let* $(x_2^2 + x_3^2 + \cdots + x_n^2 + F^2)^{1/2} \leq M$, *and let* F *satisfy a Lipschitz condition there. Then, on the interval* $|t - a| \leq \min(T, K/M)$, *the DE* (18) *has one and only one solution which satisfies the initial conditions* $u^{(i)}(a) = c_{i+1}$, $0 \leq i \leq n - 1$.

10* Analytic equations

We shall now consider the vector DE (2) under the assumption that $\mathbf{X}(\mathbf{x}, t)$ is an analytic function of all variables $x_1, \ldots, x_n, t$. The essential principle to be established is that *all solutions of analytic DE's are analytic functions.*†

The result is true whether the variables are real or complex; we shall first consider the complex case. To emphasize that we are dealing with complex variables, we rewrite the vector DE (2) as

$$d\mathbf{z}/dt = \mathbf{z}'(t) = \mathbf{Z}(\mathbf{z}, t), \qquad t = r + is, \qquad (19)$$

where $z_j = x_j + iy_j$ and $Z_j = X_j + iY_j$ are complex-valued functions.

We assume that the $Z_j(z_1, \ldots, z_n, t)$ are analytic functions of the variables $z_1, z_2, \ldots, z_n$ and t in the closed cylindrical domain C: $|t - a| \leq T$, $|\mathbf{z} - \mathbf{c}| \leq K$, with maximum M there. By the lemma of § 2, this implies that a Lipschitz condition holds in C, for some constant L.

Vector notation can be adapted to complex vectors with the following changes. The length (or norm) of a vector $\mathbf{z} = (z_1, z_2, \ldots, z_n)$ with complex components z_k is defined as

$$|\mathbf{z}| = (z_1 z_1^* + z_2 z_2^* + \cdots + z_n z_n^*)^{1/2}.$$

The *Hermitian inner product* of two complex vectors $\mathbf{z}$ and

$$\mathbf{w} = (w_1, w_2, \ldots, w_n)$$

is defined as

$$\mathbf{z} \cdot \mathbf{w} = (z_1 w_1^* + z_2 w_2^* + \cdots + z_n w_n^*).$$

note that $\mathbf{z} \cdot \mathbf{w} = (\mathbf{w} \cdot \mathbf{z})^*$. (The set of complex n-vectors with the above inner product is called a unitary space.)

---

† This section requires a knowledge of elementary complex function theory such as is found in the books by Hille (Vol. 1) and Ahlfors.

Now let γ be any path in the complex t-plane, defined parametrically by the equation $t = t(\sigma) = r(\sigma) + is(\sigma)$, where $r, s \in \mathscr{C}^1$ and σ is a *real* parameter. On the path γ, (19) is equivalent to the system of *real* DE's

$$x'(\sigma) = \mathbf{X}(\mathbf{x}, \mathbf{y}, \sigma)r'(\sigma) - \mathbf{Y}(\mathbf{x}, \mathbf{y}, \sigma)s'(\sigma),$$
$$y'(\sigma) = \mathbf{X}(\mathbf{x}, \mathbf{y}, \sigma)s'(\sigma) + \mathbf{Y}(\mathbf{x}, \mathbf{y}, \sigma)r'(\sigma). \tag{19'}$$

Theorems 1 through 8 apply to this system, which satisfies a Lipschitz condition.

Using the complex vector notation described above, we can also prove analogs of these theorems directly, for the DE $\mathbf{z}'(\sigma) = \mathbf{Z}(\mathbf{z}, t(\sigma))t'(\sigma)$ equivalent to (19'), and hence to (19), on the path γ.

The analog of the operator U of formula (12) is the operator W, defined by the line integral

$$\mathbf{w}(t) = W[\mathbf{z}(t)] = \mathbf{c} + \int_a^t \mathbf{Z}(\mathbf{z}(\zeta). \ \zeta) \, d\zeta. \tag{20}$$

Since each component function Z_j is analytic, the line integral defining the operator W is independent of the path from 0 to t in the complex t-plane, provided that this path stays within the domain C where the function $\mathbf{Z}$ is defined.† By Morera's theorem, the function $\mathbf{w}$ is therefore also analytic, in the sense that each component $w_j(z)$ is. Thus, the operator W transforms analytic functions into analytic functions. Moreover, the lemma of § 9 still holds, because the integrals in (20) can be taken along straight line segments in the complex ζ-plane. This gives the following lemma.

■ LEMMA.   *For $|t - a| \leq \min (T, K/M)$, the operator W defined by (20) takes analytic complex-valued vector functions $\mathbf{z}(t)$ with $|\mathbf{z}(t) - \mathbf{c}| \leq K$ into analytic vector functions $\mathbf{w}(t)$ with $|\mathbf{w}(t) - \mathbf{c}| \leq K$.*

By repeated applications of this lemma, it follows that the functions $W^n[\mathbf{w}^0] = \mathbf{w}^n(t)$ defined by the Picard process of iterated quadrature, in the domain $|t - a| \leq \min (T, K/M)$ of the complex t-plane, are all analytic.

We now apply the following result‡ from function theory.

Weierstrass Convergence Theorem.   If a sequence $\{f_n(t)\}$ of complex analytic functions converges uniformly to $f(t)$ in a domain D, then $f(t)$ is analytic in D.

---

† This is true because the disc $|t - a| \leq T$ where $\mathbf{Z}$ is defined is *simply connected*.

‡ Ahlfors p. 173. The result contrasts sharply with the case of functions of a real variable. By the Weierstrass approximation theorem, every continuous function on a real interval $a \leq x \leq b$ is a uniform limit of polynomial (hence analytic) functions.

By this theorem, the sequence of functions $w^n(t)$ converges uniformly for $|t - a| \leq \min (T, K/M)$ to an *analytic* solution $w^\infty(t)$ of the integral equation

$$\mathbf{z}(t) = \mathbf{c} + \int_a^t \mathbf{Z}(\mathbf{z}(\zeta), \zeta) \, d\zeta = W[\mathbf{z}(t)], \qquad (21)$$

and hence of the complex DE (19). Applying the Existence Theorem of § 8 for *real* DE's to the system (21), we infer the next theorem.

■ THEOREM 9.   *In Theorem 8, replace the real variables t, x_j, X_j with complex variables t, z_j, Z_j. Under the same hypotheses, if the $Z_j(\mathbf{z}, t)$ are complex analytic functions, the vector DE (19) has a unique complex analytic solution $\mathbf{z}(t)$ for given initial conditions.*

From this result and the uniqueness theorem, again for real DE's, we obtain

■ COROLLARY 1.   *Let $\mathbf{Z}(\mathbf{z}, t)$ be analytic in any simply-connected domain of the complex t-plane, and let $\mathbf{z}(t)$ be any solution of the DE (19). Then $\mathbf{z}(t)$ is analytic.*†

Real analytic DE's. A *real* function $X(\mathbf{x}, t)$ of real variables $x_1, \ldots, x_n$ and t is said to be analytic at $(\mathbf{c}, a)$ when it can be expanded into a power series with real coefficients in the variables $(x_k - c_k)$ and $(t - a)$, convergent in the cylinder $|\mathbf{x} - \mathbf{c}| < \eta$, $|t - a| < \epsilon$, for sufficiently small positive η and ϵ. When $X(\mathbf{x}, t)$ is analytic, its power series is convergent also in the *complex* cylinder $|\mathbf{z} - \mathbf{c}| < \eta$, $|t - a| < \epsilon$ (t complex), and defines a complex-valued analytic function there.

Now, let a normal system of real DE's (1) be given, the $X_j(x, t)$ being analytic. From Theorem 9, it follows that the resulting complex DE $d\mathbf{x}/dt = \mathbf{X}(\mathbf{x}, t)$ has a unique complex analytic solution for given real initial values. On the other hand, it also has a unique (local) real solution by Theorems 1 and 8. Hence the two solutions must coincide, proving

■ COROLLARY 2.   *If $\mathbf{X}(\mathbf{x}, t)$ is an analytic real function of the real variables $x_1, \ldots, x_n$ and t, then every solution of (1) is analytic.*

EXERCISES E

1. (a) Obtain an equivalent first-order system for $d^2x/dt^2 = t^2x$. Find the nth term of the Picard sequence of iterates for the initial values $x(0) = 1$, $x'(0) = 0$.

---

† An alternative proof can be based directly on (19). If the $z_k(t)$ satisfy (19), they are continuously differentiable. Hence, they are analytic (Ahlfors, pp. 24, 105; Hille, Vol. 1, pp. 72, 88).

(b) Prove that this initial-value problem has one and only one solution on $(-\infty, \infty)$.

2. (a) Obtain an equivalent first-order system for the DE $d^2x/dt^2 = x^2 + t^2$, and find the Lipschitz constant for the resulting system in the domain $|t| \leq A, |x| \leq B, |x'| \leq C$.

(b) State and prove a local existence theorem for solutions of this DE, for the initial conditions $x(0) = b$, $x'(0) = c$. Estimate the largest T, U such that a solution is defined on $-U \leq t \leq T$.

3. Show that, if $F(y)$ is continuous for $|y| \leq K$, and $|F(y)| \leq M$, every solution of $y' = F(y)$ can be uniformly approximated arbitrarily closely for $|x| \leq K/M$ by a solution of a DE $y' = P(y)$, where P is a polynomial.

4. Compute the nth Picard approximation to the solution of the complex system $dw/dt = iz$, $dz/dt = w$, which satisfies the initial conditions $w(0) = 1$, $z(0) = i$.

5. In the complex t-plane, determine a domain in which the system $dw/dt = tz^2$, $dz/dt = tw^2$ has an analytic solution satisfying given initial conditions $w(0) = w_0$, $z(0) = z_0$.

6. Show that the solution of the complex analytic DE

$$w'(z) = M\left[\frac{1}{2}\left(1 + \frac{w}{K}\right)\right]^{1/n}, \qquad (|z| < K)$$

which satisfies the initial condition $w(0) = 0$, is the function

$$w(z) = K\left[\left(1 + \frac{z}{c}\right)^{n/(n-1)} - 1\right], \qquad c = \frac{2^{1/n}Kn}{(n-1)M}.$$

7*. Using the result of Exercise 6, show that the bound given by Theorem 8 for the domain of existence of a solution is "best possible" for analytic functions of a complex variable.

11   Continuation of solutions

Even when the function† $\mathbf{X}(\mathbf{x}, t)$ is of class $\mathscr{C}^1$ and is defined for all $\mathbf{x}$ and t, Theorem 8 establishes the existence of solutions only in the neighborhood of a given initial value. In other words, it establishes only the *local* existence of solutions. We shall now study how such local solutions can be joined together to give a *global* solution defined up to the boundary of the domain of definition of the function $\mathbf{X}$.

■ THEOREM 10.   *Let* $\mathbf{X}(\mathbf{x}, t)$ *be defined and of class* $\mathscr{C}^1$ *in an open region $\mathscr{R}$ of* ($\mathbf{x}$, t)-*space. For any point* (**c**, a) *in the region $\mathscr{R}$, the DE* (2) *has a unique solution* $\mathbf{x}(t)$ *satisfying the initial condition* $\mathbf{x}(a) = \mathbf{c}$ *and defined for an interval* $a \leq t < b$ $(b \leq \infty)$ *such that, if* $b < \infty$, *either* $\mathbf{x}(t)$ *approaches the boundary of the region or* $\mathbf{x}(t)$ *is unbounded as* $t \to b$.

† In this Section we consider only *real* vectors and functions. The results can, however, be extended to complex-valued and analytic functions, in much the same way as in § 10. When (2) is analytic, the continuation of solutions described here coincides with *analytic continuation* in the sense of complex function theory, by Theorem 9 (cf. Chapter 9, § 1).

Proof — Consider the set S of all local solutions of the system (2) which satisfy the given initial condition $\mathbf{x}(a) = \mathbf{c}$. These are defined on intervals of varying lengths of the form $[a, T)$. Given two solutions $\mathbf{x}$ and $\mathbf{y}$ in this set, defined on intervals I and I' respectively, the function $\mathbf{z}$, defined to be equal to $\mathbf{x}$ or to $\mathbf{y}$ wherever either is defined, and hence also where both are defined, is also a solution defined on their union $I \cup I'$.

We now construct a single solution $\mathbf{x}$, called the *maximal* solution, defined on the union of *all* the intervals in which some local solution is defined, by letting $\mathbf{x}(t)$ be equal to the value of any of the solutions of S defined at the point t. This maximal solution $\mathbf{x}(t)$ is a well-defined function of class $\mathscr{C}^1$, by the Uniqueness Theorem. Furthermore, the interval of definition of this solution is the union of all the intervals of definition and, therefore, is itself an interval of the form $a \leq t < b$.

Consider the limiting behavior of $\mathbf{x}(t)$, as $t \uparrow b$. By the Bolzano-Weierstrass Theorem,† any infinite bounded set of points $(\mathbf{x}(t_n), t_n)$ in $\mathbf{x}t$-space must contain a limit point; hence, either $b = +\infty$, or $\lim_{t \uparrow b} |\mathbf{x}(t)| = +\infty$, or at least one finite point $(\mathbf{d}, b)$ is approached by at least one sequence of points $(\mathbf{x}(t_n), t_n)$ on the above solution curve. In the first case, $\mathbf{x}(t)$ is unbounded. In the second case, the maximal solution may be said to "recede to infinity."

It remains to consider the third case; a typical example is provided by choosing the region $\mathscr{R}$ as the left-half-plane $t < 0$ and $x'(t) = t^{-2}$ $\cos t^{-1}$. with general solution $x = C - \sin t^{-1}$.

We shall now prove that, in the third case above, *every* limit point $(\mathbf{d}, b)$ on $t = b$ of the maximal solution curve must lie on the boundary of $\mathscr{R}$. Indeed, suppose that it were in the interior; there would then exist a closed neighborhood $D\colon |\mathbf{x} - \mathbf{d}| \leq \epsilon, |t - b| \leq \epsilon$ of $(\mathbf{d}, b)$ also in $\mathscr{R}$; let $M = \max_D |\mathbf{X}|$. Take $\delta < \min(\epsilon, \epsilon/2M)$, and let $G \subset D$ be the open rectangle $|\mathbf{x} - \mathbf{d}| < \epsilon, |t - b| < \delta$. Finally, choose k so that $(\mathbf{x}(t_k), t_k) \in G$. Then, applying Theorem 8 (in G) to the solution through $(\mathbf{x}(t_k), t_k)$, we see that it stays in G until $t = b$. Since this is true for any $\epsilon > 0$, $\lim_{t \to b} \mathbf{x}(t) = \mathbf{d}$. Hence $\mathbf{x}(t)$ would have to coincide with the unique (by Theorem 1) local solution of (2) through $(\mathbf{d}, b)$. Therefore $\mathbf{x}(t)$ would not be maximal, a contradiction.

The maximum length $b - a$ of definition of the solution $\mathbf{x}$ is called the *escape time* of the solution for $t > a$. There is a similar notion of the escape time for $t < a$.

A solution with a *finite* escape time is one for which $|\mathbf{x}(t)|$ becomes unbounded as $t \to b < \infty$; on the other hand, a solution with an infinite

---

† Cf. Courant, Vol. 2, pp. 95 ff, where the Bolzano-Weierstrass Theorem in several dimensions is proved.

escape time is one that remains within the domain of definition of X as $t \to \infty$. For example, every solution of the DE $dx/dt = x$ has infinite escape time, whereas every nonzero solution of the DE $dx/dt = x^2$, namely every function $x = 1/(c-t)$, has finite escape time.

12* The perturbation equation

It is easy to derive a formula for the dependence on $\mathbf{c}$ of the solution $\mathbf{x} = \mathbf{f}(t, \mathbf{c})$ of the initial-value problem defined by the system $\mathbf{x}'(t) = \mathbf{X}(\mathbf{x}, t)$ and the initial condition $\mathbf{x}(a) = \mathbf{c}$. For simplicity, consider first the case $n = 1$ of a single first-order DE. Assuming that $f(t, c)$ is analytic, that is, that f has a convergent Taylor series expansion, we have

$$\frac{\partial}{\partial t}\left(\frac{\partial f}{\partial c}\right) = \frac{\partial}{\partial c}\left(\frac{\partial f}{\partial t}\right) = \frac{\partial}{\partial c}[X(f(t, c), t)]$$

$$= \left[\frac{\partial X}{\partial x}(f(t, c), t)\right] \cdot \left[\frac{\partial f}{\partial c}(t, c)\right]. \tag{22}$$

When we expand around $c = 0$, this gives formally

$$f(t, c) = f_0(t) + cf_1(t) + (c^2/2!)f_2(t) + \cdots, \tag{23}$$

where, by (23), $f_1(t) = \partial f/\partial c(t, 0)$ satisfies the linear perturbation equation

$$f_1'(t) = \left[\frac{\partial X}{\partial x}(f_0(t), t)\right]f_1(t), \qquad f_1(0) = 0. \tag{24}$$

Hence, if we know $f_0(t)$, we can compute $f_1(t)$ in closed form by quadrature (Chapter 1). Illustrations of this "perturbation method" are given in Exercises F5 and F6 below.

We now drop the assumption that X is a one-dimensional vector as well as the assumption that the solution has a convergent Taylor expansion, and we derive analogous results. We show that the solutions of a normal first-order system (1) depend differentiably on the initial values.

■ THEOREM 11.   *Let the vector function* $\mathbf{X}$ *be of class* $\mathscr{C}^1$, *and let* $\mathbf{x}(t, \mathbf{c})$ *be the solution of the normal system* (2), *taking the initial value* $\mathbf{c}$ *at* $t = a$. *Then* $\mathbf{x}(t, \mathbf{c})$ *is a continuously differentiable function of each of the components* c_j *of* $\mathbf{c}$.

The proof is subdivided into three steps.

A.   Consider the system of DE's for the unknown functions h_i, the components of the vector $\mathbf{h} = (h_1, \ldots, h_n)$:

$$\frac{dh_i}{dt} = \sum_{k=1}^{n} \frac{\partial X_i(\mathbf{x}(t, \mathbf{c}), t)}{\partial x_k} h_k + H_i(\mathbf{h}, t, \mathbf{c}, \eta_j) \tag{25}$$

when $\mathbf{x}(t, \mathbf{c})$ is the solution of the normal system (2) for which $x(t, \mathbf{a}) = \mathbf{c}$. We assume that the functions H_i are bounded for $|t - a| \leq T$ and $|\mathbf{h} - \mathbf{\delta}^j| \leq K$, where $\mathbf{\delta}^j$ is the vector whose components are the Kronecker deltas δ_i^j. We also assume that H_i tends to zero as $\eta_j \to 0$, uniformly for $|t - a| \leq T$ and $|\mathbf{h} - \mathbf{\delta}^j| \leq K$. Then, applying the Corollary of Theorem 3, with $\epsilon = \eta_j$, we find that the solution $\mathbf{h}^j = \mathbf{h}(t, \mathbf{c}, \eta_j)$ of (25) satisfying the initial condition $h_i^j(a) = \delta_i^j$ tends, as $\eta_j \to 0$, to the solution $\mathbf{f}^j$ of the linear system

$$\frac{df_i}{dt} = \sum_{k=1}^{n} \frac{\partial X_i(x(t, \mathbf{c}), t)}{\partial x_k} \cdot f_i \tag{25'}$$

satisfying the same initial conditions, namely, $f_i^j(a) = \delta_i^j$.

In addition, we infer from the same Corollary that the vector functions $\mathbf{h}^j$ remain *bounded* as $\eta_j \to 0$.

B.   Set

$$g_i^j(t, \mathbf{c}, \eta_j) = \frac{x_i(t, c_1, c_2, \ldots, c_{j-1}, c_j + \eta_j, c_{j+1}, \ldots, c_n) - x_i(t, \mathbf{c})}{\eta_j}.$$

We next find a differential equation satisfied by the vector partial difference $\mathbf{g}^j = (g_1^j, g_2^j, \ldots, g_n^j)$.

By definition,

$$\frac{dg_i^j(t, \mathbf{c}, \eta_j)}{dt} = \eta_j^{-1}[X_i(\mathbf{x}(t, \mathbf{c}) + \eta_j \mathbf{g}^j(t, \mathbf{c}), t) - X_i(t, \mathbf{x}(t, \mathbf{c}))].$$

We now use the assumption that X_i is $\mathscr{C}^1$. By Taylor's theorem for functions of several variables, we infer that the right side equals

$$\sum_{k=1}^{n} \frac{\partial X_i(\mathbf{x}(t, \mathbf{c}), t)}{\partial x_k} \cdot g_k^j(t, \mathbf{c}) + \epsilon_i |g_k(t, \mathbf{c})|,$$

where ϵ_i is a function of t, $\mathbf{c}$ and η_j which tends to zero as $\eta_j \to 0$, uniformly as the variables t and $\mathbf{c}$ range over closed intervals. Setting $H_i(\mathbf{h}, t, \mathbf{c}, \eta_j) = \epsilon_i |\mathbf{h}(t, \mathbf{c})|$, we find that the vector function $\mathbf{g}^j$ is a solution $\mathbf{g}^j = \mathbf{h}$ of a system (25). The function $\mathbf{H}$ satisfies the conditions stated under Step A.

C.   The initial conditions satisfied by the g_i^j are, by definition,

$$g_i^j(a, \mathbf{c}, \eta_j) = \frac{x_i(a, c_1, c_2, \ldots, c_{j-1}, c_j + \eta_j, c_{j+1}, \ldots, c_n) - x_i(t, \mathbf{c})}{\eta_j} =$$

$$= \begin{cases} \dfrac{c_i - c_i}{\eta_j} = 0 & \text{if} \quad i \neq j, \\[2ex] \dfrac{c_j + \eta_j - c_j}{\eta_j} = 1 & \text{if} \quad i = j. \end{cases}$$

Combining with the results of steps A and B, we conclude that, as $\eta_j \to 0$, the function $\mathbf{g}^j$ tends to the solution $\mathbf{h}^j$ of (25′) satisfying the same initial condition. But we know that

$$\lim_{\eta_j \to 0} \mathbf{g}^j(t, \mathbf{c}, \eta_j) = \partial \mathbf{x}(t, \mathbf{c})/\partial c_j.$$

We have, therefore, shown that the derivative $\partial \mathbf{x}/\partial c_j$ exists and is indeed a solution of (25′), q.e.d.

The linear DE (24) is called the *perturbation equation* or *variational equation* of the normal system (2), because it describes approximately the perturbation of the solution caused by a small perturbation of the initial conditions.

In the course of the preceding argument we have also proved the

■ COROLLARY. *If* $\mathbf{x}(t, \mathbf{c})$ *is a solution of the normal system* (2) *satisfying the initial condition* $\mathbf{x}(a) = \mathbf{c}$ *for each* $\mathbf{c}$, *and if each component of the function* $\mathbf{X}$ *is of class* $\mathscr{C}^1$, *then for each* j *the partial derivative* $\partial \mathbf{x}(t, \mathbf{c})/\partial c_j$ *is a solution of the perturbation equation* (25) *of the system.*

In the case of *linear* systems $d\mathbf{x}/dt = A(t)\mathbf{x} + \mathbf{b}(t)$, the perturbation equation is the reduced equation $d\mathbf{h}/dt = A(t)\mathbf{h}$ of the given system and is the same for all solutions. But in *nonlinear* systems, the perturbation equation (25) depends on the particular solution $\mathbf{x}(t, \mathbf{c})$ whose initial value is being varied.

13   Plane autonomous systems

We now apply the results of the preceding section to the trajectories of autonomous systems. The main result is that, near any noncritical point, the trajectories of an autonomous system look like a regular family of parallel straight lines. We give the proof for the case $n = 2$. Recall that a plane autonomous system is

$$dx/dt = X(x, y), \qquad dy/dt = Y(x, y). \tag{26}$$

■ THEOREM 12.   *Any plane autonomous system where* X *and* Y *are of class* $\mathscr{C}^1$ *is equivalent, under a diffeomorphism in a neighborhood of any point which is not a critical point, to the system* $du/dt = 1$, $dv/dt = 0$.

Proof — Let the point be (a, b); without loss of generality, we may assume that $X(a, b) \neq 0$. Let the solution of the system for the initial values $x(0) = a$, $y(0) = c$ be $x = \xi(t, c)$, $y = \eta(t, c)$, so that $\partial \xi/\partial t = X$, $\partial \eta/\partial t = Y$. Then, by Theorem 11, the transformation $(t, c) \to (\xi(t, c),$

$\eta(t, c))$ is of class $\mathscr{C}^1$; moreover, since $x(0)$ does not vary with c, the Jacobian

$$\frac{\partial(\xi, \eta)}{\partial(t, c)} = \frac{\partial \xi}{\partial t} \cdot \frac{\partial \eta}{\partial c} - \frac{\partial \xi}{\partial c} \cdot \frac{\partial \eta}{\partial t} = X(a, b) \cdot 1 - 0 \cdot Y(a, b)$$

is nonvanishing at (a, b). Hence, by the Implicit Function Theorem, the inverse transformation $u = t(x, y)$, $v = c(x, y)$ is of class $\mathscr{C}^1$. In the (u, v)-coordinates, the solutions reduce to $u = t$, $v = c = \text{constant}$; hence, the DE assumes the form stated, q.e.d.

■ COROLLARY 1.   *Any two plane autonomous systems are locally equivalent under a diffeomorphism except near critical points.*

The system $\dot{u} = 1$, $\dot{v} = 0$ is, therefore, locally a canonical form for plane autonomous systems near noncritical points. In hydrodynamics, the velocity field associated with this system is called a *uniform flow.*

■ COROLLARY 2.   *If the functions X and Y of the plane autonomous system (26) satisfy local Lipschitz conditions, then its integral curves form a regular curve family in any domain which contains no critical points.*

Proof—By Theorem 1, there is a unique integral curve of (26) passing through each point c not a critical point. As shown in § 12, each such integral curve goes all the way to the boundary. Finally, since Lipschitz conditions imply continuity, the directions of the vectors $(X(x, y), Y(x, y))$ vary continuously with position except near a critical point, which completes the proof.

14*   The Peano existence theorem

The existence theorems for normal systems (1) proved so far have assumed that the functions X_i satisfy Lipschitz conditions. We shall now derive an existence theorem, assuming only continuity. As shown in Chapter 1, solutions of such systems need not be uniquely determined by their initial values.

■ THEOREM 13 (Peano existence theorem).   *If the function $\mathbf{X}(\mathbf{x}, t)$ is continuous for $|\mathbf{x} - \mathbf{c}| \leq K$, $|t - a| \leq T$, and if $|\mathbf{X}(\mathbf{x}, t)| \leq M$ there, then the vector DE (2) has at least one solution $\mathbf{x}(t)$, defined for*

$$|t - a| \leq \min(T, K/M),$$

satisfying the initial condition $\mathbf{x}(a) = \mathbf{c}$.

Proof — Using an elegant method due to Tonelli, we shall consider the equivalent integral equation (11) of Theorem 5,

$$\mathbf{x}(t) = \mathbf{c} + \int_a^t \mathbf{X}(\mathbf{x}(s), s)\, ds \tag{27}$$

and prove that this has a solution. Let $T_1 = \min(T, K/M)$. We may assume that $a = 0$ and that the interval is $0 \le t \le T_1$. In this interval we construct a sequence of functions $\mathbf{x}^n(t)$ as follows. For $0 \le t \le T_1/n$, set $\mathbf{x}^n(t) \equiv \mathbf{c}$. For $T_1/n < t \le T_1$ define $\mathbf{x}^n(t)$ by the formula

$$\mathbf{x}^n(t) = \mathbf{c} + \int_0^{t - T_1/n} \mathbf{X}(\mathbf{x}^n(s), s)\, ds. \tag{28}$$

This formula defines the value of $\mathbf{x}^n(t)$ in terms of the previous values of $\mathbf{x}^n(s)$ for $0 \le s \le t - T_1/n$.

It follows, as in the lemma of § 9, that the functions $\mathbf{x}^n(t)$ are defined for $0 \le t \le T_1$. Also, we have

$$|\mathbf{x}^n(t)| \le |\mathbf{c}| + \int_0 M\, ds \le |\mathbf{c}| + T_1 M.$$

Hence, the sequence of functions $|\mathbf{x}^n(t)|$ $(n = 1, 2, \ldots)$ is uniformly bounded.

Next, we prove that the sequence $\mathbf{x}^n$ is *equicontinuous* in the following sense.

■ DEFINITION. *A family $\mathscr{F}$ of vector-valued functions $\mathbf{x}(t)$, defined on an interval $I: |t - a| \le T$, is said to be* equicontinuous *when, given $\epsilon > 0$, a number $\delta > 0$ exists such that*

$$|t - s| < \delta \qquad implies \qquad |\mathbf{x}(t) - \mathbf{x}(s)| < \epsilon$$

for all functions $\mathbf{x} \in \mathscr{F}$, provided that $s, t \in I$.

Indeed, using the inequality (3), we have

$$|\mathbf{x}^n(t_1) - \mathbf{x}^n(t_2)| \le \int_{t_1 - T_1/n}^{t_2 - T_1/n} |\mathbf{X}(\mathbf{x}^n(s), s)|\, ds \le M\,|t_2 - t_1|,$$

from which it is evident that the $\mathbf{x}^n(t)$ are equicontinuous.

We now apply to the sequence $\mathbf{x}^n$ the Theorem of Arzelà-Ascoli, which is stated below without proof.†

■ ARZELÀ-ASCOLI THEOREM. *Let $\mathbf{x}^n(t)$ $(n = 1, 2, 3, \ldots)$ be a bounded equicontinuous sequence of scalar or vector functions, defined for $a \le t \le b$.*

---

† Rudin, pp. 144 ff. The proof given here is for real-valued functions, but the same proof applies to vector-valued functions.

Then there exists a subsequence $\mathbf{x}^{n_i}(t)$ $(i = 1, 2, \ldots)$ *which is uniformly convergent in the interval.*

Applying this result to the sequence $\mathbf{x}^n(t)$, we see that it must contain a uniformly convergent subsequence $\mathbf{x}^{n_i}(t)$, converging to a continuous function $\mathbf{x}^\infty(t)$ as $n_i \to \infty$.

It is now easy to verify that this limit function $\mathbf{x}^\infty(t)$ satisfies the integral equation (27). Indeed, (28) can be written in the form

$$\mathbf{x}^{n_i}(t) = \mathbf{c} + \int_0^t \mathbf{X}(\mathbf{x}^{n_i}(s), s)\, ds - \int_{t - T_1/n_i}^i \mathbf{X}(\mathbf{x}^{n_i}(s), s)\, ds. \tag{29}$$

As $n_i \to \infty$, $\int_0^t \mathbf{X}(\mathbf{x}^{n_i}(s), s)\, ds \to \int_0^t \mathbf{X}(\mathbf{x}^\infty(s), s)\, ds$ because $\mathbf{X}(\mathbf{x}, t)$ is uniformly continuous; and the last term of (29) tends to zero, because, by the inequality (3),

$$\left| \int_{t - T_1/n_i}^t \mathbf{X}\, ds \right| \leq \int_{t - T_1/n_i}^t M\, ds = M\, \frac{T_1}{n_i} \to 0.$$

Therefore, taking limits on both sides of (29) as $n_i \to \infty$, we find that $\mathbf{x}^\infty$ satisfies the integral equation (27), q.e.d.

EXERCISES F

1. Let $F(x, y)$ be continuous for $|x - a| \leq T$, $|y - c| \leq K$. Show that the set of all solutions of $y' = F(x, y)$, satisfying the same initial condition $f(a) = c$, is equicontinuous.

2. Show that, if $\mathbf{X}(\mathbf{x}, t)$ is continuous and satisfies a Lipschitz condition for $a \leq t \leq b$, every solution of DE (2) satisfying $\mathbf{x}(a) = \mathbf{c}$ is bounded for $a \leq t \leq b$. Show that the corresponding result is not true for open intervals $a < t < b$.

3. Let $xX(x, y) + y^3 Y(x, y) = 0$, where X and Y are of class $\mathscr{C}^1$. Show that the system $x' = X(x, y)$, $y' = Y(x, y)$ has infinite escape time. [HINT: Show that $2x^2 + y^4$ is an integral of the system.]

4. Let the function $\mathbf{X}(\mathbf{x}, t)$ be defined for $0 \leq t < \infty$ and for all $\mathbf{x}$, and let $|\mathbf{X}(\mathbf{x}, t) - \mathbf{X}(\mathbf{y}, t)| \leq L(t)|\mathbf{x} - \mathbf{y}|$, where $\int_0^\infty L(t)\, dt < \infty$. Show that the DE $d\mathbf{x}/dt = \mathbf{X}(\mathbf{x}, t)$ has a solution on $0 \leq t < +\infty$ for every initial condition $\mathbf{x}(a) = \mathbf{c}$. Show that, if one solution is bounded, then all are.

5. Let $\mathbf{X}(\mathbf{x}, t, s)$ be of class $\mathscr{C}^1$ for $|\mathbf{x} - \mathbf{c}| \leq K$, $|t - a| \leq T$, $|s - s_0| \leq S$. Let $\mathbf{x}(t, s)$ be the solution of $\mathbf{x}' = \mathbf{X}(\mathbf{x}, t, s)$ satisfying $\mathbf{x}(a) = \mathbf{c}$. Show that $\mathbf{x}$ is a differentiable function of s.

6*. Under the assumptions of Exercise 5, suppose that $\mathbf{X}(\mathbf{x}, t, s)$ is of class $\mathscr{C}^n$. Show that $\mathbf{x}(t, s)$ has n continuous partial derivatives relative to s.

7*. Show that if there are two distinct solutions f and g of $y' = F(x, y)$ satisfying the same initial condition $c = f(a) = g(a)$ (F continuous in $|x - a| \leq T$, $|y - c| \leq K$), there are infinitely many of them.

8*. Show that there is a *maximal* and a *minimal solution* $f_M(x)$ and $f_m(x)$ of the DE in Exercise 7, such that $f_m(x) \leq f(x) \leq f_M(x)$ for any other solution f such that $f(a) = f_M(a) = f_m(a)$. [HINT: See Chapter 1, Exercise E4.]

9*. Let $F(x, y)$ and $G(x, y)$ be continuous for $a \leq x \leq T$, $|y - c| \leq K$, and $F(x, y) \leq$

$G(x, y)$. Let f be a solution of $y' = F(x, y)$, and let g be the maximal solution of $y' = G(x, y)$. Show that, if $f(a) \leqq g(a)$, then $f(x) \leqq g(x)$ for $x > a$.

ADDITIONAL EXERCISES

1*. Let $dx/dt = X(x, y, t)$ and $dy/dt = Y(x, y, t)$, where

$$(x - x')[X(x, y, t) - X(x', y', t)] + (y - y')[Y(x, y, t) - Y(x', y', t)]$$

is everywhere negative or zero. Show that, for $t > 0$, the above system has at most one solution satisfying a given initial condition at $t = 0$.

In Exercises 2 through 4, f'_+ means the right-derivative; prove the implication specified. You may assume the existence of f'_+ and g'_+ freely.

2. If $f'_+(x) \leqq g'_+(x)$, then $f(x) - f(y) \leqq g(x) - g(y)$ for $x \geqq y$.
3. If $|f'_+(x)| \leqq K|f(x)|$ then $|f(x)| \leqq |f(a)|e^{K|x-a|}$ for $x \geqq a$.
4. If $|f'_+(x)| \leqq K|f(x)| + \epsilon$, then $|f(x)| \leqq |f(a)|e^{K|x-a|} + (\epsilon/K)(e^{K|x-a|} - 1)$.
5. Let $dz_i/dt = Q_i(z_1, \ldots, z_n)$, where the Q_l are quadratic polynomials. Show that, for any initial condition, the nth Picard approximation to the solution is a polynomial in t of degree at most $2^n - 1$.
6. (a) Prove that, if there is a normal kth-order ordinary DE satisfied by two functions u and v and if $n > k$, there is a normal nth-order DE satisfied by both functions. State your differentiability assumptions.
   (b) Prove that, if the given kth-order DE is linear, then the nth-order DE can also be chosen to be linear.
   (c) Prove that there is no fourth-order normal DE $u^{iv} = F(u, u', u'', u''', t)$ satisfied by both $u = t^4$ and $v = t^6$ for all real t.
   (d) Prove that $u = t^6$ satisfies no normal linear homogeneous DE of degree six or less with continuous coefficients.
7. Show that, if $X_1, \ldots, X_n$ satisfy Lipschitz conditions on a compact domain, so does any polynomial function of the X_i.
8. Show that, if $X(t) = \|x_{ij}(t)\|$ is a matrix whose columns are solutions of the homogeneous linear system $X' = A(t)X$, then $\det X(t) = (\det X(a)) \exp \int_a^t \Sigma\, a_{kk}(s)ds$.
9. A matrix $X(t)$ is a *fundamental matrix* for $a \leqq t \leqq a + T$ of a homogeneous linear system $X' = A(t)X$ if its columns are solutions of the system and $\det (X(t)) \neq 0$. Show that, if the columns of X are solutions of the system and if $\det X(a) \neq 0$, then X is a fundamental matrix.
10*. Show that, if $X(t)$ is a fundamental matrix of the reduced linear system, the function $x(t) = X(t) \int_a^t X^{-1}(s)b(s)\, ds$ is the solution of the inhomogeneous system such that $x(a) = 0$ (X^{-1} is the matrix inverse of X).
11*. (Nagumo). Let X be continuous for $|t - a| \leqq T$, $|\mathbf{x} - \mathbf{c}| \leqq K$, and $|t - a|\,|X(\mathbf{x}, t) - X(\mathbf{y}, t)| \leqq |\mathbf{x} - \mathbf{y}|$. Show that the solution of (2) satisfying $\mathbf{x}(a) = \mathbf{c}$ is unique. [HINT: Use the equivalent integral equation, and consider the maximum of $|\mathbf{x}(t) - \mathbf{y}(t)|/(t - a)$ for $t \geqq a$].
12. Let X be continuous for $|\mathbf{x} - \mathbf{c}| \leqq K$, $|t| \leqq T$, and let

$$2(\mathbf{x} - \mathbf{c}) \cdot \mathbf{X}(\mathbf{x}, t) \leqq \psi(|\mathbf{x} - \mathbf{c}|^2, t),$$

where $\psi(u, t)$ is positive and increasing in u for fixed t, ($u \geqq 0$. Let $\phi \in \mathscr{C}^1$ satisfy $\phi'(t) > \psi(\phi(t), t)$, and $\phi(0) = 0$. Show that if $\mathbf{x}$ is a solution of (2) such that $\mathbf{x}(0) = c$, then $|\mathbf{x}(t) - c| \leqq \sqrt{\phi(t)}$. [HINT: Show that $\sigma'(t) \leqq \psi(\sigma(t), t)$, where $\sigma(t) = |x(t) - c|^2$.]

13*. Assume that $\mathbf{X}$ is continuous for $|t - a| \leqq T$, $|\mathbf{x} - \mathbf{c}| \leqq K$, and that

$$|\mathbf{X}(\mathbf{x}, t)| \leqq \psi(|\mathbf{x} - \mathbf{c}|, |t - a|),$$

where $\psi(u, t)$ is nonnegative, continuous, increasing in u for fixed t, defined for $|t - a| \leqq T$ and $u \geqq 0$. Let $\phi(t)$ be of class $\mathscr{C}^1$ and $\phi'(t) > \psi(\phi(t), t)$ for $|t - a| \leqq T$, and $\phi(0) = 0$. Let $\mathbf{x}(t)$ be a solution of (2) such that $\mathbf{x}(a) = \mathbf{c}$. Show that

$$|\mathbf{x}(t) - \mathbf{c}| \leqq \phi(|t - a|).$$

14*. Let X be continuous for $|t - a| \leqq T$, let $\phi(u)$ be continuous and increasing for $u \geqq 0$, and let $\lim_{N \to \infty} \int_1^N du/\phi(u) = \infty$. Show that, if $|\mathbf{X}(\mathbf{x}, t)| \leqq \boldsymbol{\phi}(|\mathbf{x}|)$, all solutions of (2) are bounded on $|t - a| \leqq T$. [HINT: Use Ex. 13]

7 *Approximate Solutions*

1 Introduction

In many problems, one wants to know not the exact solution of a DE for given initial conditions but only a good approximation to the solution over a limited range, together with an estimate of the error. Such approximate solutions are usually constructed as functions which *nearly* satisfy the given DE, deviating from it by very little.

■ DEFINITION. *A vector function* $\mathbf{y}(t)$ *is an* approximate solution *with* deviation *at most* ϵ *in the interval* $a \leq t \leq a + T$ *of the vector* DE

$$d\mathbf{x}/dt = \mathbf{X}(\mathbf{x}, t), \qquad a \leq t \leq a + T, \tag{1}$$

when $\mathbf{y}(t)$ *is continuous and satisfies the differential inequality*

$$|\mathbf{y}'(t) - \mathbf{X}(\mathbf{y}(t), t)| \leq \epsilon \tag{2}$$

for all except a finite number of points t of the interval $[a, a + T]$.

Note that the definition requires the function $\mathbf{y}$ to be differentiable except at a finite, possibly empty, set of points. Such a function is said† to be of class $\mathscr{D}^1$.

EXAMPLE 1. The function $y(t) \equiv 1$ is an approximate solution of the DE $dx/dt = x/100$ on the interval $[0, \infty)$, with deviation 0.01.

EXAMPLE 2. The function $y(t) \equiv 10^{-6}$ is an approximate solution of the DE $dx/dt = 3x^{2/3}$ on the interval $[0, \infty)$ with deviation .0003. The exact solution to this DE for the initial value $x(0) = 10^{-6}$ is $x = (t + .01)^3$; at $t = 1$, it assumes the value $x(1) = 1.030301$ instead of $y(1) = .000001$.

---

† See Widder, p. 330.

The preceding example shows that the deviation of an approximate solution of a DE is not necessarily a good measure of the difference between it and the exact solution satisfying the same initial conditions, that is, of the *error*.

In this chapter and the next, we shall study methods for computing approximate solutions of ordinary DE's and for estimating their errors. These methods will differ radically from those considered so far. They are typically *numerical*, depending primarily on the techniques of arithmetic. Though tedious if done by hand or even with a desk machine, they can be very quickly and cheaply performed on high-speed computers. One only needs to program a subroutine for computing $\mathbf{X}(\mathbf{x}_n, t_n)$ from given numerical values of t_n and of the components of $\mathbf{x}_n$. One need not assume that formulas are available for integrating or differentiating the components of $\mathbf{X}$ or for expanding them in power series. Provided that $\mathbf{X}(\mathbf{x}, t)$ is reasonably smooth (say, of class $\mathscr{C}^4$), convergence is rapid as the time step tends to zero.

Approximate function tables. The most effective methods for computing approximate solutions of DE's proceed directly to the construction of an approximate *function table*, giving approximate values of the solution at a sequence of points $t_0 < t_1 < t_2 < t_3 < \cdots$. These tabulated values are computed recursively; between them, the approximate solution is defined by a suitable *interpolation formula*.

Actually, the most effective methods for computing approximate solutions (Runge-Kutta, Milne) are too complicated to serve as a good introduction to the underlying theory. Therefore, in this chapter, we will discuss only a few of the simpler methods for computing approximate function tables, deferring the subject of efficient numerical integration of ordinary DE's to the next chapter.

2 Cauchy polygons

The simplest way to contruct an approximate function table for the solution of DE (1) satisfying a given initial condition is to generalize the *Riemann sum* formula used in establishing the Fundamental Theorem of the Calculus. This formula is, as in Chapter 1, (5'),

$$\int_a^{t_m} f(t)\, dt \simeq \sum_1^m f(t_{k-1})\, \Delta t_k, \qquad \Delta t_k = t_k - t_{k-1}, \quad t_0 = a, \quad t_k < t_{k+1}, \quad (3)$$

where the symbol $\simeq$ is to be read "is approximately equal to." The generalization referred to may be described as follows.

Divide the interval $[a, b]$ into m parts by a partition

$$\pi: a = t_0 < t_1 < t_2 < \cdots < t_m = b. \qquad (4)$$

For any given initial value $\mathbf{x}(a) = \mathbf{c}$, the entry $\mathbf{x}_k = \mathbf{x}_\pi(t_k)$ in the approximate function table for $\mathbf{x}(t)$ is defined by

$$\mathbf{x}_0 = \mathbf{c}, \qquad \mathbf{x}_k = \mathbf{x}_{k-1} + \mathbf{X}(\mathbf{x}_{k-1}, t_{k-1})(t_k - t_{k-1}), \qquad k = 1, \ldots, m. \quad (5)$$

This formula is *recursive*; each value $\mathbf{x}_k$ can be computed knowing $\mathbf{x}_{k-1}$ alone. For this reason, formula (5) is also called a *one-level* formula (see § 12*).

From the approximate function table just defined, one can also construct an *approximate solution* by linear interpolation. This approximate solution is defined by the formula

$$\mathbf{x}_\pi(t) = \mathbf{x}_{k-1} + \mathbf{X}(\mathbf{x}_{k-1}, t_{k-1})(t - t_{k-1}) \qquad \text{on} \quad [t_{k-1}, t_k]. \quad (5')$$

Evidently, the graph of the approximate solution $(5')$ consists of m segments of straight lines; it is a *polygon* in the $(n + 1)$-dimensional $(t, \mathbf{x})$-space. The function defined by (5) and $(5')$ for each partition π and initial value $\mathbf{c}$ is called the *Cauchy polygon* approximation to the solution.†

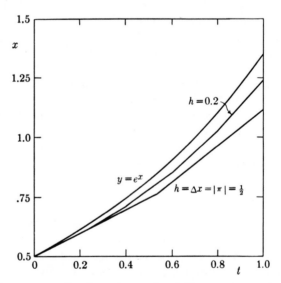

FIGURE 7.1   Cauchy polygons for $dx/dt = x$, $x(0) = 1/2$.

The Cauchy polygon approximation is continuous throughout the interval $[a, b]$, and differentiable at all points except $t_0, t_1, \ldots, t_m$, where it has a left-hand and a right-hand derivative. It is intuitively

† It was Cauchy who first proved their convergence to exact solutions, though Euler had used "Cauchy polygons" a century earlier.

plausible that, if the partition π is made sufficiently fine, the Cauchy polygon $\mathbf{x}_\pi(t)$ will be a good approximation to an actual solution. To make this idea precise, we now introduce a numerical measure for the fineness of a partition.

■ DEFINITION. *The* norm *of the partition* (4) *of the interval* $[a, b]$ *is*

$$|\pi| = \max\{\Delta t_1, \ldots, \Delta t_m\} = \max_{k=1,\ldots,m}\{t_k - t_{k-1}\}. \tag{6}$$

For continuous functions X not satisfying a Lipschitz condition, such as the function $x^{2/3}$ of Example 2, the intuitive idea stated above is not always correct. However, for functions which satisfy a Lipschitz condition

$$|\mathbf{X}(\mathbf{x}, t) - \mathbf{X}(\mathbf{y}, t)| \leqq L|\mathbf{x} - \mathbf{y}|, \tag{7}$$

we can always make the *deviation* arbitrarily small by making the norm of the partition sufficiently small. This result is contained in the following theorem.

■ THEOREM 1. *Let* $\mathbf{X} \in \mathscr{C}^1$ *satisfy* $|\mathbf{X}| \leq M$, $|\partial\mathbf{X}/\partial t| \leq C$, *and* (7) *in the cylinder* D: $|\mathbf{x} - \mathbf{c}| \leq K$, $a \leq t \leq a + T$. *Then any Cauchy polygon in* D *is an approximate solution of* $\mathbf{x}'(t) = \mathbf{X}(\mathbf{x}, t)$ *with deviation at most* $(C + LM)|\pi|$.

Proof — On each subinterval (t_{i-1}, t_i) of π, it is clear, by (7), that $|\mathbf{X}(\mathbf{x}(t), t) - \mathbf{X}(\mathbf{x}_i, t)| \leq L|\mathbf{x}(t) - \mathbf{x}_i|$;

$$|\mathbf{X}(\mathbf{x}(t), t) - \mathbf{X}(\mathbf{x}_i, t)| \leq LM|t - t_i| \leq LM|\pi|$$

since $|\mathbf{x}(t) - \mathbf{x}_i| = |\int_{t_i}^t \mathbf{X}(\mathbf{x}(s), s)\, ds| \leq M|t - t_1|$. Also,

$$|\mathbf{X}(\mathbf{x}_i, t) - \mathbf{X}(\mathbf{x}_i, t_i)| = \left|\int_{t_i}^t \partial\mathbf{X}/\partial t(s)\, ds\right| \leqq C|\pi|.$$

Adding together the two inequalities just obtained, and using the triangle inequality, we get the desired conclusion:

$$|\mathbf{X}(\mathbf{x}(t), t) - \mathbf{X}(\mathbf{x}_i, t_i)| \leq (LM + C)|\pi|.$$

REMARK. The following generalization of Theorem 1 can be proved under the weakened hypothesis $\mathbf{X} \in \mathscr{C}$.

■ THEOREM 2. *Let the vector function* $\mathbf{X}(\mathbf{x}, t)$ *be continuous on the cylinder* R: $|\mathbf{x} - \mathbf{c}| \leq K$, $a \leq t \leq a + T$, *and let* $|\mathbf{X}(\mathbf{x}, t)|$ *be bounded by* M *there. Let* T_1 *be the lesser of the two numbers* T, K/M, *and let* $\epsilon > 0$ *be given.*

Then we can find $\delta > 0$ *such that every Cauchy polygon* $\mathbf{x}_\pi(t)$ *with* $|\pi| < \delta$, *satisfying the initial condition* $\mathbf{x}_\pi(a) = \mathbf{c}$, *is an* approximate solution *of* (1) *with deviation at most* ϵ *in the interval* $[a, a + T_1]$.

Proof — First, we show that the Cauchy polygons are well-defined by (5) and (5′). This requires only that, for $t_k \in [a, a + T_1]$, every vertex $(\mathbf{x}_k, t_k)$ shall lie in the cylinder R where $\mathbf{X}(\mathbf{x}, t)$ is given. But, by formula (5),

$$\mathbf{x}_k = \mathbf{c} + \mathbf{X}(\mathbf{x}_0, t_0)(t_1 - t_0) + \cdots + \mathbf{X}(\mathbf{x}_{k-1}, t_{k-1})(t_k - t_{k-1}),$$

whence, by the triangle inequality,

$$|\mathbf{x}_k - \mathbf{c}| \leq \sum_{i=1}^{k} |\mathbf{X}(\mathbf{x}_{i-1}, t_{i-1})| \cdot |t_{i-1} - t_{i-1}| \leq M \sum_{i=1}^{k} (t_i - t_{i-1}) \leq M T_1 \leq K.$$

We shall work exclusively in the interval $[a, a + T_1]$, as has already been done with the local existence theorem of Chapter 6, §9. Given $\epsilon > 0$, choose $\delta > 0$ so that

$$|\mathbf{X}(\mathbf{x}, t) - \mathbf{X}(\mathbf{y}, s)| < \epsilon \tag{8}$$

whenever $|\mathbf{x} - \mathbf{y}| < \delta$ and $|t - s| < \delta$. This is possible since any function continuous on a compact (i.e., closed, bounded) region is uniformly continuous.† The idea of the proof is to make the sides of the Cauchy polygon so short that, by (8), the variation in $\mathbf{X}$ along any one side is at most ϵ.

This is accomplished by taking any partition whose norm satisfies

$$|\pi| \leq \delta/(M + 1).$$

We show that this choice of the norm gives deviation at most ϵ. For t in the open interval (t_{k-1}, t_k), using formula (5′), we obtain

$$|\mathbf{x}'_\pi(t) - \mathbf{X}(\mathbf{x}_\pi(t), t)| = |\mathbf{X}(\mathbf{x}_{k-1}, t_{k-1}) - \mathbf{X}(\mathbf{x}_\pi(t), t)|. \tag{9}$$

But we know that $|t_{k-1} - t_k| < \delta/(M + 1)$ and, again by (5′),

$$|\mathbf{x}_\pi(t) - \mathbf{x}_{k-1}| = |t - t_{k-1}| \cdot |\mathbf{X}(\mathbf{x}_{k-1}, t_{k-1})| \leq \frac{\delta}{M + 1} M < \delta.$$

It follows from (8) that the right-hand side of (9) is less than ϵ. Hence so is the left side, except at the points t_k of the partition, which are finite in number. Thus $\mathbf{x}_\pi$ is an approximate solution with deviation at most ϵ, q.e.d.

---

† Graves, p. 66; Rudin, p. 78.

3   Error bounds

We now prove a theorem which yields as a corollary an easily computed *a priori* error bound for the Cauchy-polygon method in terms of $|\pi|$, $|\mathbf{X}|_{\max}$, the Lipschitz constant, and the deviation.

■ THEOREM 3.   *Let* $\mathbf{x}(t)$ *be an exact solution and* $\mathbf{y}(t)$ *an approximate solution, with deviation* ϵ, *of the* DE $\mathbf{x}'(t) = \mathbf{X}(\mathbf{x}, t)$. *Let* $\mathbf{X}$ *satisfy the Lipschitz condition* (7). *Then, for* $t \geq a$, *we have*

$$|\mathbf{x}(t) - \mathbf{y}(t)| \leq |\mathbf{x}(a) - \mathbf{y}(a)| e^{L(t-a)} + (\epsilon/L)(e^{L(t-a)} - 1). \qquad (10)$$

Proof — Consider $\sigma(t) = |\mathbf{x}(t) - \mathbf{y}(t)|^2$. Differentiating,

$$\sigma'(t) = 2[\mathbf{X}(\mathbf{x}(t), t) - \mathbf{X}(\mathbf{y}(t), t)] \cdot [\mathbf{x}(t) - \mathbf{y}(t)]$$
$$+ 2[\mathbf{X}(\mathbf{y}(t), t) - \mathbf{y}'(t)] \cdot [\mathbf{x}(t) - \mathbf{y}(t)]$$

Hence, adding inequalities, we obtain

$$\sigma'(t) \leq 2L\sigma(t) + 2\epsilon\sqrt{\sigma(t)}.$$

Now, set $\sigma = v^2$; the above gives $v' \leq Lv + \epsilon$ (for $\sigma > 0$). Applying Lemma 2 of Chapter 1, §10, we get the desired inequality (10), much as in Chapter 6, § 9. This completes the proof.

Finally, substituting from Theorem 1 into Theorem 3, we obtain the following.

■ COROLLARY.   *Let* $\mathbf{y}(t)$ *be an approximate solution of* (1) *with deviation at most* ϵ, *and let* $\mathbf{x}(t)$ *be the exact solution assuming the same initial value* $\mathbf{x}(a) = \mathbf{y}(a) = \mathbf{c}$. *Then, assuming the Lipschitz condition* (7), *we have*

$$|\mathbf{y}(t) - \mathbf{x}(t)| \leq [(C/L) + M]\{e^{L(t-a)} - 1\} \cdot |\pi|. \qquad (11)$$

EXERCISES A

1. (a) What is the deviation of the approximate solution $x = t^2/2 - t^{24}/24$ of the initial value problem defined by $dx/dt = \sin t$, $x(0) = 0$ on the interval $0 \leq t \leq 1$?
   (b) Compare the difference $1 - (\cos 1) - \frac{11}{24}$ with the bound given by formula (11), for the deviation computed in (a).
   (c) For the initial value $x(0) = 1$, bound the difference between the solutions of $dx/dt = \sin t$ and $dx/dt = t - (t^3/6)$.

In Exercises 2–5, for the initial value problem specified: (a) use the Cauchy polygon method to compute an approximate function table for $t_k = 0.1, 0.2, \ldots, 1.0$, (b) find the deviation of the approximate solution obtained from this table by linear interpolation, (c) find the exact solution, (d) find the error.

2. $\dot{x} = x$, $x(0) = 1$.   3. $\dot{x} = 1 - 2x$, $x(0) = 0$.
4. $\dot{x} = y$, $\dot{y} = -x$, $x(0) = 0$, $y(0) = 1$.   5. $\dot{x} = y$, $\dot{y} = x$, $x(0) = 1$, $y(0) = 0$.

6. (a) Find the deviation of the approximate solution $y \equiv 10^{-10}$ of the DE
$x'(t) = 5x^{4/5}$.
   (b) What is the exact solution of this DE on $[0, \infty]$ for the initial value
$x(0) = 10^{-10} = y(0)$?
   (c) Prove in detail the uniqueness of this solution.

7. On the interval $[0, 1]$, for any $\epsilon > 0$, construct an approximate solution with deviation ϵ to a suitable first-order DE, for which the exact solution with the same initial value is unbounded.

8*. For the DE $x'(t) = f(t) - x$, show that

$$|x_\pi(t) - x(t)| \leq C\,|\pi|, \qquad \text{where} \quad C = \sup |f'(t)|.$$

9*. (a) Sharpen (10) and (11) in the stable case $[X(x, t) - Y(x, t)] \cdot [x - y] \leq 0$. Compare with the limiting case $L = 0$ of these formulas.
   (b) When $X(x, t)$ satisfies the one-sided Lipschitz condition $[X(x, t) - X(y, t)] \cdot [x - y] \leq L\,|x - y|^2$, how can (10) and (11) be sharpened? [HINT: See Exercise 8.]

4   Order of accuracy

A slight variant of the analysis leading to Theorem 3 yields a closely related bound to the cumulative error of the Cauchy polygon approximation, as follows.

Define the *directional derivative* $\partial X / \partial \xi$ of the vector function $X(x, t)$ in the direction $\xi = (\xi_0, \xi_1, \ldots, \xi_n)$ in t, x-space, for any vector ξ of unit length, as the sum $\xi_0 \partial X / \partial t + \sum_{k=1}^n \xi_k\, \partial X / \partial x_k$. It follows as in the proof of the lemma of Chapter 5, § 2, that

$$|X(t, x) - X(u, y)| \leq |\partial X / \partial \xi| \cdot |(t, x) - (u, y)|,$$

where ξ is the unit vector in (t, x)-space pointing in the direction $(t - u,$ $x - y)$. This inequality gives a bound on the change in $X(x, t)$ along any side of a Cauchy polygon, which we use to prove the following result.

■ THEOREM 3'.   *In the cylinder* $R: |t - a| \leq T_1, |x - c| \leq K$ *of Theorem 1, let* $X(x, t) \in \mathcal{C}^1$. *Let*

$$\sup_R |X(x, t)| = M \qquad and \qquad \sup_{R, |\xi| = 1} |\partial X / \partial \xi| = L_1. \tag{12}$$

Then, x_π *and* x *being as in Theorems 2 and 3 above, we have*

$$|x_\pi(t) - x(t)| \leq \{e^{L_1|t - a|} - 1\}(1 + M)|\pi|. \tag{13}$$

Proof — The kth side of the Cauchy polygon defined by $x_\pi(t)$ is the hypotenuse of a right triangle with base at most $|\pi|$ and altitude at most $M\,|\pi|$; hence its length is at most $(1 + M)|\pi|$. Thus, by the inequality displayed above and (12), the change in $X(x_\pi(t), t)$ along the side is at most $L_1(1 + M)|\pi|$. But the *deviation* of $x_\pi(t)$ from the DE (1) is equal to the maximum of this change. Therefore, the deviation of $x_\pi(t)$ is at most $L_1(1 + M)|\pi|$. By (11), this implies the desired result.

■ COROLLARY.   *Under the hypotheses of Theorem 3, let the interval* $[a, a + T_1]$ *of Theorem 2 be divided into n equal parts of length* $h = T_1/n$. *Then the error of the Cauchy polygon approximation is bounded by* Nh, *where N is a constant independent of h.*

Proof — Set $N = [\exp(L_1 T_1) - 1](1 + M)$, and use inequality (13). This result can be rephrased as follows. A method of numerical integration based on a subdivision of the interval of integration into "steps" or subintervals of length h is said to have the *order of accuracy* $O(h^n)$ when the cumulative error is bounded by Nh^n for all sufficiently smooth functions, where the constant N depends on the function **X** but is independent of h. Theorems 3, 3′ assert that the Cauchy polygon approximation has order of accuracy $O(h)$. By contrast, the order of accuracy of the other methods of numerical integration to be studied in this Chapter is $O(h^2)$, while the emphasis in Chapter 8 will be on more complicated methods whose order of accuracy is $O(h^4)$.

EXAMPLE 3.   Consider the linear DE $dx/dt = x$, with a constant mesh-length h. The Cauchy-polygon method gives $x_k = (1 + h)x_{k-1}$, and so $x_n = (1 + h)^n x_0$.

Thus, if we tabulate values of the solution of the DE for the initial value $x_0 = 1$, calculated by the Cauchy polygon method applied to the interval $[0, 1]$ with the constant mesh-length $h = 1/n$, we get $[1 + (1/n)]^n$ instead of e. By the binomial theorem, the cumulative error over the interval is thus the difference between

$$e = 1 + 1 + 1/2! + 1/3! + 1/4! + \cdots,$$

and

$$[1 + (1/n)]^n = 1 + 1 + n(n - 1)/2n^2 + n(n - 1)(n - 2)/6n^3 + \cdots.$$

This difference exceeds $1/2n$, so that it would take 5000 steps to achieve four-place accuracy!

Note that, in Example 3, the error made in each individual step is only $O(h^2)$. Since the number of steps is proportional to $1/h$, the cumulative error is still $O(h)$. More generally, the order of magnitude of the cumulative error is an infinitesimal of order one less than that of the error per step. It is the same as that of the *relative error* per step, defined as the error divided by the length of the step.

5   Midpoint quadrature

In studying formulas for numerical integration having higher orders of accuracy than the Cauchy polygon formula, it is helpful to begin with *quadrature* formulas for integrating numerically DE's of the form

$y' = F(x)$. For such DE's, the Cauchy polygon formula reduces to

$$\int_a^b F(x)\, dx \simeq \sum_{i=1}^n F(x_{i-1})\, \Delta x_i\,, \qquad \Delta x_i = x_i - x_{i-1}, \tag{14}$$

where the symbol $\simeq$ again means "is approximately equal to."

The simplest formula for numerical quadrature having a higher order of accuracy than the Cauchy polygon formula (14) is the *midpoint quadrature* formula

$$\int_a^b F(x)\, dx \simeq M_\pi[F] = \sum_{i=1}^n F(m_i)\, \Delta x_i\,, \qquad m_i = (x_{i-1} + x_i)/2. \tag{15}$$

Given the partition π of the interval of integration $[a, b]$ by points of subdivision $a = x_0 < x_1 < \cdots < x_n = b$, the midpoint approximation $M_\pi[F]$ is easily computed; it takes its name from the fact that m_i is the midpoint of the ith interval of subdivision. We now derive an *error bound* for the midpoint quadrature formula (15).

■ **Theorem 4.**   *If $F \in \mathscr{C}^2$, then*

$$\left| \int_a^b F(x)\, dx - \sum_{i=1}^n F(m_i)\, \Delta x_i \right| \leq |F''|_{\max} |\pi|^2 (b - a)/24. \tag{16}$$

Proof — On each interval $[x_{i-1}, x_i] = [m_i - \Delta x_i/2,\ m_i + \Delta x_i/2]$, Taylor's formula implies that

$$F(m_i + t) - F(m_i) - t F'(m_i) = t^2 F''(m_i + \tau)/2,$$

where τ is between 0 and t. But $F''(m_i + \tau)$ is bounded below by the minimum $F''_{\min}$ of $F''(x)$ on $[a, b]$ and above by its maximum value $F''_{\max}$. Therefore, we have

$$F''_{\min} t^2/2 \leq F(m_i + t) - F(m_i) - t F'(m_i) \leq F''_{\max} t^2/2.$$

Integration of this inequality over $-\Delta x_i/2 \leq t \leq \Delta x_i/2$ gives

$$F''_{\min} \Delta x_i^3/24 \leq \int_{x_{i-1}}^{x_i} F(x)\, dx - F(m_i)\, \Delta x_i \leq F''_{\max} \Delta x_i^3/24.$$

Summing over i and noting that $0 \leq \Delta x_i^2 \leq |\pi|^2$, we get (16).

Theorem 4 shows that the midpoint quadrature formula (15) has order of accuracy $O(h^2)$, one order higher than the Cauchy polygon method.

Error estimate.   By considering the higher-order terms in Taylor's formula, we can derive a much more accurate estimate of the error of the midpoint quadrature formula, at least for subdivisions into intervals of constant length.

■ THEOREM 5.   *For $F \in \mathscr{C}^6$, let all intervals of subdivision have the same length $\Delta x_i = 2k = h$.   Then*

$$M_\pi[F] = \int_a^b F(x) \, dx - \frac{h^2}{24} [F'(b) - F'(a)]$$

$$+ \frac{7h^4}{5760} [F'''(b) - F'''(a)] + O(h^6). \qquad (17)$$

Proof — By Taylor's formula with remainder, since $F \in \mathscr{C}^6$, we have

$$F(m_i + t) = \sum_{r=0}^{5} F^{(r)}(m_i) \, t^r/(r!) + F^{(6)}(\xi) \, t^6/720,$$

where ξ is some number between m_i and $m_i + t$. On each ith interval (x_{i-1}, x_i), the final term ("remainder") is bounded in magnitude by $Mk^6/720$, where $M = \max |F^{(6)}(\xi)|$, the maximum being taken on the entire interval $a \leq \xi \leq b$. Integrating over $-k \leq t \leq k$, we get

$$\int_{x_{i-1}}^{x_i} F(x) \, dx = 2kF(m_i) + k^3 F''(m_i)/3 + k^5 F^{\text{iv}}(m_i)/60 + O(k^6) \, \Delta x_i,$$

where the factor $O(k^6)$ is bounded in magnitude by $Mk^6/720$. When we sum over i, there results the estimate

$$\sum_{i=1}^{n} F(m_i) \, \Delta x_i = \int_a^b F(x) \, dx - (k^2/6) \sum_{i=1}^{n} F''(m_i) \, \Delta x_i$$

$$- (k^4/120) \sum_{i=1}^{n} F^{\text{iv}}(m_i) \, \Delta x_i + 0(k^6). \quad (18)$$

An application of (18) to the function $F''(x) \in \mathscr{C}^4$ gives similarly (one term being dropped because of the loss in differentiability),

$$\sum_{i=1}^{n} F''(m_i) \, \Delta x_i = \int_a^b F''(x) \, dx - (k^2/6) \sum_{i=1}^{n} F^{\text{iv}}(m_i) \, \Delta x_i + O(k^4); \quad (18')$$

applied to $F^{\text{iv}}(x) \in \mathscr{C}^2$, it gives

$$\sum_{i=1}^{n} F^{\text{iv}}(m_i) \, \Delta x_i = \int_a^b F^{\text{iv}}(x) \, dx + O(k^2). \qquad (18'')$$

Substituting from (18′) and (18″) back into (18), and combining terms, we get

$$\sum_{i=1}^{n} F(m_i) \, \Delta x_i = \int_a^b F(x) \, dx - \frac{k^2}{6} \int_a^b F''(x) \, dx + \frac{7k^4}{360} \int_a^b F^{\text{iv}}(x) \, dx + O(k^6).$$

When we set $k = h/2$, formula (17) follows immediately.

Note that the error estimate (17) implies the very accurate *corrected* midpoint formula

$$\int_a^b F(x)\,dx = \sum_{i=1}^n F(m_i)\,\Delta x_i + h^2[F'(b) - F'(a)]/24$$
$$- 7h^4[F'''(b) - F'''(a)]/5760 + O(h^6). \quad (19)$$

EXERCISES B

In each of Exercises 1–4, a numerical quadrature formula is specified for approximately evaluating $\int_{-h}^h f(x)\,dx$. In each case: (a) compute the truncation error for $f(x) = x^n$, $n = 0, 1, 2, 3, \ldots$, and (b) find the order of accuracy of the formula, using Taylor's formula with remainder, assuming $f(x)$ to be analytic.

1. Simpson's rule

$$S[f] = \frac{h}{3}[f(-h) + 4f(0) + f(h)].$$

2. Cotes' rule:

$$C[f] = \frac{h}{4}[f(-h) + 3f\left(\frac{-h}{3}\right) + 3f\left(\frac{h}{3}\right) + f(h)].$$

3. Weddle's rule:

$$W[f] = \frac{h}{10}\left[f(-h) + 5f\left(-\frac{2h}{3}\right) + f\left(-\frac{h}{3}\right) + 6f(0) + f\left(\frac{h}{3}\right) + 5f\left(\frac{2h}{3}\right) + f(h)\right].$$

4. Hermite rule:

$$H[f] = h[f(h) + f(-h)] + \frac{h^2}{3}[f'(h) - f'(-h)].$$

5. (a) By expanding in Taylor's series about each point, show that if $h = (b - a)/n$ and $x_i = a + ih$, then

$$\int_a^b f(x)\,dx = h\sum_{i=0}^{n-1}\left[f(x_i) + \frac{h}{2}f'(x_i) + \frac{h^2}{6}f''(x_i)\right] + O(h^3).$$

(b) By using the preceding formula on $f'(x)$, show that

$$\int_a^b f(x)\,dx = h\sum_{i=0}^{n-1} f(x_i) + \frac{h}{2}[f(x_n) - f(x_0)] - \frac{h^2}{12}\sum_{i=0}^n f''(x_i) + O(h^3).$$

(c) Applying the result of (a) to $f''(x)$, show that

$$\int_a^b f(x)\,dx = \frac{h}{2}\sum_{i=1}^n [f(x_i) + f(x_{i-1})] - \frac{h^2}{12}[f'(b) - f'(a)] + O(h^3).$$

6*. In Exercise 3, find weighting coefficients w_k such that the approximation

$$w_0 f(-h) + w_1 f\left(-\frac{2h}{3}\right) + w_2 f\left(-\frac{h}{3}\right) + w_3 f(0) + w_4 f\left(\frac{h}{3}\right) + w_5 f\left(\frac{2h}{3}\right) + w_6 f(h)$$

to $\int_{-h}^h f(x)\,dx$ has a maximum order of accuracy. Compare with Weddle's rule.

7. Use (17) to estimate the difference

$$\ln 2 - 1 \left[\sum_{k=1}^{10} \frac{2}{19 + 2k} - \frac{1}{800} \right].$$

Use (17), with $h = 0.2$, to evaluate the following numbers, approximately:

8. $\ln 2 = \int_1^2 dx/x$.   9. $\arctan 1 = \int_0^1 dx/(1 + x^2)$.

10. $\int_0^1 \sqrt{1 + x^4}\, dx$.   11. $\int_0^1 \sin (x^2)\, dx$.

12. Show that, if $|F''(x)| \leqq \epsilon$ on $[x_{i-1}, x_i]$, the error in the midpoint quadrature formula is bounded by $\epsilon(b - a)|\Delta x_i|^2/24$.

6 Trapezoidal quadrature

The formula for *trapezoidal quadrature* is

$$\int_a^b F(x)\, dx \simeq T_n[F] = \sum_{i=1}^{n} [F(x_{i-1}) + F(x_i)]\, \Delta x_i/2. \qquad (20)$$

Though more familiar than the midpoint quadrature formula, it is less accurate and harder to analyze theoretically.

To find an *error bound* for trapezoidal quadrature, when $F \in \mathscr{C}^2$, consider first the case $n = 1$ of a single interval $a = x_0 < x_1 = b$. Consider the linear function

$$L(x) = F(a) + (x - a)[F(b) - F(a)]/h, \qquad h = b - a, \qquad (21)$$

defined by linear interpolation between the values $F(a)$ and $F(b)$, and let $R(x) = F(x) - L(x)$. Then $R''(x) \equiv F''(x)$, and $R(a) = R(b) = 0$. We now prove the following lemma.

■ LEMMA 1.   *For any s in the interval* (a, b),

$$R(s) = (s - a)(s - b)F''(\sigma)/2 \qquad \text{for some} \quad \sigma \in (a, b). \qquad (22)$$

Proof — Since L is linear, $L''(x) \equiv 0$ and $R''(x) \equiv F''(x)$; moreover, we know that $R(a) = R(b) = 0$ since $L(x)$ interpolates to $F(x)$ at a and b. This defines $R(x)$ as the solution of a two-endpoint problem which was solved in Chapter 2, § 10, by the formula

$$R(x) = \int_a^b G(x, t)F''(t)\, dt. \qquad (23)$$

Moreover, the Green's function $G(x, t)$ for this problem is easily verified to be

$$G(x, t) = \begin{cases} -(x - a)(b - t)/(b - a) & \text{if} \quad x \leqq t, \\ -(t - a)(b - x)/(b - a) & \text{if} \quad t \leqq x, \end{cases} \qquad (23')$$

since $G(a, t) = G(b, t) = 0$, $G_{xx} = \partial^2 G/\partial x^2 \equiv 0$ for $x \neq t$, and $G_x = \partial G/\partial x$ has a jump of one when $x = t$.

Further, since $G(x, t) \leq 0$ for all x, $t \in [a, b]$, we can use the Second Mean Value Theorem of the Calculus to prove that

$$R(x) = F''(s) \int_a^b G(x, t) \, dt \qquad \text{for some} \quad s, \ a < s < b.$$

The proof of (22) is completed by computing

$$(b - a) \int_a^b G(x, t) \, dt = \int_a^x (x - b)(t - a) \, dt + \int_x^b (x - a)(t - b) \, dt$$

$$= \tfrac{1}{2}(x - b)(x - a)^2 - \tfrac{1}{2}(x - a)(x - b)^2$$

$$= \tfrac{1}{2}(x - b)(x - a)[b - a].$$

This proves (22); the result is also a special case of Chapter 8, (12), which will be proved by another method.

It is a corollary of (22) that

$$(x - a)(x - b)F''_{\max}/2 \leq R(x) \leq (x - a)(x - b)F''_{\min}/2,$$

where $(x - a)(x - b) \leq 0$ for $x \in [a, b]$. Integrating from $x = a$ to $x = b$, we get, finally

$$F''_{\min}(b - a)^3/12 \leq T_\pi[F] - \int_a^b F(x) \, dx \leq F''_{\max}(b - a)^3/12$$

since $\int_a^b (x - a)(x - b) \, dx = -(b - a)^3/6$; we omit the details. Since $F'' \in \mathscr{C}$ and a continuous function assumes every value between its minimum and its maximum, this proves the next lemma.

■ **LEMMA 2.** *If $F \in \mathscr{C}^2$, then for some ξ_i in (x_{i-1}, x_i),*

$$\tfrac{1}{2}[F(x_{i-1}) + F(x_i)] \, \Delta x_i - \int_{x_{i-1}}^{x_i} F(x) \, dx = \tfrac{1}{12} F''(\xi_i) \, \Delta x_i^3.$$

Since $\Delta x_i^3 \leq |\pi|^2 \, \Delta x_i$, summation over i now gives our final result.

■ **THEOREM 6.** *The error bound for trapezoidal quadrature is given by the inequality*

$$\left| T_\pi[F] - \int_a^b F(x) \, dx \right| \leq |F''|_{\max}(b - a)|\pi|^2/12. \tag{24}$$

7*   Accurate error estimates

Error estimates having higher-order accuracy can also be derived for trapezoidal quadrature with intervals of subdivision of constant length

$\Delta x_i = 2k = h$. For any $F \in \mathscr{C}^6$, Taylor's formula with remainder gives, much as in the proof of Theorem 5,

$$F(m_i + k) + F(m_i - k) = 2F(m_i) + k^2 F''(m_i) + k^4 F^{iv}(m_i)/12 + O(k^6).$$

Multiplication by $\Delta x_i/2$, followed by summation over i, now gives the further estimate

$$T_\pi[F] = M_\pi[F] + \frac{k^2}{2} M_\pi[F''] + \frac{k^4}{24} M_\pi[F^{iv}] + O(k^6). \tag{25}$$

The right side of (25) can be evaluated by repeated use of the midpoint quadrature formula error estimate (17). The conclusion is the truncated Euler-Maclaurin formula.

■ THEOREM 7. *For $F \in \mathscr{C}^6$, let all intervals of subdivision have the same length $\Delta x_i = 2k = h$. Then*

$$T_\pi[F] = \int_a^b F(x)\, dx + h^2[F'(b) - F'(a)]/12$$
$$- h^4[F'''(b) - F'''(a)]/720 + O(h^6). \tag{26}$$

Proof — Replacing h by $2k$ in (17) and then substituting from (17) into (25), we obtain, as the contribution from the first term on the right-hand side of (25),

$$\int_a^b F(x)\, dx - k^2[F'(b) - F'(a)]/6 + 7k^4[F'''(b) - F'''(a)]/360 + O(k^6).$$

That from the second term is

$$(k^2/2)\left\{\int_a^b F''(x)\, dx - (k^2/6)[F'''(b) - F'''(a)] + O(k^4)\right\},$$

while the third term gives $(k^4/24)[F'''(b) - F'''(a)] + O(k^6)$. Adding these three contributions together, simplifying, and writing $k = h/2$, we get (26).

Simpson's Rule. Comparing the error estimates (17) and (26) for midpoint and trapezoidal quadrature, we are led to an error estimate for Simpson's rule. For a given partition π, this is defined as

$$S_\pi[F] = \tfrac{2}{3}M_\pi[F] + \tfrac{1}{3}T_\pi[F] = \sum_{i=1}^n [F(x_{i-1}) + 4F(m_i) + F(x_i)]\, \Delta x_i/6. \tag{27}$$

Forming the linear combination indicated for subdivisions into double steps of constant length $2k = h$, we obtain

$$S_\pi[F] = \int_a^b F(x)\, dx + \frac{k^4}{180}[F'''(b) - F'''(a)] + O(k^6). \tag{28}$$

Simpson's rule will be studied further in Chapter 8, § 9.

Exact error. Using the Green's function for the two-endpoint problem $u'' = r(x)$, $u(-k) = u(k) = 0$, we can also obtain an exact formula for the error in trapezoidal quadrature over a single interval. As in Chapter 2, § 10, we have

$$R(x) = \int_{-k}^{k} G(x,\,\xi) R''(\xi)\,d\xi = \int_{-k}^{k} G(x,\,\xi) F''(\xi)\,d\xi,$$

where $R(x)$, defined as in §6 to be the difference between the function $F(x)$ and its trapezoidal approximation $L(x)$, vanishes at the endpoints and satisfies $R'' = F''$. The Green's function $G(x,\,\xi)$ is given by

$$G(x,\,\xi) = \begin{cases} (\xi x/k + \xi - x - k)/2, & \xi < x, \\ (\xi x/k - \xi + x - k)/2, & \xi > x. \end{cases} \tag{29}$$

The error in trapezoidal quadrature over $(-k,\,k)$ is

$$T_\pi[F] - \int_{-k}^{k} F(x)\,dx = \int_{-k}^{k} [L(x) - F(x)]\,dx = \int_{-k}^{k} R(x)\,dx.$$

Substituting for $R(x)$ the integral expression displayed above and interchanging the order of integration in the resulting double integral, we get

$$T_\pi[F] - \int_{-k}^{k} F(x)\,dx = \int_{-k}^{k} \left\{ \int_{-k}^{k} G(x,\,\xi)\,dx \right\} F''(\xi)\,d\xi.$$

But by direct calculation, $\displaystyle\int_{-k}^{k} G(x,\,\xi)\,dx = (k^2 - \xi^2)/2$. Hence

■ THEOREM 8.   *The error in trapezoidal quadrature over a single interval* $(-k,\,k)$ *is* $\displaystyle\int_{-k}^{k} (k^2 - \xi^2) F''(\xi)\,d\xi/2$.

EXERCISES C

1. Use (26) to estimate the difference

$$\ln 2 - \left[\frac{1}{20} + \frac{1}{40} + \sum_{k=1}^{9} \frac{1}{10+k} + \frac{1}{400} \right].$$

In Exercises 2–5, use (26) with $h = 0.2$ to evaluate the following numbers approximately:

2. $\ln 2 = \int_1^2 dx/x$.   3. $\arctan 1 = \int_0^1 dx/(1+x^2)$.

4. $\int_0^1 \sqrt{1 + x^4}\,dx$.   5. $\int_0^1 \sin(x^2)\,dx$.

In Exercises 6–9, use Simpson's rule (27) with double step $2k = h = 0.2$ to evaluate approximately the numbers defined in Exercises 2–5, respectively.

10. For a subdivision into $2n$ intervals of length $h = (b-a)/2n$, Simpson's approximation to $\int_a^b f(x)\,dx$ is $\sum_{i=1}^{n} (h/3)[f(x_{2i-2}) + 4f(x_{2i-1}) + f(x_{2i})]$. Show that the truncation error is $(h^5/90) \sum_{i=1}^{n} f^{\mathrm{iv}}(x_{2i-1}) + O(h^6)$.

11. Derive (23) from Theorem 8, noting that $\int_{-k}^{k}(k^2 - \xi^2)\,d\xi = 4k^3/3$.

12*. Show that $\int_{-h}^{h} F(x)\,dx = 2hF(0) + \frac{1}{6}[\int_{-h}^{h}(|h| - |x|)^3 F''(x)\,dx]$. [HINT: Construct the Green's function for the initial value problem defined by $u'' = F''(x)$ and $F(0) = F'(0) = 0$, and study the proof of Theorem 8.]

8   Trapezoidal integration

The trapezoidal quadrature formula has an immediate extension to arbitrary systems of first-order DE's—and hence to DE's of arbitrary order.† Namely, for the system $dx/dt = \mathbf{X}(\mathbf{x}, t)$, *trapezoidal integration* is defined *implicitly*‡ by the recursion formula

$$y_k = y_{k-1} + [\mathbf{X}(\mathbf{y}_{k-1}, t_{k-1}) + \mathbf{X}(\mathbf{y}_k, t_k)]\,\Delta t_k/2, \qquad (30)$$

where $\Delta t_k = t_k - t_{k-1}$. From a given initial value $\mathbf{y}_0 = \mathbf{c}$ and partition π, formula (30) defines a sequence of values $\mathbf{y}_k = \mathbf{y}_\pi(t_k)$, that is, a *function table* describing approximately the solution of the DE $\dot{\mathbf{x}} = \mathbf{X}(\mathbf{x}, t)$ satisfying the initial value $\mathbf{x}(a) = \mathbf{c}$.

■ EXAMPLE 4.   Consider the solution of the *linear* DE

$$dx/dt + 2tx = 1, \qquad (31)$$

taking the initial value $x(0) = 0$. By the formula of Chapter 1, § 5, the solution is the function $x = e^{-t^2}\int_0^t e^{s^2}\,ds$. Looking up values of the definite integral in a table,†† we get the first row of entries in the following display.

t	0.1	0.2	0.3	0.4	0.5	0.6	0.7	0.8	0.9
x	0.0993	0.1948	0.2826	0.3599	0.4244	0.4748	0.5105	0.5321	0.5407
y	0.0990	0.1941	0.2818	0.3590	0.4235	0.4739	0.5097	0.5315	0.5404
z	0.100	0.195	0.283	0.360	0.424	0.474	0.509	0.531	0.539

These entries may be compared with values y_k of the approximate function table constructed using the trapezoidal integration formula (30), with constant mesh-length $h = 0.1$, $a = c = 0$, and $b = 0.9$. With this value of h, the formula in Example 4 reduces to

$$y_k = [1 + (10 - t_{k-1})y_{k-1}]/[10 + t_k].$$

---

† As in Chapter 6, §4. This does not mean that reduction to a first-order system is recommended in numerical integration.

‡ For large Δt_k, Equation (30) may have more than one solution. This difficulty will be taken up in §10.

†† E. Jahnke and F. Emde, *Tables of Functions*, Dover, 1943, p. 32; W. L. Miller and A. R. Gordon, *J. Phys. Chem.* **35** (1931), p. 2878.

The entries in the second row of the above table were calculated from the preceding formula, rounding off all numbers to six decimal digits, and then rounding off the final values to four decimals.

Above, we used a table of $\int_0^t e^{s^2}\,ds$; we next ask: How should one construct this table? For large t, numerical quadrature formulas tend to be inefficient, because the integrand e^{s^2} varies so rapidly (by more than 10% between 5 and 5.01, for example). For this reason, it is more efficient to calculate the solution $x(t)$ of DE (31) satisfying $x(0) = 0$, by one of the efficient processes of numerical integration to be described in Chapter 8, and then compute the integral in question as the product $\int_0^t e^{s^2}ds = e^{t^2}x(t)$.

The preceding discussion illustrates an important point. Elaborate manipulations with special tricks of integration and special functions are not usually helpful in obtaining numerical values for solutions of DE's; they are more useful for describing the singularities of such solutions and for indicating the dependence of the solutions on parameters which may be involved in the DE's defining them.

Asymptotic expansion. For very large t (say $t \geq 25$) it is still better to substitute $s = t - r$ above and to expand e^{r^2} in a Taylor's series, getting

$$e^{-t^2}\int_0^t e^{s^2}\,ds = \int_0^t e^{-2tr}(1 + r^2 + r^4/2! + r^6/3! + \cdots)\,dr.$$

For large t, the kth term gives the integral

$$\frac{t^{-2k-1}}{(k!)2^{2k+1}}\int_0^{2t^2} e^{-\rho}\rho^{2k}\,d\rho \sim \frac{(2k)!\,t^{-2k-1}}{(k!)2^{2k+1}}, \qquad \rho = 2tr.$$

By truncating the series at the kth term, an asymptotic error estimate can, moreover, be obtained.

Knowing (or having guessed) the form of the asymptotic series $x(t) \sim \sum_{k=0}^{\infty} a_k/t^{2k+1}$, we can also derive from (31) purely formally, by the method of undetermined coefficients, that $a_0 = \frac{1}{2}$ and $a_{k+1} = (2k+1)a_k/2$, whence (asymptotically) we obtain

$$x \sim \frac{1}{2t} + \frac{1}{4t^3} + \frac{3}{8t^5} + \frac{15}{16t^7} + \cdots \qquad \text{as } t \to \infty.$$

Though the series is (ultimately) divergent, the first few terms give an extremely accurate approximation to $x(t)$ for $t \geq 25$.

9   Order of accuracy

The cumulative error in the function table constructed by the trapezoidal integration formula (30) can be bounded in terms of properties of the vector-valued function $\mathbf{X}$ alone. This will be shown below, for simplicity, only in the case $dx/dt = X(x, t)$ of a single first-order DE. In this section, we will actually bound only the error made in a single step; the cumulative effect of such errors will be derived later, in §12.

Let the *discrepancy* of an exact solution $x(t)$ of the DE $dx/dt = X(x, t)$ from the approximate solution given by the recursion formula (30) at the kth step be defined as the difference

$$\delta_k = x_k - x_{k-1} - [X(x_{k-1}, t_{k-1}) + X(x_k, t_k)]\, \Delta t_k/2,$$

where $\Delta t_k = t_k - t_{k-1}$ and $x_k = x(t_k)$ as usual. Lemma 2 of §6 shows that the discrepancy is $(\Delta t_k{}^3/12)\ddot{X}(x(t), t)$, where t is some number in the interval (t_{k-1}, t_k), and

$$\ddot{X} = \frac{d^3x}{dt^3} = \frac{\partial^2 X}{\partial t^2} + 2X \frac{\partial^2 X}{\partial x\, \partial t} + X^2 \frac{\partial^2 X}{\partial x^2} + \frac{\partial X}{\partial x} \frac{\partial X}{\partial t} + X\left(\frac{\partial X}{\partial x}\right)^2. \quad (32)$$

In Example 4, this gives $\ddot{X} = -4 + 12xt + 4t^2 - 8xt^3$. If we substitute calculated values of (x_k, t_k) into (32), we get an estimate of the discrepancy δ_k at the kth step. By considering the range of these values, we can also *bound* this discrepancy.

Having estimated the discrepancy δ_k of the exact solution $x(t)$ of $dx/dt = X(x, t)$ at the kth step from (32), it is easy to bound the error introduced by the approximate integration formula (30). The first step is typical; for given $x_0 = y_0 = c$, the error introduced at the first step is $\gamma_1 = y_1 - x_1$. If the function X satisfies a Lipschitz condition with Lipschitz constant L, then (30) implies

$$y_1 - x_1 = [X(y_1, t) - X(x_1, t)]\, \Delta t_k/2 - \delta_1.$$

Since $|X(y_1, t) - X(x_1, t)| \leq L|y_1 - x_1|$, it follows that

$|\gamma_1| \leq |\delta_1| + L|\gamma_1|\, \Delta t_1/2,$ or

$$|\gamma_1| = |y_1 - x_1| \leq |\delta_1|/(1 - L\, \Delta t_1/2). \quad (33)$$

Hence, if $\Delta t_1 \leq 1/L$, the inequality $|\gamma_1| \leq 2|\delta_1|$ follows.

Since $|\delta_k| \leq (|\pi|^2 |\ddot{X}|_{\max}/12)\, \Delta t_k$, by Lemma 2 of §6, it follows that the *absolute* error $\gamma_k = \epsilon_k\, \Delta t_k$ introduced at the kth step† is at most twice this amount, and so the *relative* error $\epsilon_k = \gamma_k/\Delta t_k$ is bounded by $|\pi|^2 |\ddot{X}|_{\max}/6$, provided that $|\pi| \leq 1/L$. As will be shown in §12, the cumulative error has the same order of magnitude as the relative error. Hence we conclude that the order of accuracy of trapezoidal integration is $O(h^2)$.

---

† This is defined (for one-step processes) as the difference $y_k - \tilde{x}_k$ between the computed value y_k and the exact solution $\tilde{x}_{k-1}(t_k)$ of the given DE for the initial condition $\tilde{x}(t_{k-1}) = y_{k-1}$.

EXERCISES D

In Exercises 1–4, compute the trapezoidal approximations to the solutions of the initial value problems specified, over the range $0 \leq t \leq 1$ with $h = 0.1$.

1. $\dot{x} = -tx$, $x(0) = 1$.   2. $\dot{x} = 1 + x^2$, $x(0) = 0$.
3. $\dot{x} = y$, $\dot{y} = 0$, $x(0) = 0$, $y(0) = 1$.
4. $\dot{x} = y$, $\dot{y} = x + y$, $x(0) = 0$, $y(0) = 1$.

5. For the DE $y' = F(x, y)$, show that the truncation error of the Cauchy polygon method, in one step $0 \leq x \leq h$, is

$$\frac{h^2}{2}\left[\frac{\partial F}{\partial x}(0, y_0) + F(0, y_0)\frac{\partial F}{\partial y}(0, y_0)\right] + O(h^3), \qquad y_0 = y(0).$$

In Exercises 6–9, compute the truncation error for trapezoidal integration over one interval of length h, in terms of the Taylor series expansions of the functions involved:

6. $\dot{x} = p(t)x$, p analytic.   7. $\dot{x} = 1 + x^2$.
8. $\dot{x} = y$, $\dot{y} = 0$.   9. $\dot{x} = y$, $\dot{y} = x + y$.

10. For the DE $y'' = F(x, y)$ what is the order of accuracy of the formula

$$y_{n+1} = y_{n-1} + 2hF(x_n, y_n),$$

if all $\Delta x_k = h$?

10   The improved Euler method

The trapezoidal method is very convenient for getting approximate solutions to *linear* DE's like (31), when moderate (two- or three-decimal place) accuracy is desired. But it is awkward when it comes to *nonlinear* DE's because of the difficulty of solving (30) for $\mathbf{y}_k$. In general, formula (30) does not define the vectors $\mathbf{y}_k$ recursively but only implicitly. To determine each $\mathbf{y}_k$, we have to solve an equation† (30) where $\mathbf{y}_k$ is the unknown, $\mathbf{y}_{k-1}$ having been previously determined.

For small Δt_k, we can do this by *iteration*: start with a trial value of $\mathbf{y}_k$ (say $\mathbf{y}_{k-1} + \mathbf{X}(\mathbf{y}_{k-1}, t_{k-1})\,\Delta t_k$), substitute this trial value $\mathbf{y}_k^0$ into the right-hand side of (30) to get a better approximation $\mathbf{y}_k^1$, and then repeat the process

$$\mathbf{y}_k^{r+1} = \mathbf{y}_{k-1} + [\mathbf{X}(\mathbf{y}_{k-1}, t_{k-1}) + \mathbf{X}(\mathbf{y}_k^r, t_k)]\,\Delta t_k/2$$

until (30) is satisfied up to the error tolerated.

Rather than solving the implicit equation (30) accurately by many iterations, one usually gets greater accuracy for the same amount of

---

† The vector equation (30) is, of course, equivalent to a system of n simultaneous equations in the components. For linear systems, these equations can be solved by Gauss elimination instead of iteration.

work by using a finer mesh and stopping after one or two iterations. If one stops after a single iteration, one has the *improved Euler method*, which is useful for many nonlinear engineering problems requiring moderate accuracy (two significant decimal digits, say).

In the improved Euler method, therefore, one constructs an *approximate function table* for the solution of $dx/dt = X(x, t)$ for a given initial value $x(a) = c$ and partition defined by points of subdivision $a = t_0 < t_1 < t_2 < \cdots$, as follows. (More generally, for any vector DE $d\mathbf{x}/dt = \mathbf{X}(\mathbf{x}, t)$ and vector initial value $\mathbf{x}(a) = \mathbf{c}$, one computes an approximate function table for each *component* $x_i(t)$ of $\mathbf{x}(t)$.)

Starting with $z_0 = c$, the improved Euler method gives an approximate function table of values $z_1, z_2, z_3, \ldots$, using *two* formulas at each step.

A *first* approximation to the true value is, by the Cauchy polygon construction applied to z_{k-1},

$$p_k = z_{k-1} + X(z_{k-1}, t_{k-1}) \, \Delta t_k. \tag{34}$$

The number p_k thus computed is a first approximation to the number z_k desired. It is called the *predictor*. Next, we compute the number z_k, using the predictor by applying formula (30),

$$z_k = z_{k-1} + ([X(z_{k-1}, t_{k-1}) + X(p_k, t_k)] \, \Delta t_k)/2. \tag{34'}$$

This formula is called the *corrector formula*. The slope used in computing z_k by the corrector formula is the average of the slope at the point (z_{k-1}, t_{k-1}) and the slope at the point (p_k, t_k) computed by means of the predictor. In this way, the sequence z_k is calculated *explicitly* without solving any implicit equations such as (30), employing two steps to determine each of the z_k.

The improved Euler method consists in determining the sequence of z_k by performing these two substitutions in alternation. In the case $X(x, t) = F(t)$ of quadrature, it is equivalent to the trapezoidal method.

Applied to the initial value problem of Example 4, the improved Euler method gives the approximate solution tabulated in the last row of the table of § 8; in this example, the work was carried to three decimal places to reduce the cumulative error to 0.01.

To apply the improved Euler method to first-order systems, simply substitute vectors for scalars in formulas (34), (34'). We illustrate the procedure by an example.

EXAMPLE 5.   Consider the initial value problem defined by the non-linear system

$$dx/dt = x^2 + y^2, \qquad dy/dt = 1 + x^2 - y^2, \qquad x(0) = y(0) = 0. \tag{35}$$

There is little hope that formal methods of integration will help in the computation, but a straightforward application of the improved Euler method enables one to calculate an approximate solution.

The calculations to be performed give, for this example, the double sequence of numbers x_k, y_k defined by $x_0 = y_0 = 0$ and by the formulas

$$p_k = x_{k-1} + (x_{k-1}^2 + y_{k-1}^2)\,\Delta t_k,$$
$$q_k = y_{k-1} + (1 + x_{k-1}^2 - y_{k-1}^2)\,\Delta t_k \tag{36}$$

and

$$x_k = x_{k-1} + (x_{k-1}^2 + y_{k-1}^2 + p_k^2 + q_k^2)\,\Delta t_k/2,$$
$$y_k = y_{k-1} + (2 + x_{k-1}^2 - y_{k-1}^2 + p_k^2 - q_k^2)\,\Delta t_k/2. \tag{36'}$$

Each step requires squaring four numbers and performing fourteen additions and subtractions and four multiplications. These can all be accomplished by hand in a total of ten minutes per time step or less, especially if $h = \Delta t_k = 0.1$, say, and a table of squares is available.

For a subdivision into intervals of constant length h, the relative error committed in using the improved Euler method is $O(h^2)$, provided that the function $X(x, t)$ is of class $\mathscr{C}^2$. For, expanding the exact solution $x(t)$ of $dx/dt = X(x, t)$ by Taylor's Theorem with remainder, we have

$$x_k = x(t_k) = x_{k-1} + hX_{k-1} + \frac{h^2}{2}\left[X\frac{\partial X}{\partial x} + \frac{\partial X}{\partial t}\right]_{k-1} + O(h^3), \tag{37}$$

where X_{k-1} denotes $X(x_{k-1}, t_{k-1}) = X(x(t_{k-1}), t_{k-1})$ and the subscript $k-1$ on the term in square brackets has a similar meaning. The improved Euler method (34)–(34′) gives

$$y_k = y_{k-1} + hY_{k-1} + \frac{h^2}{2}\left[Y\frac{\partial Y}{\partial x} + \frac{\partial Y}{\partial t}\right]_{k-1} + O(h^3), \tag{38}$$

where Y_{k-1} denotes $X(y_{k-1}, t_{k-1})$, and so on. The *relative* error committed in substituting (38) for (37) is thus $O(h^2)$.

A more explicit error bound is deduced in § 12.

11   The modified Euler method

The improved Euler method has the advantage over the trapezoidal method of being explicit. Various other explicit methods about as accurate as the improved Euler and trapezoidal methods can also be constructed. For instance, one can use the following adaptation of the midpoint quadrature formula:

$$w_k = w_{k-1} + hX(w_{k-1} + hX_{k-1}/2,\ t_{k-1} + h/2), \qquad h = \Delta t_k. \tag{39}$$

This *midpoint* or *modified Euler* method is about twice as accurate as the trapezoidal and improved Euler methods in the special case $dx/dt = F(t)$ of quadrature, as a comparison of formulas (17) and (26) shows. (In this case, the improved Euler method *is* the trapezoidal method.)

But, for first-order DE's generally no such simple error comparison holds. To see this, let $X = \sum b_{jk} t^j x^k$ be expanded into a double power series, and let $x(t)$ satisfy $\dot{x} = X(x, t)$. Then, just as in Chapter 3, § 8, we have $\ddot{x} = X_t + X X_x$, and

$$d^3 x/dt^3 = X_{tt} + 2 X X_{tx} + X^2 X_{xx} + X_t X_x + X X_x^2.$$

We now introduce the abbreviations

$$C = b_{10} + b_{00} b_{01}, \qquad B = b_{20} + b_{11} b_{00} + b_{02} b_{00}^2,$$
$$B^* = b_{10} b_{01} + b_{00} b_{01}^2.$$

Expanding out to infinitesimals of the fourth order, we find that the *exact* solution of the DE $dx/dt = X(x, t)$ for the initial condition $x(0) = 0$ has the expansion

$$x(h) = h b_{00} + h^2 C/2 + h^3 (2B + B^*)/6 + O(h^4). \tag{40}$$

With the trapezoidal approximation (30), we obtain

$$y(h) = h b_{00} + h^2 C/2 + h^3 (2B + B^*)/4 + O(h^4), \tag{41}$$

giving a truncation error $h^3(B/6 + B^*/12) + O(h^4)$. With the improved Euler approximation (34)–(34′), we get

$$z(h) = h b_{00} + h^2 C/2 + h^3 B/2 + O(h^4), \tag{42}$$

with error $h^3(B - B^*)/6 + O(h^4)$. With the midpoint approximation (39), we finally obtain

$$w(h) = h b_{00} + h^2 C/2 + h^3 B/4 + O(h^4), \tag{43}$$

so that the error is $-h^3(B/12 + B^*/6) + O(h^4)$.

Corrected trapezoidal method. Theorem 7, when combined with Theorem 5 of Chapter 6, shows that the exact solution $x(t)$ of the first-order DE $dx/dt = X(x, t)$ satisfies

$$x_k = x_{k-1} + [X_{k-1} + X_k] \Delta t_k/2 + [\dot{X}_{k-1} - \dot{X}_k] \Delta t_k^2/12 + O(\Delta t_k^4), \tag{44}$$

where X_k denotes $X(x_k, t_k)$ and $\dot{X}$ denotes $\partial X/\partial t + X \partial X/\partial x$. Dropping the last term, we get a *corrected* trapezoidal integration formula, which may be expected to have a cumulative error of only $O(|\pi|^3)$.

For instance, when applied to the linear DE $\dot{x} = 1 - 2tx$ of Example 4, in which $\dot{X} = -2x - 2t + 4xt^2$, this formula gives the approximate recursion formula

$$x_k[1 + t_k\,\Delta t_k + (-1 + 2t_k{}^2)\,\Delta t_k{}^2/6] = x_{k-1}[1 - t_{k-1}\,\Delta t_k +$$
$$(-1 + 2t_{k-1}^2)\,\Delta t_k{}^2/6] + \Delta t_k + \Delta t_k{}^3/6,$$

with absolute error $O(\Delta t_k{}^4)$ and relative error $O(\Delta t_k{}^3)$.

EXERCISES E

In Exercises 1–4, compute approximate function tables on $[0, 1]$, with $\Delta t_k = 0.1$, by the improved Euler method for the following initial value problems:

1. $\dot{x} = -tx,\ x(0) = 1$. 2. $\dot{x} = (1 + x^2),\ x(0) = 0$.
3. $\dot{x} = y,\ \dot{y} = 0,\ x(0) = 0,\ y(0) = 1$. 4. $\dot{x} = y,\ \dot{y} = x + y,\ x(0) = 0,\ y(0) = 1$.

In Exercises 5–8, compute approximate function tables for the data of Exercises 1–4, using the *midpoint* (or modified Euler) method instead of the improved Euler method.

9. Obtain an expression through terms in h^5 for the error committed in applying (a) the improved Euler method and (b) the midpoint method to the DE $\dot{x} = p(t)x$, $p(t)$ analytic.

10. For the analytic DE $y' = F(x, y)$ and one interval $0 \leqq x \leqq h$, let the exact solution be given by $y(h) = a_0 + a_1 h + a_2 h^2 + a_3 h^3 + O(h^4)$ and let

$$y = c_0 + c_1 h + c_2 h^2 + c_3 h^3 + O(h^4)$$

be the approximate value given by trapezoidal formula. Show that $c_0 = a_0$, $c_1 = a_1$, $c_2 = a_2$, and $c_3 = 3a_3/2$.

11. Show that, through the terms computed in Exercise 10, the improved Euler method gives the same result for c_0, c_1, c_2 as trapezoidal integration.

12* The cumulative error

All the methods for constructing approximate function tables which have been described in this chapter have had one feature in common. Namely, the kth entry in the table has been constructed from the immediately preceding entry alone, the $(k-1)$-st entry, without reference to the earlier entries. Such methods are called *one-level* or *one-step* methods.

Given a one-level method for approximately integrating the DE $dx/dt = X(x, t)$, that is, for constructing an approximate function table with entries $y_k = y(t_k)$, we can express the preceding property by writing

$$y_k = \phi(y_{k-1}, t_{k-1}, t_k; X). \tag{45}$$

Here ϕ is the function expressing y_k in terms of y_{k-1} and the data of the problem. Bounds for the errors associated with one-level methods can be obtained by using the following general theorem, which applies equally to the Cauchy polygon method, the trapezoidal method, and the improved Euler and mid-point methods.

■ THEOREM 9.   *In any one-level method for numerical integration of the*
DE $dx/dt = X(x, t)$, *where X satisfies the Lipschitz condition*

$$|X(x, t) - X(y, t)| \leq L|x - y|,$$

let the relative error at each step be at most ϵ. Then, over an interval of length
T, the cumulative error is at most $(\epsilon/L)(e^{LT} - 1)$.

Proof — For any partition π, let ϵ_k denote the error introduced at the
kth step. That is, if $\tilde{x}_k(t)$ is that exact solution of the given DE satisfying the initial condition $\tilde{x}_k(t_k) = y_k$, where y_k is the value of the computed approximate solution at t_k, let

$$\epsilon_k = |y_k - \tilde{x}_{k-1}(t_k)| = |\tilde{x}_k(t_k) - \tilde{x}_{k-1}(t_k)|.$$

By the definition of "relative error," we have $\epsilon_k \leq \epsilon \Delta t_k$. The magnitude of the cumulative error is, by definition,

$$|y_m - x(t_m)| = |\tilde{x}_m(t_m) - \tilde{x}_0(t_m)| = \left| \sum_{k=1}^{m} [\tilde{x}_k(t_m) - \tilde{x}_{k-1}(t_m)] \right|$$

$$\leq \sum_{k=1}^{m} |\tilde{x}_k(t_m) - \tilde{x}_{k-1}(t_m)|.$$

But $|\tilde{x}_k(t_m) - \tilde{x}_{k-1}(t_m)|$ is the magnitude of the difference, at $t = t_m$, of
two solutions of the given DE which differ by ϵ_k at $t = t_k$. By Theorem
2 of Chapter 6, this is at most

$$\epsilon_k e^{L(t_m - t_k)} \leq \epsilon e^{L(t_m - t_k)} \Delta t_k$$

since $\epsilon_k \leq \epsilon \Delta t_k$. Here ϵ is any upper bound to the relative error.
Summing over k, we get the following upper bound to the cumulative
error:

$$|y_\pi(t_m) - x(t_m)| \leq \epsilon \sum_{k=1}^{m} [e^{L(t_m - t_k)} \Delta t_k] \leq \epsilon e^{Lt_m} \sum_{k=1}^{m} [e^{-Lt_k} \Delta t_k].$$

But the final sum is the Riemann lower sum approximation to the
definite integral $\int_{t_0}^{t_m} \exp(-Lt) \, dt = [\exp(-Lt_0) - \exp(-Lt_m)]/L$. Hence

$$|y_\pi(t_m) - x(t_m)| \leq \epsilon[e^{LT} - 1]/L,$$

and Theorem 9 follows.

Trapezoidal integration. For trapezoidal integration, the discussion
of § 9 shows that the truncation error ϵ_k at the kth step is bounded by

$$(|\pi|^2 |\dddot{X}|_{\max}) \Delta t_k / 12[1 - (L \Delta t_k / 2)].$$

Hence, in this case, an error bound is given by the

■ COROLLARY.   *The error in the approximate function table constructed by the trapezoidal formula* (30) *is at most*

$$|\pi|^2 |\ddot{X}|_{\max}(e^{Lt} - 1)/12L[1 - L|\pi|/2] \qquad if \quad |\pi| \leq 1/L. \qquad (46)$$

Similar error bounds can be found for the midpoint and improved Euler approximate integration methods.

Approximate solutions.   The error bound (46) refers to the approximate function table constructed by the trapezoidal integration formula (30). Using linear interpolation between successive values, we can obtain from this function table a continuous approximate solution to the DE $dx/dt = X(x, t)$. Since the error in linear interpolation is bounded by $|\ddot{x}|_{\max}|\pi|^2/2$, where $\ddot{x} = \dot{X} = \partial X/\partial t + X \partial X/\partial x$, we see that the order of accuracy of this approximate solution is also $O(|\pi|^2)$.

EXERCISES F

1. Let $x(t)$ and $y(t)$ be approximate solutions of the system (1) with deviations ϵ_1 and ϵ_2, defined for $a \leq t \leq b$. Show that (9) implies that:

$$|x(t) - y(t)| \leq |x(a) - y(a)|e^{L|t-a|} + (\epsilon_1 + \epsilon_2)[(e^{L|t-a|} - 1)/L].$$

2. Let $F(x, y)$ and $G(x, y)$ be everywhere continuous, let F satisfy a Lipschitz condition with Lipschitz constant L, and let $|F(x, y) - G(x, y)| \leq K$. Show that if $f(x)$ and $g(x)$ are approximate solutions of the DE's $y' = F(x, y)$ and $z' = G(x, z)$ with deviations ϵ and η, then

$$|f(x) - g(x)| \leq |f(a) - g(a)| e^{L|x-a|} + (K + \epsilon + \eta)[e^{L|x-a|} - 1]/L.$$

3*. Assume that, for equally spaced subdivisions of mesh length h, the truncation error of a given approximate method $I_h[f]$ is $Mh^n + O(h^{n+1})$, where M is independent of h. Prove that the *extrapolated* estimate

$$I_h^*[f] = (2^n I_{h/2}[f] - I_h[f])/(2^n - 1)$$

has a truncation error $O(h^{n+1})$.

4*. (a) Show that the extrapolation of Exercise 3 gives the trapezoidal approximation from the Cauchy polygon approximation and Simpson's rule from the trapezoidal approximation.

(b) Show that Simpson's rule satisfies the hypotheses of Exercise 3 with $n = 4$. Derive an extrapolation estimate for Simpson's rule.

5*. For the DE $dx/dt + tx = 0$ and the mesh length $h_n = 1/(10|t_n| + 1)$, show that the truncation error of the trapezoidal method tends to zero as $t \to \infty$, regardless of the initial value $x(0)$. What is the limiting truncation error as $t \to -\infty$?

6*. Let $f(t)$ be an analytic function, and $f(t + 1) = f(t)$. Show that trapezoidal integration of $\int_0^1 f(t) \, dt$ for $h = 1/n$ has an infinite order of accuracy as $n \to \infty$.

7. Show that the error is $O(h^7)$ in the extended Simpson's rule

$$\int_{x-h}^{x+h} F(x) \, dx$$

$$\simeq \frac{h}{90} \{114F(x) + 34[F(x + h) + F(x-h)] - [F(x + 2h) + F(x - 2h)]\}.$$

8. (a) Let $z_k = z_0 + i^{k-1}h$, $i = \sqrt{-1}$. Show that, if $F(z)$ is any complex polynomial of degree five or less, then we have

$$\int_{z_3}^{z_1} F(z)\, dz = \frac{h}{15}[24F_0 + 4(F_1 + F_3) - (F_2 + F_4)]. \qquad (*)$$

(b) Infer that, if $F(z)$ is a complex analytic function, (*) holds with an error which is $O(h^7)$.

9*. Let $F(x, y)$ be bounded and continuous on the strip $0 \leq x \leq 1$, $-\infty < y < +\infty$; let $\{\pi_n\}$ be any sequence of partitions of $[0, 1]$ with $|\pi_n| \to 0$; and let $f_n(x)$ be the Cauchy polygon approximate solution, defined by π_n for the initial value $y(0) = 0$.

(a) Show that, if the $f_n(x)$ converge to a limit function $f(x)$, then $f(x)$ is a solution of $y' = F(x, y)$.

(b) Show that, in any case, a uniformly convergent subsequence $\{f_{n(i)}(x)\}$ can be found, $n(i) < n(i + 1)$. [HINT: See Chapter 6, § 13.]

10*. In Exercise 9, show that, if the DE $y' = F(x, y)$ admits only one solution for the initial value $y(0) = 0$, any sequence of Cauchy polygon approximations defined for $y(0) = 0$ by partitions whose norms tend to zero must converge to the exact solution.

8 Efficient Numerical Integration

1 Introduction

The concepts of approximate solution of a DE and approximate function table were introduced in Chapter 7, with some simple but instructive examples. These referred exlusively to normal first-order systems

$$d\mathbf{x}/dt = \mathbf{X}(\mathbf{x}, t). \tag{1}$$

The simplicity of the methods treated made possible a rigorous theoretical analysis of their errors.

However, the methods studied in Chapter 7 are rarely used when more than two decimal places of accuracy are wanted, because they converge so slowly (require so many steps). To obtain more accurate results with less effort, one uses more refined methods having higher orders of accuracy. Such methods are available provided $\mathbf{x}$ is really smooth, say $\mathbf{x} \in \mathscr{C}^4$, an assumption which makes (exact) solutions of (1) be of class $\mathscr{C}^5$. When such methods are used, the numerical integration of most ordinary DE's becomes a routine and very economical process on modern computing machines.

Like the schemes already analyzed in Chapter 7, the schemes for numerical integration to be studied below will refer to an assumed partition π of the interval $[a, b]$ of integration by a finite number of points (the *mesh*),

$$\pi\colon a = t_0 < t_1 < t_2 < \cdots < t_n = b = a + T. \tag{2}$$

Typically, the partition is into *steps* $\Delta t_k = t_k - t_{k-1}$ of constant length h, so that $t_r = a + rh$; we then speak of a *uniform mesh*.

On the mesh (2), the DE (1) is approximated by a suitable *difference equation*. This difference equation is then solved step-by-step in hand computations, using ordinary arithmetic supplemented by readings from available function tables. In machine computations, function tables are usually replaced by simple subroutines giving accurate approximations by rational functions.

One can obtain difference approximations to DE's by simply replacing derivatives by difference quotients, as in the Cauchy polygon method. With ordinary DE's, it is more usual to replace the system (1) by the equivalent vector integral equation (Chapter 6, (11)),

$$\mathbf{x}(t) = \mathbf{x}(a) + \int_a^t \mathbf{X}(\mathbf{x}, s)\, ds, \tag{3}$$

using a numerical quadrature formula (e.g., trapezoidal quadrature or Simpson's Rule) to replace (3) by a discrete approximation.

In either case, the step-by-step solution of the resulting difference equations yields an *approximate function table*, where the interval of tabulation is constant if the mesh is uniform. This function table, when combined with a suitable *interpolation* formula, then defines an *approximate solution*, whose value $\mathbf{y}(t)$ for any t can be computed to the degree of accuracy desired.

From these introductory remarks, it is clear that we must make a preliminary study of difference equations and interpolation formulas, before we can understand the art of efficient numerical integration. This preliminary study will be the subject of §§ 2–7 below.

2   Difference Operators

In the study of difference equations (or ΔE's, as we shall write for short), we are concerned with the *forward* difference operator Δ, the *backward* difference operator ∇, and the *central* difference operator δ, defined by the formulas

$$\Delta f(x) = f(x + h) - f(x), \tag{4a}$$

$$\nabla f(x) = f(x) - f(x - h), \tag{4b}$$

$$\delta f(x) = f(x + \tfrac{1}{2}h) - f(x - \tfrac{1}{2}h). \tag{4c}$$

In the preceding formulas, the symbols Δ, ∇, δ stand for *linear operators* transforming functions into functions. Unlike the linear differential operators of Chapter 2, §5, they aply to *all* functions.

These operations are useful in obtaining approximate solutions because they yield approximations to the derivative $f'(x)$. If $f \in \mathscr{C}^1$, the derivative $f'(x)$ is the limit of the *divided differences*:

$$f'(x) = \lim_{h \to 0} (\Delta f)/h = \lim_{h \to 0} (\nabla f)/h = \lim_{h \to 0} \delta f/h.$$

These are called, respectively, the *forward*, *backward*, and *central* divided differences of f at x.

The difference operators (4a)–(4c) can be applied to any *function table* defined on a uniform mesh with step h, consisting of the equally spaced points

$$x_r = x_0 + rh, \qquad r = 0, \pm 1, \pm 2, \dots; \qquad h > 0. \tag{5}$$

Using the standard abbreviations $y_r = f_r = f(a + rh)$, we obtain the identity

$$f_1 - f_0 = f(x + h) - f(x) = \Delta f_0 = \nabla f_1 = \delta f_{\frac{1}{2}}.$$

This shows that the usual difference notation is highly redundant.†

This redundancy is apparent also when we *iterate* the difference operators (4a)–(4c) to define the *second differences*

$$\Delta^2 f(x) = \Delta(\Delta(fx)) = \Delta(f(x + h) - f(x)) = f(x + 2h)$$
$$- 2f(x + h) + f(x), \tag{6a}$$

$$\nabla^2 f(x) = \nabla(\nabla f(x)) = \nabla(f(x) - f(x - h)) = f(x)$$
$$- 2f(x - h) + f(x - 2h), \tag{6b}$$

$$\delta^2 f(x) = f(x + h) - 2f(x) + f(x - h). \tag{6c}$$

We easily verify the identities $\delta^2 f(x) = \Delta(\nabla f(x)) = \nabla(\Delta f(x))$.

In formulas (6a)–(6c), the exponent 2 describes the effect of applying the operators of formulas (4a)–(4c) twice, or "*squaring*" them. More generally, we can form *polynomials* (with constant coefficients) of difference operators, like $\Delta^2 - 3\Delta + 2$. Such linear difference operators with constant coefficients commute (are permutable); those with variable coefficients do not (cf. Exercise A4 below).

3   Characteristic equation; stability

A *linear* ΔE *with constant coefficients* is one of the form

$$y_{n+m} = a_0 y_n + a_1 y_{n+1} + \cdots + a_{m-1} y_{n+m-1}, \tag{7}$$

where a_k are given constants. The solutions of such a ΔE can be obtained by a substitution similar to the exponential substitution of Chapter 4, § 1. Try the sequence $y_r = \rho^r$, where ρ is a number to be determined. This gives from (7) the *characteristic equation*

$$\rho^m - a_0 - a_1 \rho - \cdots - a_{m-1} \rho^{m-1} = 0. \tag{8}$$

---

† It is also inconsistent with the usual notation $\Delta t_i = t_i - t_{i-1}$ employed in writing Riemann sums, used in Chapter 7.

For each root ρ_k of this characteristic equation, the sequence $y_r = \rho_k^r$ is the solution of the linear ΔE (7) satisfying the initial conditions $y_0 = 1$, $y_1 = \rho_k, \ldots, y_{m-1} = \rho^{m-1}$.

EXAMPLE 1. Consider the central difference approximation $y_{k+1} - y_{k-1} = 2hy_k$ with constant mesh length h to the DE $y' = y$. This can be rewritten in the form (7) as

$$y_{k+1} = y_{k-1} + 2hy_k. \tag{9}$$

For $h = 0.1$ and $y_0 = y(0) = 1$, the exponential series truncated after five terms gives $y_1 = 1.1052$, rounded off to four decimal places. Substituting into (9), we can compute the approximate function table for $y_r = \exp (r/10)$:

x	0.1	0.2	0.3	0.4	0.5	0.6	0.7
y	1.1052	1.2210	1.3494	1.4809	1.6476	1.8204	2.0117

and so on. After ten steps, this gives the approximate value $e = 2.7159$, whose error is about -0.0023.

In Example 1, the characteristic equation is $\rho^2 = 1 + 2h\rho$, with distinct roots

$$\rho_i = h \pm \sqrt{1 + h^2} = \pm 1 + h \pm h^2/2 \mp h^4/8 \pm \cdots.$$

For $h = 0.1$, this gives $\rho_1 = 1.10499$, $\rho_2 = -0.90499$ when rounded off to five decimal places. The first root gives a fair approximation to the exact solution $e^{r/10}$, for which $\rho = 1.10517$. The discrepancy of 0.00018 is enough to explain the error in the approximate function table computed above. It indicates that little can be gained by reducing the roundoff error to less than 0.00005 per step—i.e., by carrying out computations to more than four decimal places.

When the characteristic equation (8) has m distinct roots, the sequences ρ_k^r form a *basis* of solutions of the ΔE (7). This means that every solution of (7) can be expressed as a linear combination,

$$y_r = A_1 \rho_1^r + A_2 \rho_2^r + \cdots + A_m \rho_m^r,$$

of the particular solutions ρ_k^r. The preceding result holds since the vectors $(1, \rho_k, \rho_k^2, \ldots, \rho_k^{m-1})$ are linearly independent,† so that any initial value vector $(y_0, y_1, \ldots, y_{m-1})$ is a suitable linear combination of them.

---

† Their determinant is the Vandermonde determinant and so is not zero (Birkhoff and Mac Lane, p. 284, Ex. 6c).

Even if the characteristic equation has multiple roots, a basis of solutions of the form $r^j\rho_k^{\ r}$ can still be constructed, much as in Chapter 4, Theorem 1.

Stability. In analogy with Chapter 4, §5, we say that the homogeneous linear nth-order ΔE with constant coefficients (7) is *stable* when all solutions y_r are *bounded* sequences, and *strictly stable* when all solutions are sequences tending to zero as $r \to \infty$.

Since we can obtain a basis of solutions of (7) of the form $r^j\rho_k^{\ r}$, the ΔE (7) is strictly stable if and only if all roots of the characteristic equation (8) are less than one in absolute value. This condition is obviously necessary; it is sufficient because $\lim_{r \to \infty} r^j\rho^r = 0$ whenever $|\rho| < 1$.

The concept of stability brings out a significant aspect of the effectiveness of the central difference approximation (9) for integrating numerically the DE $y' = y$. The general solution of (9) is $A\rho_1^{\ r} + B\rho_2^{\ r}$, where $\rho_i = h \pm (1 + h^2)^{1/2}$ as above and A, B are arbitrary constants. The positive root ρ_1, which is approximately equal to $e^{0.1}$, is *dominant* in the sense that $|\rho_1| > |\rho_2|$. Therefore, the term $B\rho_2^{\ r}$ can be neglected in comparison with $A\rho_1^{\ r}$ for large r, provided that $A \neq 0$.

When one uses (9) to compute an approximate function table for negative $x = -rh$, the reverse is true: we have the curious phenomenon of an *unstable* difference approximation to a *stable* DE. Unless $B = 0$, we have $A\rho_1^{-r} \ll B\rho_2^{-r}$ if r is sufficiently large. Setting $t = -x$, this shows that the central difference approximation to $dy/dt + y = 0$ can only be used to compute good approximate function tables for solutions of the initial value problem over very limited ranges.

We can avoid instabilities of the preceding type by using higher-order *backward* difference approximations to y' with small h. The simplest such approximation is

$$y_k' \simeq (3y_k - 4y_{k-2} + y_{k-1})/2h = \nabla y_k/h + \nabla^2 y_k/2h^3. \qquad (10)$$

The truncation error in (10) is $h^2 y_k'''/3 + O(h^3)$. The approximation (10) yield the *implicit* two-step difference approximation

$$y_k = \{4y_{k-1} - y_{k-2} + 2hF(x_k, y_k)\}/3 \qquad (11)$$

to the DE $y' = F(x, y)$. In the *linear* case, this implicit second-order ΔE is easily solved recursively for y_k.

EXERCISES A

1. Show that, if the function $f(x) = \Sigma a_k x^k$ is a polynomial of degree m, then $\Delta^m f = \nabla^m f = \delta^m f = h^m f^{(m)}$, where $f^{(m)}$ denotes the mth derivative of f.
2. Show that, if $y \in \mathscr{C}^r$, then $\delta^r y = 0(h^r)$ and $\Delta^r y = 0(h^r)$.

3. Show that

$$\delta^r y_j = \sum_{k=0}^{r} (-1)^k \, \frac{r!}{k!(r-k)!} \, y_{j-k+r/2} \, .$$

4. Show that, if $f(x) = x^2$, then $x(\Delta x) = 2x^2$ whereas $\Delta(xf) = 3x^2$.

5. Solve the ΔE $u_{n+1} = 2u_n - u_{n-1}$ for the initial conditions $u_0 = 1$, $u_1 = -1$.

6. The nth Fibonacci number F_n is the value at n of the solution of the ΔE,

$$F_{n+1} = F_n + F_{n-1},$$

for the initial conditions $F_0 = 0$, $F_1 = 1$.

   (a) Show that $F_n = (\rho^n - \sigma^n)/\sqrt{5}$, where $\rho = (\sqrt{5} + 1)/2$, $\sigma = (1 - \sqrt{5})/2$.
   (b) What is the solution G_n of the Fibonacci ΔE for the initial conditions $G_0 = 2$, $G_1 = 1$?

7. Test the following ΔE's for stability or instability, by calculating the roots of their characteristic equations:

   (a) $u_{n+1} = 2u_n - u_{n-1}$,   (b) $u_{n+1} = u_n + u_{n-1}$,
   (c) $u_{n+1} - 5u_n + 6u_{n-1} = 0$,   (d) $u_{n+1} = -u_{n-1}$.

8. Show in detail that $|a + ab| + b^2 < 1$ is a necessary and sufficient condition for the strict stability of the ΔE $y_{n+2} = ay_{n+1} + by_n$.

9. Derive necessary and sufficient conditions for the strict stability of a general linear third-order ΔE with constant coefficients.

4   Polynomial interpolation

The difference notation of §2 permits us to write down simple expressions for the polynomials of least degree interpolated through given values on any uniform mesh. Simplest is the *linear* interpolation formula (for fixed h and variable k)

$$p(x_0 + k) = y_0 + \frac{k}{h}(y_1 - y_0), \qquad 0 < k < h. \tag{12}$$

The next easiest case is that of *parabolic* interpolation. Using the second central difference notation of formula (6c),

$$\delta^2 y_i = y_{i+1} - 2y_i + y_{i-1},$$

we obtain the quadratic interpolation formula

$$q(x_1 + k) = y_1 + \frac{k}{2h}\Big(y_2 - y_0 + \frac{k}{h}\,\delta^2 y_1\Big). \tag{13}$$

If second differences are tabulated, as they are in many tables, this formula requires only two multiplications and three additions†.

In a similar way, we can derive the *quartic* (fourth order) *interpolation formula*

---

† We do not count the division required to calculate k/h since this requires only a decimal-point shift in most tabulations.

$$f(x_2 + k) = y_2 + \frac{k}{2h}\left(y_3 - y_1 + \frac{k}{h}\,\delta^2 y_2\right)$$

$$+ k(k^2 - h^2)[(\delta y_3 - \delta^2 y_1)/12h^3 + k\delta^4 y_2/24h^4]. \qquad (14)$$

Here $\delta^4 y_2 = \delta^2(\delta^2 y_2) = y_4 - 4y_3 + 6y_2 - 4y_1 + y_0$.

The preceding formulas are based on central differences. For polynomial interpolation between $n + 1$ successive values on a uniform mesh, one often uses the *Gregory-Newton interpolation formula*,

$$p(x) = f(x_0) + \sum_{k=1}^{n} \Delta^k f(x_0)\left[\prod_{j=0}^{k-1}(x - x_0 - jh)\right]\Big/ h^k(k!), \qquad (15)$$

where $n = (x_n - x_0)/h$, and where Δ^k is the iterated forward-difference operator. This formula gives an approximation to $f(x)$ in terms of the differences of n equally spaced values of f. This formula is a difference analog of Taylor's formula, without a remainder term.

Lagrange interpolation formula. The Gregory-Newton formula, in turn, can be regarded as a special case of a very general interpolation formula due to Lagrange. Given the numbers $x_0 < x_1 < \cdots < x_n$ and $y_0, y_1, \ldots, y_n$, one can show† that there exists a unique polynomial $p(x)$ of degree n or less which satisfies $p(x_k) = y_k$ for $k = 0, 1, \ldots, n$, that is, which assumes the $n + 1$ given values at the points specified. Let

$$Q(x) = (x - x_0)(x - x_1) \cdots (x - x_n),$$

$$p_k(x) = Q(x)/(x - x_k) = \prod_{j \neq k}(x - x_j).$$

Then the polynomial

$$p(x) = \sum_{k=0}^{n} \frac{p_k(x_k)}{p_k(x_k)}\, y_k = Q(x) \sum_{k=0}^{n} \frac{y_k}{Q'(x_k)(x - x_k)} \qquad (16)$$

takes exactly the values $p(x_k) = y_k$, $0 \leq k \leq n$. Indeed, $p_k(x_j) = 0$ for $j \neq k$, so that, substituting $x = x_j$ into (16), we have

$$p(x_j) = \sum_{k=0}^{n} \frac{p_k(x_j)}{p_k(x_k)}\, y_k = \frac{p_j(x_j)}{p_j(x_j)}\, y_j = y_j.$$

Formula (16) is the Lagrange interpolation formula. Since the polynomial $p(x)$ in (16) is unique, (16) is equivalent to (15) if $x_j = a + jh$,

---

† Birkhoff and Mac Lane, pp. 58–69.

$j = 0, 1, \ldots, n$. Hence, regarded as approximations to a function tabulated at equal intervals, (15) and (16) have the same error.

Hermite interpolation. The limiting case of Lagrange interpolation of order $2m$, obtained by letting $x_0, \ldots, x_{m-1}$ approach a and x_m, $\ldots, x_{2m-1}$ approach b, is called *osculatory* interpolation of order m on $[a, b]$. The limit exists if $f \in \mathscr{C}^{m-1}[a, b]$, and is that polynomial $p(x)$ of degree $2m - 1$ which satisfies $p^{(j)}(a) = f^{(j)}(a)$ and $p^{(j)}(b) = p^{(j)}(b)$ for $j = 0, \ldots, m - 1$. *Hermite* interpolation of order m means, for any partition π of $[a, b]$, just osculatory interpolation of order m on each subinterval.

The case $m = 2$ of *cubic* Hermite interpolation is especially useful. On $[0, 1]$, this gives (writing $f(0) = y_0, f'(0) = y_0', f(1) = y_1, f'(1) = y_1'$)

$$p(x) = y_0 + y_0' x + [3y_1 - 3y_0 - 2y_0' - y_1']x + [y_1' - y_0' - 2y_1 + 2y_0]x^2.$$

5   The interpolation error

Let a function $f(x)$ be tabulated at $n + 1$ points $x_0 < x_1 < \cdots < x_n$, and let $p(x)$ be the unique interpolation polynomial, of degree n or less, which satisfies $p(x_k) = f(x_k), k = 0, 1, \ldots, n$. What is the *error* of $p(x)$, considered as an approximation to $f(x)$? An answer to this question, when $f(x)$ is sufficiently smooth, is provided by the following result.

■ THEOREM 1.   *Let $p(x) = a_0 + a_1 x + \cdots + a_n x^n$ be the polynomial satisfying $p(x_i) = f(x_i)$, for $x_0 < x_1 < \cdots < x_n$. If $f \in \mathscr{C}^{n+1}[x_0, x_n]$, then for every x in $[x_0, x_n] = I$ there exists ξ in I, such that*

$$f(x) - p(x) = \frac{(x - x_0) \cdots (x - x_n)}{(n + 1)!} f^{(n+1)}(\xi). \tag{17}$$

Proof — Let $e(x) = f(x) - p(x)$ denote the error function. Since $p(x)$ is a polynomial of degree n, $p^{(n+1)}(x) \equiv 0$, hence

$$e^{(n+1)}(x) = f^{(n+1)}(x)$$

for all x, and $e(x_0) = e(x_1) = \cdots = e(x_n) = 0$. Consider now the function

$$\phi(t) = Q(x)e(t) - Q(t)e(x), \tag{18}$$

where Q is the polynomial $Q(x) = (x - x_0)(x - x_1) \cdots (x - x_n)$. We consider ϕ as a function of t on I, for x fixed. Clearly $\phi \in \mathscr{C}^{n+1}$; moreover $\phi(x_k) = 0$, $k = 0, 1, \ldots, n$, and in addition $\phi(x) = 0$. By Rolle's Theorem, between any two points where ϕ vanishes there is at least one point where ϕ' vanishes. Since the function ϕ vanishes at $n + 2$ points (if $x \neq x_k$ for all x), the function ϕ' vanishes for at least $n + 1$ points.

Repeating the same argument for higher derivatives, we eventually conclude that $\phi^{(n+1)}(t)$ vanishes for at least one point ξ in the interval I. Differentiating (18) relative to t, $n + 1$ times, we obtain

$$0 = \phi^{(n+1)}(\xi) = Q(x)\, e^{(n+1)}(\xi) - (n + 1)!\, e(x).$$

Since $e^{(n+1)}(\xi) = f^{(n+1)}(\xi)$ and $e(x) = f(x) - p(x)$, this gives

$$f(x) - p(x) = e(x) = \frac{1}{(n + 1)!}\, f^{(n+1)}(\xi) Q(x), \qquad \text{q.e.d.}$$

■ COROLLARY. *If p is the Lagrange interpolation polynomial of a function $f(x)$ of class $\mathscr{C}^{n+1}$ in the interval $[x_0, x_n]$ at $x_0 < x_1 < \cdots < x_n$, the error at any point $x \in [x_0, x_n]$ is at most*

$$|f(x) - p(x)| \leqq \frac{1}{(n + 1)!}\, N_n M_n,$$

where $M_n = \max\limits_{x_0 \leqq \xi \leqq x_n} |f^{(n+1)}(\xi)|$ *and* $N_n = \max\limits_{x_0 \leqq x \leqq x_n} |Q_n(x)|.$

When the mesh points are equally spaced, we can compute N_n explicitly. Thus, we have $N_2 = h^2/4$; if $x_1 < x < x_2$, $N_4 = 9h^2/16$, and so on.

Applications. For example, if $x = x_j + k$, $0 < k < h$, the magnitude of the error in linear interpolation is $|k(h - k)f''(\xi)|/2 \leqq h^2 |f''(\xi)|/8$, for some $\xi \in [x_j, x_j + h]$. Likewise, parabolic interpolation through $f(x_j - h), f(x_j)$, and $f(x_j + h)$ gives an approximate value differing from $f(x_j + k)$ by $|k(h^2 - k^2)f'''(\xi)|/6$. For $|k| \leqq h/2$, the error is therefore bounded by $h^3 |f'''|_{\max}/16$. Since we would naturally choose j to minimize $|x - x_j|$, this bounds the error in parabolic interpolation. The maximum error in the interval $(x_j - h, x_j + h)$ is slightly larger; see Exercise 8.

Ordinarily, parabolic interpolation is sufficiently accurate. For example, with $\sin x$, $|f'''|_{\max} = 1$; hence the error is bounded by $h^3/16$ in radian units. Therefore parabolic interpolation gives one four-place accuracy in a table at 6° intervals! More generally, unless $|f'''|_{\max} > 10$, six-place tables can be extended by parabolic interpolation to all x if $h = 0.01$, without an appreciable loss of accuracy. The same is true of nine-place tables if $h = 0.001$ (and of three-place tables if $h = 0.1$).

For these reasons, higher-order interpolation is unnecessary for most tables in common use.

CAUTION. The *approximations* to a given function $f(x)$ on a fixed interval, defined by polynomial *interpolation* over that interval, are not necessarily *good* approximations to $f(x)$, even if $f(x)$ is analytic. Thus, the approximations to the analytic function $f(x) = 1/(1 + x^2)$ obtained by the Gregory-Newton interpolation formula (15) *do not converge*† to $f(x)$ on the interval $-5 \leq x \leq 5$, but oscillate more and more wildly as the step length h tends to zero.

This shows that Newtonian interpolation cannot be used to define the approximating polynomials referred to in the Weierstrass Approximation Theorem. To get the best such *uniform* polynomial approximations, one must use a very different method due to Chebyshev (see Ch. 11, § 7).

EXERCISES B

In Exercises 1–4, verify the formulas indicated for $f \in \mathscr{C}^4$, a uniform mesh with step h, $0 < \theta < 1$, and $\bar{\theta} = (1 - \theta)$:

1. $f(x_0 + \theta h) = y_0 + \theta \Delta y_0 - (\theta\bar{\theta}/2)\Delta^2 y_0 + O(h^3)$ (Newton).

2. $f(x_0 + \theta h) = y_0 + \theta \delta y_{1/2} - (\theta\bar{\theta}/4)(\delta^2 y_0 + \delta^2 y_1) + O(h^3)$ (Bessel).

3. $f(x_0 + \theta h) = (\bar{\theta}y_0 + \theta y_1) + [(\bar{\theta}^3 - \bar{\theta})\delta^2 y_0 + (\theta^3 - \theta)\delta^2 y_1]/6 + O(h^4)$ (Everett).

4. $f(x_0 + \theta h) = \frac{1}{2}(y_0 + y_1) + (\theta - \frac{1}{2})\delta y_{1/2} - (\theta\bar{\theta}/4)(\delta^2 y_0 + \delta^2 y_0)$
$\qquad\qquad\qquad - [\theta\bar{\theta}(2\theta - 1)/12]\delta^3 y_{1/2} + O(h^4)$ (Bessel).

5. Find the truncation errors of the formulas of Exercises 1–3, for quartic polynomials $q(x) = a + bx + cx^2 + dx^3 + ex^4$.

6. (a) Find the cubic polynomial $c(x)$ which satisfies $c(0) = y_0$, $c'(0) = y_0'$, $c(h) = y_1$, $c'(h) = y_1'$.
   (b) Derive your formula as a limiting case of the four-point Lagrange interpolation formula.

7. Estimate the largest h such that parabolic interpolation in a six-place table of $\log_{10} x$ on $2 \leq x \leq 3$, with mesh-length h, will yield five-place accuracy.

8. Show that, with parabolic interpolation between $y(-h)$, $y(0)$, and $y(h)$, the maximum error is normally near $x = \pm h/\sqrt{3}$ and is about $h^3|f'''(x)|/9\sqrt{3}$ there.

6 Roundoff errors

In the preceding discussion, as in the error estimates and error bounds derived in Chapter 7, it has been tacitly assumed that all arithmetic operations and readings from function tables were *exact*, to an unlimited number of decimal places. In reality, however, only a finite number of significant figures are used. This leads to a source of error called the *roundoff error*, which has been ignored previously in this book. The errors discussed previously are referred to technically as *truncation errors*, or *discretization errors*.

In polynomial interpolation of low order, the roundoff error is not a serious problem. For $|k| < h$, formulas (12)–(14) show that the roundoff error affects only the last decimal place tabulated. For instance, writing $k/h = r$, parabolic interpolation gives $f(x_1 + rh) = w_0 y_0 + w_1 y_1 +$

† See J. F. Steffensen, *Interpolation*, Williams and Wilkins, Baltimore, 1927, pp. 35–38 and the references given there.

$w_2 y_2$, where $w_0 = (r^2 - r)/2$, $w_1 = 1 - r^2$, $w_2 = (r + r^2)/2$, and $|r| < \frac{1}{2}$ if the three nearest tabulated values are used. Since

$$|w_0| + |w_1| + |w_2| \leq 1 + |r| + 2r^2 \leq 2,$$

and tabulated values are correct to $\frac{1}{2}$ in the last decimal place, the roundoff error is at most one in the last decimal place.

In numerical quadrature formulas, which also have the form $\sum w_k y_k$ per step with $\sum w_k$ equal to the mesh-length, the *maximum* roundoff error is similarly bounded by the length of the interval multiplied by the maximum tabulation error (ordinarily $\frac{1}{2}$ in the last decimal place).

Moreover the roundoff errors are nearly independent, and randomly distributed in the first untabulated decimal place with mean nearly zero. Hence,† the cumulative roundoff error has a roughly normal distribution on a Gaussian curve, and the *probable* cumulative roundoff error with n equal subdivisions is only $O(1/\sqrt{n})$ times the maximum cumulative roundoff error.

Similar results hold for the numerical integration formulas to be considered. The roundoff errors may be thought of as "noise," super-imposed on the systematic truncation error. Both are amplified in the course of the calculation by a factor of at most $e^{L(b-a)}$, where $L = \sup \partial F/\partial x$ is the one-sided Lipschitz constant and $(b - a)$ is the interval of integration.‡ The reason for this is that, for L as defined above,

$$[y(x) - z(x)]' = F(x, y) - F(x, z) \leq L(y - z) \qquad \text{if} \quad y > z;$$

see also Chapter 1, Exercise E12.

7 Numerical differentiation

The idea of using divided differences (or difference quotients) to approximate derivatives of tabulated functions has already been suggested in §2. Using Taylor's formula, we can obtain estimates of the truncation errors incurred in such formulas for *numerical differentiation*.

For example, if $f \in \mathscr{C}^5$, the first two approximations to $f'(x)$ mentioned in § 2 give rise to the truncation error estimates

$$\Delta f/h - f'(x) = f''(x)h/2 + f'''(x)h^2/6 + f^{\text{iv}}(\xi)h^3/24, \qquad (19a)$$

$$\delta f/h - f'(x) = f'''(x)h^2/24 + f^{\text{v}}(\xi)h^4/1920, \qquad (19b)$$

where ξ is in the interval over which the difference is being taken. This illustrates the general principle that *central* difference quotients give

---

† By the central limit theorem of probability theory.
‡ For a careful analysis of the cumulative roundoff error, see Henrici.

more accurate approximations to derivatives than forward or backward difference quotients of the same order. We can obtain *truncation error bounds* similarly:

$$|[f(x+h)-f(x-h)]/2h-f'(x)| \leq |f'''|_{\max} h^2/6. \qquad (19c)$$

Note that the interval in (19c) is twice as long as in (19b); hence, the truncation error is multiplied by about four.

It is interesting to compare the preceding truncation error bound with the corresponding *roundoff error* bound, which is $10^{-m}/2h$ if an m-place table is used. When $h < (3/10^m|f'''|_{\max})^{1/3}$, therefore, the roundoff error exceeds the truncation error. To minimize the sum $(|f'''|_{\max} h^2/6)+(10^{-m}/2h)$, which is the maximum total error if both terms have the same sign, set $2h^3 = 3/10^m|f'''|_{\max}$. This shows that the maximum total error cannot be reduced below

$$\tfrac{1}{4}\sqrt[3]{18\,|f'''|_{\max}/10^{2m}}$$

and that one loses accuracy if $|f''_{\max}| < 2$, by choosing h smaller than 0.04 if a four-place table is used to approximate $f'(x)$ by a central difference quotient.

Similar approximations can be made to $f''(x)$, using second difference quotients. For $f \in \mathscr{C}^2$, we have

$$\begin{aligned}
\delta^2 f(x) &= f(x+h) - 2f(x) + f(x-h) \\
&= [f(x) + hf'(x) + h^2 f''(\xi_1)/2] - 2f(x) \\
&\quad + [f(x) - hf'(x) + h^2 f''(\xi_2)/2] \\
&= h^2[f''(\xi_1) + f''(\xi_2)]/2,
\end{aligned}$$

for some numbers ξ_1 and ξ_2 in the intervals $[x, x+h]$ and $[x-h, x]$, respectively. Hence $\delta^2 f/h^2$ lies between the minimum and maximum values of $f''(\xi)$ for ξ in the interval $x-h \leq \xi \leq x+h$. Since a continuous function assumes all values between its minimum and its maximum, and since $f''(x)$ is continuous in the interval, we conclude that $\delta^2 f = h^2 f''(\xi)$ for some ξ in $[x-h, x+h]$. This shows that the difference quotient $\delta^2 f/h^2$ is a good approximation to the derivative f'' for small h. Since $\delta^2 f/h^2$ can be computed by consulting a numerical table of $f(x)$, the preceding formula may again be regarded as one for *approximate numerical differentiation*. This is written in the form $f''(x) \simeq \delta^2 f(x)/h^2$, where the symbol $\simeq$ means "is approximately equal to," as in Chapter 7, § 2.

For $f \in \mathscr{C}^4$, the preceding analysis can be refined to give an estimate of the truncation error. Taylor's formula with remainder gives

$$f(x \pm h) = f(x) \pm hf'(x) + h^2 f''(x)/2 \pm h^3 f'''(x)/6 + h^4 f^{\mathrm{iv}}(\xi)/24,$$

where $x - h \leq \xi \leq x + h$. Since $f^{iv}(\xi)$ assumes all values between its minimum and maximum values on the above interval, we can write

$$\delta^2 f - h^2 f''(x) = h^4 f^{iv}(\xi)/12, \qquad x - h \leq \xi \leq x + h. \qquad (20)$$

This formula gives the truncation error estimate

$$f''(x) - \delta^2 f/h^2 = h^2 f^{iv}(\xi)/12,$$

in the formula $f''(x) \simeq \delta^2 f(x)/h^2$ for numerical differentiation. This formula shows that the truncation error is of the order of h^2, and tends to zero fairly rapidly when the step h is taken smaller and smaller.

However, for small h, the roundoff error is again dominant. Using m-place tables, the maximum roundoff error in the formula $f'' - \delta^2 f/h^2$ is found to be $2 \times 10^{-m}/h^2$, a quantity which increases without limit as h tends to zero.

For example, for the function $f(x) = \sin x$, where $f^{(iv)}(x) = \sin x$, since $f^{iv}(x)$ ranges between -1 and 1, the maximum truncation error is approximately $h^2/12$, and the maximum roundoff error is $2 \times 10^{-5}/h^2$, using five-place tables. To minimize the greater of the truncation error (which tends to zero with h) and the maximum roundoff error, one must make $h^2/24 \simeq 10^{-5}/h^2$. Hence, we minimize the maximum total error of $f'' \simeq \delta^2 f/h^2$ near $h^4 = 2.4 \times 10^{-4}$ or $h \simeq 0.13$ radian, $\simeq 8°$, roughly, a surprisingly large interval!

Roundoff errors are not considered further in this chapter. This is partly because, with high-speed computing machines, truncation errors are usually bigger unless h is very small (most modern machines carry at least ten decimal digits), and partly because the analysis of roundoff errors involves difficult statistical considerations.

Higher-order derivatives. The preceding truncation error estimates and bounds are special cases of a general result, namely:

■ THEOREM 2. *If $f \in \mathscr{C}^{(n+2)}$ on $[x - nh/2, x + nh/2]$, then*

$$f^{(n)}(x) = \delta^n f/h^n - nh^2 f^{(n+2)}(\xi)/24, \qquad \xi \in I. \qquad (21)$$

Proof — The cases $n = 1, 2$ have been treated above. Proceeding by induction, we get

$$\delta f(x) = \int_{-h/2}^{h/2} f'(x + t)\, dt, \qquad \delta^2 f(x) = \int_{-h/2}^{h/2} dt \int_{-h/2}^{h/2} f''(x + t + u)\, du, \ldots,$$

$$\delta^n f(x) = \int_{-h/2}^{h/2} dt_1 \int_{-h/2}^{h/2} dt_2 \cdots \int_{-h/2}^{h/2} f^{(n)}(x + t_1 + \cdots + t_n)\, dt_n.$$

This is a multiple integral over an n-dimensional domain D with center $\mathbf{t} = \mathbf{0}$ and volume h^n, symmetric under the reflection $t_i \to -t_j$ $(j = 1, \dots, n)$. The arithmetic mean of the integrands at symmetrically placed points $x - T$ and $x + T$ is, by Taylor's formula,

$$\tfrac{1}{2}[f^{(n)}(x + T) + f^{(n)}(x - T)] = f^{(n)}(x) + (T^2/2)f^{(n+2)}(x + \theta T)$$

for some θ, $0 \le \theta \le 1$. Hence, setting $T = t_1 + \cdots + t_n$ and integrating over D, we have

$$(m/2) \int T^2 \, dt_1 \dots dt_n \le \delta^n f - h^n - f^{(n)}(x) \le (M/2) \int T^2 \, dt_1 \dots dt_n,$$

where m and M are the least and greatest values of $f^{(n+2)}(\xi)$ for ξ in the given interval. Since

$$\int_{-h/2}^{h/2} t_k{}^2 \, dt_k = h^3/12 \qquad \text{and} \qquad \int_{-h/2}^{h/2} t_\ell t_k \, dt_\ell = 0, \qquad k \ne \ell,$$

and since $f^{(n+2)}(\xi)$, being continuous, assumes all values between its extreme values m and M, formula (21) follows.

■ COROLLARY. *Under the hypothesis of Theorem 2, we have the truncation error bound*

$$|f^{(n)}(x) - \delta^n f / h^n| \le nMh^2/24, \tag{22}$$

where M is the maximum of $f^{(n+2)}(\xi)$ as ξ ranges over the given interval.

8 Difference approximations

The truncation error estimate (19a) is related to that obtained in Chapter 7 for the Cauchy polygon formula

$$y_{k+1} - y_k = F(x_k, y_k)(x_{k+1} - x_k). \tag{23}$$

Formula (23) is obtained from the DE $y' = F(x, y)$ if we approximate y' by the forward† difference quotient $\Delta y_k / \Delta x_k = (y_{k+1} - y_k)/(x_{k+1} - x_k)$. In the case $\Delta x_k = h$ of a uniform mesh, the central difference quotient $(y_{k+1} - y_{k-1})/2h$ approximates y'_k much better, by (19b).

This comparison suggests that a more accurate function table for the solution of $y' = F(x, y)$ satisfying $y(x_0) = y_0$ will result if (23) is replaced by the *two-level midpoint formula*

$$y_{k+1} - y_{k-1} = F(x_k, y_k)(x_{k+1} - x_{k-1}) = 2hF(x_k, y_k). \tag{24}$$

This is an explicit *two-step* difference equation, in the following sense.

---

† *N.B.* The forward difference notation $\Delta x_k = x_{k+1} - x_k$ of (4a) is used here, and *not* the notation $\Delta x_k = x_k - x_{k-1}$ of the calculus, used in Chapter 7.

■ DEFINITION.   *A difference equation of order m, or an* m-step ΔE, *is an expression of the form*

$$\Delta^m y_n = F(n, y_n, \Delta y_n, \ldots, \Delta^{m-1} y_n), \tag{25}$$

where F is a given function. A solution of (25) *is a sequence* $y_0, y_1, y_2, \ldots, y_n, \ldots$ *which satisfies* (25) *for* $n \geq m$.

Since $\Delta^k y_n$ is a linear combination of $y_n, y_{n+1}, \ldots, y_{n+k}$, we can re-write the ΔE (25) in the equivalent form

$$y_{n+m} = \phi(n, y_n, y_{n+1}, \ldots, y_{n+m-1}), \tag{26}$$

where ϕ is a function determined by F. Thus, the solutions of (25) are the sequences y_n satisfying (26).

The ΔE (25) is the difference analog of the normal mth order DE

$$y^{(m)} = F(x, y, \ldots, y^{(m-1)}).$$

In contrast to the case of DE's, however, the problem of proving the existence and uniqueness of solutions of the ΔE (25) for given initial values $y_0, y_1, \ldots, y_{m-1}$ is trivial. Clearly, (26) determines y_m from $y_0, y_1, \ldots, y_{m-1}$. By induction on n, the same is true for y_{m+n} for any positive integer n.

The preceding remark brings out a disadvantage in using two-step ΔE's like (24) for integrating first-order DE's. To apply such two-step methods, one must first calculate y_1, knowing y_0, by a separate process. A like extra calculation by a separate process must be made every time the mesh-length is changed. For *analytic* DE's, power series (Chapter 3) are often used for this purpose.

Another possible disadvantage (that of getting an unstable difference approximation to a stable DE) has already been noted in §3. Thus, schemes for numerically integrating DE's need not be good just because they have a high order of accuracy.

EXERCISES C

1. Show that the effect of roundoff errors on tenth differences is bounded by about 500×10^{-n} in n-place tables.

2. Show that $hf'(x_0 + h/2) = \delta y_{1/2} - (1/24)\delta^3 y_{1/2} + O(h^5)$.

3. Show that $hf'(x_0 + h/2) = \delta y_{1/2} - \delta^3 y_{1/2}/24 + 3\delta^5 y_{1/2}/640 + O(h^7)$.

4. Given a six-place table of $\sin x$ (x in radians), show that the approximate formula $f_0'' \simeq \delta^2 f_0/h^2$ has a combined truncation and roundoff error bounded by $2/10^6 h^2 + h^2/12$, and that this expression has a minimum of about 0.0008, assumed for h about 0.07.

5. (a) Show that $h^2 f'' = \delta^2 f - \delta^4 f/12 + O(h^6)$.
   (b*) Show that $h^2 f'' = \delta^2 f - \delta^4 f/12 + \delta^6 f/90 + O(h^8)$.

6. Show that for, $y \in \mathscr{C}^8$, we have $\delta^2 y_0 = h^2[y'' + \delta^2 y_0''/12 - \delta^4 y_{..}/240] + O(h^8)$.

7. Show that, for small h, the ΔE (10) provides a strictly stable approximation

to the strictly stable DE $y' + y = 0$, with truncation error $2h^3|y_k'''|/3 + O(h^4)$.

8. Show that, if $y' = F(x, y)$ and $F \in \mathscr{C}^3$, then:

$$y_{k+1} = y_{k-1} + 2hF_k + h^3F_k''/3 + O(h^4), \qquad \text{(cf. (24))}$$

where $F_k = F(x_k, y_k)$ and $F'' = (d/dx + F\partial/\partial y)^2 F$.

9. Show that, under the hypotheses of Exercise 8,

$$y_{k+1} = \{4y_k - y_{k-1} + 2hF_{k+1}\}/3 + 2h^3F_{k+1}''/9 + O(h^4) \qquad \text{(cf. (10))}.$$

10*. (a) What is the order of accuracy of the explicit three-step Adams formula

$$y_{n+3} = y_{n+2} + h[F_{n+2} + \tfrac{1}{2}\Delta F_{n+1} + \tfrac{5}{12}\Delta^2 F_n]$$

for integrating numerically the DE $y' = F(x, y)$?

(b) Show that the resulting ΔE is strictly stable for $y' + y = 0$, provided that h is sufficiently small.

9 Simpson's rule

The results on polynomial interpolation obtained in §§ 4, 5 will now be used to derive a truncation error estimate for Simpson's rule (cf. Chapter 7, (27) and (28)). Since Simpson's rule approximates the definite integral in the integral equation equivalent to $y' = F(x, y)$, this error estimate applies to *Milne's formula*

$$y_{k+2} = y_k + \frac{h}{3}[F(x_k, y_k) + 4F(x_{k+1}, y_{k+1}) + F(x_{k+2}, y_{k+2})] \quad (27)$$

for the numerical integration of $y' = F(x, y)$, see § 11.

The method to be used applies to a wide class of formulas for numerical quadrature. Let $0 \leq r_0 < r_1 < \cdots < r_n \leq 1$ be given, and let $x_i = a + r_i h$, $h > 0$. For any function $f \in \mathscr{C}^{n+2}$, let $p(x)$ be the Lagrange interpolation polynomial for the function $f(x)$ associated with the partition

$$a \leq x_0 < x_1 < \cdots < x_n \leq a + h = b.$$

Then the formula $f(x) \simeq p(x)$ is associated with a formula for numerical quadrature, namely

$$\int_a^b f(x)\, dx \simeq \int_a^b p(x)\, dx = \sum_{i=0}^n w_i y_i = \sum_{i=0}^n w_i f(x_i). \qquad (28)$$

The coefficients w_i are the integrals of the polynomials $p_i(x)/p_i(x_i)$ by (16);

$$w_i = \frac{1}{p_i(x_i)} \int_a^b p_i(x)\, dx, \qquad p_i(x) = \prod_{j \neq i}(x - x_j). \qquad (28')$$

Formula (28) is exact for all polynomials of degree $\leq n$, since then $f(x) = p(x)$. For other functions, the error in (28) is $-\int_a^b e(x)\, dx$, where

$-e(x) = p(x) - f(x)$. Hence, by Theorem 1, the error in (28) for any given n is of the order of h^{n+2} at most. We have proved

■ **THEOREM 3.** *For any choice of real numbers r_i with $0 \leq r_0 < r_1 < \cdots < r_n \leq 1$ and weights w_i defined by formula (28'), we have, for all $f \in \mathscr{C}^{n+2}[a, b]$:*

$$\int_a^b f(x)\,dx - \sum_{i=0}^n w_i f(a + r_i h) = O(h^{n+2}).$$

Setting $n = 1$ and $r_0 = 0$, $r_1 = 1$ in the preceding formulas, we get $p_0(x) = x - x_1$, $p_1(x) = x - x_0$, and so

$$w_1 = \int_{x_0}^{x_1} (x - x_0)\,dx / (x_1 - x_0) = (x_1 - x_0)/2 = h/2.$$

A similar calculation gives $w_0 = h/2$, so that the formula for *trapezoidal quadrature* (Chapter 7, §6),

$$\int_a^{a+h} f(x)\,dx \simeq \frac{h}{2}[f(a) + f(a + h)] = \frac{h}{2}(y_0 + y_1), \qquad (29)$$

is obtained as a special case of (28) and (28'). In this special case, the error $e(x)$ satisfies, by Theorem 1,

$$e(x) = L(x) - f(x) = \tfrac{1}{2}(x - x_0)(x_1 - x)f''(\xi),$$

for some $\xi = \xi(x)$ in the interval $x_0 \leq \xi \leq x_0 + h = x_1$. Since

$$\int_{x_0}^{x_1} L(x)\,dx = h(y_0 + y_1)/2,$$

the error $\int_{x_0}^{x_1} e(x)\,dx = \int_0^h e(x_0 + t)\,dt$ in trapezoidal quadrature satisfies

$$\tfrac{1}{2}f''_{\min} \int_0^h t(h - t)\,dt \leqq \int_{x_0}^{x_1} e(x)\,dx \leqq \tfrac{1}{2}f''_{\max} \int_0^h t(h - t)\,dt.$$

Since $\tfrac{1}{2} \int_0^h t(h - t)\,dt = h^3/12$, we obtain formula (24) of Chapter 7:

$$\frac{h}{2}(y_0 + y_1) - \int_{x_0}^{x_1} f(x)\,dx = \frac{h^3}{12}f''(\xi), \qquad x_0 < \xi < x_1. \qquad (30)$$

Applying (30) to each component of any *vector*-valued function $\mathbf{x}(t) \in \mathscr{C}^2$, we have

$$\int_{t_0}^{t_1} x_k(t)\,dt - \frac{h}{2}[x_k(t_0) + x_k(t_1)] = -\frac{h^3}{12}x_k''(\tau),$$

for some τ in the interval $[t_0, t_0 + h]$, and for each component x_k. By choosing one axis parallel to the error vector $\int_{t_0}^{t_1} \mathbf{x}(t)\,dt - h(\mathbf{x}_0 + \mathbf{x}_1)/2$, we obtain as a special case of the preceding result the inequality

$$\left| \int_{t_0}^{t_1} \mathbf{x}(t)\, dt - \frac{h}{2}\,(\mathbf{x}_0 + \mathbf{x}_1) \right| \leqq \frac{h^3}{12} \sup |\mathbf{x}''(\tau)|, \qquad t_0 < \tau < t_1.$$

The *relative* truncation error is thus $O(h^2)$, as is to be expected from a formula which neglects quadratic terms.

Note that the vector analogs of the Mean Value Theorem and of (30) are false. For example, let $\mathbf{x}(t) = (t^3, t^4)$, $t_0 = 0$, and $t_1 = 1$. Then

$$\int_0^1 \mathbf{x}(t)\, dt - (\tfrac{1}{2})(\mathbf{x}_0 + \mathbf{x}_1) = -(\tfrac{1}{4}, \tfrac{3}{10})$$

is not equal to $-\mathbf{x}''(\tau)/12 = -(6\tau, 12\tau^2)/12 = -(\tau, 2\tau^2)/2$ for any τ in $[0, 1]$.

Formula (13) for parabolic interpolation leads similarly to *Simpson's rule*:

$$\int_{x_0}^{x_2} f(x)\, dx \simeq \frac{h}{3}\,[y_0 + 4y_1 + y_2] = \frac{h}{3}\,[f(x_0) + 4f(x_1) + f(x_2)], \qquad (31)$$

$h = x_2 - x_1 = x_1 - x_0$. This formula is exact for quadratic polynomials. Since $\int_{-h}^{h} x^3\, dx = 0$, Simpson's rule is also exact for cubic polynomials; this coincidence makes Simpson's rule especially practical.

The error estimate for Simpson's rule (31) will now be derived for any $f \in \mathcal{C}^4$. Consider the *cubic* polynomial

$$p(x) = a_0 + a_1 x + a_2 x^2 + a_3 x^3,$$

satisfying $p(x_0) = y_0$, $p(x_1) = y_1$, $p'(x_1) = y_1' = f'(x_1)$, $p(x_2) = y_2$, with $x_0 = x_1 - h$, $x_2 = x_1 + h$. These conditions amount to $a_0 = y_1$, $a_1 = y_1'$, $a_2 = \delta^2 y_1 / 2h^2$, and $a_3 = -a_1/h^2 + (y_2 - y_0)/2h^3$. Hence they can be satisfied for any y_0, y_1, y_2.†

To estimate the error $e(x) = p(x) - f(x)$, translate coordinates so that $x_0 = -h$, $x_1 = 0$, $x_2 = h$. Consider the function of t for *fixed* x,

$$\phi(t) = x^2(x^2 - h^2)e(t) - t^2(t^2 - h^2)e(x), \qquad (32)$$

analogous to the function (18) used in proving Theorem 1. We have $\phi(0) = \phi(\pm h) = 0(x) = 0$, and further, $\phi'(0) = 0$ since $e'(0) = 0$. By Rolle's Theorem, the function $\phi'(t)$ vanishes at three places besides $t = 0$ in the interval $-h < t < h$. Hence, $\phi''(t)$ vanishes at least three times in $-h < t < h$, $\phi'''(t)$ vanishes twice, and $\phi^{\mathrm{iv}}(t)$ vanishes once, at some point $t = \xi$. We thus have, much as in (17),

$$0 = \phi^{\mathrm{iv}}(\xi) = x^2(x^2 - h^2)e^{\mathrm{iv}}(\xi) - 24e(x). \qquad (33)$$

---

† The resulting interpolation formulas are limiting cases of Lagrangian interpolation, for "infinitely near" points x_0, $x_0 + dx$, $x_1 - dx$, x_1.

Since $p(x)$ is a cubic polynomial, $p^{\mathrm{iv}}(x) \equiv 0$; therefore; $-e^{\mathrm{iv}}(\xi) = f^{\mathrm{iv}}(\xi)$. Substituting in (33) and solving for $e(x)$, we get the error estimate

$$e(x) = x^2(h^2 - x^2)f^{\mathrm{iv}}(\xi)/24, \qquad -h \leq \xi \leq h. \tag{34}$$

Integrating (34) with respect to x, since $x^2(h^2 - x^2) \geq 0$, it follows that the truncation error in using Simpson's Rule for quadrature over $-h \leq x \leq h$ lies between $m = \min f^{\mathrm{iv}}(\xi)$ and $M = \max f^{\mathrm{iv}}(\xi)$ times the definite integral

$$\int_{-h}^{h} x^2(h^2 - x^2)\,dx/24 = h^5/90.$$

Since $f(x) \in \mathscr{C}^{\mathrm{iv}}$, $f^{\mathrm{iv}}(\xi)$ assumes every value between m and M. This gives

■ **THEOREM 4.** *If $f(x) \in \mathscr{C}^{\mathrm{iv}}$, the truncation error for Simpson's Rule on the interval $-h \leq x \leq h$ is equal to $h^5 f^{\mathrm{iv}}(\xi)/90$ for some ξ in the interval $[-h, h]$.*

The *relative* truncation error is therefore $h^4 f^{\mathrm{iv}}(\xi)/180$. For example, to achieve five decimal places of accuracy in computing $\ln 2 = \int_1^2 dx/x$, about 10^4 points must be taken if Riemann sums are used, about one hundred with trapezoidal quadrature, while ten are sufficient using Simpson's rule! See also formula (28) of Chapter 7.

10* Gaussian quadrature

In formulas (28) and (28′) for numerical quadrature, with the x_i as free parameters, we have $2n + 2$ adjustable constants in all. This suggests the hope that, by properly locating the x_i, we can get a formula which is exact for all polynomials of degree $2n + 1$ or less, since these form a $(2n + 1)$-parameter family.

Such a formula was obtained by Gauss; in deriving it, it is convenient to renormalize to the interval $(-1, 1)$ and to label the points $\xi_1, \ldots, \xi_m$, so that $m = n + 1$. The formula uses two properties of the Legendre polynomials $P_m(x)$ defined in Chapter 3, § 2, which will be proved later in Chapter 11, § 6. These properties are

(i) $P_m(x)$ has m distinct zeros $x = \xi_1 < \xi_2 < \cdots < \xi_m$ in the open interval $(-1, 1)$, whence $P_m(x) = c_m(x - \xi_1)(x - \xi_2) \cdots (x - \xi_m)$ for some constant c_m,

(ii) $P_m(x)$ is orthogonal to any polynomial of lower degree:

$$\int_1^1 x^n P_m(x)\,dx = 0 \qquad \text{if} \quad n < m.$$

We shall assume these results, and also the following definition.

■ DEFINITION.   *The Gaussian quadrature formula of order m is the special case of formulas* (28)–(28'), *in which* $r_{i-1} = (1 + \xi_i)/2$, $i = 1, \ldots, m$, *and* ξ_i *is the ith zero of the Legendre polynomial* $P_m(x)$.

■ THEOREM 5.   *Gaussian quadrature of order m is exact if* $f(x)$ *is a polynomial of degree* $2m - 1$ *or less.*

Proof — By centering the origin and change of scale, we can assume the interval of integration to be $[-1, 1]$ without loss of generality. Let $f(x)$ be any polynomial of degree $2m - 1$ or less; let $p(x)$ be the Lagrange interpolation polynomial of degree at most $m - 1$ satisfying $p(\xi_i) = f(\xi_i)$, $i = 1, 2, \ldots, m$. Then $e(x) = f(x) - p(x)$ vanishes at $\xi_i, \ldots, \xi_m$. Hence † we have $e(x) = (x - \xi) \cdots (x - \xi_m)b(x)$, where $b(x)$ is a polynomial of degree at most $m - 1$.

Therefore, by (i), $e(x) = c_m^{-1} P_m(x)b(x) = s(x)P_m(x)$, where $s(x)$ is a polynomial of degree at most $m - 1$. But, by (ii), $P_m(x)$ is orthogonal to any polynomial of degree less than m. Hence,

$$\int_{-1}^{1} e(x)\, dx = \int_{-1}^{1} s(x)P_m(x)dx = 0,$$

so that (28)–(28') is exact for $e(\xi)$ by the choice of the ξ_i. Moreover Gaussian quadrature is exact for $p(x)$ by the choice of the w_i; hence it is exact also for the given $f(x)$, completing the proof.

Now, let $f(x) \in \mathscr{C}^{2m}[a, b]$, and let $q(x)$ be the polynomial of degree $2m - 1$ (or less) satisfying $q(x_j) = f(x_j)$ for $x_j = a + jh/(2m + 1)$, $j = 1, \ldots, 2m$. Then, by Theorem 1, we have $e(x) = q(x) - f(x) = O(h^{2m})$ and so

$$\int_{a}^{a+h} q(x)\, dx - \int_{a}^{a+h} f(x)\, dx = \int_{a}^{a+h} e(x)\, dx = O(h^{2m+1}).$$

But, by Theorem 5, we have

$$\int_{a}^{a+h} q(x)\, dx = \sum_{j=1}^{m} w_j\, q(a + r_j h) = \sum_{j=1}^{m} w_j f(a + r_j h).$$

Substituting back into the preceding equation, we get

$$\int_{a}^{a+h} f(x)\, dx - \sum_{j=1}^{m} w_j f(a + r_j h) = O(h^{2m+1}) \qquad \text{if} \quad r_j = (1 + \xi_j)/2. \quad (35)$$

This proves the following result.

■ COROLLARY.   *For* $f(x) \in \mathscr{C}^{2m}$, *Gaussian quadrature of order m has an absolute error* $O(h^{2m+1})$ *and a relative error* $O(h^{2m})$.

---

† By the Remainder Theorem; see Birkhoff-MacLane, p. 65.

EXERCISES D

1. Using a five-place table of sin x, x in radians (but not tables of SI(x)), evaluate

$$\int_0^x t^{-1} \sin t \, dt \qquad \text{for} \quad x = 0.1, 0.2, \ldots, 1.0$$

by Simpson's rule, with $h = 0.1$.

2. Show that $\int_1^2 dx/x = \ln 2$ is given by various numerical quadrature formulas, with $h = 1/10$, as follows: (a) initial point 0.73654401, (b) trapezoidal 0.69377139, (c) midpoint 0.6928354, (d) Simpson 0.6931474.

3. Use Weddle's rule (Exercise B3, Chapter 7) with 12 subdivisions to compute the approximation 0.69314935 to $\ln 2 = 0.69314718056$.

4. Use Cotes' rule (Exercise B2, Chapter 7) with 12 subdivisions, to compute the approximation $\ln 2 \simeq 0.69319535$.

5*. Show that

$$\int_{x_0}^{x_1} f(x) \, dx = \frac{h}{2} [f_0 + f_1 - \frac{1}{12} (\delta^2 f_0 + \delta^2 f_1) + \frac{11}{720}(\delta^4 f_0 + \delta^4 f_1)] + O(h^7).$$

6*. Show that, for $n = 3$, the Gauss quadrature formula on $(-h, h)$ is

$$\frac{h}{9} \{8f(0) + 5[f(-h\sqrt{\tfrac{3}{5}}) + f(h\sqrt{\tfrac{3}{5}})]\}$$

with truncation error $h^6 f^{\text{vi}}(\xi)/15{,}750$, where $-h < \xi < h$.

7*. Show that the error in Hermite's tangent cubic quadrature formula,

$$\int_0^h y \, dx \simeq \frac{h}{2} (y_0 + y_1) - \frac{h^2}{12} (y_0' - y_1'),$$

is $h^5 f^{\text{iv}}(\xi)/720$, where $0 < \xi < h$, if $y = f(x) \in \mathscr{C}^4$.

8. (Simpson's Five-Eight Rule). Show that, if $f \in \mathscr{C}^3$, then

$$\int_0^h f(x) \, dx = \frac{h}{12} [5f(h) + 8f(0) - f(-h)] + O(h^4).$$

11   Milne's method

As mentioned in § 9, Simpson's Rule suggests an efficient procedure for calculating approximate function tables for the solutions of any first-order DE

$$y' = F(x, y), \qquad F \in \mathscr{C}^4. \tag{36}$$

Namely, given an initial value $f(a) = c$ and a mesh-length $h > 0$, one first computes $y_1 = f(a + h)$ by a suitable *starting process* (see below) such as expansion in power series. One then solves recursively the *implicit, two-step* ΔE

$$y_{k+2} = y_k + \frac{h}{3} [F(x_k, y_k) + 4F(x_{k+1}, y_{k+1}) + F(x_{k+2}, y_{k+2})]. \tag{37}$$

The ΔE (37) is obtained from the integral equation form (Chapter 5, (11)) of the DE (36), which is

$$y_{k+2} = y_k + \int_{x_k}^{x_{k+2}} F(x, y(x)) \, dx, \tag{38}$$

by approximating the integral in question by Simpson's Rule.

EXAMPLE 2.   Consider the linear DE $y' = 1 - 2xy$ of Chapter 7, §8, with initial value $y(0) = 0$ and mesh-length $h = 0.1$. In this case, (37) reduces to

$$y_{k+2} = [15 + x_{k+2}]^{-1}[3 + (15 - x_k)y_k - 4x_{k+1}y_{k+1}]. \tag{39}$$

Evaluating $y(0.1) = 0.09934$ by power series, Milne's formula (39) gives $y(0.2) = 0.19475$. This approximate value agrees to five places with the value of $y(\tfrac{1}{5})$ obtained by power series expansion; the comparison suggests that the mesh-length $h = 0.1$ is adequate for four-place accuracy. Repeated use of (39) then gives the following *approximate function table.*

x	0.1	0.2	0.3	0.4	0.5
y	0.09934	0.19475	0.28264	0.36000	0.42444

The truncation error is about 10^{-5}, as can be verified by use of the power series expansion

$$y = x - \frac{2}{3}x^3 + \frac{4}{15}x^5 + \cdots = \sum_{k=0}^{\infty} a_{2k+1}x^{2k+1}, \qquad \frac{a_{2k+1}}{a_{2k-1}} = \frac{-2}{2k+1},$$

which gives $y(1) = 0.538079$. Another check is provided by the four-place table of Chapter 7, §8.

Having been successfully used on a wide variety of DE's, Milne's method provides an excellent illustration of *implicit, two-step* methods. (An explicit two-step method was briefly discussed in §8, following formula (24).)

Starting process.   Given the initial value $y_0 = c = f(a)$, one must compute y_1 by a *one-step* method before one can begin to apply a *two-step* method. For analytic F, it is usually best to calculate $y_1 = f(a + h)$ by expanding $f(x)$ in a Taylor series as in Chapter 3, §7. When F is not analytic, but fairly smooth (say, if $F \in \mathscr{C}^4$), good approximations to $f(a + h)$ are often obtained by repeated *mesh-halving* of the interval $[a, a + h]$, using a one-step method with a lower order of accuracy. For instance, we might first compute $f(a + h/8)$ by midpoint integration, and then use Milne's formula to get $f(a + h/4) = y_{1/4}$ from y_0 and $y_{1/8}$, next computing $y_{1/2}$ from y_0 and $y_{1/4}$ by a second application of Milne's formula with mesh-length $h/4$, finally getting y_1 from y_0 and $y_{1/2}$ by a third application of the same process.

Iterative solution. To apply Milne's method, one must solve the implicit equation (37) for y_{k+2} at each step. For *linear* DE's, the equation can be solved arithmetically by division, as in (39). But for *nonlinear* DE's, one must usually resort to the iterative method of successive approximation† described briefly in Chapter 7, § 10. Namely, one rewrites Milne's equation (37) and defines a function U in the form

$$y_{k+2} = y_k + \frac{h}{3}[F_k + 4F_{k+1}] + \frac{h}{3}F(x_{k+2}, y_{k+2}) = U(y_{k+2}), \quad (40)$$

where all quantities are known except y_{k+2}. Regarded as an equation in the unknown number y_{k+2}, (40) has the form $y_{k+2} = U(y_{k+2})$, where the function U is computable. For any initial *trial value* $y_{k+2}^{(0)}$, one can hope that the sequence

$$y_{k+2}^{(1)} = U(y_{k+2}^{(0)}), \qquad y_{k+2}^{(2)} = U(y_{k+2}^{(1)}), \qquad y_{k+2}^{(3)} = U(y_{k+2}^{(2)}), \ldots$$

will *converge* fairly rapidly to the exact solution.

This hope can be justified if h is small and F satisfies a Lipschitz condition with Lipschitz constant L. More precisely, iteration *converges* if $h < 3/L$, and it converges *rapidly* if $h \ll 3/L$. For, from (40), we have

$$\left| y_{k+2}^{(r+1)} - y_{k+2}^{(r)} \right| = \frac{h}{3} \left| F(x_{k+2}, y_{k+2}^{(r)}) - F(x_{k+2}, y_{k+2}^{r-1}) \right|$$

$$\leqq (hL/3) |y_{k+2}^{(r)} - y_{k+2}^{r-1}|,$$

by induction on r, using the Lipschitz condition assumed.

Hence, if $\theta = hL/3$, we obtain

$$\left| y_{k+2}^{(r+1)} - y_{k+2}^{(r)} \right| \leqq \theta^r |y_{k+2}^{(1)} - y_{k+2}^{(0)}|.$$

For $h < 3/L$, $\theta < 1$ and the sequence of $y_{k+2}^{(r)}$ is a Cauchy sequence. Let y_{k+2} be its limit. Since U satisfies a Lipschitz condition with Lipschitz constant $\theta = hL/3$, it is continuous. Hence, passing to the limit on both sides of the equation $y_{k+2}^{(r+1)} = U(y_{k+2}^{(r)})$, we get (40).

Predictors. We can obtain good initial approximations to y_{k+2} by using numerical quadrature formulas involving equally spaced interior points. The simplest such formula is

$$y_{k+2}^{(0)} = y_k + 2hF_{k+1}, \quad (41a)$$

---

† The method is also analogous to Picard's method of successive approximation described in Chapter 6, § 7.

where F_i denotes $F(x_i, y_i)$, as above. The error is $O(h^3)$. For $k \geq 2$, we can use the more refined formula

$$y_{k+2}^{(0)} = y_{k-2} + (4h/3)[2F_{k-1} - F_k + 2F_{k+1}]. \tag{41b}$$

This would be exact if $F(x, y(x))$ were a cubic polynomial in x. Hence, by Theorem 1, its truncation error is $O(h^5)$.

By analogy with the improved Euler method of Chapter 7, §10, we can think of the Milne method as combining one of the above *predictor* formulas with the *corrector* formula (40); one or two applications of the corrector formula at each step should give sufficient accuracy.

12 Stability; error analysis

Like the second-order approximation (22) of §7, Milne's method gives an *unstable* difference approximation to the strictly stable DE $y' + y = 0$. Neglecting roundoff error, the approximate solution satisfies the ΔE, obtained by Milne's method (37),

$$y_{k+2} = y_k - \frac{h}{3}[y_k + 4y_{k+1} + y_{k+2}].$$

Equivalently, it satisfies the *linear* ΔE

$$y_{k+2} = \frac{3-h}{3+h} y_k - \frac{4h}{3+h} y_{k+1}. \tag{42}$$

The general solution of (42) is, as in §8, the sequence $x_n = A_1\rho_1{}^n + A_2\rho_2{}^n$, where ρ_1 and ρ_2 are the roots of the characteristic equation of (42), namely

$$\rho^2 + \frac{4h\rho}{3+h} - \frac{3-h}{3+h} = 0.$$

The roots of this equation satisfy the relations

$$\rho_1 = 1 - h + 0(h^2), \qquad \rho_2 = -\left(1 + \frac{h}{3}\right) + O(h^2).$$

As $h \downarrow 0$, we obtain $\rho_1{}^n = (1-h)^{t/h} + O(h)$, so that, in the limit, we get e^{-t}, an exact solution of the DE.

But $\rho_2{}^n = \left[-\left(1 + \frac{h}{3}\right)\right]^n + O(h)$ tends, as $h \to 0$ $(n \to \infty)$, to a *spurious* solution, whose magnitude $e^{t/3}$ grows exponentially and whose sign alternates! As a result, no matter how small the coefficient A_2 of $\rho_2{}^n$ is initially, and how small is subsequent roundoff error, the calculated values of $x_n = x(t_n)$ will ultimately oscillate wildly if the approximate function table is continued far enough using Milne's method.

Error bound. Since the relative error in Simpson's rule is $O(h^4)$, we readily guess that the cumulative truncation error in Milne's method, over any fixed interval $[a, a + T]$, is bounded by Mh^4 for some finite constant M independent of the mesh-length h. This is true, provided that both y_0 and y_1 are accurate to $O(h^5)$.

Indeed, let $y(x)$ be any exact solution of the DE $y' = F(x, y)$, and let $\phi(x) = F(x, y(x))$. Then by Theorem 4, we have

$$y_{k+2} = y_k + \frac{h}{3}[\phi(x_k) + 4\phi(x_{k+1}) + \phi(x_{k+2})] + e_{k+2}, \qquad (43)$$

where $|e_{k+2}| = |\phi^{iv}|_{max}h^5/90$. From this, a discussion like that of Chapter 7, § 12, yields the bound

$$M = |\phi^{iv}|_{max}(e^{LT} - 1)\Big/ 90L\Big(1 - \frac{hL}{3}\Big). \qquad (44)$$

Finally, we can express $\phi^{iv}(x)$ in terms of F and its derivatives, just as in Chapter 3, § 8:

$$\phi' = F_x + FF_y, \qquad \phi'' = F_{xx} + 2FF_{xy} + F^2F_{yy} + F_xF_y + FF_y^2 \quad (45)$$

and so on. Combining these results, we can compute M *a priori* in terms of the values of F and its derivatives, thus getting an explicit error bound.

Practical error analysis. A priori error bounds like the preceding are usually less useful than *a posteriori* error estimates which make use of numerical results. For example, let $y_k = y(x_k)$ be the value at $x = x_k$ of the exact solution of an initial value problem for the DE (36), and let $z_k = z(x_k, h)$ be the value at x_k of the *approximate* solution computed by Milne's method for a given constant mesh-length h. General theorems (not proved in this book)† assert that, as $h \downarrow 0$, the truncation error $z(x_k, h) - y(x_k)$ satisfies an asymptotic formula of the form

$$z(x_k, h) - y(x_k) = Ch^4 + O(h^5) \qquad (46)$$

for some constant C. The coefficient C of the dominant term in the asymptotic formula (46) for the truncation error is, however, not usually known *a priori*, even approximately. Though we can use (44)–(45) to compute an upper bound M for C, this bound is ordinarily much bigger than C (in symbols, $M \gg C$).

However, we can combine (46) with numerical evidence, to get a good estimate of C, as follows. First compute approximate numerical

---

†But see Chapter 7, formulas (19), (26) and (28).

tables of $z(x_k, \theta)$ for different constant mesh-lengths $\theta = h,\ h/2,\ \ldots\ldots$
The truncation error $Z(\theta) = z(x_k, \theta) - y(x_k)$ for any fixed mesh point
x_k satisfies the following lemma for some n (the "order of magnitude
of the truncation error").

■ LEMMA. *Given the function $Z(\theta) = Y + C\theta^n + O(\theta^{n+1})$, let $Z(h) = Z_0$
and $Z(h/2) = Z_1$. Then*

$$Y = Z_1 + (Z_1 - Z_0)/(2^n - 1) + O(h^{n+1}). \tag{47}$$

Proof — Straightforward substitution into the formulas given, with
$\theta = h$ and $\theta = h/2$, yields $Z_1 - Z_0 = (2^{-n} - 1)Ch^n + O(h^{n+1})$, whence

$$Z_1 + (Z_1 - Z_0)/2^{n-1} = Y + Ch^n + O(h^{n+1}) - Ch^n + O(h^{n+1}).$$

Since $Ch^n - Ch^n = 0$ and $O(h^{n+1}) + O(h^{n+1}) = O(h^{n+1})$, formula (47)
follows immediately.

Note that formula (47) *corrects* the computed value Z_1 by the *extrapolation* term $(Z_1 - Z_0)/(2^n - 1)$. If we compute $Z(h/4) = Z_2$ as well,
we get the improved estimate

$$Y = Z_2 + (Z_2 - Z_1)/(2^n - 1) + O(h^{n+1}). \tag{48}$$

The internal agreement between (47) and (48) provides the best practical
way of estimating the error. When $(Z_2 - Z_1)/(Z_1 - Z_0) \simeq 2^{-n}$, we can
be fairly confident that both the terms $O(h^{n+1})$ in (46) and the roundoff
error (neglected in (46)) are of secondary importance, and that the
error term $O(h^{n+1})$ in (48) is not much bigger than $2^{-n}(Z_2 - Z_1)$.

The preceding method, called "deferred approach to the limit" by
its inventor, L. F. Richardson, applies to partial as well as to ordinary
DE's; its usefulness for practical computation can hardly be over-
estimated.

Romberg's quadrature method†. Application of the preceding idea to
trapezoidal quadrature, for which $n = 2$, yields a very beautiful new
method of numerical quadrature. Let $T_0^{(k)}$ be the trapezoidal sum

$$h = \sum_{j=0}^{2k} F(a + jh), \qquad \text{where} \quad h = 2^{-k}(b - a),$$

and let $T_m^{(k)} = 4^m[T_{m-1}^{(k+1)} - T_{m-1}^{(k)}]/(4^m - 1)$. Then the $T_k^{(k)}$ converge
very rapidly to $\int_a^b F(x)\,dx$.

---

† See F. L. Bauer, H. Rutishauser, and E. Stiefel, *Proc. XV Symposium on Applied
Math.*, *Am. Math. Soc.* 1963, pp. 199–218.

EXERCISES E

1. (a) Show that, for the DE $y' = y$ and $h = 0.1$, Milne's method amounts to using the ΔE $y_{k+2} = (31y_k + 4y_{k+1})/29$.
   (b) Integrate the DE $y' = y$ from $x = 0$ to $x = 1$ by Milne's method with $h = 0.1$, for the starting values $y_0 = 1$ and $y_1 = 1.1052$.
2. Same question for the DE $y' = 1 + y^2$, using the starting values $y_0 = 0$ and $y_1 = 0.1003$.
3. Same question for the DE $y' = x^2 + y^2$, with the starting values $y_0 = 0$ and $y_1 = 0.00033$.

   Exercises 4–6 concern the *two-level midpoint method*, defined by (24).

4. (a) Show that, if $y' = F(x, y)$, where $F \in \mathscr{C}^2$, then $y = f(x)$ satisfies the two-level midpoint formula (19) with discrepancy $O(h^3)$.
   (b) Show that, if $F \in \mathscr{C}^4$ and y_{n-1}, y_n are exact, the truncation error is $Kh^3 + O(h^4)$.
5. (a) Integrate $y' = y$ approximately by the two-level midpoint method with $h = 0.1$, taking $y_0 = 1$, $y_1 = 1.1052$ as starting values and integrating to $y_{10} \simeq 2.7145$.
   (b) Estimate the discrepancy and the cumulative truncation error in (a), comparing them with the roundoff error.
6. (a) Do the same as in Exercise 5a but for the system $y' = z - 2y$, $z' = y - 2z$ and the starting values $y_0 = 1$, $z_0 = 0$, $y_1 = 0.8228$, $z_1 = 0.0820$, computed by the method of § 13.
   (b) Show that the system in question is stable but that the approximating ΔE is not. Explain why the computed table is approximately correct, although the method is unstable.
7. (a) For general $h > 0$, set
$$y_0 = 1, \quad y_1 = 1 + h + h^2 \left(\frac{1}{2} + \frac{h}{6} + \frac{h^2}{24} \right) \quad \text{and} \quad y_{n+1} = y_{n-1} + 2hy_n.$$
   Show that $|y_n - e^{nh}| = O(h^2)$, as $h \to 0$ with nh constant.
   (b) If $h = 10^{-p}$ and the roundoff error is 10^{-p}, infer that the cumulative *total* error is $O(10^{p-h})$.
8. For the first-order linear system $dx/dt = A(t)x$, show that the trapezoidal, improved Euler, and midpoint integration formulas give respectively:
$$\mathbf{x}_i = (I - hA_i/2)^{-1}(I + hA_{i-1}/2)\mathbf{x}_{i-1},$$
$$\mathbf{x}_i = [I + h(A_{i-1} + A_i)/2 + h^2 A_i A_{i-1}/2]\mathbf{x}_{i-1},$$
$$\mathbf{x}_i = (I + hA_{i-1/2} + h^2 A_{i-1/2} A_i/2)\mathbf{x}_{i-1}.$$

9*. Show the approximate solution obtained by Milne's method for given initial values converges to the true solution for any $F \in \mathscr{C}^2$. What is the resulting order of accuracy?

13   Local power series

In principle, it is easy to derive formulas of numerical integration for $y' = F(x, y)$ having an arbitrarily high order of accuracy, if F is sufficiently smooth. Simply evaluate the successive derivatives of y as in Chapter 3, §8, getting $y' = F$, $y'' = F' = F_x + FF_y$,

$$y''' = F_{xx} + 2FF_{xy} + F^2 F_{yy} + y'' F_y,$$

$$y^{\mathrm{iv}} = F_{xxx} + 3FF_{xxy} + 3F^2 F_{xyy} + F^3 F_{yyy} + y''(3F_{xy} + 3FF_{yy}) + y''' F_y,$$

and so on. If F is linear or a polynomial of low degree, the preceding formulas may even be practical for computation.

Then evaluate Taylor's formula, valid for $F \in \mathscr{C}^n$,

$$y(x_k + h) = y_k + hy'_k + h^2 y''_k/2 + \cdots + h^n y_k^{(n)}/(n!) + O(h^{n+1}), \quad (49)$$

ignoring the remainder $O(h^{n+1})$. The relative error in the recursion relation so obtained,

$$y_{k+1} = y_k + hy'_k + h^2 y''_k/2 + \cdots + h^n y_k^{(n)}/(n!), \quad (49')$$

is obviously of order n. Hence, by Theorem 9 of Chapter 7, so is the cumulative error. Moreover this *one-step, explicit* method has the advantages of permitting a variable mesh-length and of being stable for strictly stable DE's.

The calculation of (49'), however, is rather cumbersome since it involves many terms. Furthermore, in some cases the derivatives of F can be computed only approximately by numerical differentiation, which is inexact (§ 6). A one-step method of integration which gives a high order of accuracy and avoids these defects will now be described.

14 The Runge-Kutta method

This approach is based on the idea of obtaining as high an order of accuracy as possible, using an *explicit, one-step* method. It consists in extending the approximations of the improved Euler method (Chapter 7, § 10) further, so as to obtain a one-step formula having a higher order of accuracy. One-step methods have the advantage of permitting a change of mesh-length at any step, because no starting process is required.

The most commonly used one-step method with high order of accuracy is the Runge-Kutta† method. We now describe the ΔE used in this method, for the first-order system

$$d\mathbf{x}/dt = \mathbf{X}(\mathbf{x}, t), \qquad a \leq t \leq b, \quad (50)$$

with mesh points $a = t_0 < t_1 < t_2 < \cdots$. Let $\mathbf{y}_0 = \mathbf{x}(a)$ be the initial

---

† *Zeits. Math. Phys.* 46 (1901), 435–453; C. Runge and H. König, *Numerische Rechnung*, 1924, Chapter 10.

value. The approximate function table of values $\mathbf{y}_i$ corresponding to the points t_i is defined by the ΔE

$$\mathbf{y}_{i+1} = \mathbf{y}_i + \frac{h}{6}(\mathbf{k}_1 + 2\mathbf{k}_2 + 2\mathbf{k}_3 + \mathbf{k}_4), \tag{51}$$

$$\mathbf{k}_1 = \mathbf{X}(\mathbf{y}_i, t_i), \qquad \mathbf{k}_2 = \mathbf{X}(\mathbf{y}_i + h\mathbf{k}_1/2, t_i + h/2),$$
$$\mathbf{k}_3 = \mathbf{X}(\mathbf{y}_i + h\mathbf{k}_2/2, t_i + h/2), \qquad \mathbf{k}_4 = \mathbf{X}(\mathbf{y}_i + h\mathbf{k}_3, t_i + h),$$

where the mesh-length $h = h_i$ may vary with i.

We now show that the preceding Runge-Kutta method has an error of only $O(h^5)$ per step[†]. For simplicity, we restrict attention to the first-order DE

$$dx/dt = X(x, t), \qquad X \in \mathscr{C}^4, \qquad a \leqq t \leqq b, \tag{52}$$

and to the initial condition $x(0) = 0$. Formulas (51), (51′) reduce in this case to

$$y_{i+1} = y_i + (h/6)(k_1 + 2k_2 + 2k_3 + k_4), \tag{53}$$

where

$$k_1 = X(y_i, t_i), \qquad\qquad k_2 = X(y_i + hk_1/2, t_i + h/2),$$
$$\tag{53′}$$
$$k_3 = X(y_i + hk_2/2, t_i + h/2), \qquad k_4 = X(y_i + hk_3, t_i + h).$$

Let $x(t)$ be the exact solution of the DE satisfying $x(0) = y_0 = 0$. Set $h/2 = \theta$. Then k_2 can be written as

$$k_2 = X(x_{1/2}, \theta) + X_x(x_{1/2}, \theta)[x_0 - x_{1/2} + \theta k_1]$$
$$+ X_{xx}(x_{1/2}, \theta)[x_0 - x_{1/2} + \theta k_1]^2/2 + \cdots,$$

where $x_0 = x(0)$, $x_{1/2} = x(\theta)$, and subscripts x stand for partial derivatives. Using primes to indicate total derivatives with respect to t, so that $X' = \partial X/\partial t + X \partial X/\partial x$, we get

$$x_{1/2} = x_0 + X(0, 0)\theta + X'(0, 0)\theta^2/2 + X''(0, 0)\theta^3/6$$
$$+ X'''(0, 0)\theta^4/24 + O(h^5).$$

Since $k_1 = X(0, 0)$, it follows that

$$x_0 - x_{1/2} + \theta k_1/2 = -X'(0, 0)\theta^2/2 - X''(0, 0)\theta^3/6 + O(h^4),$$

so that

$$k_2 = X(x_{1/2}, \theta) - X_x(x_{1/2}, \theta)[X'(0, 0)\theta^2/2 + X''(0, 0)\theta^3/6] + O(h^4).$$

For k_3, we have, similarly,

$$k_3 = X(x_{1/2}, \theta) + X_x(x_{1/2}, \theta)[x_0 - x_{1/2} + \theta k_2] + \cdots$$

[†] The proof which follows was constructed by Robert E. Lynch.

From this formula, since

$$x_0 = x_{1/2} - X(x_{1/2}, \theta)\theta + X'(x_{1/2}, h/2)\theta^2/2$$
$$- X''(x_{1/2}, \theta)\theta^3/6 + X'''(x_{1/2}, \theta)\theta^4/24 + O(h^5),$$

we obtain

$$k_3 = X(x_{1/2}, \theta) + X_x(x_{1/2}, \theta)X'(x_{1/2}, \theta)\theta^2/2$$
$$- X_x(x_{1/2}, \theta)X_x(x_{1/2}, \theta)X'(0, 0)\theta^3/2$$
$$- X_x(x_{1/2}, \theta)X''(x_{1/2}, \theta)\theta^3/6 + O(h^4)$$

Similarly, we have

$$k_4 = X(x_1, h) + X_x(x_1, h)[x_0 - x_1 + hk_3] + \cdots$$

and

$$x_0 - x_1 = -hX(x_{1/2}, \theta) - X''(x_{1/2}, \theta)\theta^3/3 + O(h^4),$$

so that

$$k_4 = X(x_1, h) - X_x(x_1, h)X''(x_{1/2}, \theta)\theta^3/3$$
$$+ X_x(x_1, h)X_x(x_{1/2}, \theta)X'(x_{1/2}, \theta)\theta^3 + O(h^4)$$

Finally, we have the relations

$$X(x_{1/2}, \theta) = X(0, 0) + X'(0, 0)\theta + X''(0, 0)\theta^2/2$$
$$+ X'''(0, 0)\theta^3/6 + O(h^4),$$

$$X(x_1, h) = X(0, 0) + X'(0, 0)h + X''(0, 0)h^2/2 + X'''(0, 0)h^3/6 + O(h^4),$$

$$X_x(x_1, h) = X_x(x_{1/2}, \theta) + X_x'(x_{1/2}, \theta)\theta + O(h^2)$$

Combining these results, we find that

$$y_1 = y_0 + (h/6)[k_1 + 2k_2 + 2k_3 + k_4]$$
$$= y_0 + X(0, 0)h + X'(0, 0)\frac{h^2}{2} + X''(0, 0)\frac{h^3}{6} + X'''(0, 0)h^4/24 + O(h^5)$$

and $y_0 = x_0$. Since $x(h)$ is given by

$$x(h) = x_1 = x_0 + X(0, 0)h + X'(0, 0)h^2/2 + X''(0, 0)h^3/6$$
$$+ X'''(0, 0)h^4/24 + O(h^5),$$

we see that

$$|y_1 - x_1| = O(h^5).$$

Hence, the relative error is of order four. Therefore, by Theorem 9 of Chapter 7, so is the cumulative error. The method of proof consists in comparing various Taylor's series.

The main defect of the Runge-Kutta method is the need for evaluating $\mathbf{k}_j = \mathbf{X}(\mathbf{x}_j, t_j)$ for four values of $(\mathbf{x}_j, t_j)$ per time step. If $\mathbf{X}$ is a complicated function, this may be quite time-consuming.

To avoid this repetitive evaluation, some computer programs use the Runge-Kutta process only to start the computation or in the first few steps after the mesh-length has been changed. At other time steps, Adams type formulas are used, based on approximate quadrature formulas having a high order of accuracy. For example, we can obtain an absolute error $O(h^4)$, using the *predictor* formula of Adams-Bashforth,

$$\tilde{\mathbf{y}}_{i+1} = \mathbf{y}_i + h \sum_{m=0}^{3} \beta_m \nabla^m \mathbf{X}_i, \qquad (54)$$

where $\beta_0 = 1$, $\beta_1 = \frac{1}{2}$, $\beta_2 = \frac{5}{12}$, and $\beta_3 = \frac{3}{8}$, followed by the explicit *corrector* formula of Adams-Moulton

$$\mathbf{y}_{i+1} = \mathbf{y}_i + h \sum_{m=0}^{3} \gamma_m \nabla^m \tilde{\mathbf{X}}_{i+1}, \qquad (55)$$

where $\gamma_0 = 1$, $\gamma_1 = -\frac{1}{2}$, $\gamma_2 = -\frac{1}{12}$, $\gamma_3 = -\frac{1}{24}$, and

$$\tilde{\mathbf{X}}_{i+1} = \mathbf{X}(\tilde{\mathbf{y}}_{i+1}, t).$$

EXERCISES F

1. (a) Derive a power series expansion for $f(a + h)$ through terms in h^3 for the solution of $y' = 1 + y^2$ satisfying $f(a) = c$.
   (b) Truncating the preceding series after terms in h^3, evaluate approximately in three steps the solution of $y' = 1 + y^2$ satisfying $f(0) = 0$, setting $x_1 = 0.5$, $x_2 = 0.8$, $x_3 = 1$. What is the truncation error? [HINT: Consider $\tan x$.]
2. Same question for $y' = x^2 + y^2$. (The exact solution, rounded off to five decimal places, is 0.35023.)
3. (a) Apply the Picard process to the DE $y' = x^2 + y^2$ for the initial value $y_0 = 0$ and initial trial function $y^{(0)} \equiv 0$. Calculate the first four iterates.
   (b) Using the power series method of the text, calculate the Taylor series of the solution through terms in x^{17}, and check against the answer to (a).
   (c) Evaluate $y(1)$ numerically at $x = 1$, using the preceding truncated power series, and compare with the answer of Exercise 2.
4. Apply the Runge-Kutta method to the DE $y' = 1 + y^2$ for the initial value $y(0) = 0$, setting $x_0 = 0$, $x_1 = 0.5$, $x_2 = 0.8$, $x_3 = 1$.
5. Same question for the DE $y' = x^2 + y^2$, with $y(0) = 0$, and the same mesh.
6. For the first-order linear system $d\mathbf{x}/dt = A(t)\mathbf{x}$, show that the Runge-Kutta method is equivalent to

$$\mathbf{x}_{i+1} = \left[I + \frac{h}{6} (A_0 + 4A_1 + A_2) + \frac{h^2}{6} (A_1 A_0 + A_1^2 + A_2 A_1) \right.$$

$$\left. + \frac{h^3}{12} (A_1^2 A_0 + A_2 A_1^2) + \frac{h^4}{24} (A_2 A_1^2 A_0) \right] \mathbf{x}_i$$

where $A_0 = A(t_i)$, $A_1 = A(t_{i+1/2})$, $A_2 = A(t_{i+1})$.

In Exercises 7–11, let $y' = F(x, y) = \sum_{j,k=0}^{\infty} b_{jk} x^j y^k$ and $y(0) = 0$.

7. Show that

$$y'' = F_x + F F_y \qquad \text{and} \qquad y''' = F_{xx} + 2F F_{xy} + F^2 F_{yy} + F_x F_y + F F_y^2.$$

In Exercises 8–11, let $B = b_{20} + b_{11} b_{00} + b_{02} b_{00}^2$ and $B^* = b_{10} b_{01} + b_{00} b_{01}^2$.

8. Show that, if $y(0) = 0$, then we have

$$y(h) = h b_{00} + h^2(b_{10} + b_{00} b_{01})/2 + h^3(B/3 + B^*/6) + O(h^4).$$

9. Show that, with midpoint integration, $y(h)$ is given by the approximate formula

$$y_M(h) = h b_{00} = h^2(b_{10} + b_{00} b_{01})/2 + h^3 B/4 + O(h^4).$$

and that the truncation error is $-h^3(B/12 + B^*/6) + O(h^4)$.

10. Show that the improved Euler method gives

$$y_E(h) = h b_{00} + h^2(b_{10} + b_{00} b_{01})/2 + h^3 B/2 + O(h^4),$$

with truncation error $h^3(B - B^*)/6 + O(h^4)$.

11. Show that the trapezoidal approximation to $y(h)$ is

$$y_T(h) = h b_{00} + h^2(b_{10} + b_{00} b_{01})/2 + h^3(B/2 + B^*/4) + O(h^4)$$

with truncation error $h^3(B/6 + B^*/12) + O(h^4)$.

12. Check the formulas of Exercise E8 against those of Exercises 9–10 above in the special case $t_{i-1} = 0$, $t_i = h$, and $A(t) = p(t) = p_0 + p_1 t + p_2 t^2 + \cdots$ of a first-order linear DE.

13*. For the linear DE $dx/dt = p(t)x$, $\qquad p(t) = \sum_{k=0}^{\infty} p_k(t - a)^k$, evaluate $x(a + h)$ through terms in h^6 by the Runge-Kutta method. Compare with the Taylor series for the exact solution.

14*. *Adams three-level methods* for integrating $y' = F(x, y)$ are

(A_3) $\qquad y_{n+1} = y_n + h[23F_n - 16F_{n-1} + 5F_{n-2}]/12$ $\qquad\qquad$ (explicit),

(A_3') $\qquad y_{n+1} = y_n + h[9F_{n+1} + 19F_n - 5F_{n-1} + F_{n-2}]/24$ $\qquad$ (implicit).

Show that the truncation error of (A_3) is $O(h^4)$ per step, while that of the implicit method (A_3') is $O(h^5)$.

9 Regular Singular Points

1 The continuation principle

An *analytic*, or *holomorphic*, function $w = f(z)$ of a *complex* variable $z = x + iy$ is one having a complex derivative $f'(z) = dw/dz$ at every point.[†] This is equivalent to the definition given in Chapter 3, §5, as is proved in books on complex analysis: any complex analytic function can be expanded in a convergent power series. An analytic DE is one in which the functions involved are all analytic. Its solutions are then necessarily also analytic (Chapter 6, § 10).

The solutions of analytic DE's are best studied as functions of a complex variable, because their isolated singular points are surrounded by connected domains in the complex z-plane. This permits one to continue solutions beyond and around isolated singular points whereas, on the real line, solutions terminate abruptly at singular points.

For instance, consider the DE $du/dx = u^2$ for real x and u. The formula $u = -1/x$ defines *two* real solutions of this DE; one defined for $x > 0$; the other for $x < 0$. As $x \to 0$, one solution tends to $+\infty$, and the other to $-\infty$; the behavior of these two solutions near $x = 0$ seems to be unrelated if x is restricted to real values. On the other hand, consider the same DE $dw/dz = w^2$ for *complex* $z = x + iy$ and $w = u + iv$. The formula $w = -1/z$ defines now a *single* solution of the DE, in a domain D which includes every point of the complex z-plane except the isolated singular point at $z = 0$; hence, it includes both real solutions. The general solution of the same DE is the complex-valued analytic function $w = 1/(c - z)$. This function has an isolated singularity at $z = c$.

---

† Ahlfors, p. 24; Hille, p. 72. Some knowledge of complex function theory is assumed in the present Chapter.

The DE $dw/dz = w^2$ is defined and analytic for all z and w, real or complex. Each particular solution $w = 1/(c-z)$ of this DE is defined in the punctured z-plane with the point $z = c$ deleted. Since this domain is connected, the solution can be continued as an analytic function from any region in it to any other. This process of *analytic continuation* is uniquely defined, for any given path of continuation.†

The solution $u = -1/x$ of $dw/dz = w^2$ on the negative x-axis is obtained by analytic continuation in the complex plane from the solution $u = -1/x$ of $du/dx = u^2$ for $x > 0$. This is evident if we continue the solution as a complex analytic function $w = (-x+iy)/(x^2+y^2)$ around the origin on either side. The fact that the analytic continuation of a solution of a DE is a solution of the analytic continuation of the DE is valid in general, as we now prove.

Let $F(w_1, \ldots, w_n, z)$ be an analytic complex-valued function in a domain D of $(w_1, \ldots, w_n, z)$-space. This means that F can be expanded into a convergent power series with complex coefficients in some neighborhood of each point of D. Then, as shown in Chapter 6, § 10, every solution of the nth order DE

$$\frac{d^n w}{dz^n} = F(w, w', w'', \ldots, w^{(n-1)}, z)$$

is an analytic function. The function $w^{(n)}(z) - F(w(z), w'(z), \ldots, w^{(n-1)}(z), z)$ of the variable z is holomorphic and vanishes identically in the subdomain where the function w is defined. It follows that all analytic continuations beyond D of this function vanish identically. Therefore, any analytic continuation of the function w is also a solution of the DE, and we have

■ THEOREM 1 (Continuation Principle). *The function obtained by analytic continuation of any solution of an analytic DE, along any path in the complex plane, is a solution of the analytic continuation of the DE along the same path.*

EXAMPLE 1.   Consider the first-order Euler DE

$$dw/dz = \gamma w/z, \qquad \gamma = \alpha + i\beta, \qquad \alpha, \beta \text{ real.} \tag{1}$$

By separating variables and writing $z = re^{i\theta}$, we find the solution

$$w = z^\gamma = e^{\gamma \ln z} = e^{(\alpha+i\beta)(\ln r + i\theta)}$$
$$= e^{(\alpha \ln r - \beta\theta)}[\cos(\beta \ln r + \alpha\theta) + i\sin(\beta \ln r + \alpha\theta)].$$

† Ahlfors, p. 275; Hille, p. 184.

When $\beta = 0$ and γ is real, the analytic continuation of the real solution $u = x^\alpha$ on the positive x-axis through the upper half-plane to the negative x-axis, where $\theta = \pi$, is $(\cos \pi\alpha + i \sin \pi\alpha)|x|^\alpha$. Note that this is not equal to the real solution $|x|^\alpha$ on $x < 0$, unless α is an even integer.

The preceding example also shows that DE's involving only single-valued functions can have *multiple-valued* solutions in the complex plane. Unless γ is a real integer, the value of $w = z^\gamma$ changes by a factor $e^{2\pi i\gamma} \neq 1$ when z describes a simple closed counterclockwise loop around the origin, making θ increase by 2π and $\ln z$ by $2\pi i$. This example shows that solutions of a linear DE can have *branch points* where the DE has a singular point†, even though the DE has single-valued coefficient-functions.

EXAMPLE 2.   The second-order homogeneous Euler DE is

$$z^2 w'' + pz w' + qw = 0, \qquad p, q \quad \text{real constants.} \tag{2}$$

For positive $z = x > 0$, a basis of real solutions is provided by the real and imaginary parts of the functions $z^\nu = e^{\gamma \ln z}$, where γ is either of the roots of the *indicial equation*

$$\nu^2 + (p - 1)\nu + q = 0. \tag{2'}$$

For instance, the roots of the indicial equation of the DE

$$z^2 w'' + z w' + w = 0$$

are $\nu = \pm i$. A basis of complex solutions, real on the positive x-axis, is therefore provided, as in Chapter 4, §2, by the real and imaginary parts of the functions

$$w_1 = (z^i + z^{-i})/2 = [e^{i(\ln r + i\theta)} + e^{-i(\ln r + i\theta)}]/2$$

$$= \cosh \theta \cos (\ln r) - i \sinh \theta \sin (\ln r),$$

$$w_2 = (z^i - z^{-i})/2i = \cosh \theta \sin (\ln r) + i \sinh \theta \cos (\ln r).$$

The analytic continuation of the solution $\cos (\ln x)$, real on the positive x-axis $\theta = 0$, through the upper half-plane to the negative x-axis $\theta = \pi$ is not the solution $\cos (\ln |x|) = \cos (\ln r)$ given in Chapter 4, §2 but is the complex-valued function $\cosh \pi \cos (\ln r) - i \sinh \pi \sin (\ln r)$.

---

† We define a *singular* point of the linear DE

$$p_0(z)w^{(n)} + p_1(z)w^{(n-1)} + \cdots + p_n(z)w = p_{n+1}(z)$$

as a point where some $p_k(z)$ has a singular point, or $p_0(z) = 0$.

2* Movable singular points

The general solution of the DE $w' = w^2$ considered in §1 is $1/(c - z)$. This function has a *pole* at the variable point c. Thus, the location of the singular point of a solution depends in this example on the particular solution. This happens for most *nonlinear* DE's; one describes the situation by saying that the "general solution" has a *movable* singular point.

A second example of movable singular points is provided by the DE $w' = z/w$. The general solution of this DE, obtained by separating variables, is the two-valued function $w = (z^2 - c^2)^{1/2}$, which has branch points at $z = \pm c$. Since c is arbitrary, the general solution has a movable branch point.

There is no significant class of nonlinear first-order normal DE's whose solutions have fixed singular points. The solutions of the generalized Riccati DE $w' = p_0(z) + p_1(z)w + p_2(z)w^2$ have *fixed branch points*.† This can be shown by representing $w = v'/p_2 v$ as a quotient of solutions v of the linear DE $v'' + p_1 v' + p_0 p_2 v = 0$, as in Chapter 2, §3.

A second-order nonlinear DE having a fixed singular point at $z = 0$ is

$$w'' = (w'^2/w) - (w'/z),$$

whose general solution is $w = Cz^\gamma$, with C, γ arbitrary complex constants. But nonlinear DE's with fixed singular points are highly exceptional.

It is otherwise for linear DE's, to which this chapter will be largely devoted. An nth order normal linear DE

$$L[w] = w^{(n)} + p_1(z)w^{(n-1)} + \cdots + p_{n-1}(z)w' + p_n(z)w = f(z)$$

with holomorphic coefficient functions has holomorphic solutions in any domain where the coefficient functions are holomorphic. The argument of Chapter 6, § 8, can be applied to construct solutions along any path. Moreover, as in Chapter 6, § 10, all the functions constructed in the Picard iteration process are holomorphic in any *simply connected* domain, say in $0 \leq |z| < R$. It follows, as in Corollary 2 of Theorem 7 of Chapter 6, that the DE $L[w] = 0$ has a basis of holomorphic solutions in any such domain—and that $L[w] = f(z)$ has a solution for any choice of initial conditions compatible with the order of the DE.

It follows that the only possible singular points of the solutions of a linear DE occur where one or more of the coefficient-functions $p_k(z)$ has a singular point. In short, linear DE's have fixed singular points. In the remainder of this chapter, we will see how the nature of these singular points is determined by the singularities of the coefficient-functions.

---

† The Riccati DE is the *only* first-order DE with fixed branch points.

3 First-order equations

The study of singular points of linear DE's begins with the first-order linear DE

$$w' + p(z)w = 0. \tag{3}$$

We will treat only *isolated* singular points. For such singular points, we can assume that p is a holomorphic function in the punctured disc $\Delta: 0 < |z| < \rho$ because any singular point can be put at the origin by a translation of coordinates.

It follows that $p(z)$ can be expanded into a Laurent series†,

$$p(z) = \sum_{-\infty}^{\infty} a_k z^k, \qquad 0 < |z| < \rho,$$

convergent in Δ. When all a_k with $k < 0$ vanish, $p(z)$ is said to have a *removable singularity* at $z = 0$; when there is a largest negative integer $k = -m$ for which $a_k \neq 0$, $p(z)$ is said to have a *pole* of *order m* there; if there are an infinite number of nonzero coefficients a_k with $k < 0$, then $p(z)$ is said to have an *essential singularity* at the origin.

In all cases, the general solution of (3) is given by the indefinite integral formula (11) of Chapter 1, § 6 (with $q = 0$):

$$w = \exp\left[-\int p(z)\, dz\right]$$

$$= C \exp\left[-a_{-1}\ln z - \sum_{k=1}^{\infty}(a_{k-1}/k)z^k + \sum_{k=1}^{\infty}(a_{-k-1}/k)z^{-k}\right].$$

As a corollary, we obtain the representation of the solution w in the form

$$w = C z^\alpha g(z), \qquad \alpha = -a_{-1} \tag{3'}$$

where $g(z)$ is a *holomorphic* function in the domain Δ.

We now describe the fundamental classification of singularities for the first-order linear DE (3) at any isolated singular point of $p(z)$.

■ DEFINITION. *If $p(z)$ has a removable singularity,* (3) *has a* removable singularity; *if $p(z)$ has a pole of order one,* (3) *has a* regular singular point; *if $p(z)$ has a pole of order $m > 1$ or an essential singularity,* (3) *has an* irregular singular point.

If (3) has a removable singularity at $z = 0$, then $a_{-1} = 0$, and

$$w = C g(z), \qquad g(z) = \exp\left[-\sum_{1}^{\infty}(a_{k-1}z^k/k)\right]$$

---

† Ahlfors, p. 182; Hille, p. 209.

also has a removable singularity there. If (3) has a regular singular point, then (3′) still holds and $g(z)$ is given as above by

$$g(z) = 1 - a_0 z + (a_0{}^2 - a_1)z^2/2 + \cdots$$

and is still regular. Therefore, w has the form

$$w = Cz^\alpha(1 + c_1 z + c_2 z^2 + \cdots), \qquad \alpha = -a_{-1}. \tag{4}$$

An analytic function w having an expansion of the form (4) is said to have a *branch pole* of *order* α at $z = 0$. The number $\alpha = -a_{-1}$ can be real or complex.

Finally, if (3) has an irregular singular point, then $g(z)$ has an essential singularity.

From the representation (3′) we obtain the following result.

■ **THEOREM 2.** *Every solution of the first-order linear* DE (3), *with p holomorphic in Δ, has the form $w = z^\alpha g(z)$, where $\alpha = -a_{-1}$ and g is single-valued and analytic in Δ. Removable singularities, regular singular points, and irregular singular points of* (3) *give solutions having removable singularities, branch poles of order $-a_{-1}$, and essential singularities at $z = 0$, respectively.*

Theorem 2 was derived by explicit calculation. To extend it to higher-order linear DE's, which cannot be explicitly solved, more general arguments are needed. These require the notion of a *simple branch point* of an analytic function $w = f(z)$. This is defined as an isolated singular point z_0 near which $f(z)$ can be represented in the form $f(z) = (z - z_0)^\alpha g(z)$, where $g(z)$ is a one-valued holomorphic function in the punctured neighborhood of z_0. Expanding $g(z)$ in a Laurent series, we get the following expansion for a function f having a simple branch point at z_0:

$$f(z) = \sum_{-\infty}^{\infty} a_k(z - z_0)^{\alpha + k}.$$

Not all branch points are simple; for example, the functions $\ln(z - z_0)$ and $(z - z_0)^\alpha + (z - z_0)^\beta$ have branch points at $z = z_0$ but do not have simple branch points there, unless $\alpha - \beta$ is an integer. Any branch pole (4) is a simple branch point, but a simple branch point may not be a branch pole; thus, consider $z^{1/2}e^{-1/z^2}$ at $z = 0$.

We shall now give another proof of the first result of Theorem 2, namely that every solution $w(z)$ of (3) which is not a holomorphic function has a simple branch point at $z = 0$.

Starting at a point z_0 in the given punctured disc, we continue the function w analytically counterclockwise around a closed circuit, say the circle $|z| = |z_0|$. Returning to z_0 after a complete circuit around the origin, the function $w(e^{2\pi i}z) = \tilde{w}(z)$ obtained in a neighborhood of z_0 is still a solution of the DE, by Theorem 1. But $\tilde{w}$ may differ from the function w in a neighborhood of z_0, because the function w may have a branch point at $z = 0$ even though the coefficient $p(z)$ of the DE does not have a branch point there; the DE $w' = w/2z$ is a case in point.

However, the general solution of the DE (2) has the form $cw(z)$; from this it follows that

$$\tilde{w}(z) = w(e^{2\pi i}z) = cw(z), \qquad c \neq 0.$$

Now, write $c = e^{2\pi i \alpha}$, where α is a suitable complex number, and consider the analytic continuation of the function

$$g(z) = z^{-\alpha}w(z)$$

around the same circuit. We obtain

$$g(ze^{2\pi i}) = (ze^{2\pi i})^{-\alpha}w(ze^{2\pi i}) = z^{-\alpha}e^{-2\pi i \alpha}w(ze^{2\pi i})$$
$$= z^{-\alpha}e^{-2\pi i \alpha}cw(z) = z^{-\alpha}w(z) = g(z).$$

This shows that g is a single-valued function in the punctured disc Δ. Thus, the function w is the product of z^{α} and a function without a branch point.

The idea of the preceding alternative proof can be applied to linear DE's of any order, as we show in the following sections.

EXERCISES A

1. Show that no solution of $w' = 1/z$ which is real on the positive x-axis can be real on the negative x-axis.
2. (a) Setting $z = re^{i\theta}$, discuss the analytic continuation to the negative x-axis of the solutions z and $z \ln z$ of $z^2w'' - zw' + w = 0$ on the positive x-axis.
   (b) Show that no nontrivial solution of $z^2w'' + 3w/8 = 0$ which is real on the positive x-axis can be real on the negative x-axis.
3. Let $w^{(n)} + a_1(z)w^{(n-1)} + \cdots + a_n(z)w = 0$ be any holomorphic linear homogeneous DE satisfied by $\ln z$. Show that $a_n(z) \equiv 0$.
4*. Show that any holomorphic linear homogeneous DE which is satisfied by $z \ln z$ is also satisfied by z.
5. Find the function g of Theorem 2 when
   (a) $p(z) = 1/z^n$ (n an integer)   (b*) $p(z) = e^{1/z}$.
6. Solve the DE (3) for

$$p(z) = \sum_{k=1}^{n} \frac{1}{z - a_k}.$$

7. Let $p(z)$ be holomorphic and single-valued in $|z| < \rho$ except at points a and b. Show that any solution w_1 of (3) can be written in the form

$$w_1(z) = (z - a)^a(z - b)^\beta f(z),$$

where f is single-valued and holomorphic in $|z| < \rho$ except at a and b.

8. Generalize the result of the preceding exercise to the case where $p(z)$ is single-valued for $|z| < \rho$ and holomorphic at all points except $a_1, \ldots, a_n$.

9. Prove in detail that solutions of the generalized Riccati equation

$$w' = p_0(z) + p_1(z)w + p_2(z)w^2$$

can have branch points only where the $p_k(z)$ have singular points.

10. Show that, if the DE of Exercise 9 has no movable singularities, $p_2(z) \equiv 0$.

11. Show that, for analytic $p_l(z)$, the DE

$$dw/dz = \sum_{k=0}^{n} p_k(z)w^{-k}$$

has a regular solution. [HINT: Consider the DE satisfied by $1/w$.]

4 Circuit matrix

Let $w_1(z)$ and $w_2(z)$ be a basis of solutions of the second-order DE

$$w'' + p(z)w' + q(z)w = 0, \qquad (5)$$

where the functions p and q are single-valued and analytic in the punctured disc $\Delta: 0 < |z| < \rho$. Analytic continuation of each of these solutions counterclockwise around a circle $|z| = r < \rho$ with center at the origin yields two functions (in general different): $\tilde{w}_1(z) = w_1(ze^{2\pi i})$ and $\tilde{w}_2(z) = w_2(ze^{2\pi i})$. These are, by the Continuation Principle (Theorem 1), also solutions of the DE (5). But every solution of (5) is a linear combination of w_1 and w_2; hence, the continued functions $\tilde{w}_j$ can be expressed as linear combinations of the solutions w_1 and w_2:

$$\tilde{w}_1(z) = w_1(e^{2\pi i}z) = a_{11}w_1(z) + a_{12}w_2(z),$$
$$\tilde{w}_2(z) = w_2(e^{2\pi i}z) = a_{21}w_1(z) + a_{22}w_2(z).$$

The two-by-two matrix of complex constants $A = \|a_{ij}\|$ is called the *circuit matrix* of the DE at the singular point $z = 0$, relative to the basis of solutions (w_1, w_2).

For instance, consider the Euler DE $z^2 w'' - zw' + 3w/4 = 0$, with indicial equation $(\nu - 1/2)(\nu - 3/2) = 0$. The functions $z^{1/2}$ and $z^{3/2}$ form a basis of solutions; hence, the circuit matrix is the diagonal (scalar) matrix

$$\begin{pmatrix} -1 & 0 \\ 0 & -1 \end{pmatrix}.$$

A similar calculation shows that the DE $w'' + (2/9z^2)w = 0$ has the solution basis $z^{1/3}$, $z^{2/3}$. Relative to this basis, its circuit matrix is

$$\begin{pmatrix} \omega & 0 \\ 0 & \omega^2 \end{pmatrix},$$

where $\omega = (-1 + \sqrt{3}\,i)/2$ is a cube root of unity.

Higher-order DE's.   A similar construction can be used to define a circuit matrix (relative to any solution basis) for the nth order linear DE

$$L[w] = \frac{d^n w}{dz^n} + p_1(z)\frac{d^{n-1}w}{dz^{n-1}} + \cdots + p_n(z)w = 0, \tag{6}$$

where again all the coefficient-functions $p_k(z)$ are holomorphic in the punctured disc Δ.

If $w_1(z), \ldots, w_n(z)$ are any basis of solutions of (6) in Δ, analytic continuation of these functions once counterclockwise around a circuit $\gamma\colon |z| = r$ carries them into a new basis of solutions

$$\tilde{w}_j(z) = w_j(e^{2\pi i}z) = a_{j1}w_1(z) + \cdots + a_{jn}w_n(z), \qquad j = 1, 2, \ldots, n.$$

The matrix $A = \|a_{jk}\|$ so defined is the *circuit matrix* of DE (6) relative to the basis $w_1(z), \ldots, w_n(z)$.

The circuit matrix represents a linear transformation of the vector space of solutions of the nth-order linear analytic DE (6), as follows. If

$$w(z) = c_1 w_1(z) + c_2 w_2(z) + \cdots + c_n w_n(z)$$

is the general solution of the DE, analytic continuation of w around the same circuit γ carries $w(z)$ into the solution

$$\tilde{w}(z) = w(e^{2\pi i}z) = \sum_{j,k=1}^{n} c_j a_{jk} w_k(z). \tag{6'}$$

That is, the effect of analytic continuation around γ counterclockwise is to multiply the vector $\mathbf{c}$ by the matrix A on the right, so that $\mathbf{c} \to \mathbf{c}A$.

Using the circuit matrix A just defined, we can construct at least one "canonical" solution of (6) of the special form $zf(z)$, with f holomorphic in the disc Δ. This is because every matrix has† at least one (complex) eigenvector (characteristic vector). Hence, for some choice of $\mathbf{c} \neq 0$, we can write $\mathbf{c}A = \lambda\mathbf{c}$, where λ is a complex number, an eigenvalue of the matrix A. Choose $\mathbf{c}$ in (6') to be such an eigenvector, and let $f(z) = z^{-\alpha}w(z)$, where $\alpha = (\ln \lambda)/2\pi i$. It is clear that $\lambda \neq 0$, since otherwise we could retrace backward the circuit γ, continuing the solution $w = 0$ into a nonzero solution. Continuing the function $f(z) = z^{-\alpha}w(z)$ along the same circuit, we obtain, as in the proof of Theorem 2, the following result.

■ THEOREM 3.   *The nth order linear* DE (6) *with coefficients holomorphic in* $\Delta\colon 0 < |z| < \rho$ *admits at least one nontrivial solution of the form*

$$w(z) = z^\alpha f(z), \tag{7}$$

where the function f is single-valued in Δ.

---

† Birkhoff and MacLane, p. 293. As stated there, λ is a root of the characteristic equation $|A - \lambda I| = 0$.

5 Canonical bases

A solution of a holomorphic DE (6) in Δ has a simple branch point at $z = 0$ if and only if it is carried into a constant (scalar) multiple of itself by continuation around the circuit γ. In view of the discussion in the preceding Section, we see that a solution $w(z) = \sum_{j=1}^n c_j w_j(z)$ of (6) has a simple branch point at $z = 0$ if and only if the vector $\mathbf{c} = (c_1, c_2, \ldots, c_n)$ and the circuit matrix A satisfy the relation $\mathbf{c}A = \lambda \mathbf{c}$, where the constant λ will then be necessarily different from zero. In other words, a linear combination $\sum_{j=1}^n c_j w_j$ of solutions of (6) has a simple branch point at $z = 0$ if and only if the vector $\mathbf{c}$ is an eigenvector of the circuit matrix A associated with the basis $(w_1, w_2 \ldots, w_n)$ of solutions. Thus, there are as many linearly independent solutions of (6) with simple branch points as there are linearly independent eigenvectors of the matrix A.

We shall now look for a basis of solutions with simple branch points for any second-order linear DE (5), with coefficients holomorphic in Δ.

Given two linearly independent solutions w_1 and w_2 of (5), we can construct the circuit matrix $A = \|a_{ij}\|$ as in § 4. The linear combination $w = c_1 w_1(z) + c_2 w_2(z)$ will then have a simple branch point if and only if $\sum c_j a_{jk} = \lambda c_k$. By the theory of linear equations, this system of equations has a nontrivial solution if and only if the following determinant (the *characteristic equation* of the circuit matrix A) equals zero:

$$|A - \lambda I| = \lambda^2 - (a_{11} + a_{22})\lambda + (a_{11}a_{22} - a_{12}a_{21}) = 0. \qquad (8)$$

Ordinarily, this characteristic equation has two distinct roots λ_1, λ_2. These roots give two linearly independent solutions $F(z) = c_1 w_1(z) + c_2 w_2(z)$ and $G(z) = d_1 w_1(z) + d_2 w_2(z)$, having simple branch points: $F(e^{2\pi i}z) = \lambda_1 F(z)$ and $G(e^{2\pi i}z) = \lambda_2 G(z)$. Relative to the canonical basis of solutions F, G, the circuit matrix is thus a *diagonal* matrix

$$\begin{pmatrix} \lambda_1 & 0 \\ 0 & \lambda_2 \end{pmatrix}.$$

As in § 4, $F(z) = z^\alpha f(z)$ and $G(z) = z^\beta g(z)$,| where $\lambda_1 = e^{2\pi i \alpha}$, $\lambda_2 = e^{2\pi i \beta}$, and f and g are holomorphic in Δ. Such a basis is called a *canonical* basis.

When the characteristic equation has a single solution λ, the solutions may still† sometimes have a basis of the form (7). Every solution of the DE is then multiplied by the same nonzero constant $\lambda = e^{2\pi i \alpha}$ when continued around a counterclockwise circuit γ.

---

† This occurs when the matrix A is a multiple of the identity matrix. Otherwise, any 2×2 matrix A with only one eigenvalue is similar to a matrix of the form $A\begin{pmatrix} \lambda & 0 \\ 1 & \lambda \end{pmatrix}$. This fact is not assumed in the present discussion.

Otherwise, we choose a basis as follows. Let $w_1(z)$ be the solution of the form $z^\alpha f(z)$, where f is one-valued in the punctured disc, whose existence was established in Theorem 3, and let $w_2(z)$ be any other linearly independent solution. Continuation of $w_2(z)$ around the circuit γ gives, as in § 3, $w_2(ze^{2\pi i}) = aw_1(z) + bw_2(z)$. The circuit matrix for this basis of solutions is therefore the matrix

$$A = \begin{pmatrix} \lambda & 0 \\ a & b \end{pmatrix}$$

Since the eigenvalues of such a "triangular" matrix are λ and b, and since the only eigenvalue of A was assumed to be λ, we must have $b = \lambda$ and

$$A = \begin{pmatrix} \lambda & 0 \\ a & \lambda \end{pmatrix}, \qquad a \neq 0.$$

The continuation around the circuit γ of the function $h(z) = w_2(z)/w_1(z)$ is easily computed to be

$$h(ze^{2\pi i}) = \frac{a}{\lambda} + \frac{w_2(z)}{w_1(z)} = \frac{a}{\lambda} + h(z).$$

It follows that the function

$$f_1(z) = h(z) - \frac{a}{2\pi i \lambda} \ln z$$

is single-valued in $0 < |z| < \rho$ and, therefore, that the function $w_2(z)$ can be written in the form

$$w_2(z) = w_1(z)f_1(z) + \frac{a}{2\pi i \lambda} (\ln z)w_1(z).$$

In the exceptional case, since $a \neq 0$, we can make $a/2\pi i \lambda = 1$ by replacing w_2 by $2\pi i \lambda w_2/a$.

This completes the proof of the following theorem.

■ THEOREM 4.   *Under the hypotheses of Theorem 3, the second-order linear DE (5) has a basis of solutions in the neighborhood of the singular point $z = 0$, having one of the following forms:*

$$w_1(z) = z^\alpha f(z), \qquad w_2(z) = z^\beta g(z) \tag{9a}$$

or, exceptionally,

$$w_1(z) = z^\alpha f(z), \qquad w_2(z) = w_1(z)[f_1(z) + \ln z]. \tag{9b}$$

The functions $f(z)$, $g(z)$, and $f_1(z)$ are holomorphic and single-valued in the punctured disc $0 < |z| < r$.

Higher-order equations.† The preceding discussion can be extended to nth order DE's (6). A basis of solutions $w_1, w_2, \ldots, w_n$ is called a *canonical basis* when the associated circuit matrix A is in *Jordan canonical form* or, somewhat more generally, consists of zeros except on the main diagonal and (in the case of a repeated eigenvalue) just above it. If the eigenvalues of the circuit matrix are $\lambda_1, \lambda_2, \ldots, \lambda_n$, the continuation of the solution w_j around a small circuit γ is given by one of the two formulas‡

$$\tilde{w}_j(z) = w_j(ze^{2\pi i}) = \lambda_j w_j(z), \qquad (10a)$$

or, when $\lambda_j = \lambda_{j-1}$,

$$\tilde{w}_j(z) = w_j(ze^{2\pi i}) = \lambda_j w_j(z) + a_{j-1} w_{j-1}(z). \qquad (10b)$$

By Theorem 3, there always is at least one solution which goes into a multiple of itself. If all the eigenvalues of the circuit matrix are distinct, then the circuit matrix can be reduced to diagonal form by suitable choice of a " canonical basis" of solutions, and the exceptional case of formula (10b) does not arise.

EXAMPLE 3. Consider the nth order *Euler* DE

$$L[w] = \frac{d^n w}{dz^n} + \frac{c_1}{z}\frac{d^{n-1}w}{dz^{n-1}} + \frac{c_2}{z^2}\frac{d^{n-2}w}{dz^{n-2}} + \cdots + \frac{c_n}{z^n} w = 0. \qquad (11)$$

The trial function z^ν, with unknown exponent ν, satisfies the DE if and only if the exponent ν is a root of the indicial equation of Chapter 4, § 2,

$$I(\nu) = \nu(\nu - 1)\cdots(\nu - n + 1) + c_1\nu(\nu - 1)\cdots(\nu - n + 2) + \cdots$$
$$+ c_{n-1}\nu + c_n = 0. \qquad (12)$$

When the roots of the indicial equation are distinct, the z^{ν_j} are a canonical basis of solutions of the Euler DE (11). The circuit matrix is the diagonal matrix with diagonal elements $\lambda_j = e^{2\pi i\nu_j}$, where ν_j is a root of the indicial equation. When ν is a k-tuple root of the indicial equation, then the functions $z^\nu \log z$, $z^\nu(\log z)^2$, etc., form a basis of solutions. This basis is not "canonical" when $n > 2$ (see Exercise B2), though the circuit matrix for (11) is always triangular, relative to it.

EXERCISES B

1. Construct DE's (5) with circuit matrix

$$\begin{pmatrix} 1 & 0 \\ 0 & 1 \end{pmatrix}$$

for which the functions f and g in Theorem 4 have (a) essential and (b) removable singularities at 0.

---

† For a complete discussion see Coddington and Levinson, Chapter 4, §1.
‡ Cf. Birkhoff and MacLane, pp. 310–311.

2. (a) Compute the indicial polynomial for the homogeneous Euler DE
$w''' + 3w''/2 + w'4/ = w/8$.
   (b) Compute the circuit matrix of the preceding DE relative to the solution
basis $z^{1/2}$, $z^{1/2}(\log z)$, and $z^{1/2}(\log z)^2$.

3. Find a DE (5) with circuit matrix $\begin{pmatrix} \lambda & 0 \\ 0 & 1/\lambda \end{pmatrix}$ for which the functions f and g in
Theorem 4 have (a) poles and (b) essential singularities. Can f and g have removable singularities?

4. Show that the requirements $\operatorname{Re}\{\alpha\} \geqq 0$, $\operatorname{Re}\{\beta\} < 1$ uniquely determine the
exponents α and β in Theorem 4.

5. Show that, in the exceptional case of Theorem 4, the eigenvalues of the circuit
matrix are equal.

6. Show that $e^{\sqrt{z}}$, $e^{-\sqrt{z}}$ form a solution basis for the DE $w'' + (1/2z)w' - (1/4z)w = 0$.
Compute the circuit matrix for the given DE relative to this basis, and also find
a canonical solution basis.

7. Construct a second-order holomorphic DE (5) with a singular point at $z = 0$
whose circuit matrix has the form $\begin{pmatrix} 1 & 0 \\ 1 & 1 \end{pmatrix}$, such that f in Theorem 4 has an essential singularity at $z = 0$.

8. Show that, if $w \ln z$ satisfies a (homogeneous) linear DE with holomorphic
coefficients, and w is holomorphic, w satisfies the same DE.

6   Regular singular points

The results obtained so far apply to *all* linear analytic DE's near
isolated singular points. We now ask the question: When does the
canonical basis constructed in Theorem 4 involve functions $f(z)$ and
$g(z)$ having, at worst, *poles* at the singular point of interest? Again,
when does the function $f(z)$ of Theorem 3 have the form $\sum_{k=r}^{\infty} a_k z^k$,
$a_r \neq 0$, for some *finite* integer r? Since this implies

$$w_1(z)/a_r = z^{\alpha+r}\left[1 + \sum_{j=1}^{\infty} (a_{j+r}/a_r)z^j\right],$$

this question amounts to asking the following. What are the conditions on the coefficients of a linear analytic DE, having an isolated
singular point at the origin, which make it have a basis of solutions of
the form $z^r[1 + \sum_{j=1}^{\infty} b_j z^j]$—that is, of solutions having branch poles?

The answer to the above questions is that the singular point must be
regular in the following sense.

■ DEFINITION.   *A second-order DE*

$$w'' + p(z)w' + q(z)w = 0, \tag{13}$$

*analytic for $0 < |z - z_0| < \rho$, has a regular singular point at z_0 when $p(z)$
has at worst a simple pole at $z = z_0$, and $q(z)$ at worst a double pole there.*†

† That is, p may either be holomorphic (have a removable singularity) or have a simple
pole, and q may be holomorphic or have a pole of first or second order.

We now show that, near the regular singular point $z = 0$, there always exists a formal solution of the DE (13), namely, a formal power series of the form

$$w = z^\nu(1 + c_1 z + c_2 z^2 + c_3 z^3 + \cdots) = z^\nu + c_1 z^{\nu+1} + c_2 z^{\nu+2} + \cdots, \quad (14)$$

which, when substituted into (13), satisfies the DE. To calculate the coefficients c_k and the exponent ν of (14) it is convenient to rewrite (13) in the form

$$L[w] = z^2 w'' + z P(z) w' + Q(z) w = 0, \quad (15)$$

where $P(z) = \sum_{k=0}^{\infty} P_k z^k$ and $Q(z) = \sum_{k=0}^{\infty} Q_k z^k$ are convergent for $|z| < \rho$. Substituting (14) into (15) and equating to zero the coefficient of z^ν, we obtain the *indicial equation*

$$I(\nu) = \nu(\nu - 1) + P_0 \nu + Q_0 = 0 \quad (16)$$

for the exponent ν. The roots of this equation are called the *characteristic exponents* of the singular point, and $I(\nu)$ is called its *indicial polynomial*.

Equating to zero the coefficients of the higher powers of z, namely $z^{\nu+1}, \ldots, z^{\nu+n}, \ldots$, we obtain the relation

$$[(\nu + 1)\nu + P_0(\nu + 1) + Q_0]c_1 + P_1 \nu + Q_1 = 0$$

and, recursively,

$$[(\nu + n)(\nu + n - 1) + (\nu + n)P_0 + Q_0]c_n = -\sum_{k=0}^{n-1} [(\nu + k)P_{n-k} + Q_{n-k}]c_k.$$

Since the left side of the preceding equation is $I(\nu + n)c_n$, the equation can be written in the form

$$I(\nu + n)c_n = -\sum_{k=0}^{n-1} [(\nu + k)P_{n-k} + Q_{n-k}]c_k, \qquad n = 1, 2, 3, \ldots. \quad (17)$$

The above equations for the coefficients c_k can be solved recursively for $c_1, c_2, c_3, \ldots$, except in one case: when, for some positive integer n, both ν and $(\nu + n)$ are roots of the indicial equation. By taking a characteristic exponent having the largest real part, we can make sure that $I(\nu + n)$ does not vanish for any positive integer n, even in this case. We therefore obtain

■ THEOREM 5. *If the* DE *(13) has a regular singular point at $z = 0$, then at least one formal power series of the form (14) formally satisfies the* DE. *Unless the roots of the indicial equation differ by an integer, there are two linearly independent formal power series solutions (14) of the* DE, *whose exponents are the two roots of the indicial equation.*

EXAMPLE 4.   A remarkable class of special functions having regular
singular points at 0, 1, and ∞ (see § 12), and no other singular points,
is obtained by applying Theorem 5 to the *hypergeometric* DE

$$z(1-z)w'' + [\gamma - (\alpha + \beta + 1)z]w' - \alpha\beta w = 0. \tag{18}$$

The hypergeometric DE has regular singular points at $z = 0$ and $z = 1$.
The indicial equation at $z = 0$ is $\nu(\nu + \gamma - 1) = 0$, with roots $\nu_1 = 0$ and
$\nu_2 = 1 - \gamma$. Unless γ is an integer, by Theorem 5 the hypergeometric
DE has two formal power series solutions with exponents 0 and $1 - \gamma$.
Unless γ is a negative integer or zero, one such formal power series is
obtained from the easily computed recursion relations

$$(n+1)(\gamma + n) c_{n+1} = (\alpha + n)(\beta + n) c_n, \qquad n \geq 0. \tag{19}$$

Setting $c_0 = 1$, we obtain the hypergeometric series

$$F(\alpha, \beta, \gamma; z) = 1 + \frac{\alpha\beta}{\gamma} z + \frac{\alpha(\alpha+1)\beta(\beta+1)}{\gamma(\gamma+1)} \frac{z^2}{2!}$$

$$+ \frac{\alpha(\alpha+1)(\alpha+2)\beta(\beta+1)(\beta+2)}{\gamma(\gamma+1)(\gamma+2)} \frac{z^3}{3!} + \cdots. \tag{20}$$

From the Ratio Test, it follows that the radius of convergence of the
series is at least one, and is exactly one unless α, β, or γ is a negative
integer. This may also be expected from the existence theorems of
Chapter 6, since the radius of convergence of a solution extends to the
nearest other singular point of the coefficients of the hypergeometric
DE, which is at $z = 1$. The function $F(\alpha, \beta, \gamma; z)$ defined by the power
series (20) is the *hypergeometric function*, studied in § 10 below.

7 Bessel equation

To illustrate the behavior of solutions of second-order DE's near
regular singular points, we consider an example of great importance in
applied mathematics. This is the Bessel DE of order n:

$$z^2 w'' + zw' + (z^2 - n^2)w = 0. \tag{21}$$

The Bessel DE has a regular singular point at the origin, with indicial
equation $I(\nu) = \nu^2 - n^2 = 0$. In physical applications, n is usually an
integer or half-integer. But, for theoretical purposes, it is interesting to
let n^2 be an arbitrary complex number.

By Theorem 5, we can compute a formal power series solution
beginning with z^n, of the form $z^n(1 + c_1 z + c_2 z^2 + \cdots)$. From the
recursion formulas (17) or, more simply, by direct substitution into the
DE, we obtain the recursion relations for the coefficients c_k:

$$(2n+1)c_1 = 0; \qquad (k+2)(2n+k+2)c_{k+2} + c_k = 0, \quad k = 0, 1, 2, \ldots.$$

Since $\text{Re}(2n) \geq 0$, the factor $(k+2)(2n+k+2)$ cannot vanish. Solving recursively for c_{k+2}, we obtain the series

$$z^n \left[1 - \frac{1}{n+1} \left(\frac{z}{2}\right)^2 + \frac{1}{(2!)(n+1)(n+2)} \left(\frac{z}{2}\right)^4 - \cdots \right].$$

The series in square brackets is an entire function (convergent for all finite z). Multiplying by the normalizing factor $1/2^n\Gamma(n+1)$, we obtain the *Bessel function of order* n, already discussed in Chapter 3, § 4:

$$J_n(z) = \frac{1}{\Gamma(n+1)} \left(\frac{z}{2}\right)^n \left[1 - \frac{1}{n+1} \left(\frac{z}{2}\right)^2 + \frac{1}{(2!)(n+1)(n+2)} \left(\frac{z}{2}\right)^4 - \cdots \right].$$

$$(22)$$

The Bessel function J_n is an entire function if n is a nonnegative integer. Using the functional equation for the gamma function $\Gamma(z+1) = z\Gamma(z)$, this formula can be recast in the form

$$J_n(z) = \sum_{k=0}^{\infty} \frac{(-1)^k (z/2)^{n+2k}}{\Gamma(n+k+1)\Gamma(k+1)}.$$

Unless n is an integer, the series (22) with $-n$ in place of n defines a second, linearly independent solution of the Bessel DE (21),

$$J_{-n}(z) = \sum_{k=0}^{\infty} \{ (-1)^k (z/2)^{-n+2k} / \Gamma(k+1)\Gamma(-n+k+1) \}.$$

This solution has a branch pole at the origin. Unless n is an integer, J_n and J_{-n} form a canonical basis of solutions of the Bessel DE.

Exceptional case. When n is an integer, we have $J_{-n}(z) = (-1)^n J_n(z)$, so that another method must be used to find a basis of solutions. We can then proceed as follows (cf. Chapter 2, (13)).

Consider the Wronskian $W = J_n \phi' - J_n' \phi$ of J_n and any other solution ϕ of the Bessel DE. A straightforward computation gives $W' + (1/z)W = 0$, whence $(zW)' = 0$. Hence, for some constant A, we have

$$J_n(z)\phi'(z) - J_n'(z)\phi(z) = A/z.$$

If $g(z)$ is the quotient $\phi(z)/J_n(z)$, it follows that

$$g'(z) = W(z)/J_n^2(z) = A/zJ_n^2(z).$$

Therefore, the general soluton of the Bessel DE (21) is

$$Z_n(z) = J_n(z) \left[B + A \int \frac{dz}{zJ_n^2(z)} \right]$$

$$(23)$$

for any indefinite integral of $1/zJ_n^2(z) = K_n z^{-2n-1} \{ 1 + \sum_{k=1}^{\infty} b_k z^{2k} \}$

(cf. Chapter 3, (15)), where K_n is a suitable constant. Hence, we have

$$\int \frac{dz}{z J_n{}^2(z)} = K_n A \int z^{-1-2n} \left\{ 1 + \sum_{k=1}^{\infty} b_k z^{2k} \right\} dz, \tag{23'}$$

where the circle of convergence of the series in curly brackets extends to the point $z \neq 0$ nearest the origin, where $J_n(z)$ vanishes. Within this circle, we can integrate the series term by term. Thus, when $n = 0$, we easily compute $1/z J_0{}^2(z) = z^{-1} + z/2 + 5z^3/64 + \cdots$, and so the general solution of (21) when $n = 0$ is

$$Z_0(z) = J_0(z)\{B + A(\ln z + z^2/4 + 5z^4/256 + \cdots)\}. \tag{23''}$$

This shows that any solution of the Bessel DE of order zero which is not a constant times $J_0(z)$ is logarithmically infinite near $z = 0$.

More generally, the preceding formulas show that, when the parameter n in the Bessel DE (21) is not an integer†, we obtain the general case (9a) of Theorem 4, with $\alpha = n$ and $\beta = -n$. When n is an integer, we have the exceptional case (9b) of Theorem 4. We shall now discuss this exceptional case.

The Neumann function. In the exceptional case that n is an integer, various choices are possible for a canonical basis of solutions of the Bessel equation. The first solution $w_1(z)$ in (9b) must be chosen as a multiple of $J_n(z)$, because only such multiples have branch poles at the origin. Any choice $A \neq 0$ in (23) will give a possible second member of the canonical basis (9b). Thus, when $n = 0$, we can choose $A = 1$, $B = 0$ in (23''). Relative to this choice, the circuit matrix is $\begin{pmatrix} 1 & 0 \\ 2\pi i & 1 \end{pmatrix}$.

A more convenient choice is $A = 2/\pi$ and $B = (2\gamma - 2 \log 2)/\pi$, where $\gamma = 0.5772 \ldots$ is Euler's constant. This defines the *Neumann function* $Y_0(x)$. The choice is convenient because of the asymptotic formulas, valid as $x \to \infty$,

$$J_0(x) = \sqrt{\frac{2}{\pi x}} \left[\cos \left(x - \frac{\pi}{4} \right) + O\!\left(\frac{1}{x} \right) \right],$$

$$Y_0(x) = \sqrt{\frac{2}{\pi x}} \left[\sin \left(x - \frac{\pi}{4} \right) + O\!\left(\frac{1}{x} \right) \right]. \tag{24}$$

This asymptotic behavior will be explained in Chapter 10, § 11.

---

† Note that, though the Bessel DE of half-integral order $n + \frac{1}{2}$ has characteristic exponents which differ by an integer, it has a basis of solutions of the form (9a). This is because the recurrence relations for the coefficients in its expansion express c_{k+2} as a multiple of c_k, without involving c_{k+1}.

The Bessel and Neumann functions J_0 and Y_0 are clearly linearly independent; hence, they are a canonical basis of solutions of the Bessel DE of order zero. Using these functions, we now derive a canonical basis for the Bessel DE of integral order n.

This can be done as follows. If Z_n is a solution of the Bessel equation of order n, the function Z_{n+1} defined by the formula

$$Z_{n+1} = -z^n(z^{-n}Z_n(z))'$$

is a solution of the Bessel equation of order $n + 1$. This formula is valid whether n is an integer or not and is immediately verified by substituting Z_{n+1} into the Bessel DE of order $n + 1$. In particular, we easily verify that $J_{n+1}(z) = -z^n(z^{-n}J_n(z))'$, as in Chapter 3, (16).

We now define the Neumann function $Y_n(z)$ for integer n by the recursive formulas

$$Y_{n+1}(z) = -z^n(z^{-n}Y_n(z))', \qquad n = 0, 1, 2, \ldots.$$

Since the function $Y_0(z)$ is of the form $Y_0(z) = J_0(z)[f_0(z) + K_0 \log z]$, where f_0 is holomorphic and one-valued in a punctured disc around $z = 0$, we verify by straightforward differentiation that

$$Y_1(z) = J_1(z)[f_1(z) + K_1 \log z],$$

where f_1 has the same property as f_0, and, successively, that

$$Y_n(z) = J_n(z)[f_n(z) + K_n \log z].$$

Thus, all Neumann functions $Y_n(z)$ have a branch point at $z = 0$. From this it follows that Y_n and J_n are linearly independent, and indeed are a canonical basis of solutions for the singular point $z = 0$ of Bessel's DE.

The Neumann function is defined when ν is not an integer by the formula

$$Y_\nu(z) = \frac{J_\nu(z) \cos \nu\pi - J_{-\nu}(z)}{\sin \nu\pi}.$$

When $\nu = n$ is an integer, let $Y_n(z) = \lim_{\nu \to n} Y_\nu(z)$. The limit can be evaluated by l'Hôpital's Rule as

$$Y_n(z) = \frac{1}{\pi}\left[\frac{\partial J_\nu(z)}{\partial \nu} - (-1)^n \frac{\partial J_{-\nu}(z)}{\partial \nu}\right]_{\nu=n}.$$

It can be shown that this definition of the Neumann function for integral n agrees with that above.

Modified Bessel functions. The values of $J_n(z)$ on the imaginary axis $z = iy$ define a *real* function of the positive variable y:

$$I_n(y) = (-i)^n J_n(iy) = \left(\frac{y}{2}\right)^n \sum_{k=0}^{\infty}\left[\frac{y^k}{2^k\Gamma(k+1)\Gamma(k+n+1)}\right].$$

This function is called the *modified* Bessel function of order n. The function $I_n(y)$ satisfies the modified Bessel DE

$$y^2 \frac{d^2 I}{dy^2} + y \frac{dI}{dy} - (y^2 + n^2)I = 0$$

obtained by substituting iy for z in the Bessel DE. The coefficient-functions of the modified Bessel DE are real.

EXERCISES C

1. (a) Show that the DE $zw'' + (1 - z)w' + \lambda w = 0$ has a regular singular point at the origin, and that $\nu = 0$ is a double root of the indicial equation.
   (b) Find the power series expansion of the solution of this DE which is regular at $z = 0$.
2. State and prove an analog of Theorem 5 for $w' + p(z)w = 0$.
3. (a) Show that, if

$$w'' + p(z)w' + q(z)w = 0 \tag{*}$$

   has a regular singular point at $z = 0$, and $q(0) \neq 0$, then

$$w'' + [p - (q'/q)]w' + [q' - (pq'/q) + q]w = 0 \tag{**}$$

   has a regular singular point at $z = 0$.
   (b) Show that, if w_1, w_2 are a basis of solutions of (*), then w_1', w_2' are a basis of solutions of (**).
4*. Show that, if the roots of the indicial equation at a regular singular point differ by an integer, the eigenvalues of any circuit matrix are equal.
5. Let (13) have a regular singular point at $z = 0$, and let α be a root of its indicial equation having largest real part. Show that, if w is a solution, then $v = z^{-\alpha}w$ satisfies a DE of the form (15) with $Q_0 = 0$ and $\text{Re}\{P_0\} \geqq 1$.
6. (a) Given three pairs of nonzero complex numbers (λ_1, λ_2), (μ_1, μ_2), (z_1, z_2), construct a holomorphic second-order linear DE (13) having regular points at $z = (z_1, z_2)$, whose circuit matrices at these points have eigenvalues (λ_1, λ_2), (μ_1, μ_2).
   (b*) Generalize to n points $z_1, \ldots, z_n$.
7. Show that, for n a nonnegative integer, $J_n(z)$ and its complex multiples are the only solutions of the Bessel DE that are holomorphic at the origin.
8. (a) Find the exponents at $z = 0$ of the DE $zw'' + (n + \frac{1}{2})w' + w = 0$, and find formal power series solutions corresponding to each characteristic exponent.
   (b) Show that a basis of solutions of this DE is given by the functions

$$d^n[\sin(2\sqrt{z})]/dz^n \quad \text{and} \quad d^n[\cos(2\sqrt{z})]/dz^n.$$

9*. Show that, when n is an integer, a solution of Bessel's DE (the Neumann function $Y_n(z)$) is defined by

$$\pi^{-1}[\partial J_n(z)/\partial n - (-1)^n \partial J_{-n}(z)/\partial n].$$

10. Show that, if u_1, u_2 and v_1, v_2 are bases of solutions of the Bessel and modified Bessel DE's, respectively, u_1, u_2, v_1, v_2 form a basis of solutions of the DE

$$w^{(4)} + (2/z)w^{(3)} - [(2n^2 + 1)/z^2]w'' + [(2n^2 + 1)/z]w' + [(n^4 - n^2)/z^2 - 1]w = 0.$$

11. Show that the self-adjoint form (Chapter 2, § 5) of the hypergeometric DE (18) is:

$$\frac{d}{dz}\left[z^c(1-z)^{a+b+1-c}w'\right] - [abz^{c-1}(1-z)^{a+b-c}]w = 0.$$

12. Show that a canonical basis of solutions of the hypergeometric DE (18) is provided by $F(\alpha, \beta, \gamma; z)$ and $z^{1-\gamma}F(\alpha - \gamma + 1, \beta - \gamma + 1, 2 - \gamma; z)$ unless γ is an integer.

8 The fundamental theorem

We now establish the fact that the formal power series solutions obtained in § 6 are convergent. We begin by proving the converse of this result.

■ THEOREM 6.   *Let the analytic functions*

$$w_1 = z^\alpha\left(1 + \sum_1^\infty a_k z^k\right), \qquad w_2 = z^\beta\left(1 + \sum_1^\infty b_k z^k\right), \qquad \alpha \neq \beta, \quad (25)$$

have simple branch poles at $z = 0$ of different orders $\alpha \neq \beta$. Then the normal second-order DE satisfied by w_1 and w_2 has a regular singular point at $z = 0$, with characteristic exponents α and β.

Proof — The coefficients of the normal second-order linear DE satisfied by w_1 and w_2 are found by solving the simultaneous linear equations

$$w_j'' + p(z)w_j' + q(z)w_j = 0, \qquad j = 1, 2,$$

for the unknown coefficient functions p, q. The result is

$$p = -(w_1 w_2'' - w_2 w_1'')/(w_1 w_2' - w_2 w_1'), \quad q = (w_1' w_2'' - w_2' w_1'')/(w_1 w_2' - w_2 w_1').$$

The Wronskian $W = w_1 w_2' - w_2 w_1'$ in the denominators is equal to

$$(\beta - \alpha)z^{\alpha+\beta-1}\left(1 + \sum_1^\infty c_k z^k\right)$$

and does not vanish near $z = 0$, since $\alpha \neq \beta$. The numerators are the powers $z^{\alpha+\beta-2}$ and $z^{\alpha+\beta-3}$ multiplied by holomorphic functions of z. Dividing out, we get

$$p(z) = z^{-1}P(z), \qquad q(z) = z^{-2}Q(z),$$

where $P(z)$ and $Q(z)$ are holomorphic in some neighborhood of $z = 0$. This completes the proof of the theorem.

■ Theorem 7.   *Let the second-order linear* DE (5) *have a regular singular point at the origin, and let* α *be a root of its indicial equation* $I(\nu) = 0$. *Then the formal power series* $z^{\alpha}(1 + \sum a_k z^k)$ *of Theorem 5 converges to a solution of* (5) *in a domain* $0 < |z| < \sigma$, $\sigma > 0$.

It will be recalled that, in Theorem 5, ν was any root of the indicial equation $I(\nu) = 0$ such that $I(\nu + n) = 0$ for no positive integer n.

Proof — A method similar to the Method of Majorants of Chapter 3, § 6 can be used   The functions P and Q are holomorphic in a neighborhood of the origin; thus a closed disc $0 \leq |z| \leq \rho$ can be found in which these functions are holomorphic, with $|P(z)| \leq M$ and $|Q(z)| \leq N$. It follows from the Cauchy estimates for derivatives† that

$$|P_k| \leq M/\rho^k, \qquad |Q_k| \leq N/\rho^k, \qquad k = 0, 1, 2, \ldots.$$

Hence, we have

$$|P_k||\nu| + |Q_k| \leq \frac{M|\nu| + N}{\rho^k}, \qquad k \geq 0.$$

From formula (16) we obtain the bound $|I(\nu + n)| \geq n^2/K$ for some constant $K \geq 1$: since $I(\nu + n) \neq 0$ for all nonnegative integers n by hypothesis, the sequence $n^2/|I(\nu + n)|$ is bounded (it tends to 1 as $n \to \infty$). Set $K = 1 + \max(n^2/|I(\nu + n)|)$. Therefore, the recursion formulas (17) give the following bound for the coefficient c_n in the formal power series solution (14):

$$|c_n| \leq \frac{K}{n} \sum_{k=0}^{n-1} \left(\frac{M|\nu| + N}{n} + \frac{kM}{n} \right) \frac{|c_k|}{\rho^{n-k}}.$$

Now, let $A = M|\nu| + N + M + 1$. Clearly $(M|\nu| + N + kM)/n \leq A$ for all n and for $0 \leq k \leq n$, and $AK \geq K \geq 1$. Hence, we obtain

$$|c_n| \leq \frac{K}{n} \sum_{k=0}^{n-1} A \frac{|c_k|}{\rho^{n-k}} = \frac{AK}{n} \sum_{k=0}^{n-1} \frac{|c_k|}{\rho^{n-k}}. \qquad (25')$$

Using this formula, we now prove by induction that

$$|c_n| \leq \left(\frac{AK}{\rho} \right)^n |c_0|, \qquad n = 1, 2, \ldots.$$

This inequality is immediate for $n = 1$, namely $|c_1| \leq AK|c_0|/\rho$. Now, assume it is true for all c_k for $1 \leq k \leq n - 1$. Substituting in (25') the

---

† See Hille, pp. 197 and 202.

bounds for $c_0, \ldots, c_{n-1}$ given by the induction hypothesis, we obtain

$$|c_n| \leqq \frac{KA}{n} \sum_{k=0}^{n-1} \left(\frac{AK}{\rho}\right)^k \cdot \frac{1}{\rho^{n-k}} |c_0|$$

$$= \frac{(AK)|c_0|}{n \cdot \rho^n} [1 + (AK) + (AK)^2 + \cdots + (AK)^{n-1}].$$

Since $AK \geq 1$, each term in the brackets above is bounded by $(AK)^{n-1}$. thus, we have

$$|c_n| \leqq \frac{AK|c_0|}{\rho^n} \cdot \frac{n(AK)^{n-1}}{n} = \frac{(AK)^n|c_0|}{\rho^n},$$

and this shows that the formal power series solution (14) has a radius of convergence at least equal to ρ/AK. The proof is therefore complete.

■ COROLLARY.   *In Theorem 7, unless the roots α, β of the indicial equation differ by an integer, the DE (5) has a basis of solutions whose circuit matrix is a diagonal matrix with diagonal entries $\lambda_1 = \exp(2\pi i\alpha)$ and $\lambda_2 = \exp(2\pi i\beta)$.*

For this, one only has to choose a canonical basis of the form (25), which exists by Theorem 7.

Exceptional case. The exceptional case, namely when the roots of the indicial equation differ by an integer, can be treated by the following method. Select for α a root of the indicial equation having maximum real part. Then $\beta = \alpha - n$ for some integer $n \geqq 0$ and so, since by the indicial equation $\alpha + \beta = 1 - P_0$, it follows that $-2\alpha - P_0 = -n - 1$, where P_0 is the leading coefficient of $p(z) = P_0/z + P_1 + \cdots$ and n is a nonnegative integer.

Moreover, we know that $I(\alpha + n) \neq 0$ for all integers $n > 0$, and so by Theorem 7 the given second-order linear DE (5) has a solution

$$w_1 = z^\alpha f(z) = z^\alpha \left(1 + \sum_{k=1}^{\infty} a_k z^k\right)$$

which a branch pole at $z = 0$, nonvanishing in the punctured disc $0 < |z| < \sigma$ for some $\sigma > 0$. Hence, if we set $w = w_1 h = z^\alpha f(z)h(z)$, the DE (5) is equivalent to

$$0 = w_1 h'' + [2w_1' + p(z)w_1]h' = z^\alpha f(z)\{h'' + [(2\alpha/z) + 2(f'/f) + p(z)]h'\}.$$

This first-order DE for the unknown function h' has a regular singular point at $z = 0$, since f'/f is holomorphic there, while $2\alpha/z$ and $p(z)$ have at worst first-order poles. Therefore, we can write $h'(z) = z^\gamma(1 + \sum c_k z^k)$, where $\gamma = -2\alpha - P_0 = -n - 1$, as shown above.

Integrating $h'(z)$ term by term in the circle of convergence, we thus have

$$h(z) = \begin{cases} \ln z + \phi(z) & \text{if } n = 0, \\ c_n \ln z + z^{-n}\phi(z) & \text{if } n \neq 0, \end{cases}$$

where $\phi(z)$ is holomorphic. This shows that the exceptional case of Theorem 4 always occurs when the indicial equation has a double root and also when the roots differ by an integer n, unless $c_n = 0$.

Collecting results, we have proved (for $C = c_n$) the following theorem.

■ **THEOREM 8.** *Suppose that the roots α and $\beta = \alpha - n$ of the indicial equation of a second-order linear DE having a regular singular point at $z = 0$ differ by a nonnegative integer n. Then there exists a canonical basis of solutions of the form*

$$w_1 = z^\alpha\left(1 + \sum_{k=1}^\infty a_k z^k\right), \qquad w_2 = z^\beta\left(1 + \sum_{k=1}^\infty b_k z^k\right) + Cw_1 \ln z, \quad (26)$$

where the power series are convergent in a neighborhood of $z = 0$.

Relative to the canonical basis (26), the circuit matrix has the form

$$\begin{pmatrix} \lambda & 2\pi iC \\ 0 & \lambda \end{pmatrix},$$

with $\lambda = e^{2\pi i\alpha} = e^{2\pi i\beta}$.

9* Alternative proof of the fundamental theorem

Theorem 7 can also be given a more intrinsic proof, by relying on the following characterization of poles of analytic functions.†

■ **ORDER OF GROWTH THEOREM.** *If $f(z)$ is holomorphic in $0 < |z| \leq R$, then $z = 0$ is a pole of $f(z)$ of order at most α, or a removable singularity, if and only if there exists a positive number C such that*

$$\sup_{0 \leq \theta \leq 2\pi} |f(re^{i\theta})| < Cr^{-\alpha}, \qquad 0 < r \leq R.$$

Theorem 7 can be deduced quite easily from the following basic.

■ **LEMMA.** *If the DE (5) has a regular singular point at $z = 0$, then the function $f(z)$ in Theorem 3 has at most a pole at $z = 0$.*

---

† Hille, p. 213, Thm. 8.4.1.

Proof — For any solution $w(z)$ of (5), consider the real-valued function

$$U(z) = |w(z)|^2 + |zw'(z)|^2.$$

Setting $z = re^{i\theta}$, we shall majorize the derivative of this function relative to r for fixed θ; its differentiability follows by the Chain Rule.

For any differentiable complex-valued function $V(r)$ of a real variable r, as in Chapter 6, formula (3), we have

$$\left| \int_a^r V'(t)\, dt \right| \leq \int_a^r |V'(t)|\, dt$$

and hence, differentiating,

$$\left| \frac{d}{dr} |V(r)| \right| \leq \left| \frac{dV(r)}{dr} \right|.$$

Applying this inequality to $U(re^{i\theta})$ we obtain

$$\frac{1}{2} \left| \frac{\partial U}{\partial r} \right| \leq |ww'| + \left| \frac{z^2 w'^2}{r} \right| + |z^2 w' w''|,$$

where $z = re^{i\theta}$. Using the fact that $w'' = -(P(z)/z)w' - (Q(z)/z^2)w$ we obtain

$$\tfrac{1}{2}|\partial U/\partial r| \leq |ww'| + |z^2 w'^2|/r + |P(z)|\,|z^2 w'^2|/r + |Q(z)|\,|ww'|.$$

The functions $P(re^{i\theta})$ and $Q(re^{i\theta})$ are holomorphic in some closed disc $0 \leq |z| \leq R$, $R > 0$. Let M be a common upper bound for their absolute values, for $0 \leq \theta \leq 2\pi$ and for fixed r. This gives the inequality

$$\tfrac{1}{2}|\partial U/\partial r| \leq (M+1)|ww'| + (M+1)|z^2 w'^2|/r.$$

By definition of U, we have $|w|^2 \leq U$, $|w'|^2 \leq U/r^2$ and, hence, multiplying, $|ww'| \leq U/r$. We obtain, therefore,

$$|[\partial U(re^{i\theta})]/\partial r| \leq (4M+4)U(re^{i\theta})/r = KU/r, \qquad K > 0.$$

In particular, for $0 < r \leq R$, we obtain $\partial U/\partial r + KU/r \geq 0$, whence, integrating between the limits r and R,

$$R^K U(Re^{i\theta}) - r^K U(re^{i\theta}) \geq 0.$$

If $N = \max_{0 \leq \theta \leq 2\pi} U(Re^{i\theta})$, we obtain

$$U(re^{i\theta}) \leq N R^K r^{-K}$$

and hence, *a fortiori*, that $|w(re^{i\theta})|^2 \leq (NR^K)r^{-K}$. By the Order-of-Growth Theorem, with $C = NR^K$ and $\alpha = K$, the conclusion of the lemma follows.

Consequently, if the DE (5) has a regular singular point at the origin, then it has a solution given by a locally convergent power series of the form described in Theorems 5 and 7. The construction of a second solution can then be achieved as in Theorem 8.

The preceding method of proof can be generalized easily to nth order linear DE's.

EXERCISES D

1. Find the exponents at $z = 0$ of the DE $w'' + (\mu/z)w' + (1/z)w = 0$. Show that this DE has a power series solution $C_\mu(z) = 1 + \sum_{k=1}^{\infty} a_k z^k$, convergent for all $|z|$. Show that $C_\mu(z) = z^{(1-\mu)/2} J_{\mu-1}(2\sqrt{z})$.

2. Show that $w'' + (n + \frac{1}{2} - z^2/4)w = 0$ has a basis of solutions

$$w_1(z) = 1 - (2n + 1)z^2/4 + (4n^2 + 4n + 3)z^4/96 - \cdots, \quad \text{and}$$

$$w_2(z) = z - (2n + 1)z^3/12 + (4n^2 + 4n + 7)z^5/480 - \cdots.$$

For what values of $|z|$ do these series converge?

3. The Laguerre DE is $zw'' + (1 - z)w' + \alpha w = 0$.
   (a) Find its characteristic exponents.
   (b) Show that a nontrivial solution is given by $\sum c_k z^k$ with

$$c_{j+1} = (j - a)c_j/(j + 1)^2.$$

4. The associated Laguerre DE is $zw'' + (k + 1 - z)w' + (n - k)w = 0$. Show that this has a polynomial solution $w = L_n^k(z)$ for any positive integers k, n.

5. Show that $e^{-z/2} z^{(k-1)/2} L_n^k(z)$ satisfies the DE

$$zw'' + 2w' + [A + Bz + C/z]w = 0,$$

with $A = n - (k - 1)/2$, $B = -\frac{1}{4}$, $C = (1 - k^2)/4$.

6. Show that, if $\phi(0) \neq 0$, the substitution $w = \phi(z)v$ carries second-order linear DE's (5) having a regular singular point at the origin into DE's having the same property.

7. Generalize the result of Exercise 6 to nth order linear DE's.

8. Show that the substitution $w = z^r \phi(z)w_1$, where $\phi(0) \neq 0$ and $\phi(z)$ is regular near $z = 0$, carries a regular singular point at $z = 0$ with indicial polynomial $I(\nu)$ into one with indicial polynomial $I(\nu - r)$.

9. Do the functions $\log z$ and $(\log z)^2$ satisfy a second-order linear DE (3) with a regular singular point at $z = 0$? Do they satisfy a third-order linear DE with regular singular point at $z = 0$? Justify your answer.

10*. (a) The DE $w''' + \sum_{k=1}^{3} p_k(z)w^{(3-k)} = 0$, $p_k(z)$ holomorphic for $0 < |z| < r$, has a regular singular point at $z = 0$ if p_k has, at worst, a pole of order k. Derive an analog of the indicial equation (16) and generalize Theorem 7 to this DE.
   (b) Generalize Theorem 8 for this DE when two exponents coincide.

10* Hypergeometric functions

So far in this Chapter, the behavior of solutions of DE's has been studied only near a single isolated singular point. A fascinating topic of analysis is the relation between the behavior at different singular points of analytic functions defined by DE's. This topic is beautifully illustrated by the hypergeometric functions, defined as solutions of the hypergeometric DE (18). This illustration (Example 4 of §6) is of especial interest because many common transcendental functions can be expressed in terms of the hypergeometric functions. For example, $(1-z)^{-\alpha} = F(\alpha, \beta, \beta; z)$, $\arcsin z = zF(\frac{1}{2}, \frac{1}{2}, 3/2; z^2)$, $\log(1+z) = zF(1, 1, 2; -z)$, and so on.

According to the program laid out in Chapter 3, the properties of the hypergeometric functions can be deduced from the DE (18). For example, let us derive a formula for the derivative of the hypergeometric function $F(\alpha, \beta, \gamma; z)$. Differentiating the hypergeometric DE, we get

$$z(1-z)w''' + [\gamma + 1 - (\alpha + 1 + \beta + 1 + 1)z]w'' - (\alpha + 1)(\beta + 1)w' = 0,$$

which is again a hypergeometric DE with constants $\alpha_1 = \alpha + 1$, $\beta_1 = \beta + 1$, $\gamma_1 = \gamma + 1$. By Theorems 7 and 8, every solution of this DE holomorphic at the origin is a constant times $F(\alpha + 1, \beta + 1, \gamma + 1; z)$. Hence, we obtain $F'(\alpha, \beta, \gamma; z) = kF(\alpha + 1, \beta + 1, \gamma + 1; z)$. The constant k is determined by evaluating (20) at $z = 0$. This gives the differentiation formula

$$F'(\alpha, \beta, \gamma; z) = \frac{\alpha\beta}{\gamma} F(\alpha + 1, \beta + 1, \gamma + 1; z). \tag{27}$$

The *Jacobi identity*

$$\frac{d^n}{dz^n} [z^{\alpha+n-1}F(\alpha, \beta, \gamma; z)] = \alpha(\alpha + 1) \cdots (\alpha + n - 1)z^{\alpha-1}F(\alpha + n, \beta, \gamma; z),$$

can be similarly established by multiplying both sides of the identity by $z^{1-\alpha}$, and then verifying that both sides of the resulting identity satisfy the same hypergeometric DE with constants $a_1 = \alpha + n, \beta, \gamma$.

The study of the hypergeometric DE is greatly facilitated by its *symmetry properties*. Making the substitution $w = z^{1-\gamma}u$, we obtain, as a DE equivalent to (18) for the dependent variable u, a second hypergeometric DE with different constants (unless $\gamma = 1$):

$$z(1-z)u'' + [\gamma_1 - (\alpha_1 + \beta_1 + 1)z]u' - \alpha_1\beta_1 u = 0, \tag{28}$$

where $\alpha_1 = \alpha - \gamma + 1$; $\beta_1 = \beta - \gamma + 1$, and $\gamma_1 = 2 - \gamma$. Since this DE has the solution $w_1(z) = F(\alpha_1, \beta_1, \gamma_1; z)$, we obtain at once a power series solution of (18) corresponding to the exponent $1 - \gamma$ in the form

$$w_2(z) = z^{1-\gamma}F(\alpha - \gamma + 1, \beta - \gamma + 1, 2 - \gamma; z). \tag{29}$$

The two solutions are a *canonical basis* of solutions of (18) at the regular singular point $z = 0$.

The change of dependent variable $w = (1 - z)^{\gamma - \alpha - \beta} u$ gives another hypergeometric DE of the form (18) in the variable u with $\alpha_1 = \gamma - \alpha$, $\beta_1 = \gamma - \beta$, $\gamma_1 = \gamma$. Since the solution of this DE which is holomorphic at $z = 0$ and takes the value 1 there is $F(\gamma - \alpha, \gamma - \beta, \gamma; z)$, we obtain the identity

$$F(\alpha, \beta, \gamma; z) = (1 - z)^{\gamma - \alpha - \beta} F(\gamma - \alpha, \gamma - \beta, \gamma; z). \tag{30}$$

A change of independent variable which transforms the hypergeometric DE into itself is $t = 1 - z$. This gives the DE

$$t(1 - t)w'' + [\gamma_1 - (\alpha + \beta + 1)t]w' - \alpha\beta w = 0,$$

where $\gamma_1 = \alpha + \beta - \gamma + 1$. It follows that the hypergeometric DE has a second regular singular point at $z = 1$, and a basis of solutions

$$w_3(z) = F(\alpha, \beta, \alpha + \beta + 1 - \gamma \,;\, 1 - z), \text{ and}$$

$$w_4(z) = (1 - z)^{\gamma - \alpha - \beta} F(\gamma - \alpha, \gamma - \beta, \gamma - \alpha - \beta + 1; 1 - z).\dagger$$

These functions form a *canonical basis* of solutions relative to the singular point $z = 1$. Note that the functions w_3 and w_4 are equal to linear combinations of the functions w_1 and w_2 by the uniqueness theorem for second-order linear DE's (Chapter 2, Theorem 1).

11*   The Jacobi polynomials

Writing out the hypergeometric DE (18) with parameters $\alpha = -n$, $\beta = n + a + b + 1$, $\gamma = b + 1$, we get

$$t(1 - t)u_{tt} + [b + 1 - (a + b + 2)t]u_t + n(n + a + b + 1)u = 0. \tag{31}$$

If we set $t = (1 + z)/2$ in (31), so that $z = 2t - 1$, and then perform the indicated differentiations, we obtain

$$(1 - z^2)u'' + [b - a - (a + b + 2)z]u' + n(n + a + b + 1)u = 0. \tag{32}$$

This is called the *Jacobi* DE; it has regular singular points at ± 1 (and ∞; cf. §12). Multiplying by $(1 - z)^a(1 + z)^b$, we get the *self-adjoint* form (Chapter 2, § 5)

$$\frac{d}{dz}\left[(1 - z)^{a+1}(1 + z)^{b+1}\frac{du}{dz}\right] + n(n + a + b + 1)(1 - z)^a(1 + z)^b u = 0.$$

When $a = b$, this reduces to the *ultraspherical* DE

$$\frac{d}{dz}\left[(1 - z^2)^{a+1}\frac{du}{dz}\right] + n(n + 2a + 1)(1 - z^2)^a u = 0. \tag{32}$$

---

† Assuming, of course, that the parameters α, β, γ are not chosen in such a way that the solutions coincide: thus $\gamma \neq \alpha + \beta$.

This is obtained from the partial DE $\nabla^2[r^n u(\cos\theta)] = 0$ in $(2a+3)$-dimensional space by separation of variables; hence its solutions play an important role in potential theory and its generalizations. Familiar special cases of the ultraspherical DE are $a = b = 0$, which gives the Legendre DE $[(1-z^2)u']' + n(n+1)u = 0$ (Chapter 2, § 1), and $a = b = -\frac{1}{2}$, which gives the Chebyshev DE

$$[(1-z^2)^{1/2}u']' + n^2(1-z^2)^{-1/2}u = 0.$$

From the derivation of (32), it is evident that the hypergeometric functions $F(-n, n+a+b+1, a+1, (1-z)/2)$ are solutions of it. It follows, inspecting the hypergeometric series (20), that if n is a nonnegative integer, this is a *polynomial* in z unless a is a nonnegative integer $-m$, with $m \leqq n$. Multiplying by the normalizing factor

$$\binom{n+a}{n},$$

we get, by definition, the *Jacobi polynomials*

$$P_n^{(a,b)}(z) = \binom{n+a}{n} F(-n, n+a+b+1, a+1; (1-z)/2)$$

$$= (-1)^n \binom{n+b}{n} F(-n, n+a+b+1, b+1, (1-z)/2). \tag{34}$$

In turn, when $a = b$, these give the ultraspherical or Gegenbauer polynomials of index $a + \frac{1}{2}$. These are usually normalized by the formula

$$P_n^{(a)}(z) = \frac{\Gamma(2a+n+1)}{\Gamma(a+1/2+n+1)} P_n^{(a-1/2,a-1/2)}(z).$$

With this normalization, $P_n^{(0)}(z) = T_n(z)$ is the Chebyshev polynomial of degree n: $P_n^{(1/2)}(z)$ is the Legendre polynomial of degree n, and so on.

From the differentiation formula (27) for the hypergeometric function, we infer the differentiation formula for Jacobi polynomials (including Legendre and Chebyshev polynomials)

$$\frac{d^m}{dz^m} P_n^{(a,b)}(z) = C \cdot P_{n-m}^{(a+m,b+m)}(z), \tag{35}$$

$$C = 2^{-m}(n+a+b+1)(n+a+b+2)\cdots(n+a+b+m).$$

An expression for the Jacobi polynomials often more convenient than (34) is the *Rodrigues formula*

$$P_n^{(a,b)}(z) = \frac{(-1)^n}{n!\,2^n}(1-z)^{-a}(1+z)^{-b}\frac{d^n}{dz^n}[(1-z)^{a+n}(1+z)^{b+n}]. \tag{36}$$

We shall derive this formula from the identities for the hypergeometric function established in the preceding section. First, since $(1 - t)^a = F(-a, b, b, t)$, the binomial series is a special case of the hypergeometric series: $(1 - t)^{b+n} = F(a + 1, -n - b, a + 1, t)$. Using also the Jacobi identity, we justify the first two steps of

$$t^{-a}(1 - t)^{-b} \frac{d^n}{dt^n} [t^{a+n}(1 - t)^{b+n}]$$

$$= t^{-a}(1 - t)^{-b} \frac{d^n}{dt^n} [t^{a+n} F(a + 1, -n - b, a + 1; t)]$$

$$= (a + 1)(a + 2) \cdots (a + n)(1 - t)^{-b} F(a + n + 1, -n - b, a + 1; t)$$

$$= (a + 1)(a + 2) \cdots (a + n) F(-n, n + a + b + 1, a + 1; t).$$

In the last step, identity (30) for the hypergeometric function is used. The Rodrigues formula (36) follows by making the change of variable $t = (1 - z)/2$.

EXERCISES E

1. Verify the following identities:
   (a) $F(\alpha, \beta, \beta; z) = (1 - z)^{-\alpha}$,
   (b) $F(\frac{1}{2}, \frac{1}{2}, \frac{3}{2}; z^2) = (\text{arc sin } z)/z$,
   (c) $F(1, 1, 2; z) = -\log (1 - z)/z$,

   (d) $1 + \binom{a}{1}z + \binom{a}{2}z^2 + \cdots + \binom{a}{m}z^m = \binom{a}{m}z^m F(-m, 1, a - m + 1; -z^{-1})$,

   (e) $\cos az = F(a/2, -a/2, 1/2; (\sin z)^2)$,
   (f) $\log [(1 + z)/(1 - z)] = 2z F(1/2, 1, 3/2; z^2)$.
2. (a) Show that (18) is equivalent to
   $$[zd/dz(zd/dz + \gamma - 1) - z(zd/dz + \alpha)(zd/dz + \beta)]w = 0.$$
   (b) Show that the eigenvalues of the circuit matrix for $z = 0$ are equal if γ is an integer.
   (c) Show that the eigenvalues of the circuit matrix for $z = 1$ are equal if $\gamma - \alpha - \beta$ is an integer.
3. (a) Show that, if α is zero or a negative integer, the hypergeometric DE (18) has a polynomial solution unless $\gamma < \alpha$ is a negative integer.
   (b) Using (33), express this solution as a Jacobi polynomial.
4. (a) Compute the characteristic exponents at $z = \pm 1$ of the Legendre DE
   $$[(1 - z^2)w']' + \lambda w = 0.$$
   (b*) Describe corresponding circuit matrices, taking as basic solutions an even and an odd solution.
5. (a) Show that setting $t = z^2$ in the Legendre DE gives a hypergeometric DE.
   (b) Express the Legendre polynomials as multiples of $F(\alpha, \beta, \gamma; z^2)$ for suitable α, β, γ.
6. Find the characteristic exponents at $z = \pm 1$ of the associated Legendre DE:
   $$[(1 - z^2)w']' + [n(n + 1) - m^2/(1 - z^2)]w = 0.$$

7. Derive from (31) the self-adjoint form of the Jacobi DE displayed in the text
8*. Prove that $P_n^{(a,b)}(z) = k_n F(-n, -b-n, 1+a; (z-1)/(z+1))$, where.

$$k_n = \binom{n+a}{n}\left(\frac{z+1}{2}\right)^n.$$

[HINT: Show the right-hand side satisfies (31), using appropriate identities for F.]
9. Find the roots of the indicial equation of the Jacobi DE (31) at $z = 1$ and $z = -1$.
10. Show that (34) defines a solution of (32) even when n is not a positive integer. What happens when n is a negative integer?
11. Using (36), show that, for $a > b > -1$,

$$\int_{-1}^{1} P_m^{(a,b)}(x) P_n^{(a,b)}(x)(1-x)^a(1+x)^b \, dx = 0 \qquad \text{for} \quad m \neq n.$$

12* Singular points at infinity

Even when the coefficient-functions p and q of the second-order linear DE (5) are regular at infinity, the point at infinity may be neither a removable singularity nor a regular singular point, but an *irregular singular point*. For instance, this is true of $w'' = w$, whose solutions $e^{\pm z}$ have essential singularities at infinity.

One determines when the point at infinity is a regular singular point by making the substitution $z = 1/t$. This substitution transforms the second-order linear DE (5) into the DE

$$\frac{d^2v}{dt^2} + \left[\frac{2}{t} - \frac{1}{t^2}p\left(\frac{1}{t}\right)\right]\frac{dv}{dt} + \frac{1}{t^4}q\left(\frac{1}{t}\right)v(t) = 0, \qquad (37)$$

where $v(t) = w(1/t)$. The point at infinity is said to be a *regular* singular point of the DE (5) when the origin is a regular singular point for the DE (37). This happens when the function

$$\left[\frac{2}{t} - \left(\frac{1}{t^2}\right)p\left(\frac{1}{t}\right)\right]$$

has, at worst, a pole of the first order at $t = 0$, that is, when the first coefficient in the power series expansion of $p(1/t)$ vanishes. Also, the function $t^{-4}q(1/t)$ must have at most a pole of the second order at $t = 0$; this happens when the first two coefficients in the power series for $q(1/t)$ vanish. This gives

■ THEOREM 9. *The point at infinity is a regular singular point for the second-order linear* DE (5) *if and only if the coefficients p and q have power series expansions, convergent for sufficiently large $|z|$, of the form*

$$p(z) = \frac{p_1}{z} + \frac{p_2}{z^2} + \cdots, \qquad q(z) = \frac{q_2}{z^2} + \frac{q_3}{z^3} + \cdots. \qquad (38)$$

That is, it is necessary and sufficient that the function p have a zero of at least the first order and the function q have a zero of at least the second order at infinity. In particular, the solutions of the DE are holomorphic at $z = \infty$, or $t = 0$, if and only if the coefficients

$$\left[\frac{2}{t} - \left(\frac{1}{t^2}\right)p\left(\frac{1}{t}\right)\right] \quad \text{and} \quad \left(\frac{1}{t^4}\right)q\left(\frac{1}{t}\right)$$

are regular at $t = 0$. Hence, the following corollary.

■ COROLLARY. *If the coefficients $p(z)$ and $q(z)$ of the DE (5) are holomorphic for sufficiently large z, then all solutions of (5) have removable singularities at $z = \infty$ if and only if $p_1 = 2$ and $q_2 = q_3 = 0$ in (38).*

It follows from Theorem 7 that, if $z = \infty$ is a regular singular point, and if the indicial equation of (37) at $t = 0$ has roots α and β not differing by an integer, then the DE (5) has a basis of solutions of the form

$$w_j(z) = z^{-\nu}\left(1 + \frac{a_1}{z} + \frac{a_2}{z^2} + \cdots\right), \qquad \nu = \alpha, \beta.$$

The indicial equation at infinity is defined, because of Theorem 9, to be the following equation for ν:

$$\nu(\nu - 1) + (2 - p_1)\nu + q_2 = 0; \tag{39}$$

its roots are called the *characteristic exponents* at $z = \infty$. If they differ by an integer, then there is still a solution of the form $(1/z^\nu)(1 + (a_1/z) + \cdots)$, but a second linearly independent solution may contain a logarithmic term.

EXAMPLE 5.   The hypergeometric DE (18) has, by Theorem 9, a regular singular point at infinity with characteristic exponents α and β. In order to derive a canonical basis at infinity, it is convenient to make the substitution $u(t) = t^{-\alpha}w(1/t)$. This transforms the DE into another hypergeometric DE

$$t(1 - t)u'' + [\gamma_2 - (\alpha_2 + \beta_2 + 1)t]u' - \alpha_2\beta_2 u = 0$$

with $\alpha_2 = \alpha$, $\beta_2 = \alpha - \gamma + 1$, $\gamma_2 = \alpha - \beta + 1$. It follows that the hypergeometric DE has the solution

$$w_5(z) = z^{-\alpha}F(\alpha, \alpha - \gamma + 1, \alpha - \beta + 1; 1/z),$$

convergent when $|z| > 1$. From the symmetry between α and β we obtain a second solution

$$w_6(z) = z^{-\beta}F(\beta, \beta - \gamma + 1, \beta - \alpha + 1; 1/z).$$

The functions w_5 and w_6 form a canonical basis at infinity, unless $\alpha = \beta$.

13* Fuchsian equations

A homogeneous linear DE with single-valued analytic coefficients is called a *Fuchsian* DE when it has, at worst, regular singular points in the extended complex plane, including the point at infinity. Since functions whose only singular points are poles necessarily are rational functions,[†] it follows that the coefficients of any Fuchsian DE are rational functions. The most general first-order Fuchsian DE has the form (see Exercise F8)

$$w' + \left(\sum_{k=1}^{n} \frac{A_k}{z - z_k} \right) w = 0.$$

The general solution of this DE is the elementary function

$$w(z) = c \prod_{k=1}^{n} (z - z_k)^{-A_k}.$$

Second-order Fuchsian DE's offer much more variety; they are classified according to the number of their singular points. When the number of these is small, their study is greatly simplified by making *linear fractional transformations*[‡] of the independent variable, of the form

$$\zeta = (az + b)/(cz + d), \qquad ad \neq bc.$$

Any such transformation can be obtained by successive changes of variable of the forms $\zeta = z + k$, $\zeta = az$, and $\zeta = 1/z$. Each such change of variable shifts the position of the singular points of a DE, carrying branch poles of solutions into branch poles. Therefore, by Theorems 6, 7, and 8, a general linear fractional transformation transforms regular singular points into regular singular points, and the indicial equations of the transformed DE coincide with those of the original DE at corresponding points.

We first consider second-order Fuchsian DE's having at most two singular points, say at $z = z_1$ and $z = z_2$. By a linear fractional transformation of the form $\zeta = (z - z_1)/(z - z_2)$, we can send these singular points to zero and infinity. It follows from the definition of a regular singular point and from Theorem 9 that $p(z) = p_1/z$ and $q(z) = q_2/z^2$. Hence, the most general Fuchsian DE of the second order with two regular singular points is equivalent to the *Euler* DE of Example 2,

$$w'' + \frac{p_1}{z} w' + \frac{q_2}{z^2} w = 0,$$

after a linear fractional transformation.

---

† Hille, p. 217, Theorem 8.5.1.
‡ See Hille, pp. 46–50, or Ahlfors, pp. 76–89.

The simplest Fuchsian DE of the second order whose solutions do not reduce to elementary functions is, therefore, one having three regular singular points. By a linear fractional transformation of the independent variable we may put these singular points at 0, 1, ∞. From the definition of a regular singular point and from Theorem 9 of §12, we can determine the coefficient-functions of a second-order Fuchsian DE with three regular singular points at 0, 1, ∞ as follows. The coefficient $p(z)$ must have, at worst, poles of the first order at $z = 0$ and $z = 1$. It can therefore be written in the form

$$p(z) = \frac{A_1}{z} + \frac{B_1}{z-1} + p_1(z),$$

where the function $p_1(z)$ is regular throughout the plane. However, by Theorem 9, the function $zp(z)$ has a finite limit as $|z|$ tends to infinity. Since $z[(A_1/z) + (B_1/(z-1))]$ is bounded as $|z|$ tends to infinity, it follows that the function $zp_1(z)$ is uniformly bounded. By Liouville's Theorem† it must, therefore, vanish identically.

Similarly, the coefficient $q(z)$ has at worst poles of the second order at $z = 0$ and $z = 1$, and can therefore be written in the form

$$q(z) = \frac{A_2}{z^2} + \frac{A_3}{z} + \frac{B_2}{(z-1)^2} + \frac{B_3}{z-1} + q_1(z),$$

where the function $q_1(z)$ is holomorphic in the finite complex plane. By Theorem 9, the function $z^2 q(z)$ remains bounded as $|z|$ tends to infinity; hence, so does the function

$$z^2 \left(\frac{A_3}{z} + \frac{B_3}{z-1} + q_1(z) \right) = z^2 \left(\frac{(A_3 + B_3)z - A_3 + q_1(z)z(z-1)}{z(z-1)} \right).$$

Therefore, $A_3 = -B_3$ and, again by Liouville's Theorem, the function $q_1(z)$ vanishes identically. This completes the proof of

■ THEOREM 10.   *A second-order Fuchsian DE with three regular singular points can be transformed by a linear fractional transformation into the form*

$$w'' + \left(\frac{A_1}{z} + \frac{B_1}{z-1} \right) w' + \left[\frac{A_2}{z^2} + \frac{B_2}{(z-1)^2} - \frac{A_3}{z(z-1)} \right] w = 0, \quad (40)$$

where A_i and B_i are constants.

The differential equation (40) is called the *Riemann* DE; it evidently depends on five parameters.

---

† Hille, p. 204, Theorem 8.2.2.

With the Riemann DE are associated three pairs of characteristic exponents (λ_1, λ_2), (μ_1, μ_2), (ν_1, ν_2), belonging to the singular points $0, 1, \infty$, respectively. These exponents are the roots of the indicial equations (cf. (16) and (39))

$$\lambda_i(\lambda_i - 1) + A_1\lambda_i + A_2 = 0, \qquad \mu_i(\mu_i - 1) + B_1\mu_i + B_2 = 0,$$

$$\nu_3{}^2 + (1 - A_1 - B_1)\nu_i + A_2 + B_2 - A_3 = 0.$$

By means of these equations, we can express the parameters in the DE (40) in terms of the (characteristic) exponents:

$$A_1 = 1 - \lambda_1 - \lambda_2, \qquad\qquad A_2 = \lambda_1\lambda_2,$$

$$B_1 = 1 - \mu_1 - \mu_2, \qquad\qquad B_2 = \mu_1\mu_2,$$

$$A_1 + B_1 = \nu_1 + \nu_2 + 1, \qquad A_2 + B_2 - A_3 = \nu_1\nu_2.$$

From the identities in the first column, we obtain the *Riemann identity*

$$\lambda_1 + \lambda_2 + \mu_1 + \mu_2 + \nu_1 + \nu_2 = 1. \tag{41}$$

Substituting into (40) we find the Riemann DE

$$w'' + \left(\frac{1 - \lambda_1 - \lambda_2}{z} + \frac{1 - \mu_1 - \mu_2}{z - 1}\right)w'$$

$$+ \left(\frac{\lambda_1\lambda_2}{z^2} + \frac{\mu_1\mu_2}{(z-1)^2} + \frac{\nu_1\nu_2 - \lambda_1\lambda_2 - \mu_1\mu_2}{z(z-1)}\right)w = 0. \tag{42}$$

The preceding discussion shows that the Riemann DE (40) is completely determined by assigning the values of the exponents and the location of the singular points:

■ THEOREM 11.   *A Fuchsian DE of the second order with three regular singular points in the extended complex plane is uniquely determined by prescribing the two exponents at each singular point. The exponents satisfy Riemann's identity* (41).

The *hypergeometric* DE of §6 is a special case of the Riemann DE with three singular points at $0, 1, \infty$. As shown in §6 and in §12, the hypergeometric DE has three regular singular points at $0, 1, \infty$ with exponents $0, 1 - \gamma$; $0, \gamma - \alpha - \beta$; α, β respectively.

From Theorems 6–8 and from the fact that the Riemann DE is the *unique* DE satisfying the conditions of Theorem 11, several identities for the solutions can be derived. If we make the change of dependent variable $v(z) = z^\lambda w(z)$, the function $v(z)$ has a branch pole at each of the singular points $0, 1, \infty$. Therefore (cf. Theorem 9, Corollary), $v(z)$ satisfies a DE with three regular singular points at $0, 1, \infty$. By Theorem

11, this must be the Riemann DE (42). The exponents of this DE are unchanged at $z = 1$, whereas they are changed to $\alpha_i + \lambda$ at $z = 0$ and to $\gamma_i - \lambda$ at infinity. A similar result holds for the more general change of dependent variable

$$v(z) = z^\lambda(z - 1)^\mu w(z).$$

Using these identities, we can prove the following fundamental

■ THEOREM 12. *Every Riemann DE (40) can be reduced to the hypergeometric DE (18) by a change of dependent variable of the form* $w = z^\lambda(1 - z)^\mu v(z)$.

■ COROLLARY. *Every second-order Fuchsian DE with three regular singular points can be reduced to the hypergeometric DE by changes of independent and dependent variable.*

Proof — The general solution $w(z)$ of the Riemann DE can be written in the form

$$w(z) = z^{\lambda_1}(1 - z)^{\mu_1} v(z),$$

where v is the general solution of a Riemann DE with exponents 0, $\lambda_2 - \lambda_1$; 0, $\mu_2 - \mu_1$; $\nu_1 + \lambda_1 + \mu_1$, $\nu_2 + \lambda_1 + \mu_1$. Thus, the function v is a solution of a hypergeometric DE with $\alpha = \nu_1 + \lambda_1 + \mu_1$, $\beta = \nu_2 + \lambda_1 + \mu_1$, and $\gamma = 1 - \lambda_2 + \lambda_1$, q.e.d.

Other identities are obtained by making a change of independent variable. Any linear fractional transformation which permutes the singular points $0, 1, \infty$ transforms the Riemann DE (42) into another DE with the same regular singular points which, again by Theorem 10, is a Riemann DE. For example, make the change of independent variable $t = 1/z$, which permutes 0 and ∞. If $w(z)$ is a solution of the DE (42), then the function $v(t) = w(1/z)$ satisfies a Riemann DE with singular points at $0, 1, \infty$ for which the exponents at 0 and ∞ are permuted. Similarly, the change of independent variable $t = 1 - z$ permutes the singular points 0 and 1 and leads to the conclusion that $w(1 - z)$ is a solution of a Riemann DE whenever $w(z)$ is a solution. The exponents at the singular points are permuted accordingly.

EXERCISES F

1. Show that the only second-order linear DE which has just two regular singular points, at 0 and ∞, is the Euler DE.
2. Show that no analytic linear DE (5) can have only removable singularities if the point $z = \infty$ is included.
3. Prove in detail that any linear fractional transformation carries regular singular points into regular singular points.

4. If p and q are constant in (5), is the singular point at ∞ regular? Justify your statement.

5. Show that, unless $B = A^2/4$, the DE $(z^2 + Az + B)w'' + (Cz + D)w' + Ew = 0$ can be reduced to the hypergeometric equation by a linear substitution $z = a\zeta + b$.

6. Show that the Bessel DE has an irregular singular point at $z = \infty$.

7. Find necessary and sufficient conditions on $p(z)$ for $w' + p(z)w = 0$ to have
   (a) a removable singularity and (b) a regular singular point at ∞.

8. Show that the most general first-order linear DE with $n + 1$ distinct regular singular points at $z_1, \ldots, z_n$ and ∞ is

$$w' + \left[\sum_{k=1}^{n} q_k/(z - z_k)\right] w = 0.$$

Integrate this DE explicitly.

9*. Find the most general second-order linear DE (5) having regular singular points at $a_1, \ldots, a_n$ and ∞.

10*. Find the most general linear DE having regular singular points at 0, ∞ and no other singular points. Show that any such DE can be integrated in terms of elementary functions.

ADDITIONAL EXERCISES

1. Show that $\int_0^{\pi/2} d\theta/(1 - k^2 \sin^2 \theta)^{1/2} = \frac{1}{2}F(\frac{1}{2}, \frac{1}{2}, 1; k^2)$.

2. Show that the substitution $z = \zeta^m$ (m a nonzero integer) transforms DE's (5) having a regular singular point at $z = 0$ into DE's having a regular singular point at $\zeta = 0$, with characteristic exponents divided by m.

3. Show that the DE $w'' + [(1 - z^2)/4z^2]w = 0$ has a basis of solutions of the form $w_1(z) = z^{1/2}[1 + z^2/16 + z^4/1024 + \cdots]$ and $w_2(z) = w_1 \log z - z^{3/2}/16 + \cdots$.

4. Find an entire function $f(z)$ and constant c for which the functions

$$w_i = f(z)^{1/2} \exp \pm \left\{c \int_c^z dz/[f(z)\sqrt{z(1 - z)}]\right\}$$

are a basis of solutions of $z(1 - z)w'' + (1 - 2z)w'/2 + (az + b)w = 0$.

5. The algebraic form of the Mathieu equation is

$$4\xi(1 - \xi)u_{\xi\xi} + 2(1 - 2\xi)u_\xi + (\lambda - 16k + 32k\xi)u = 0.$$

Show that this has a regular singular point at $\xi = 0$, calculate the exponents, and find a recurrence relation on the coefficients of the power series solutions.

6*. (a) If P and Q are given polynomials without common factors and if $c_{n+1}/c_n = P(n)/Q(n)$ and $\sum c_n z^n$ is convergent, show that $\sum c_n z^n$ satisfies the DE $zP(zd/dz)w - Q(zd/dz)w = 0$.
   (b) Find all quadratic polynomials P and Q for which the preceding DE has regular singular points only, and express the solutions in terms of hypergeometric functions.

7*. (a) Find the eigenvalues of the circuit matrix of (18) for $z = 0$.
   (b) Using the change of variable $t = 1 - z$, solve the same problem for the circuit matrix for $z = 1$.

8. Show that the function $\ln(\ln z)$ satisfies no linear DE of finite order with holomorphic coefficients.

9. Show that, if $f(0) = 0$ but $f'(0) \neq 0$, the substitution $z = f(\zeta)$ carries a regular singular point of (5) at $z = 0$ into one at $\zeta = 0$ having the same indicial equation.

10. Show that, for any nontrivial solution of the Euler DE $z^2w'' + zw' + w = 0$ and any integer n, there exists a spiral path $\theta = h(r)$ approaching the origin, along which $\lim_{z \to 0} |z^n w| = \infty$.

11*. Let the DE $w'' + p_1(z)w' + p_2(z)w = 0$ have an isolated singular point at $z = \infty$. Show that this singular point is regular if and only if, for some $n > 0$, every solution satisfies $\lim_{z \to \infty} z^{-n}w(re^{i\theta}) = 0$ for $0 \leqq \theta \leqq 2\pi$.

10 Sturm-Liouville Systems

1 Sturm-Liouville systems

A Sturm-Liouville equation is a second-order homogeneous linear DE of the form

$$\frac{d}{dx}\left[p(x)\frac{du}{dx}\right] + [\lambda\rho(x) - q(x)]u = 0. \tag{1}$$

Here λ is a parameter, while p, ρ, and q are real-valued functions of x; the functions p and ρ are positive. In operational notation, with $L = D[p(x)D] - q(x)$, we can rewrite (1) in the abbreviated form

$$L[u] + \lambda\rho(x)u = 0. \tag{1'}$$

Such a DE (1) is *self-adjoint* for real λ; to insure the existence of solutions, the functions q and ρ are assumed to be continuous and p to be continuously differentiable (of class $\mathscr{C}^1$). For a given value of λ, (1) defines a *linear operator* transforming any function $u \in \mathscr{C}^2$ into $L[u] + \lambda\rho u$. The Sturm-Liouville equation (1) is called *regular* in a *closed* finite interval $a \leq x \leq b$ when the functions $p(x)$ and $\rho(x)$ are different from zero for $a \leq x \leq b$. The functions p, q, and ρ, being continuous, are bounded in the interval.

For each λ, it follows from the existence theorem of Chapter 6, §8, that a regular Sturm-Liouville equation for $a \leq x \leq b$ has a basis of two linearly independent solutions of class $\mathscr{C}^2$.

A *Sturm-Liouville system* (or S-L system) is a Sturm-Liouville equation together with *endpoint* (or boundary) *conditions* to be satisfied by the solutions, for example $u(a) = u(b) = 0$. One type of endpoint condition we shall study is the following.

■ **DEFINITION.**   A regular S-L system *is a regular S-L equation* (1) *on a finite closed interval* $a \leq x \leq b$, *together with two* separated *endpoint conditions, of the form*

$$\alpha u(a) + \alpha' u'(a) = 0, \qquad \beta u(b) + \beta' u'(b) = O. \tag{2}$$

Here α, α', β, β' *are given real numbers. We exclude the trivial conditions* $\alpha = \alpha' = 0$ *and* $\beta = \beta' = 0$.

A nontrivial solution of an S-L system is called an *eigenfunction*, and the corresponding λ is called its *eigenvalue*. Each eigenfunction is also said to *belong* to its eigenvalue. The set of all eigenvalues of a regular S-L system is called the *spectrum* of the system.

EXAMPLE 1.   The system consisting of the DE $u'' + \lambda u = 0$ in the interval $0 \leq x \leq \pi$, with the boundary conditions $u(0) = 0$, $u(\pi) = 0$, has the eigenfunctions $u_n(x) = \sin nx$ and the eigenvalues $\lambda_n = n^2$, $n = 1, 2, 3, \ldots$.

EXAMPLE 2.   For fixed n, the Bessel equation

$$\frac{d}{dr}\left[r\frac{du}{dr}\right] + \left(k^2 r - \frac{n^2}{r}\right)u = 0, \qquad a \leq r \leq b, \tag{3}$$

is an S-L equation with $p = \rho = r$, $\lambda = k^2$, and $q = n^2/r$. When $0 < a < b$, a regular S-L system is obtained by imposing the endpoint conditions $u(a) = u(b) = 0$, or by imposing any other separated endpoint conditions of the form (2).

With $a = 0$, the DE (3) does not define a regular S-L system, because the coefficient $p(r)$ vanishes at $r = 0$. We then obtain a *singular* S-L system, which is treated in § 4.

For fixed k and variable n, the Bessel equation (3) defines a different S-L equation, because the parameter is different.

Periodic endpoint conditions.   For S-L equations whose coefficients are periodic functions of x with period $b - a$, the *periodic* endpoint conditions

$$u(a) = u(b), \qquad u'(a) = u'(b) \tag{4}$$

are sometimes imposed, and give another type of S-L system, a *periodic* S-L system.

EXAMPLE 3.   The system consisting of the DE $u'' + \lambda u = 0$, for $-\pi \leq x \leq \pi$, with the periodic endpoint conditions $u(-\pi) = u(\pi)$ and $u'(-\pi) = u'(\pi)$, has the eigenfunctions 1, $\cos nx$, $\sin nx$, where n is any positive integer. The corresponding eigenvalues are the squares of integers; if $n > 0$, there are two linearly independent eigenfunctions having the same eigenvalue n^2.

EXAMPLE 4.   A regular S-L system is obtained from the *Mathieu equation*

$$u'' + (\lambda + 16d \cos 2x)u = 0, \qquad 0 \leq x \leq \pi, \tag{5}$$

by imposing separated endpoint conditions. In this example, $p = \rho \equiv 1$, and $q(x) = -16d \cos 2x$. With the periodic endpoint conditions $u(0) = u(\pi)$, $u'(0) = u'(\pi)$, or with $u(0) = -u(\pi)$ and $u'(0) = -u'(\pi)$, S-L systems are obtained which are not regular but periodic.

2 Sturm-Liouville series

Examples 1 and 3 define two S-L systems from the same S-L equation, $u'' + \lambda u = 0$, but with different endpoint conditions. The eigenfunctions of Example 3 are the functions used in the theory of Fourier series, studied in the advanced calculus. It is shown there that these functions are *orthogonal* on the interval $-\pi \leq x \leq \pi$. This means that the following relations hold:†

$$\int_{-\pi}^{\pi} \sin mx \sin nx \, dx = \int_{-\pi}^{\pi} \cos mx \cos nx \, dx = 0 \qquad \text{if} \quad m \neq n,$$

$$\int_{-\pi}^{\pi} \sin mx \cos nx \, dx = 0 \qquad \text{for all integers} \quad m, n.$$

The eigenfunctions $\sin nx$ of Example 1 are also orthogonal on the interval $0 \leq x \leq \pi$ on which the S-L system in question is defined:

$$\int_{0}^{\pi} \sin mx \sin nx \, dx = 0 \qquad \text{if} \quad m \neq n.$$

We will now show that analogous orthogonality relations hold for the eigenfunctions of regular S-L systems generally, and for the eigenfunctions of S-L systems with periodic endpoint conditions.

■ DEFINITION.   *Two integrable real-valued functions f and g are orthogonal* with *weight function $\rho > 0$ on an interval I if and only if*

$$\int_{I} \rho(x)f(x)g(x) \, dx = 0. \tag{6}$$

The interval I may be finite and open or closed at either end; or it may be semi-infinite or infinite.

■ THEOREM 1.   *Eigenfunctions of a regular* S-L *system* (1)–(2) *having different eigenvalues are* orthogonal *with weight function ρ. Thus, let u*

---

† Courant and John, pp. 274, 583; Widder, p. 395.

and v be eigenfunctions belonging to distinct eigenvalues λ *and* μ. *Then*

$$\int_a^b \rho(x)u(x)v(x)\,dx = 0. \tag{7}$$

Proof — We use the operator notation $L[u] = [p(x)u']' - q(x)u$. Then u and v are eigenfunctions of (1) with eigenvalues λ and μ if and only if

$$L[u] + \lambda\rho(x)u = L[v] + \mu\rho(x)v = 0.$$

We next establish the following lemma.

■ LEMMA. *If* u *and* v *satisfy an* S-L *equation* (1) *on a closed interval* $a \leq x \leq b$, *for values* λ *and* μ *of the parameter, then*

$$(\lambda - \mu)\int_a^b \rho(x)u(x)v(x)\,dx = p(x)[u(x)v'(x) - v(x)u'(x)]\Big|_{x=a}^{x=b}. \tag{8}$$

To prove (8), we apply the hypothesis to the *Lagrange identity* of Chapter 2, § 6, namely the identity

$$uL[v] - vL[u] = \frac{d}{dx}\{p(x)[u(x)v'(x) - v(x)u'(x)]\},$$

which is easily verified directly. Integrating this identity between the endpoints $x = a$ and $x = b$ and substituting $-\mu\rho v$ for $L[v]$ and $-\lambda\rho u$ for $L[u]$, we get (8) as claimed. The right-hand side of (8) is called its *boundary term*.

To prove Theorem 1, it suffices to show that the boundary term vanishes in the case of separated endpoint conditions. But (2) implies that

$$p(a)[u(a)v'(a) - v(a)u'(a)] = [\alpha p(a)/\alpha'][u(a)v(a) - v(a)u(a)] = 0$$

if $\alpha' \neq 0$. If $\alpha \neq 0$, the right side of (8) reduces similarly at $x = a$ to

$$[\alpha'p(a)/\alpha][u'(a)v(a) - v'(a)u(a)] = 0.$$

Hence $p(a)[u(a)v'(a) - v(a)u'(a)] = 0$ unless $\alpha = \alpha' = 0$. Similar formulas cover the boundary term at $x = b$. Since the possibilities $\alpha = \alpha' = 0$ and $\beta = \beta' = 0$ are excluded, this shows that the right side of (8) vanishes. Formula (7) now follows from identity (8), after dividing through by the nonzero factor $(\lambda - \mu)$.

From the Lemma we also obtain the

■ COROLLARY. *The result of Theorem 1 holds also for* S-L *systems with periodic endpoint conditions.*

For, in this case, the contributions to the boundary term on the right side of (8) from $x = a$ and $x = b$ are equal in magnitude and opposite in sign; hence, they cancel.

The orthogonality relations just proved enable one to expand given functions as infinite linear combinations of the eigenfunctions of regular S-L systems, and of the eigenfunctions of S-L systems with periodic endpoint conditions. The resulting infinite series are called *Sturm-Liouville series*. The most important property of Sturm-Liouville series, which will be derived in Chapter 11, is that *any* reasonably smooth function can be expanded into an infinite linear combination of the eigenfunctions of any *regular* Sturm-Liouville system. Fourier series are the most familiar example of such an expansion.

In the present chapter, our main objective is to prove that the eigenfunctions of any regular S-L system behave like the eigenfunctions of $u'' + \lambda u = 0$ for the same endpoint conditions, in a sense to be made precise.

EXERCISES A

1. (a) Show that every solution of the Airy DE $v'' + xv = 0$ vanishes infinitely often on the positive x-axis and at most once on the negative x-axis.
   (b) Show that, if $v(x)$ satisfies the Airy equation, $u(x) = v(kx)$ satisfies $u'' + k^3 xu = 0$.
   (c) Show that the S-L system defined for the DE $u'' + \lambda xu = 0$ by the endpoint conditions $u(0) = u(1) = 0$ has an infinite sequence of positive eigenvalues and no negative eigenvalue. [HINT: See Chapter 2, § 4.]
2. For the S-L system defined by $u'' + \lambda u = 0$ and the endpoint conditions $u(0) = u(\pi) + u'(\pi) = 0$, show that there is an infinite sequence of eigenfunctions with distinct eigenvalues. What are its eigenvalues?
3. Determine the eigenvalues of the DE $u'' + \lambda u = 0$, for the endpoint conditions $u(0) = u(\pi)$, $u'(0) = 2u'(\pi)$.
4. (a) Show that $u = U(kr)$ satisfies (3) if and only if $U(x)$, $(x = kr)$, satisfies the Bessel DE $U'' + (1/x)U' + [1 - (n^2/x^2)]U = 0$.
   (b) Show that if $U(x)$ and $V(x)$ satisfy the Bessel DE and if

$$U(ka) = U(kb) = V(k_1 a) = V(k_1 b) = 0, \qquad k \neq k_1,$$

   then $\int_a^b U(kr)V(k_1 r)r\, dr = 0$.
5. (a) Show that if $u(x)$ and $v(x)$ are periodic solutions of the Mathieu equation (Example 4) with period π having distinct eigenvalues, then

$$\int_0^\pi u(x)\, v(x)\, dx = 0.$$

   (b) Show that, for any eigenvalue λ, the Mathieu equation has either an odd eigenfunction or an even eigenfunction.
6. Determine the eigenvalues λ such that $u^{\mathrm{iv}} + \lambda u = 0$ admits a nontrivial eigenfunction satisfying $f(0) = f'(0) = f(\pi) = f'(\pi) = 0$.
7. Show that, if $f_1(x)$ and $f_2(x)$ are eigenfunctions of Exercise 6 having distinct eigenvalues, $\lambda_1 \neq \lambda_2$, then $\int_0^\pi f_1(x)f_2(x)\, dx = 0$.

8. Show that the substitution $\xi = \cos^2 x$ transforms the Mathieu equation into

$$4\xi(1 - \xi)u_{\xi\xi} + (2 - 4\xi)u_\xi + (\lambda - 16\,d + 32\,d\xi)u = 0.$$

9*. Consider the boundary value problem defined by the first-order DE

$$u' + [\lambda + q(x)]u = 0, \qquad q \in C, \quad q \text{ real},$$

and one nontrivial side condition $B[u] = \alpha u(a) + \alpha'u'(a) + \beta u(b) + \beta'u'(b) = 0$. Show that this problem admits at most three real eigenvalues.

3* Physical interpretations

Sturm-Liouville systems arise typically from *vibration* problems in continuum mechanics. In physical language, they describe boundary-value problems corresponding to simply harmonic *standing waves*. It is commonly assumed in physics that *any wave motion can be resolved into simply harmonic standing waves*, each of which oscillates with its proper frequency.

Though physicists commonly *assume* this result on the basis of experimental evidence and intuition, it can actually be *deduced* rigorously from the mathematical theory of wave motion as a boundary value problem in differential equations, as will be shown below.

We illustrate the physical interpretation of eigenfunctions of Sturm-Liouville systems by three classic examples.

The partial DE of a vibrating string is†

$$y_{tt} = c^2 y_{xx}, \qquad \text{where} \quad c^2 = T/\rho.$$

Here y is the lateral displacement from equilibrium; T is the tension and ρ the density of the string, both assumed constant. Simply harmonic standing waves are defined by the separation of variables

$$y(x, t) = u(x) \cos k(t - t_0).$$

For $y(x, t)$ to satisfy the vibrating string equation $y_{tt} = c^2 y_{xx}$, it is necessary and sufficient that $u'' + \lambda u = 0$, $\lambda = k^2/c^2$.

For the vibrating string, it is natural physically to have *fixed endpoints*, so that $y(a, t) = y(b, t) = 0$. This makes $u(a) = u(b) = 0$ and leads to the S-L problem of Example 1. The eigenvalue belonging to each eigenfunction is proportional to the *squared frequency* $k^2/4\pi^2$. This relation, combined with the analogy between mechanical and electromagnetic waves, has led mathematicians to call the set of eigenvalues the *spectrum* of an S-L system.

Another physical interpretation of S-L systems is furnished by the longitudinal vibrations of an *elastic bar* of local stiffness $p(x)$ and

---

† Widder, pp. 413–421. In this Section, subscript letters denote differentiation with respect to the variable indicated.

density $\rho(x)$. The mean longitudinal displacement $v(x, t)$ of the section of such a bar from its equilibrium position x satisfies the wave equation

$$\rho(x) \frac{\partial^2 v}{\partial t^2} = \frac{\partial}{\partial x}\left[p(x) \frac{\partial v}{\partial x} \right].$$

The *simple harmonic* vibrations (the *normal modes* of vibration) given by the separation of variables

$$v = u(x) \cos k(t - t_0)$$

are the solutions of the Sturm-Liouville equation

$$\frac{d}{dx}\left[p(x) \frac{du}{dx} \right] + k^2 \rho(x) u = 0.$$

This is the special case $q = 0$ of (1), with $\lambda = k^2$.

For a finite bar, extending over the interval $a \leqq x \leqq b$, various physical boundary conditions arise naturally:

$$
\begin{array}{ll}
u(a) = u(b) = 0 & \text{(rigidly fixed ends),} \\
u'(a) = u'(b) = 0 & \text{(free ends),} \\
u'(a) + \alpha u(a) = u'(b) + \beta u(b) = 0 & \text{(elastically held ends),} \\
u(a) = u(b), \quad u'(a) = u'(b) & \text{(periodic constraints).}
\end{array}
$$

Each of these endpoint conditions on u implies a corresponding condition on $v(x, t)$, with d/dx replaced by $\partial/\partial x$. The natural frequencies of longitudinal vibration (musical fundamental tone and overtones) of a bar, whose ends are held in each of the ways described, are thus the solutions of the S-L systems defined by (1) and the appropriate conditions above. Finally, the partial DE of a *vibrating membrane* is

$$w_{tt} = c^2(w_{xx} + w_{yy}) = c^2(w_{rr} + r^{-1}w_r + r^{-2}w_{\theta\theta}),$$

where r, θ denote polar coordinates. A basis of standing wave solutions can be found by trying the separation of variables

$$w(r, \theta, t) = u(r) \begin{Bmatrix} \cos \\ \sin \end{Bmatrix} n\theta \cos \kappa(t - t_0).$$

For w to satisfy the membrane equation with $\kappa = ck$, it is necessary and sufficient that u be a solution of the Bessel equation (3). The singularity at $r = 0$ of the Bessel equation is associated with the singularity in polar coordinates at the origin.

If the membrane is a circular disc of radius a (vibrating drumhead), the physically natural boundary conditions are $u(a) = 0$ and $u(0)$ nonsingular. The latter condition characterizes the *Bessel functions* among other solutions of the Bessel equation, up to a constant normalizing factor.

EXERCISES B

1. Show that, if $U_n(x)$ satisfies the Bessel equation of order n (Exercise A4), then $\phi = U_n(kr) \sin n\theta$ and $U_n(kr) \cos n\theta$ satisfy the Helmholtz equation $\nabla^2\phi + k^2\phi = 0$ for polar coordinates in the plane.

2. The partial DE of a vibrating membrane is $\nabla^2 U + k^2 U = 0$. Using Exercise 1, show that this equation has solutions satisfying $U(x, y) \equiv 0$ on $x^2 + y^2 = 1$ for all numbers k_{mn} such that $J_n(k_{mn}) = 0$.

3. A string of density $\frac{1}{100} + \frac{1}{1000} \cos 2x$ grams/cm is stretched taut between pegs at $x = -\pi/2$ and $x = \pi/2$, under a tension of 2 Kg. Determine its natural frequencies, in cycles per second.

4. For the Bessel DE $(xu')' + \lambda x u = 0$, with the endpoint conditions that $u(1) = 0$ and u is bounded on $0 < x \leq 1$, show that the first five eigenvalues are approximately $\lambda_1 = 5.78$, $\lambda_2 = 30.5$, $\lambda_3 = 74.9$, $\lambda_4 = 139$, and $\lambda_5 = 223$. [HINT: Consult a table of zeros of $J_0(x)$.]

5. A vibrating reed, with one clamped end and one free end, executes simple harmonic vibrations with transverse displacement $y(x, t) = u(x) \cos kt$ if and only if $u^{iv} = k^2 u$, $u(0) = u'(0) = 0$, and $u''(L) = u'''(L) = 0$. Find the characteristic frequencies $2\pi/k$. [HINT: Consider the ultraspherical polynomials of Ch. 9, § 11.]

6. Show that the general solution of the Airy DE is $x^{1/2} U_{1/3}(2x^{3/2}/3)$, where $U_{1/3}$ is the general solution of the Bessel DE of order one-third.

7. Show that the function $J_{d/c}(e^{cx}\sqrt{b}/c)$ satisfies the DE $u'' + (be^{2cx} - d^2)u = 0$.

8. Show that the function $xJ_{d/c}(e^{c/x}\sqrt{b}/c)$ satisfies the DE

$$u'' + x^{-4}(be^{2c/x} - d^2) = 0.$$

9*. Show that the general solution of the DE

$$v'' + (a^2 b^2 x^{2a-2} + [(1 - 4n^2 a^2)/4x^2])v = 0$$

is the function $v(x) = \sqrt{x}U(bx^a)$, where U is the general solution of the Bessel DE of order n.

4   Singular systems

An S-L equation (1) can be given on a finite, semi-infinite, or infinite interval I. In the finite case, I may include neither, one, or both end points. The exclusion of an endpoint a may be necessary when $\lim_{x \to a} p(x) = 0$, $\lim_{x \to a} \rho(x) = 0$, or when any one of the functions p, q, ρ is singular at a.

Only when I is a closed, finite interval $a \leq x \leq b$ can an S-L equation be associated with a *regular* S-L system. If I is semi-infinite or infinite, or if I is finite and p or ρ vanishes at one or both endpoints, or if q is discontinuous, we cannot obtain from (1) a regular S-L system. In any such case, the given S-L equation (1) is called *singular*.

We can obtain *singular S-L systems* from singular S-L equations by imposing suitable homogeneous linear endpoint conditions. These conditions cannot always be described by formulas like (2). For example, the condition that u be bounded near a singular endpoint is a common boundary condition defining a singular S-L system.

EXAMPLE 5.   The Legendre DE

$$((1 - x^2)u')' + \lambda u = 0, \qquad -1 < x < 1, \tag{9}$$

together with the condition that a solution u be *bounded* in the interval, is an example of a singular S-L system. As shown in Chapter 3, § 2, the *Legendre polynomials* $P_n(x)$ are real eigenfunctions of this S-L system belonging to the eigenvalues $\lambda_n = n(n + 1)$.

EXAMPLE 6.   For fixed n, the Bessel equation of Example 2,

$$\frac{d}{dr}\left[r\frac{du}{dr}\right] + \left(k^2 r - \frac{n^2}{r}\right)u = 0, \qquad 0 < r \leq a,$$

is a singular S-L equation with $p = \rho = r$, $\lambda = k^2$, and $q = n^2/r$. A singular S-L system is obtained for any $a > 0$ by imposing the endpoint conditions $u(a) = 0$, and $u(r)$ bounded as $r \to 0$.

The eigenfunctions of the preceding singular S-L systems are the Bessel functions $J_n(k_j r)$, where $k_j a$ is the jth zero of the Bessel function $J_n(x)$ of order n. It has been shown in Chapter 2, § 4, that $J_n(x)$ has infinitely many zeros; it follows that the singular S-L system just defined has infinitely many eigenvalues.

The eigenfunctions of singular S-L systems are also orthogonal, provided that they are *square-integrable* relative to the weight function ρ, in the following sense.

■ DEFINITION.   *A real-valued function f is* square-integrable *on the interval I relative to a given weight function $\rho(x) > 0$ when*

$$\int_I f^2(x)\rho(x)\,dx < +\infty. \tag{10}$$

When the weight function ρ is identically equal to 1, we say simply that the function f is *square-integrable* on the interval I.

The *Schwarz inequality* holds† for square-integrable functions:

$$\left(\int_I |f(x)g(x)|\,\rho(x)\,dx\right)^2 \leq \int_I f^2(x)\,\rho(x)\,dx \int_I g^2(x)\rho(x)\,dx. \tag{11}$$

This inequality implies in particular that the product of two such square-integrable functions is an integrable function relative to the weight function ρ, that is, the integral in parentheses on the left-hand of (11) is finite.

The right side of the boundary term in (8) vanishes in the limit, for any endpoint conditions which imply that

$$\lim_{\alpha \downarrow a, \beta \uparrow b} p(x)[u(x)v'(x) - v(x)u'(x)]\Big|_{x=\alpha}^{\beta} = 0. \tag{12}$$

---

† Birkhoff and Mac Lane, p. 177.

The conditions $p(a) = p(b) = 0$ and $u'(x)$ bounded on a finite interval have this property, for example.

When (12) holds, we obtain from (8) the identity

$$(\lambda - \mu) \int_a^b \rho(x)u(x)v(x)\, dx = 0$$

for any two square-integrable eigenfunctions u and v with eigenvalues λ and μ. The integral here may be an improper integral. If $\lambda \neq \mu$, this implies, as in the proof of the lemma of § 2, that u and v are orthogonal. This proves the next theorem.

■ THEOREM 2.   *Square-integrable eigenfunctions u and v belonging to different eigenvalues of a singular S-L system are orthogonal with weight ρ whenever the boundary term vanishes, as in (12).*

Applying this result to Example 5, we obtain the orthogonality relation for the Legendre polynomials

$$\int_{-1}^{1} P_m(x)P_n(x)\, dx = 0, \qquad m \neq n, \tag{13}$$

after verifying that the boundary term vanishes. Applying it to the Bessel equation, we obtain the orthogonality relations for Bessel functions

$$\int_0^a x J_n(k_i x)J_n(k_j x)\, dx = 0, \qquad k_i \neq k_j, \tag{14}$$

if $J_n(k_i a) = J_n(k_j a) = 0$.

EXAMPLE 7.   The *Hermite* DE is

$$u'' - 2xu' + \lambda u = 0, \qquad -\infty < x < +\infty, \tag{15}$$

as in Chapter 3, § 2. Using the recursion formula

$$a_{k+2} = (2k - \lambda)a_k/(k + 1)(k + 2), \qquad k = 0, 1, 2, \ldots \tag{16}$$

of Chapter 3, (9′), we obtain a polynomial solution of degree n for $\lambda = 2n$. These polynomials are commonly normalized by the condition that $a_n = 2^n$ (and $a_{n-1} = 0$); this defines the *Hermite polynomials* $H_n(x)$. For example, $H_0(x) = 1$, $H_1(x) = 2x$, $H_2(x) = 4x^2 - 2$, etc. Evidently, $H_n(x)$ is an even function for even n, and an odd function for odd n.

The Hermite DE is not an S-L equation, because it is not self-adjoint. Making the substitution $y = e^{-x^2/2}u$ in (15), we obtain the following equivalent self-adjoint S-L equation for the *Hermite functions* $y(x)$:

$$y'' + [\lambda - (x^2 - 1)]y = 0, \qquad -\infty < x < \infty, \tag{17}$$

among whose solutions for $\lambda = 2n$ are the functions $e^{-x^2/2}H_n(x)$; these functions are square-integrable and tend to zero as $x \to \pm\infty$.

That is, the functions $\phi_n(x) = e^{-x^2/2}H_n(x)$ are eigenfunctions for the singular S-L system defined by (17) and by the endpoint condition that a solution $y(x)$ shall tend to zero as $x \to \pm\infty$. We shall now derive the orthogonality relations for the Hermite polynomials

$$\int_{-\infty}^{\infty} H_m(x)H_n(x)\, e^{-x^2}dx = 0, \qquad m \neq n. \tag{18}$$

For, substituting into the identity (8), we obtain

$$2(m - n)\int_{-a}^{a} H_m(x)H_n(x)\, e^{-x^2}\, dx = [\phi_m(x)\phi_n'(x) - \phi_m'(x)\phi_n(x)]_{x=-a}^{x=a}.$$

Since the boundary terms are e^{-x^2} times a polynomial in x, and

$$\lim_{x \to +\infty} x^n\, e^{-x^2} = 0 \tag{19}$$

for all n, the boundary term vanishes in the limit, as in (12).

EXERCISES C

1. (a) Prove the orthogonality relations for the Bessel functions

$$\int_0^L xJ_n(\alpha x)J_n(\beta x)\, dx = 0 \qquad \text{if} \quad J_n'(\alpha L) = J_n'(\beta L) = 0, \quad \alpha^2 \neq \beta^2 \tag{*}$$

for any nonnegative integer n.
  (b) Prove the equality (*) if $\alpha J_n'(\alpha L)J_n'(\beta L) = \beta J_n'(\beta L)J_n(\alpha L)$.
2. Show that the Legendre polynomials (and their constant multiples) are the only solutions of the Legendre DE which are bounded on $(-1, 1)$.
3. Show that the S-L system $[(x - a)(b - x)u']' + \lambda u = 0$, $a < b$, with $u(x)$ bounded on $a < x < b$, has the eigenvalues $\lambda = 4n(n + 1)(b - a)^2$. Describe the eigenfunctions.
4. (a) (Laguerre polynomials) Consider the singular S-L system

$$(xe^{-x}u')' + \lambda e^{-x}u = 0 \qquad \text{on} \quad 0 < x < +\infty,$$

with endpoint conditions that $u(0^+)$ is bounded and that $e^{-x}u(x) \to 0$ as $x \to +\infty$. Show that the values $\lambda = n$ give polynomial eigenfunctions.
  (b) Show that the preceding system has no other polynomial eigenfunctions. [HINT: Obtain the power series expansion of the general solution of the DE].
5. Show that the eigenvalues of the singular S-L system defined by

$$\frac{d}{dx}\left[(1 - x^2)^{a+1}\frac{du}{dx}\right] + \lambda(1 - x^2)^a u = 0, \qquad a > -1,$$

and the condition of being bounded on $(-1, 1)$, are $\lambda_n = n\,(n + 2\alpha)$.

5 Prüfer substitution

We now develop a powerful method for the study of the solutions of a self-adjoint second-order linear DE

$$\frac{d}{dx}\left[P(x)\frac{du}{dx}\right] + Q(x)u = 0, \qquad a < x < b, \tag{20}$$

where $P(x) > 0$ is of class $\mathscr{C}^1$ and Q is continuous. One often wants to find out how often the solutions of (20) *oscillate* on the interval under consideration, that is, the number of zeros they have for $a < x < b$. This can be done by using the Poincaré phase plane, already introduced in Chapter 2, § 5. Modifying slightly the formulas used there, we make in (20) the *Prüfer substitution*

$$P(x)u'(x) = r(x)\cos\theta(x); \qquad u(x) = r(x)\sin\theta(x). \tag{21}$$

The new dependent variables r and θ are defined by the formulas

$$r^2 = u^2 + P^2u'^2, \qquad \theta = \arctan(u/Pu'). \tag{21'}$$

r is called the *amplitude* and θ the *phase* variable. When $r \neq 0$, the correspondences $(Pu', u) \rightleftharpoons (r, \theta)$ defined by (21) are *analytic* with non-vanishing Jacobian.

For nontrivial solutions, r is always positive since, if $u(x) = u'(x) = 0$ for a given x, by the Uniqueness Theorem of Chapter 2, § 2, u would be the trivial solution $u \equiv 0$.

We now derive an equivalent system of DE's for $r(x)$ and $\theta(x)$. Differentiating the relation† $\cot\theta = Pu'/u$, we get

$$-\csc^2\theta\,\frac{d\theta}{dx} = \frac{(Pu')'}{u} - \frac{Pu'^2}{u^2} = -Q(x) - \frac{1}{P}\cot^2\theta.$$

If we multiply through by $-\sin^2\theta$, this expression becomes

$$\frac{d\theta}{dx} = Q(x)\sin^2\theta + \frac{1}{P(x)}\cos^2\theta = F(x, \theta). \tag{22}$$

Differentiating $r^2 = (Pu')^2 + u^2$ and simplifying, we obtain

$$\frac{dr}{dx} = \left[\frac{1}{P(x)} - Q(x)\right]r\sin\theta\cos\theta = \frac{1}{2}\left[\frac{1}{P(x)} - Q(x)\right]r\sin 2\theta. \tag{23}$$

The system (22)-(23) is equivalent to the DE (20) in the sense that every nontrivial solution of the system defines a unique solution of the DE by the Prüfer substitution (21), and conversely. This system is called the *Prüfer system* associated with the self-adjoint DE (20).

---

† When $\theta \equiv 0 \pmod{\pi}$, the relation is not defined. But the final equations (22)–(23) can still be derived by differentiating the relation $\tan\theta = u/Pu'$.

The DE (22) of the Prüfer system is a first-order DE in θ, x alone, not containing the other dependent variable r, and it satisfies a Lipschitz condition with Lipschitz constant

$$L = \sup_{a < x < b} \left| \frac{\partial F}{\partial \theta} \right| \leq \sup_{a < x < b} |Q(x)| + \sup_{a < x < b} \frac{1}{|P(x)|}.$$

The constant L is finite in any closed interval in which Q and P are continuous. Hence, the existence and uniqueness theorems of Chapter 5 are applicable, and show that the DE (22) has a unique solution $\theta(x)$ for any initial value $\theta(a) = \gamma$, provided P and Q are continuous at a.

With $\theta(x)$ known, $r(x)$ is given by (23) after a quadrature:

$$r = K \exp\left\{ \frac{1}{2} \int_a^x \left[\frac{1}{P(t)} - Q(t) \right] \sin 2\theta \, dt \right\}, \tag{23'}$$

where $K = r(a)$. Each solution of the Prüfer system (22)-(23) depends on two constants: the initial *amplitude* $K = r(a)$ and the initial *phase* $\gamma = \theta(a)$. Changing the constant K just multiplies a solution $u(x)$ by a constant factor; thus, the zeros of any solution u of (20) can be located by studying only the DE (22).

6 The Sturm comparison theorem

The *zeros* of any solution $u(x)$ of the DE (20) occur where the phase function $\theta(x)$ in the Prüfer substitution (21) assumes the values 0, $\pm\pi$, $\pm 2\pi$, ..., that is, at all points x where $\sin \theta(x) = 0$. At each of these points $\cos^2 \theta = 1$ and $d\theta/dx$ is positive, by (22) (recall that $P(x) > 0$). Geometrically, this means that the curve $(P(x)u'(x), u(x))$ in the (Pu', u)-plane corresponding to a solution u of the DE can cross the Pu'-axis $\theta = n\pi$ only counterclockwise.

Now compare DE (22) with a DE of the same form $d\theta/dx = F_1(x, \theta)$ with coefficients $Q_1(x) \geq Q(x)$ and $P_1(x) \leq P(x)$:

$$\frac{d\theta}{dx} = Q_1(x) \sin^2 \theta + \frac{1}{P_1(x)} \cos^2 \theta = F_1(x, \theta).$$

If $Q_1(x) \geq Q(x)$ and $P_1(x) \leq P(x)$ in an interval I, then $F_1(x, \theta) \geq F(x, \theta)$ there. By the Comparison Theorem of Chapter 1, § 11, we conclude that, if $\theta_1(x)$ is a solution of the second DE whose initial value satisfies $\theta_1(a) \geq \theta(a)$, and $\theta(x)$ is a solution of (22), then $\theta_1(x) \geq \theta(x)$ for $a \leq x \leq b$. Furthermore, we have $\theta_1(b) = \theta(b)$ only if $\theta(x) \equiv \theta_1(x)$, which implies that $u(x) \equiv cu_1(x)$, whence $F(x, \theta(x)) \equiv F_1(x, \theta_1(x))$. This implies that $Q(x) \equiv Q_1(x)$ since $d\theta/dx = 1/P_1(x) > 0$, where $\sin \theta = 0$; therefore, $\sin \theta$ can vanish only at isolated points. It also implies that $P(x) \equiv P_1(x)$, except in intervals where $\cos \theta \equiv 0$ and so $Q(x) \equiv Q_1(x) \equiv 0$ (cf.

Chapter 1, § 11, Corollary 1). Therefore, if $\sin \theta(a) = 0$, the number of zeros of $\sin \theta_1(x)$ for $a < x < b$ is greater than the number of zeros of $\sin \theta(x)$, except when $P \equiv P_1$ and $Q \equiv Q_1$, when it is equal, and when $Q \equiv Q, \equiv 0$ in an interval, when it may be equal. This completes the proof of

■ THEOREM 3 (Sturm Comparison Theorem). *Let* $P(x) \geq P_1(x) > 0$ *and* $Q_1(x) \geq Q(x)$ *in the* DE's

$$\frac{d}{dx}\left(P(x)\frac{du}{dx}\right) + Q(x)u = 0, \qquad \frac{d}{dx}\left(P_1(x)\frac{du_1}{dx}\right) + Q_1(x)u_1 = 0. \quad (24)$$

Then, between any two zeros of a nontrivial solution $u(x)$ *of the first* DE, *there lies at least one zero of every solution of the second* DE, *except when* $u(x) \equiv cu_1(x)$. *This implies* $P \equiv P_1$ *and* $Q \equiv Q_1$ *except possibly in intervals where* $Q \equiv Q_1 \equiv 0$.

In the case of S-L equations, since $\rho(x) > 0$, $Q(x) \equiv Q_1(x)$ evidently implies that $\lambda = \lambda_1$.

Sturm's Separation Theorem of Chapter 2, §4 follows as a corollary by comparing two linearly independent solutions of the same DE.

A short and easily remembered if somewhat imprecise summary is this: as Q increases and P decreases, the number of zeros of every solution increases.

Maxima and minima. For the self-adjoint DE (20), the inequality $Q(x) > 0$ implies that

$$d\theta/dx > 0 \qquad \text{if} \quad \theta = (n + \tfrac{1}{2})\pi.$$

For, in (22), $\cos \theta = 0$ and $|\sin \theta| = 1$ if $\theta = (n + \tfrac{1}{2})\pi$. Since $\cos \theta = 0$ if and only if $u' = 0$, it follows that, if $Q(x)$ is positive, any nontrivial solution of (20) has exactly one maximum or minimum between successive zeros.

7   The Oscillation theorem

We now consider the variation with λ in the number of zeros of the eigenfunctions of a regular S-L system (1)–(2). Setting $P(x) = p(x)$ and $Q(x) = \lambda\rho(x) - q(x)$ in (1), we obtain (20). Since $u = 0$ if and only if $\sin \theta = 0$ in (21), the zeros of any solution of (1) are the points where $\theta = 0, \pm\pi, \pm 2\pi, \ldots, \pm n\pi, \ldots$, since θ is a solution of the associated Prüfer equation

$$\frac{d\theta}{dx} = [\lambda\rho(x) - q(x)]\sin^2 \theta + \frac{1}{p(x)}\cos^2 \theta, \qquad a \leq x \leq b. \quad (25)$$

Here $p(x) > 0$, $\rho(x) > 0$ for $a \leq x \leq b$.

We now fix γ, and denote by $\theta(x, \lambda)$ the solution of (25) which satisfies an initial condition $\theta(a, \lambda) = \gamma$ for all λ, where γ is defined by the conditions†

$$\tan \gamma = u(a)/p(a)u'(a) = -\alpha'/p(a)\alpha, \qquad 0 \leq \gamma < \pi. \qquad (25')$$

The constants α and α' come from the initial condition $\alpha u(a) + \alpha'u'(a) = 0$. For fixed γ, the function $\theta(x, \lambda)$ is defined on the domain $a \leq x \leq b, -\infty < \lambda < \infty$; we shall consider its behavior there.

Applying the comparison theorem of Chapter 1, § 11 (and especially Corollary 1 there) to (25), we obtain the following lemmas.

■ **LEMMA 1.** *For fixed $x > a$, $\theta(x, \lambda)$ is a strictly increasing function of the variable λ.*

■ **LEMMA 2.** *Suppose that for some $x_n > a$, $\theta(x_n, \lambda) = n\pi$, where $n \geq 0$ is an integer. Then $\theta(x, \lambda) > n\pi$ for all $x > x_n$.*

Proof — If x_n is any point where $\theta(x, \lambda) = n\pi$, then, by the DE (25), we have $d\theta(x_n, \lambda)/dx_n = 1/p(x_n) > 0$. Thus, the function $\theta = \theta(x_n, \lambda)$, considered as a function of x_n, is increasing where it crosses the line $\theta = n\pi$, as shown in Figure 10.1. Hence, $\theta(x, \lambda)$ stays above this line for $x > x_n$, q.e.d.

FIGURE 10.1   Direction field of

$$\frac{d\theta}{dx} = Q(x)\sin^2 \theta + \frac{1}{P(x)}\cos^2 \theta = F(x, \theta).$$

Lemma 2, combined with the condition $0 \leq \gamma = \theta(a, \lambda) < \pi$, makes the first zero of $u(x)$ in the open interval $a < x < b$ occur where $\theta = \pi$, and the nth zero, where $\theta = n\pi$.

Our next aim is to show that, for fixed x, $\theta(x, \lambda) \to \infty$ as $\lambda \to \infty$.

In view of Lemma 2, we will have shown that $\lim_{\lambda \to \infty} \theta(x, \lambda) = \infty$ for each x if we can show that, for every integer $n > 0$, we can find

---

† We have assumed $\alpha \neq 0$. When $\alpha = 0$, set $\gamma = \pi/2$, $\tan \gamma = \infty$.

number $x_n < x$ such that $\theta(x_n, \lambda) = n\pi$ for sufficiently large λ. Stated in different terms, let $x_n(\lambda)$ be the smallest x such that $\theta(x, \lambda) = n\pi$. Then, all we need to show is that $x_n(\lambda)$ exists for large λ and that $\lim_{\lambda \to \infty} x_n(\lambda) = a$. This is done in the following lemma.

■ LEMMA 3.   *For a given fixed positive integer n and sufficiently large λ, the function $x_n(\lambda)$ is defined and continuous. It is a decreasing function of λ, and $\lim_{\lambda \to \infty} x_n(\lambda) = a$.*

Proof — By Theorem 3 of Chapter 6, the function $\theta(x, \lambda)$ is a continuous function of both variables x and λ for $a \leq x \leq b$ and $-\infty < \lambda < \infty$. We shall first prove that, if the function $x_n(\lambda)$ is well-defined, that is, if $\theta(x, \lambda) = n\pi$ for some x, then $x_n(\lambda)$ is a monotonic decreasing function of λ. To prove this result, it suffices to prove that $\theta(x, \lambda)$ is an increasing function of λ. But this is the conclusion of Lemma 1.

We now show that, for fixed n, the function $x_n(\lambda)$ is well-defined for large enough λ. This amounts to saying that, for large enough λ, there is an x in the interval $a \leq x \leq b$ for which $\theta(x, \lambda) = n\pi$. We can translate this statement into an equivalent statement for the solutions of the DE (1), using (21). It is equivalent to saying that every nontrivial solution of (1) has at least n zeros in the interval $a < x < b$, since $\theta(x, \lambda)$, being a continuous function of x, must take all values between $\theta(a, \lambda) = \gamma < \pi$ and $n\pi$.

Now, let q_M and p_M be the maxima of $q(x)$ and $p(x)$, respectively, and ρ_m be the minimum of $\rho(x)$ for $a \leq x \leq b$. A solution of the DE

$$p_M u'' + (\lambda \rho_m - q_M)u = 0, \qquad \lambda > q_M/\rho_m, \qquad (26)$$

is the function $u_1(x) = \sin kx$, where $k^2 = (\lambda \rho_m - q_M)/p_M$. The successive zeros of this function are spaced at a distance $\pi \sqrt{p_M/(\lambda \rho_m - q_M)}$ apart. By the Sturm Comparison Theorem (Theorem 3 above), any nontrivial solution $u(x)$ of the Sturm-Liouville equation (1) must have at least one zero between any two zeros of the function $u_1(x)$. Since $u_1(x)$ has n zeros on (a, b) when λ is sufficiently large, it follows that $u(x)$ has at least n zeros and, therefore, that $\theta(x, \lambda)$ takes the value $n\pi$ for sufficiently large λ, as we wanted to show.

The number $x_n(\lambda)$ falls between the $(n-1)$st and the nth zero of $u_1(x)$, and both these zeros tend to a as $\lambda \to \infty$. Therefore, we have $x_n(\lambda) \to a$ as $\lambda \to \infty$, q.e.d.

We are now ready to prove the following result.

■ THEOREM 4 (Oscillation Theorem).   *The solution $\theta(x; \lambda)$ of DE (25) satisfying the initial condition $\theta(a, \lambda) = \gamma$, $0 \leq \gamma < \pi$ for each λ, is a* *continuous and strictly increasing function of* λ *for fixed* x *on* $a < x \leq b$. *Moreover,*

$$\lim_{\lambda \to \infty} \theta(x; \lambda) = \infty, \qquad \lim_{\lambda \to -\infty} \theta(x; \lambda) = 0, \qquad (27)$$

for $a < x \leq b$.

The first sentence was proved in Lemmas 1–3. The first formula of (27) was proved above.

We shall now prove the second formula of (27). Choose numbers $\gamma < \gamma_1 < \pi$ and $\epsilon > 0$. The slope of the segment in the $x\theta$-plane joining the points (a, γ_1) and (x_1, ϵ) where $a < x_1 \leq b$, equals $(\epsilon - \gamma_1)/(x_1 - a)$. For a point (x, θ) on this segment, the slope of $\theta(x, \lambda)$, as given by (25), will be less than the slope of the segment for large negative λ. Therefore, the function $\theta(x, \lambda)$ will lie below the segment for $a \leq x \leq x_1$, for all sufficiently large negative λ. We conclude that $\theta(x_1, \lambda) < \epsilon$ for sufficiently large negative λ. Since, by the argument used to prove Lemma 2, $\theta(x_1, \lambda) > 0$, it follows that $|\theta(x_1, \lambda)| < \epsilon$. And since ϵ and x_1 are arbitrary, the proof is complete.

We now derive an estimate for the position of the zeros of the solutions of a regular S-L equation (1) by comparing it with equation (26) and with

$$p_m u'' + (\lambda \rho_M - q_m)u = 0, \qquad (28)$$

where p_m and q_m are the minima of $p(x)$ and $q(x)$, and ρ_M the maximum of $\rho(x)$ for $a \leq x \leq b$.

Consider solutions of (26) and (28) for which $u(a)/p(a)u'(a) = \tan \gamma$. The zeros of these solutions can be determined by inspection. They are $a + (n\pi - \gamma)/\sqrt{(\lambda \rho_m - q_M)/p_M}$ and $a + (n\pi - \gamma)/\sqrt{(\lambda \rho_M - q_m)/p_m}$, respectively. Applying the Sturm Comparison Theorem, we obtain the

■ COROLLARY. *Let* x_n *be the* nth *zero of a nontrivial solution of the* S-L *equation* (1). *Then*

$$\sqrt{\frac{p_m}{\lambda \rho_M - q_m}} \leq \frac{x_n - a}{n\pi - \gamma} \leq \sqrt{\frac{p_M}{\lambda \rho_m - q_M}}. \qquad (29)$$

The preceding results have been proved under the assumption that $\alpha \neq 0$ in (2). If $\alpha = 0$, we can use the same argument when $\beta \neq 0$, by changing the independent variable to $t = a + b - x$. If $\alpha = \beta = 0$, we can still prove the above results with $\gamma = \pi/2$.

EXERCISES D

1. For $u'' + [\lambda - q(x)]u = 0$, with separated endpoint conditions (2), show that all eigenvalues are positive if $q(x) > 0$, $\alpha \alpha' < 0$, and $\beta \beta' > 0$.

2. Show that the number of negative eigenvalues of a regular S-L system is always finite, and is at most 1 if $q(x) > 0$.

3. Show that any infinite sequence of eigenvalues of a regular S-L system is unbounded.

4. Find all solutions of the DE $\theta' = A \sin^2 \theta + B \cos^2 \theta$, where A and B are positive constants. [HINT: Relate it to a Prüfer system.]

5. Show that, at all points x where a solution $u(x)$ of $(Pu')' + Qu = 0$ has a minimum or a maximum, $d\theta/dx = Q(x)$.

6. Extend the Sturm Oscillation Theorem to the case where $\alpha = \beta = 0$ in (2).

7. Derive Theorem 3 from the Sturm Comparison Theorem of Chapter 2 by introducing the new dependent variables $t = \int_a^x ds/P(s)$ and $t_1 = \int_a^x ds/P_1(s)$.

8. For any solution of $u'' + q(x)u = 0$, $q(x) < 0$, show that the product $u(x)u'(x)$ is an increasing function. Infer that a nontrivial solution can have at most one zero.

9. Show that, if $q(x) < 0$ in $u'' + p(x)u' + q(x)u = 0$, no nontrivial solution of the DE can have more than one zero.

10. (a) Show that $J_n(x)$ is increasing for $0 < x \leq |n|$. [HINT: Use the identity $x(xJ_n')' \equiv (n^2 - x^2)J_n$.]

   (b) Prove that, if x_0 is the first positive zero of J_n and y_0 is that of J_n', then

$$|n| \leq y_0 < x_0.$$

11*. (a) Let $u(x)$ be a solution of $(Pu')' + Qu = 0$, where $P > 0$, $P' > 0$, $Q > 0$, and $(P'/Q)' > 1$. Show that the zeros of u, u', u'' follow each other cyclically.

   (b) Infer that the zeros of J_n, J_{n+1}, J_{n+2} follow one another cyclically.

12. (Sturm Convexity Theorem) In $u'' + Q(x)u = 0$, let $Q(x)$ be increasing. Show that $x_n - x_{n-1} < x_{n+1} - x_n$, where $\{x_n\}$ is the sequence of successive zeros of a nontrivial solution u.

13. For the modified Bessel function $I_0(y) = J_0(iy)$, without considering its Taylor series, show that $I_0'(y) > 0$ and $1 < I_0(y) < \cosh y$ for all $y > 0$.

14. Show that, in the Sturm Oscillation Theorem, $\theta(x, \lambda) \to \infty$ as $\lambda \to \infty$, uniformly in any subinterval $a' \leq x \leq b$, $a' > a$.

15. Show that $\theta(x, \lambda) \to 0$ as $\lambda \to -\infty$, uniformly in any subinterval $a' \leq x \leq b$, $a' > a$.

8   The sequence of eigenfunctions

The existence of an infinite sequence of eigenfunctions of a regular S-L system consisting of the DE (1) together with the separated endpoint conditions (2), that is, the conditions

$$A[u] = \alpha u(a) + \alpha' u'(a) = 0, \qquad B[u] = \beta u(b) + \beta' u'(b) = 0 \quad (30)$$

will now be proved.

We first transform these endpoint conditions into equivalent endpoint conditions for the phase function $\theta(x, \lambda)$ of the Prüfer system (22), (23) associated with the DE (1). If $\alpha \neq 0$, then the function $\theta(x, \lambda)$ must satisfy the initial condition $\theta(a, \lambda) = \gamma$, where γ is the smallest positive number $0 \leq \gamma < \pi$ such that $p(a) \tan \gamma = -\alpha'/\alpha$. When $\alpha = 0$, we choose $\gamma = \pi/2$. Similarly, we choose $0 < \delta \leq \pi$ so that $\tan \delta = -\beta'/\beta p(b)$.

A solution $u(x)$ of the DE (1) for $a \leq x \leq b$ is an eigenfunction of the regular S-L problem obtained by imposing the endpoint conditions (30) if and only if, for the corresponding phase function defined by (21'),

$$\theta(a, \lambda) = \gamma, \qquad \theta(b, \lambda) = \delta + n\pi, \qquad n = 0, 1, 2, \ldots, \tag{31}$$

$$0 \leq \gamma < \pi, \qquad 0 < \delta \leq \pi.$$

Clearly, any value of λ for which conditions (31) are satisfied is an eigenvalue of the given regular S-L system, and conversely. Let $\theta(x, \lambda)$ be the solution of (25) for the initial condition $\theta(a, \lambda) = \gamma$. Figure 10.2

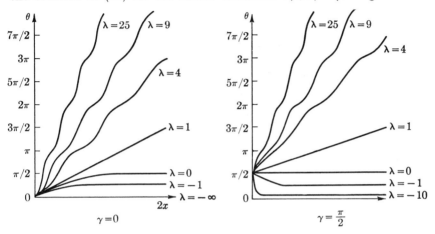

FIGURE 10.2 $\theta(x, \lambda)$ for $u'' + \lambda u = 0$.

shows graphs of the function $\theta = \theta(x, \lambda)$ for various values of the parameter λ. The waviness of the lines expresses the fact that $1/P(x)$ in (23) is independent of λ, whereas $Q(x) = \lambda\rho - q$ tends to infinity with λ. As a result, the slope of the graph is $1/p(x)$ for all λ when $\theta \equiv 0 \pmod{\pi}$, although it tends to infinity with λ for all other θ.

Since $\theta(b, \lambda)$ is an increasing function of λ, and $\theta(b, \lambda) > 0$ by Lemma 2 of § 7, as λ increases from $-\infty$, there is a first value λ_0 for which the second of the conditions (31) is satisfied. For this eigenvalue, we have $\theta(b, \lambda_0) = \delta$. As λ increases, there is an infinite sequence of λ_n for which the second boundary condition is satisfied, namely those for which $\theta(b, \lambda_n) = \delta + n\pi$ for some nonnegative integer n. Each of these values gives an eigenfunction

$$u_n(x) = r(x) \sin \theta(x, \lambda_n) \tag{32}$$

of the S-L system. Furthermore, the eigenfunction belonging to λ_n has exactly n zeros in the interval $a \leq x \leq b$, by Theorem 4. This proves all but the last statement of the following theorem.

■ THEOREM 5.   *Any regular* S-L *system has an infinite sequence of real eigenvalues* $\lambda_0 < \lambda_1 < \lambda_2 < \cdots$ *with* $\lim_{n \to \infty} \lambda_n = \infty$. *The eigenfunction $u_n(x)$ belonging to the eigenvalue λ_n has exactly n zeros in the interval $a < x < b$, and is uniquely determined up to a constant factor.*

Only the last assertion wants verification. Any two solutions of (1) which satisfy the same initial condition $\alpha u(a) + \alpha' u'(a) = 0$ are linearly dependent, by the Uniqueness Theorem of Chapter 2, § 2.

EXERCISES E

1. Show that, for a regular S-L system, if $q(x)$ is increased to $q_1(x) > q(x)$, each nth eigenvalue of the new system is smaller than that of the old.
2. Show that, for a regular S-L system, if $\rho(x)$ is increased to $\rho_1(x) > \rho(x)$, all positive eigenvalues decrease and any negative eigenvalue increases.
3. Derive an analog of the Prüfer system for the variables defined by

$$u = R \cos \phi, \qquad Pu' = R \sin \phi.$$

4. For regular S-L systems with two sets of endpoint conditions, (30) and

$$\alpha_1 u(a) + \alpha_1' u'(a) = 0, \qquad \beta u(b) + \beta_1' u'(b) = 0,$$

show that, if $\alpha_1'/\alpha_1 < \alpha'/\alpha$, the eigenvalues of the second system are smaller than the corresponding eigenvalues of the first.
5. (a) Given $(Pu')' + Qu = 0$, and $(P_1 v')' + Q_1 v = 0$, $P_1(x) > 0$, $Q_1(x)$ continuous, establish *Picone's identity*.

$$\int_a^b (Q_1(x) - Q(x))u(x)\,dx + \int_a^b (P(x) - P_1(x))u'(x)^2\,dx$$

$$+ \int_a^b P_1(x)\left[u'(x) - \frac{u(x)v'(x)}{v(x)} \right]^2 dx = 0,$$

where $u(a) = u(b) = 0$ and $v(x) \neq 0$ in $[a, b]$.
(b) Infer the Sturm Comparison Theorem from Picone's Identity.
6*. (Szegö's Comparison Theorem) Under the hypothesis of the Sturm Comparison Theorem for $a < x < b$, $P \equiv P_1$, $Q \not\equiv Q_1$, let $u(x) > 0$, $u_1(x) > 0$ for $a < x < b$ and $\lim_{x \to a} P(x)[u'u_1 - uu_1'] = 0$. Show that, if $u(b) = 0$, there is an x_2 in (a, b) such that $u_1(x_2) = 0$.

9   The Liouville normal form

By changes of dependent and independent variables of the form

$$u = y(x)w, \qquad t = \int h(x)\,dx; \qquad y > 0, \quad h > 0, \tag{33}$$

we can simplify S-L equations (1) considerably. If the functions y and h are positive and continuous in the given interval, the first substitution leaves the location of zeros unchanged, while the second one distorts the range of the independent variable, preserving the order, and leaves the number of zeros of a solution in corresponding intervals unchanged. The equivalent DE in w and t is obtained from the identity $d/dx = h(x)\,d/dt$, which is obtained from the second of equations (33). When substituted into the S-L equation (1), this identity gives

$$0 = h(hp(yw)_t)_t + (\lambda\rho - q)yw$$

$$= h\{pyhw_{tt} + [(hp)_t\,y + 2hpy_t]w_t + (hpy_t)_t\,w\} + (\lambda\rho - q)yw.$$

Dividing through by the coefficient pyh^2 of w_{tt}, we obtain the equivalent DE (for $h,\,y \in \mathscr{C}^2$),

$$w_{tt} + (pyh)^{-1}[(hp)_t\,y + 2hpy_t]w_t$$

$$+ [(pyh)^{-1}(hpy_t)_t + h^{-2}p^{-1}(\lambda\rho - q)]w = 0.$$

The term $\lambda(\rho/ph^2)w$ reduces to λw if and only if $h^2 = \rho/p$. The coefficient of w_t vanishes if and only if $(hp)_t/hp = -2y_t/y$, which can be achieved by choosing $y^2 = (hp)^{-1}$. Therefore, a simplified equivalent DE in w and t is obtained by choosing

$$u = w/\sqrt[4]{p(x)\rho(x)}, \qquad t = \int\sqrt{\rho(x)/p(x)}\,dx. \tag{34}$$

This substitution is the *reduction* to *Liouville normal form*. Since p and ρ are positive throughout the interval of definition (cf. § 1), this change of variables makes $h(x)$ and $y(x)$ positive and of class $\mathscr{C}^2$ whenever p and ρ are of class $\mathscr{C}^2$.

■ **THEOREM 6.** *Liouville's substitution* (34) *transforms the S-L equation* (1) *with coefficient functions* p, $\rho \in \mathscr{C}^2$ *and* $q \in \mathscr{C}$ *into the normal form*

$$\frac{d^2w}{dt^2} + [\lambda - \hat{q}(t)]w = 0, \tag{35}$$

where

$$\hat{q} = \frac{q}{\rho} + (p\rho)^{-1/4}\frac{d^2}{dt^2}[(p\rho)^{1/4}]. \tag{36}$$

Evaluating the second derivative in (36) and using the identity $d/dt = (p/\rho)^{1/2}d/dx$, we get the alternative rational form

$$\hat{q} = \frac{q}{\rho} + \frac{p}{4\rho}\left[\left(\frac{p'}{p}\right)' + \left(\frac{\rho'}{\rho}\right)' + \frac{3}{4}\left(\frac{p'}{p}\right)^2 + \frac{1}{2}\left(\frac{p'}{p}\right)\left(\frac{\rho'}{\rho}\right) - \frac{1}{4}\left(\frac{\rho'}{\rho}\right)^2\right]. \tag{36'}$$

If the DE (1) is defined in $a \le x < b$, and t is the definite integral $t = \int_a^x \sqrt{\rho(s)/p(s)}\,ds$, then the equivalent DE (35) is defined in the interval $[0, c)$, where $c = \int_a^b \sqrt{\rho(x)/p(x)}\,dx$. An S-L equation (1) with p, $\rho \in \mathscr{C}^2$ and $q \in \mathscr{C}$ is transformed by Liouville's substitution into an S-L equation (35) with $\hat{q} \in \mathscr{C}$, since the denominator in (36) remains bounded away from 0.

■ COROLLARY 1. *Liouville's reduction* (34) *transforms regular* S-L *systems into regular* S-L *systems, separated and periodic boundary conditions into separated and periodic boundary conditions. The transformed system has the same eigenvalues as the original system.*

Let $u(x)$ and $v(x)$ be transformed into the functions $f(t)$ and $g(t)$ by Liouville's reduction (34). From the identity

$$\int_0^c f(t)g(t)\,dt = \int_a^b u(x)v(x)\sqrt{p(x)\rho(x)}\,\sqrt{\frac{\rho(x)}{p(x)}}\,dx = \int_a^b u(x)v(x)\rho(x)\,dx, \quad (37)$$

we infer the following result

■ COROLLARY 2. *Liouville's reduction* (34) *transforms functions orthogonal with weight ρ into orthogonal functions with unit weight.*

The Bessel equation (3) of Example 2, § 1,

$$(xu')' + \left(k^2 x - \frac{n^2}{x}\right)u = 0, \quad (38)$$

is the special case $p = \rho = x$, $q = n^2/x$ of the DE (1). Hence Liouville's reduction (34) is $u = w/\sqrt{x}$ and $x = t$, which leads to the equivalent DE

$$\frac{d^2 w}{dx^2} + \left[k^2 - \frac{n^2 - 1/4}{x^2}\right]w = 0, \qquad w = x^{1/2}u.$$

If $n = \frac{1}{2}$, this is the trigonometric DE $w'' + k^2 w = 0$, having a basis of solutions $\cos kx$ and $\sin kx$ $(k = 1, 2, 3, \ldots)$. Since $J_{1/2}(0) = 0$, it follows that $J_{1/2}(x)$ is a constant multiple of $(\sin x)/\sqrt{x}$.

EXERCISES F

1. (a) Show that the self-adjoint form of the Hermite DE (15) is the S-L equation

$$[e^{-x^2}u']' + \lambda e^{-x^2}u = 0.$$

   (b) Show that the Liouville normal form of this is the S-L equation (17) for the Hermite functions.

2. Show that the Liouville normal form of the self-adjoint form of the Jacobi DE is, for $x = \cos t$,

$$w_{tt} + [(\tfrac{1}{4} - \alpha^2)/4\sin^2(t/2) + (\tfrac{1}{4} - \beta^2)/4\cos^2(t/2) + (n + (\alpha + \beta + 1)/2)^2]w = 0.$$

3. Show that the self-adjoint form of the hypergeometric DE is the singular S-L equation

$$[x^\gamma(1-x)^{\alpha+\beta+1-\gamma}u']' - [\alpha\beta x^{\gamma-1}(1-x)^{\alpha+\beta-\gamma}]u = 0.$$

What is the Liouville normal form for this DE?

4. Compute the Liouville normal form for the Legendre DE, setting $x = -\cos t$, $-\pi < t < 0$.

5*. Show that every solution of the Legendre DE is square-integrable on $[-1, 1]$ and satisfies the endpoint conditions $\lim_{x \to \pm 1}(1 - x^2)u(x) = 0$.

6*. The Laguerre DE is $xu'' + (1 - x)u' + \lambda u = 0$. Show that its self-adjoint form is the S-L equation $[xe^{-x}u']' + \lambda e^{-x}u = 0$. What is its Liouville normal form?

7*. Show that the Legendre polynomial $P_n(x)$ has exactly n zeros. [HINT: Reduce the Legendre DE to Liouville normal form and apply Exercise E6.]

8*. If $x_1 = \cos t_1, \dots, x_n = \cos t_n$ are the zeros of $P_n(x)$, $x_j < x_{j+1}$, show that $2\pi(j - 1)/(2n + 1) < t_j < 2\pi j/(2n + 1)$ for $2 \leqq j \leqq n$. [HINT: Use the Liouville normal form and Exercise E6.]

10   Modified Prüfer substitution

By applying a modification of the Prüfer substitution to the Liouville normal form of an S-L system, we can obtain asymptotic formulas for the nth eigenfunction $u_n(x)$, valid for large n.

Using the Liouville substitution, any regular S-L system can be transformed into a regular S-L system consisting of the equation

$$u'' + [\lambda - q(x)]u = u'' + Q(x)u = 0, \qquad Q(x) = \lambda - q(x), \qquad (39)$$

and separated boundary conditions of the same form

$$\alpha u(a) + \alpha' u'(a) = 0. \qquad \beta u(b) + \beta' u'(b) = 0. \qquad (40)$$

The constants α, α', β, β' are usually changed, but we still have $\alpha^2 + \alpha'^2 \neq 0$ and $\beta^2 + \beta'^2 \neq 0$. By Theorem 6, Corollary 1, the eigenvalues of this system are the same as those of the original system, and the eigenfunctions are obtained from those for the Liouville normal form through the Liouville substitution. To study the distribution of eigenvalues and magnitude of the eigenfunctions, it therefore suffices to treat the system (39), (40). In §§ 10–11, we shall use mainly (40).

We shall assume from now on that $Q(x) > 0$ for $a \leq x \leq b$, that is, that $\lambda > q(x)$ and $Q \in \mathscr{C}^1$. We introduce the functions $R(x, \lambda)$ and $\phi(x, \lambda)$, the *modified amplitude* and *modified phase*, which are defined in the terms of a given solution $u(x, \lambda)$ of (39) by the equations

$$u = \frac{R}{\sqrt[4]{Q}} \sin \phi, \qquad u' = R\sqrt[4]{Q} \cos \phi. \qquad (41)$$

These equations constitute the *modified Prüfer* system for the DE (39).

We shall now derive a pair of DE's for R and ϕ which are equivalent to (39). We have†

$$\cot \phi = \frac{1}{\sqrt{Q}} \frac{u'}{u}, \qquad R^2 = \sqrt{Q}\, u^2 + \frac{1}{\sqrt{Q}}\, u'^2. \qquad (42)$$

---

† When $u \neq 0$. When $u = 0$, set $\tan \phi = \sqrt{Q}\, u/u'$ and proceed similarly.

Differentiating the first of these equations, we obtain (using $u'' = -Qu$)

$$(\csc^2 \phi)\phi' = \frac{Qu^2 + u'^2}{Q^{1/2}u^2} + \frac{1}{2}\frac{Q'}{Q^{3/2}}\frac{u'}{u}.$$

Using the second equation, this simplifies to

$$(\csc^2 \phi)\phi' = \frac{R^2}{u^2} + \frac{1}{2}\frac{Q'}{Q}\cot \phi$$

and, multiplying by $\sin^2 \phi$ and simplifying,

$$\phi' = Q^{1/2} + \frac{1}{4}\frac{Q'}{Q}\sin 2\phi \tag{43}$$

To derive the DE satisfied by R, differentiate the second equation in (42), obtaining the identity

$$2RR' = 2Q^{-1/2}(Quu' + u'u'') + (Q'/2Q)(Q^{1/2}u^2 - Q^{-1/2}u'^2).$$

The first term vanishes since $u'' = -Qu$, leaving the DE

$$\frac{R'}{R} = \frac{Q'}{4Q}(\sin^2 \phi - \cos^2 \phi) = \frac{-Q'}{4Q}\cos 2\phi. \tag{44}$$

In terms of λ and q, the *modified Prüfer system* is

$$\phi' = \sqrt{\lambda - q} + \frac{q'}{4(\lambda - q)}\sin 2\phi, \tag{45a}$$

$$\frac{R'}{R} = \frac{q'}{4(\lambda - q)}\cos 2\phi. \tag{45b}$$

Clearly, to every nontrivial solution of (39) there corresponds a solution of the modified Prüfer system, and conversely. Furthermore, we know that $R > 0$, unless R vanishes identically.

Equations (45a) and (45b) determine the asymptotic behavior of the solutions of (39) as $\lambda \to \infty$. The fundamental result is the following.

■ **Theorem 7.** *Let $\phi(x, \lambda)$ and $R(x, \lambda)$ be solutions of the system* (45a) *and* (45b), *where $q(x) \in \mathscr{C}^1$ is bounded. Then, as $\lambda \to \infty$,*

$$\phi(x, \lambda) = \phi(a, \lambda) + \sqrt{\lambda}(x - a) + O(1)/\sqrt{\lambda} \tag{46}$$

and

$$R(x, \lambda) = R(a, \lambda) + O(1)/\lambda. \tag{47}$$

Intuitively, Theorem 7 states that for large λ the modified phase ϕ is approximately a linear function of $\sqrt{\lambda}$, and the modified amplitude function R is approximately constant.

The symbol $O(1)$.   The symbol $O(1)$ used here and below signifies a function $f(x, \lambda)$ of x and λ, defined for all sufficiently large λ, which is uniformly bounded for $a \leq x \leq b$ as $\lambda \to \infty$. Hence, $O(1)/\lambda^s$ signifies a function $f(x, \lambda)$ such that $\lambda^s f(x, \lambda)$ is uniformly bounded. The symbol $O(1)/\lambda^s$ is also often written $O(\lambda^{-s})$, as has been done in analogous contexts in Chapters 7 and 8.

The formula $f(x, \lambda) = O(1)$, where f is a given function, is not an ordinary equation. Thus, to write $O(1) = f(x, \lambda)$ would be meaningless since $O(1)$ is not a function. The formula means simply that f remains uniformly *bounded* for all x as $\lambda \to \infty$, and that no other property of the function f is needed for the purposes at hand. Using this definition, the following important properties of the symbol $O(1)$ can be easily verified:

$$O(1) + O(1) = O(1); \qquad O(1)\,O(1) = O(1); \qquad \int_a^b O(1)\,dx = O(1)$$

for any finite a, b. Again, if α and β are real numbers with $\alpha \leq \beta$, then $O(1)/\lambda^\alpha + O(1)/\lambda^\beta = O(1)/\lambda^\alpha$. Finally, if $q(x)$ is any bounded function of x, then by Taylor's formula we have, as $\lambda \to \infty$,

$$[\lambda - q(x)]^\alpha = \lambda^\alpha [1 - q(x)/\lambda]^\alpha = \lambda^\alpha - \alpha q(x)\lambda^{\alpha-1} + O(1)\lambda^{\alpha-2}.$$

The preceding formulas will be used freely in the computations below.

Proof — For all λ for which $|q(x)| < \lambda$ on $[a, b]$, we have as above,

$$\frac{q'}{\lambda - q} = \frac{q'}{\lambda}\Bigl(1 + \frac{O(1)}{\lambda}\Bigr) = \frac{q'}{\lambda} + \frac{O(1)}{\lambda^2}.$$

$$\sqrt{\lambda - q} = \sqrt{\lambda}\Bigl(1 - \frac{q}{\lambda}\Bigr)^{1/2} = \sqrt{\lambda} - \frac{q}{2\sqrt{\lambda}} + \frac{O(1)}{\lambda^{3/2}}.$$

We now compare the solutions of the DE's (45a) and (45b) with the solutions $\phi_1(a, \lambda) = \phi(a, \lambda) + \sqrt{\lambda}(x - a)$ and $R_1(x, \lambda) \equiv R_1(a)$ of

$$\phi' = \sqrt{\lambda} \qquad \text{and} \qquad (\log R)' = 0,$$

using Theorem 3 of Chapter 6. In making this comparison, we set $\epsilon = O(1)/\sqrt{\lambda}$, and replace **x** and **y** with the functions $\phi(x, \lambda)$ and $\phi_1(x, \lambda)$, respectively. If $\phi_1(a, \lambda) = \phi(a, \lambda)$, the inequality (7) of Chapter 6 gives $|\phi(x, \lambda) - \phi_1(x, \lambda)| \leq O(1)/\sqrt{\lambda}$, and since $\phi_1(x, \lambda) = \phi(a, \lambda) + \sqrt{\lambda}(x - a)$, equation (46) follows.

Similarly, to derive (47), compare $R(x, \lambda)$ with $R_1(x, \lambda)$, using the identity $e^{O(1)/\lambda} = 1 + O(1)/\lambda$, obtained from Taylor's formula.

11*   The asymptotic behavior of Bessel functions

We shall now use the modified Prüfer substitution to study the asymptotic behavior of solutions of the Bessel DE (3) as $x \to \infty$. The substitution $u = w/\sqrt{x}$ reduces (3) to the Liouville normal form

$$w'' + [1 - (M/x^2)]w = 0, \qquad 0 < x < \infty, \qquad M = n^2 - \tfrac{1}{4}, \qquad (48)$$

whose solutions are $w(x) = \sqrt{x}\, Z_n(x)$, where $Z_n(x)$ is a solution of the Bessel DE (see (38)). The modified Prüfer system for (48) is obtained by setting $Q(x) = 1 - M/x^2$ in (43) and (44). This gives

$$\phi'(x) = \sqrt{1 - \frac{M}{x^2}} + \frac{M \sin 2\phi}{2(x^3 - Mx)}, \qquad (49a)$$

$$\frac{R'(x)}{R(x)} = \frac{-M \cos 2\phi}{2(x^3 - Mx)}. \qquad (49b)$$

Expanding the right sides of these equations for large x, and using $(1 - M/x^2)^{1/2} = 1 - M/2x^2 + O(1)/x^4$, we have, as $x \to \infty$,

$$\phi'(x) = 1 - \frac{1}{2}\frac{M}{x^2} + \frac{O(1)}{x^3}, \qquad \frac{R'(x)}{R(x)} = \frac{O(1)}{x^3}.$$

Here $O(1)$ denotes a function of x which remains bounded as $x \to \infty$. Integrating the first of these equations between any $x > \sqrt{M}$ and $y > x$, we obtain

$$\phi(x) - \phi(y) = x - y - M/2x - M/2y + O(1)/x^2.$$

Keeping x fixed and letting $y \to \infty$, we find that $\phi_\infty = \lim_{y \to \infty}[y - \phi(y)]$ is finite. This gives $\phi(x) = \phi_\infty + x - M/(2x) + O(1)/x^2$.

If $\sqrt{M} < x < y$, integration of the second equation gives, similarly, $\log R(x) - \log R(y) = O(1)/x^2$. Taking exponentials and letting $y \to \infty$, we get

$$R(x) = R_\infty \exp [O(1)/x^2] = R_\infty + O(1)/x^2,$$

where $R_\infty = \lim_{y \to \infty} R(y)$.

It follows that every solution of the Bessel DE (48) has the asymptotic form

$$Z_n(x) = x^{-1/2}\left[R_\infty + \frac{O(1)}{x^2} \right] \sin \left(\phi_\infty + x - \frac{M}{2x} + \frac{O(1)}{x^2} \right).$$

Since $\sin (A + O(1)/x^2) = \sin A + O(1)/x^2$, the preceding display can be rewritten as

$$Z_n(x) = R_\infty x^{-1/2} \sin (x + \phi_\infty - M/2x) + O(1)/x^{5/2}.$$

The solution Z_n is uniquely determined by the constants R_∞ and ϕ_∞, for if two solutions had the same asymptotic amplitude R_∞ and phase ϕ_∞, their difference would be a solution having modified amplitude $R(x) = O(1)/x^{5/2}$. Since

$$R(x) = R_\infty \exp\left[O(1)/x^2\right],$$

this would imply $R \equiv u \equiv 0$. Setting $x_\infty = \pi/2 + \phi_\infty$, this proves

■ THEOREM 8. *To every nontrivial solution of the Bessel DE (3), there corresponds an asymptotic phase constant x_∞ and a limiting modified amplitude R_∞. The solution is uniquely determined by x_∞ and R_∞; every solution $Z_n(x)$ of Bessel's DE can be expressed as $x \to \infty$ in the form*

$$Z_n(x) = \frac{R_\infty}{\sqrt{x}} \cos\left(x + x_\infty - \frac{(n^2 - 1/4)}{2x}\right) + \frac{O(1)}{x^{5/2}}. \tag{50}$$

For the Bessel function $J_n(x)$, it can be shown that $x_\infty = n\pi/2 + \pi/4$ and $R_\infty = \sqrt{2/\pi}$. The Neumann function $Y_n(x)$ is defined by the conditions $x_\infty = n\pi/2 + 3\pi/4$ and $R_\infty = \sqrt{2/\pi}$. Thus, the Neumann function $Y_n(x)$ is defined by the condition that it has the same asymptotic amplitude as $J_n(x)$, with an asymptotic phase lag of $\pi/2$ radians.

That is, the asymptotic relation between $J_n(x)$ and $Y_n(x)$ is, for large positive x, the same as that between $\cos x$ and $\sin x$. The *Hankel function* $H_n(x) = J_n(x) + i Y_n(x)$ is, therefore, analogous to the complex exponential function $e^{ix} = \cos x + i \sin x$.

12 Distribution of eigenvalues

The asymptotic distribution of the eigenvalues of a regular S-L system is determined by the boundary conditions; the case of the trigonometric DE $u'' + \lambda u = 0$ is typical. For the boundary conditions $u(a) = u(b) = 0$, the nth eigenfunction is $\sin[n\pi(x - a)/(b - a)]$ and the nth eigenvalue is $\lambda_n = n^2\pi^2/(b - a)^2$, $n = 1, 2, 3, \ldots$. For $u(a) = u'(b) = 0$, similarly, $u_n(x) = \sin\sqrt{\lambda_n}(x - a)$, where $\lambda_n = (n + \frac{1}{2})^2\pi^2/(b - a)^2$. For $u'(a) = u'(b) = 0$, the $(n + 1)$st eigenfunction is $\cos\sqrt{\lambda_n}(x - a)$, where $\lambda_n = n^2\pi^2/(b - a)^2$ and $n = 0, 1, 2, \ldots$.

We will treat below in detail the case of separated endpoint conditions (2) with $\alpha'\beta' \neq 0$. We will show that $\sqrt{\lambda_n} = [n\pi/(b - a)] + O(1)/n$ in this case, $n = 0, 1, 2, \ldots$. That is, unless $\alpha' = 0$ or $\beta' = 0$ in (40), the asymptotic behavior of the eigenvalues and eigenfunctions is similar to that for $u'' + \lambda u = 0$, with the endpoint conditions $\alpha = \beta = 0$.

■ THEOREM 9. *For the regular S-L system (39)-(40), let $\alpha'\beta' \neq 0$. Then the eigenvalues λ_n are given, as $n \to \infty$, by the formula*

$$\sqrt{\lambda_n} = \frac{n\pi}{b-a} + \frac{O(1)}{n}, \qquad n = 0, 1, 2, \ldots. \tag{51}$$

Here $O(1)$ denotes a function of n which is uniformly bounded for all integers $n \geq 0$.

Proof — Let $A = -\alpha/\alpha'$ and $B = -\beta/\beta'$. By assumption, A and B are finite. Choose a solution $\phi(x, \lambda)$ satisfying the initial condition

$$\cot \phi(a, \lambda) = \frac{A}{\sqrt{\lambda - q(a)}}, \qquad -0 \leq \phi(a, \lambda) < \pi. \tag{52}$$

According to (41), the solution $u(x, \lambda)$ corresponding to ϕ will be an eigenfunction if and only if

$$\cot \phi(b, \lambda) = \frac{B}{\sqrt{\lambda - q(b)}}. \tag{53}$$

Condition (52) can be simplified by expanding arccot x around $x = \pi/2$ to a first-order approximation in $1/\sqrt{\lambda}$. This gives, as $\lambda \to \infty$,

$$\phi(a, \lambda) = \frac{\pi}{2} + \frac{A}{\sqrt{\lambda}} + \frac{O(1)}{\lambda^{3/2}}. \tag{54}$$

Condition (53) can be simplified by a similar expansion. For the $(n+1)$st eigenvalue, the modified phase function changes asymptotically to $n\pi + O(1)/\sqrt{\lambda_n}$. This gives, for $x = A/\sqrt{\lambda - q(a)}$,

$$\phi(b, \lambda_n) = \frac{\pi}{2} + n\pi + \frac{O(1)}{\sqrt{\lambda_n}}. \tag{54'}$$

Subtracting (54) from (54'), and comparing with (46) of Theorem 7, we obtain the equation

$$\phi(b, \lambda_n) - \phi(a, \lambda_n) = n\pi + \frac{O(1)}{\sqrt{\lambda_n}} = \sqrt{\lambda_n}\,(b - a) + \frac{O(1)}{\sqrt{\lambda_n}}. \tag{55}$$

Letting $\lambda_n \to \infty$, we obtain $\lim_{n \to \infty} n\pi \lambda_n^{-1/2} = (b - a)$, or $\sqrt{\lambda_n} = K_n n$, where K_n is some sequence of numbers tending to $\pi/(b - a)$. Substituting into (55), we obtain

$$\sqrt{\lambda_n} = \frac{n\pi}{b-a} + \frac{O(1)}{\sqrt{\lambda_n}} = \frac{n\pi}{b-a} + \frac{O(1)}{n}, \qquad \text{q.e.d.}$$

■ COROLLARY. *If λ_n is the sequence of nonzero eigenvalues of a regular S-L system, then $\sum_{n=0}^{\infty} \lambda_n^{-2} < \infty$.*

13 Normalized eigenfunctions

A square-integrable function u on an interval $a < x < b$ is *normalized* relative to a weight function ρ when

$$\int_a^b u^2(x)\,\rho(x)\,dx = 1.$$

In the case of the eigenfunctions of (39), $\rho(x) \equiv 1$. Our aim is to show that the normalized eigenfunctions of (39) and (40) behave approximately like cosine functions: provided that $\alpha'\beta' \neq 0$. (The cases, $\alpha = 0$ and $\beta = 0$ are similar, after phase-shifts of $\pi/2$ in (54) and (54').))

■ THEOREM 10.   *Let $u_n(x)$ $(n = 0, 1, 2, \ldots)$ be the sequence of normalized eigenfunctions of the regular S-L system (39)–(40), with $\alpha'\beta' \neq 0$. Then*

$$u_n(x) = \sqrt{\frac{2}{b-a}}\cos\frac{n\pi(x-a)}{b-a} + \frac{O(1)}{n}. \tag{56}$$

The proof of this theorem will be carried out in three steps. For an eigenfunction $u_n(x)$, with eigenvalue λ_n, we have, by (41),

$$u_n(x) = \frac{R(x, \lambda_n)}{\sqrt[4]{\lambda_n - q(x)}}\sin\phi(x, \lambda_n), \qquad a \leq x \leq b. \tag{57}$$

In order to obtain formula (56) we obtain asymptotic expressions separately in terms of n for each of the three factors appearing in (57). This is done in the following three lemmas.

■ LEMMA 1.   *Let $\phi(x, \lambda)$ be as in the proof of Theorem 9. Then, as $\lambda \to \infty$,*

$$\int_a^b \sin^2\phi(x, \lambda)\,dx = \frac{b-a}{2} + \frac{O(1)}{\lambda^{1/2}}. \tag{58}$$

Proof — Using $\phi(x, \lambda)$ as the variable of integration in (55), and, recalling from (46) that $dx/d\phi = (d\phi/dx)^{-1} = -\lambda^{-1/2} + O(1)\lambda^{-3/2}$, we have

$$\int_a^b \sin^2\phi(x, \lambda)\,dx = \int_{\phi(a,\lambda)}^{\phi(b,\lambda)} \sin^2\phi\,\frac{dx}{d\phi}\,d\phi$$

$$= (\lambda^{-1/2} + O(1)\lambda^{-3/2})\int_{\phi(a,\lambda)}^{\phi(b,\lambda)} \sin^2\phi\,d\phi.$$

The last integral can be evaluated explicitly. Apply Theorem 7, to obtain

$$\int_{\phi(a,\lambda)}^{\phi(b,\lambda)} \sin^2\phi\,d\phi = \left[\frac{\phi}{2} - \frac{\sin 2\phi}{4}\right]_{\phi(a,\lambda)}^{\phi(b,\lambda)} = \frac{\lambda^{1/2}(b-a)}{2} + O(1).$$

Substituting into the previous displayed formula and simplifying, we obtain (58).

A second step toward our result is the following Lemma.

■ **LEMMA 2.**   *Let $u(x, \lambda)$ be a solution of (39). Then, as $\lambda \to \infty$,*

$$\left(\int_a^b u^2(x)\, dx \right)^{1/2} = R(a, \lambda)\lambda^{-1/4} \sqrt{\frac{b-a}{2}} \left(1 + \frac{O(1)}{\lambda^{1/2}} \right) + \frac{O(1)}{\lambda^{5/4}}. \qquad (59)$$

Proof — Expressing u in terms of R by (41), and then expanding R as in Theorem 7, formula (47), we have

$$\int_a^b u^2(x)\, dx = \left[R(a, \lambda) + \frac{O(1)}{\lambda} \right]^2 \int_a^b [\lambda - q(x)]^{-1/2} \sin^2 \phi \, dx.$$

Since $(\lambda - q)^{-1/2} = \lambda^{-1/2} + O(1)\lambda^{-3/2}$, this gives, after simplifying and using (58),

$$\int_a^b u^2(x)\, dx = \left[R(a, \lambda) + \frac{O(1)}{\lambda} \right]^2 (\lambda^{-1/2} + O(1)\lambda^{-3/2}) \left(\frac{b-a}{2} + O(1)\lambda^{-1/2} \right)$$

$$= \left[R(a, \lambda) + \frac{O(1)}{\lambda} \right]^2 \left(\frac{b-a}{2\lambda^{1/2}} + \frac{O(1)}{\lambda} \right).$$

Hence, taking square roots,

$$\left(\int_a^b u^2(x)\, dx \right)^{1/2} = \left(R(a, \lambda) + \frac{O(1)}{\lambda} \right) \left(\frac{b-a}{2\lambda^{1/2}} + \frac{O(1)}{\lambda} \right)^{1/2}$$

$$= \frac{R(a, \lambda)}{\lambda^{1/4}} \sqrt{\frac{b-a}{2}} \left(1 + \frac{O(1)}{\lambda^{1/2}} \right) + \frac{O(1)}{\lambda^{5/4}}, \quad \text{q.e.d.}$$

■ **COROLLARY.**   *If, in addition, $\int_a^b u^2(x, \lambda)\, dx = 1$, then*

$$R(a, \lambda) = \sqrt{\frac{2}{b-a}} \, \lambda^{1/4}[1 + O(1)\lambda^{-1/2}]. \qquad (60)$$

Proof — Formula (59) gives the following condition on the amplitude function of a normalized solution:

$$1 - \frac{O(1)}{\lambda^{5/4}} = \frac{R(a, \lambda)}{\lambda^{1/4}} \sqrt{\frac{b-a}{2}} \left(1 + \frac{O(1)}{\lambda^{1/2}} \right).$$

Solving for R, and taking the asymptotic form of the quotient, we get (60), q.e.d.

■ LEMMA 3. *Let* λ_n *be the nth eigenfunction* $(\lambda_0 \leqq \lambda_1 < \lambda_2 < \cdots)$ *of the* S-L *system* (39), (40). *Then, as* $n \to \infty$, *unless* $\alpha'\beta' = 0$,

$$\sin \phi(x, \lambda_n) = \cos \frac{n\pi(x-a)}{b-a} + O(1)\lambda_n^{-1/2}. \qquad (61)$$

Proof — By Theorem 7, (46), we have

$$\phi(x, \lambda_n) = \phi(a, \lambda_n) + \sqrt{\lambda_n}(x-a) + O(1)/\sqrt{\lambda_n}.$$

Moreover by (54), $\phi(a, \lambda_n) = \pi/2 + O(1)/\sqrt{\lambda_n}$. Substituting back into the preceding formula, we get

$$\sin \phi(x, \lambda_n) = \sin \left[\sqrt{\lambda_n}(x-a) + \pi/2\right] + O(1)/\sqrt{\lambda_n}. \qquad (62)$$

$$= \cos\left[\sqrt{\lambda_n}(x-a)\right] + O(1)/n.$$

We now apply Theorem 9 to this formula. By formula (51) and the mean value theorem, we have

$$\cos\left[\sqrt{\lambda_n}(x-a)\right] - \cos\left[n\pi(x-a)/(b-a)\right] = O(1)n^{-1} = O(1)\lambda_n^{-1/2}.$$

Substituting into the right-hand side of (62), we obtain (61), q.e.d.

The proof of Theorem 10 can now be completed as follows. Of the three factors in equality (57), the first can be simplified by taking the first-order approximation $(\lambda - q)^{-1/4} = \lambda^{-1/4} + O(1)\lambda^{-5/4}$. The factor $R(x, \lambda_n)$ is estimated by the Corollary to Lemma 2, and the factor $\sin \phi(x, \lambda_n)$ is estimated by Lemma 3. Substituting all these expressions into (57) and simplifying, we obtain

$$u_n(x) = \sqrt{\frac{2}{b-a}} \cos\left[\frac{n\pi(x-a)}{b-a}\right] + O(1)\lambda_n^{-1/2}.$$

Since $\lambda_n^{-1/2} = O(1)n^{-1}$, this gives Theorem 10.

EXERCISES G

1. For any DE $u'' + u + \rho(x)u = 0$ with $\rho(x) = O(x^{-2})$ as $x \to +\infty$, show that, for every solution $u(x)$, constants A and x_1 can be found for which

$$u(x) = A \cos(x - x_1) + O(x^{-1}) \qquad \text{as} \quad x \to \infty.$$

2*. Establish the following formula for Legendre polynomials:

$$P_n(\cos \theta) = \frac{A}{(\sin \theta)^{1/2}} \cos\left[\left(n + \frac{1}{2}\right)\theta - \frac{\pi}{4}\right] + O(n^{-3/2}) \qquad \text{for} \quad 0 < \theta < \pi,$$

for some constant A. [HINT: Find a DE satisfied by $P_n(\cos \theta)$.]

3. Show that the relative maxima of $x^{1/2}|J_n(x)|$ form an increasing sequence if $0 < n < \frac{1}{2}$ and a decreasing sequence if $n > \frac{1}{2}$.

4*. (Sonin-Polya Theorem) Show that if, in $(Pu')' + Qu = 0$, $P, Q \in \mathscr{C}^1[a, b]$, $Q(x) \neq 0$, and $P(x)Q(x)$ are nondecreasing, the successive maxima of $|u(x)|$ form a nonincreasing sequence, and that equality occurs if and only if $Q(x) = 1/P(x)$ [HINT: Show that the derivative of $\phi(x) = u(x)^2 + P(x)u'(x)^2/Q(x)$ is nonpositive.]

5*. Show that the values of $|P(x)Q(x)|^{1/2}|u(x)|$ at those points where $u'(x) = 0$ are a monotonic increasing or decreasing sequence, according as the values of $P(x)Q(x)$ are decreasing or increasing.

[HINT: Consider $v(x) = P(x)Q(x)\phi(x)$, ϕ as in Exercise 4.]

14 Inhomogeneous equations

Inhomogeneous second-order linear equations, of the form

$$L[u] = p_0(x)u'' + p_1(x)u' + p_2(x)u = f(x), \qquad p_0(x) \neq 0, \qquad p_0(x) \in \mathscr{C}^1,$$

$$(63)$$

subject to *homogeneous* separated endpoint conditions (30), can be solved by use of *Green's functions*. The method of solution generalizes that for *two-endpoint* problems described in Chapter 2, §§ 9, 10. The discussion given there, which covers the case $\alpha' = \beta' = 0$ of (30), can now be reviewed to advantage.

Before introducing Green's functions, we first analyze the problem with *inhomogeneous* separated endpoint conditions:

$$A[u] = \alpha u(a) + \alpha' u'(a) = \alpha_1, \qquad B[u] = \beta u(b) + \beta' u'(b) = \beta_1. \quad (64)$$

Let $U(x)$ be the solution of $L[u] = 0$ satisfying the initial conditions $U(a) = \alpha'$, $U'(a) = -\alpha$; let $V(x)$ be the solution of $L[u] = 0$ satisfying $V(b) = \beta'$, $V'(b) = -\beta$; let $F(x)$ be the solution of $L[u] = f(x)$ satisfying $F(a) = F'(a) = 0$ The existence and uniqueness of these functions follow from Theorem 7, Corollary 2, of Chapter 6, §8. For any constants, c, d, the function

$$w(x) = cU(x) + dV(x) + F(x)$$

satisfies the inhomogeneous DE (63). Moreover, we have

$$A[w] = d(\alpha V(a) + \alpha' V'(a)) = dA[V],$$
$$B[w] = c(\beta U(b) + \beta' U'(b)) + B[F] = cB[U] + B[F]$$

$$(65)$$

If U and V are linearly independent, their Wronskian $W = UV' - VU'$ never vanishes. Hence,

$$A[V] = \alpha V(a) + \alpha' V'(a) = -U'(a)V(a) + U(a)V'(a) \neq 0;$$

similarly, $B[U] = -W(b) \neq 0$. Therefore equations (65) for the unknowns c and d have a unique solution for any values given to $A[w]$ and $B[w]$.

On the other hand, if U and V are linearly dependent, their Wronskian vanishes identically. Hence, $U(x)$ satisfies $A[U] = \alpha\alpha' + \alpha'(-\alpha) = 0$ and $B[U] = 0$. This proves the following theorem.

■ **Theorem 11.**   *Either* DE (63) *has a solution w satisfying the boundary conditions* $A[w] = \alpha_1$ *and* $B[w] = \beta_1$ *for any given constants* α_1 *and* β_1 *or else the homogeneous* DE $L[u] = 0$ *has an eigenfunction with eigenvalue* 0 *satisfying the homogeneous conditions* $A[u] = 0$ *and* $B[u] = 0$.

15   Green's functions

We now show that, in the first case of the preceding theorem, there exists a *Green's function* $G(x, \xi)$ defined for $a \leq x,\ \xi \leq b$, such that the solution of (63) subject to the boundary conditions (30) is given by

$$u(x) = \int_a^b G(x, \xi) f(\xi)\, d\xi = \mathscr{G}[f]. \tag{66}$$

Note that $\mathscr{G}$ is an *integral operator* (Chapter 2, §5) whose kernel is Green's function $G(x, \xi)$.

This result has already been established in Chapter 2, § 10, for the endpoint conditions $u(a) = u(b) = 0$; it will now be generalized to arbitrary *homogeneous* separated endpoint conditions (30): $A[u] = B[u] = 0$.

In this general case, $G(x, \xi)$ can be constructed by the method used in Chapter 2. For each fixed ξ, $G(x, \xi)$ is a solution of the homogeneous DE $L[G] = 0$ on the intervals $[a, \xi]$ and $[\xi, b]$, satisfying the homogeneous endpoint conditions $A[u] = 0$ and $B[u] = 0$, respectively. It is continuous across $x = \xi$ (i.e., across the principal diagonal of the square $a \leq x,\ \xi \leq b$), and its derivative $\partial G/\partial x$ jumps by $1/p_0(x)$ across this diagonal . That is, we have

$$G(x, \xi) = \begin{cases} \epsilon(\xi) U(x) V(\xi), & a \leq x \leq \xi, \\ \epsilon(\xi) V(x) U(\xi), & \xi \leq x \leq b, \end{cases}$$

where the factor $\epsilon(\xi)$ above is chosen to give $\partial G/\partial x$ a jump of $1/p_0(\xi)$ across $x = \xi$:

$$\frac{\partial G}{\partial x}(\xi^+, \xi) - \frac{\partial G}{\partial x}(\xi^-, \xi) = \epsilon(\xi)\{U(\xi) V'(\xi^+) - V(\xi) U'(\xi^-)\} = 1/p_0(\xi).$$

We are therefore led to try the kernel

$$G(x, \xi) = \begin{cases} U(x) V(\xi)/p_0(\xi) W(\xi), & a \leq x \leq \xi, \\ U(\xi) V(x)/p_0(\xi) W(\xi), & \xi \leq x \leq b, \end{cases} \tag{67}$$

where $W = UV' - VU'$ is the Wronskian of U and V.

■ **Theorem 12.**   *Unless* $W \equiv 0$, *equations* (66), (67) *yield for any continuous function f on* $[a, b]$ *a solution* $u(x)$ *of the* DE $L[u] = f(x)$ *which satisfies the boundary conditions* $A[u] = B[u] = 0$.

That is, unless the homogeneous linear boundary-value problem $L[u] = A[u] = B[u] = 0$ admits an eigenfunction, the function defined by (67) is a Green function for the system $L[u] = f$, $A[u] = B[u] = 0$.

The proof is like that given in Chapter 2, § 10. Rewriting (66) as

$$u(x) = \int_a^x G(x, \xi) f(\xi) \, d\xi + \int_x^b G(x, \xi) f(\xi) \, d\xi,$$

and differentiating, we have, by Leibniz' rule,

$$u'(x) = \int_a^x G_x(x, \xi) f(\xi) \, d\xi + \int_x^b G_x(x, \xi) f(\xi) \, d\xi.$$

The endpoint contributions give $G(x, x^-) f(x^-) - G(x, x^+) f(x^+) = 0$; they cancel since $G(x, \xi)$ and f are continuous for $x = \xi$. Differentiating again, we have, by Leibniz' rule,

$$u''(x) = \int_a^x G_{xx}(x, \xi) f(\xi) \, d\xi + G_x(x, x^-) f(x^-)$$
$$+ \int_x^b G_{xx}(x, \xi) f(\xi) \, d\xi - G_x(x, x^+) f(x^+).$$

The two terms corresponding to the contributions from the endpoints come from the sides $x > \xi$ and $x < \xi$ of the diagonal; since f is continuous, their difference is $[G_x(x^+, x) - G_x(x^-, x)] f(x) = f(x)/p_0(x)$. Simplifying, we obtain

$$u''(x) = \int_a^b G_{xx}(x, \xi) f(\xi) \, d\xi + f(x)/p_0(x).$$

From the above identities, we can calculate $L[u]$. It is

$$L[u] = \int_a^b L_x[G(x, \xi)] f(\xi) \, d\xi + f(x) = f(x),$$

where $L_x[G(x, \xi)]$ stands for the sum $p_0 G_{xx} + p_1 G_x + p_2 G$. This sum is zero except on the diagonal $x = \xi$, where it is undefined. This gives the identity (63).

Since $G(x, \xi)$, as a function of x, satisfies the boundary conditions (30) for all ξ, it follows from (66), by differentiating under the integral sign and using Leibniz' Rule again, that u satisfies the same boundary conditions. This completes the proof of the theorem.

In operator language (cf. Chapter 2, §1), we have shown that the operator $f \rightarrow \mathcal{G}[f]$ transforms the space $\mathscr{C}[a, b]$ of continuous functions on the interval $[a, b]$ into the space $\mathscr{C}^2[a, b]$ of functions of class $\mathscr{C}^2$, and that this operator is a *right inverse* of the operator L. That is, we have $L[\mathcal{G}[f]] = f$ for all continuous f. In operator notation, we can write $\mathcal{G} = L^{-1}$.

EXERCISES H

In Exercises 1–5 show that Green's function is as specified.

1. $u'' = f$, $u(0) = u'(1) = 0$;

$$G(x, \xi) = \begin{cases} x & \text{for } x \leqq \xi, \\ \xi & \text{for } x > \xi. \end{cases}$$

2. $u'' = f$, $u(-1) = u(1) = 0$; $G(x, \xi) = -[|x - \xi| + x\xi - 1]/2$.
3. $xu'' + u' = f$, $u(x)$ bounded as $x \to 0$, $u(1) = 0$.

$$G(x, \xi) = \begin{cases} (\log \xi)/x & \text{for } x \leqq \xi, \\ (\log x)/\xi & \text{for } x > \xi. \end{cases}$$

4. $u'' - u = f$, $u(x)$ bounded as $|x| \to \infty$; $G(x, \xi) = -[\exp(-|x - \xi|/2)]/2$.
5. $x^2 u'' - 2xu' + 2u = f$, $u(1) = u(2) = 0$; $G(x, \xi) = (\xi^2 - 2\xi)(x^2 - x)/(-2\xi^3)$ if $x \leqq \xi$; $G(\xi, x) = G(x, \xi)$.
6. Find Green's function for $u'' - u = f$ with $u(-a) = u(a) = 0$. Show that, as $a \to \infty$, it approaches that of Exercise 4.
7. Show that $L[u] + \lambda u = 0$ for nontrivial u, $\lambda \neq 0$ and given homogeneous endpoint conditions (30), if and only if $\mathscr{G}[u] = \mu u$ for $\mu = 1/\lambda$.
8*. Show that Green's function G of a regular S-L system is a symmetric function of x and ξ.

16* The Schroedinger equation

The *Schroedinger equation* of quantum mechanics in one space dimension is the DE

$$\psi'' + (2m/\hbar^2)[E - V(x)]\psi = 0. \tag{68}$$

Physically, the function $V(x)$ has the significance of potential energy; the constant m stands for the mass of the particle; the constant E is an energy parameter; $\hbar = h/2\pi$ is a universal constant, whose numerical value depends on the units used. The "wave function" $\psi(x)$ may be real or complex; $\psi\psi^* \, dx = |\psi|^2 \, dx$ is the probability that the particle under consideration will be "observed" in the interval $(x, x + dx)$. The *eigenvalues* of (68) for varying E are the *energy levels* of the associated physical system.

The DE (68) is precisely the Liouville normal form

$$u'' + [\lambda - q(x)]u = 0 \tag{69}$$

of a general S-L equation, with $\lambda = 2mE/\hbar^2$ and $q = 2mV/\hbar^2$. But, in most physical applications, one is concerned with the *infinite interval* $(-\infty, \infty)$. On this interval, the "endpoint" condition that a solution remain bounded as $x \to \pm\infty$ defines a *singular* S-L system (cf. § 4). In problems involving the Schroedinger equation, it is customary among physicists to define the *spectrum* of this S-L system as the set of all eigenvalues for which eigenfunctions exist. The set of isolated points (if any) in this spectrum is called the *discrete spectrum*; the part (if any) consisting of entire intervals is called the *continuous spectrum*. We shall adopt this suggestive terminology below, but noting that its logical extension to boundary value problems generally is very technical, even for ordinary DE's.†

For regular S-L systems, we have proved that the spectrum is always discrete, and the eigenfunctions are (trivially) square-integrable. We now describe a simple singular S-L system whose spectrum is continuous and whose eigenfunctions are not square-integrable.

EXAMPLE 8.   The S-L system of a *free particle* is

$$u'' + \lambda u = 0, \qquad -\infty < x < +\infty. \tag{70}$$

For every positive number $\lambda > 0$, this DE has two linearly independent bounded solutions $\sin(\sqrt{\lambda}x)$ and $\cos(\sqrt{\lambda}x)$. For $\lambda = 0$, it has the bounded solution $x = 1$, and no other linearly independent eigenfunction. For $\lambda < 0$, it has the linearly independent unbounded solutions $\sinh(\sqrt{\lambda}x)$ and $\cosh(\sqrt{\lambda}x)$, and no nontrivial bounded solution. Hence, the *spectrum* of the free particle is *continuous*: it consists of the half-line $\lambda \geqq 0$.

EXAMPLE 9.   In the case of a *harmonic oscillator*, the potential energy $V(x)$ is a constant multiple of x^2. By a change of unit $x \to kx$, we can reduce the resulting Schroedinger DE to the normal form

$$u'' + (\lambda - x^2)u = 0. \tag{71}$$

Comparing with Example 7 of § 4, we see that this has the eigenfunctions $e^{-x^2/2}H_n(x)$ for $\lambda = 2n + 1$ $(n = 0, 1, 2, \ldots)$. These eigenfunctions are even *square-integrable*.

For any value of λ not an odd positive integer, the recurrence relation $a_{k+2} = (2k - \lambda + 1)a_k/(k + 1)(k + 2)$ satisfied by $H_\lambda(x)$ may be compared with that for the Taylor series $e^{\beta x^2} = \sum \beta^r x^{2r}/(r!)$, namely $c_{2r+2} = \beta c_{2r}/(r + 1)$. Setting $2r = k$, we see that, for all sufficiently large k,

$$a_{k+2}/a_k > c_{k+2}/c_k > 0 \qquad \text{if} \quad \beta < 1.$$

Hence $|H_\lambda(x)| > Be^{\beta x^2} - p_\lambda(x)$, where $B > 0$, $p_\lambda(x)$ is a polynomial, and (say) $\beta = \frac{3}{4}$. It follows that $|e^{-x^2/2}H_\lambda(x)| > Be^{x^2/4} - O(1)$ is *unbounded* unless λ is an odd positive integer.—Finally, if $u(x)$ is any bounded nontrivial solution of (71), the same is true of $u(-x)$ and of $[u(x) + u(-x)]/2$, $[u(x) - u(-x)]/2$. This shows that, if (71) has an eigen-

---

† See, for example, Coddington and Levinson, pp. 252–269.

function, it must have an odd eigenfunction or an even eigenfunction. Since either of these would be defined up to a constant factor by the relation

$$a_{k+2} = (2k - \lambda + 1)a_k/(k+1)(k+2)$$

on its coefficients, we see that the *Hermite functions* $e^{-x^2/2}H_n(x)$ are the *only eigenfunctions* of the harmonic oscillator.

17* The square-well potential

In Example 8, the spectrum is continuous; in Example 9, it is discrete. We now describe a Schroedinger equation whose spectrum is partly continuous and partly discrete.

EXAMPLE 10.   A *square-well* potential is one satisfying $V(x) = -C^2$ on $|x| < a$, and $V(x) = 0$ when $|x| > a$. This leads to the Schroedinger DE with *discontinuous* $q(x)$:

$$u'' + \lambda u = \begin{cases} 0 & \text{on} \quad |x| > a, \\ -C^2 u & \text{on} \quad |x| < a. \end{cases} \tag{72}$$

The eigenfunctions can again be determined explicitly.†

If $u(x)$ is any eigenfunction, then so is $u(-x)$, and so are the even part $[u(x) + u(-x)]/2$ and the odd part $[u(x) - u(-x)]/2$ of $u(x)$. Hence, (72) has a basis of eigenfunctions consisting exclusively of *even* and *odd* eigenfunctions, that is, satisfying $u'(0) = 0$ or $u(0) = 0$.

For $\lambda > 0$, every solution of (72) has the form $A \cos \sqrt{\lambda}\, x + B \sin \sqrt{\lambda}\, x$ for $|x| > a$. Hence, every nontrivial solution of (72) is an eigenfunction and, as in Example 8, the spectrum includes the entire half line $\lambda \geqq 0$.

For $\lambda < -C^2$, on the other hand, the continuation to $|x| > a$ of both the even solution $\cosh (\sqrt{-\lambda - C^2}\, x)$ and the odd solution $\sinh (\sqrt{-\lambda - C^2}\, x)$, from the interval $|x| < a$, can be shown (see Theorem 14 below) to satisfy $u(x) > 0$, $u'(x) > 0$, and $u''(x) > 0$ for all positive x. Hence, they are both unbounded. In summary, the spectrum contains no points on $\lambda < -C^2$: there is no bounded solution with eigenvalue $\lambda < -C^2$.

In the interval $-C^2 < \lambda < 0$, one can show that the spectrum is discrete by working out the implications of the Sturm Oscillation Theorem. The solutions bounded for $x > a$ are the functions $A \exp (-\sqrt{-\lambda}\, x)$

---

† With the usual understanding (Chapter 2, Exercise A14) that a "solution" of (72) is a function $u \in \mathscr{C}^1$ which satisfies (72) and so is of class $\mathscr{C}^2$ where $q(x)$ is continuous.

which satisfy $u'(a)/u(a) = -\sqrt{-\lambda}$. Writing $\mu = \sqrt{\lambda + C^2}$, we see that the even solutions $A \cos \mu x$ of (72) satisfy the same boundary condition $u'(a)/u(a) = -\sqrt{-\lambda}$ if and only if $\mu \tan \mu a = \sqrt{-\lambda}$; the odd solutions $B \sin \mu x$ satisfy it if and only if $\mu \cot \mu a = -\sqrt{-\lambda}$. Solving the preceding transcendental equations graphically, we see that the number of even eigenfunctions and the number of odd eigenfunctions belonging to the discrete spectrum are both approximately equal to aC/π. Moreover, every eigenfunction which corresponds to the discrete spectrum is square-integrable, and conversely.

18*   Mixed spectrum

The preceding example is typical of a wide class of Schroedinger equations—namely, all those having a "potential well" dying out at infinity. We first treat the continuous portion of the spectrum.

■ LEMMA 1.   *In the normalized Schroedinger equation (69), let q be continuous and satisfy $q(x) = B/x + 0(1/x^2)$ as $x \to \infty$ for some constant B. Then, for $\lambda > 0$, every solution has infinitely many zeros and is bounded.*

Proof — The first statement follows from the Sturm Comparison Theorem, comparing with the DE $u'' + \lambda u/2 = 0$.

To prove the second statement, first change the independent variable to $t = \sqrt{\lambda} x$, giving the DE $u_{tt} + Q(t)u = 0$, with $Q(t) = 1 - q(t/\sqrt{\lambda})/\lambda$. Applied to the new DE, the Prüfer substitution (21) gives, by (22),

$$\frac{d\theta}{dt} = Q(t) \sin^2 \theta + \cos^2 \theta = 1 + \frac{A}{t} \sin^2 \theta + \frac{O(1)}{t^2}, \qquad A = -B/\sqrt{\lambda}. \quad (73)$$

Moreover, $r^2 = u^2 + u_t{}^2$ is given by (23'), as

$$r^2 = K^2 \exp\left\{ \int_a^t \left[\frac{A}{s} + O\left(\frac{1}{s^2}\right)\right](\sin 2\theta)\,\frac{ds}{d\theta}\, d\theta \right\} = K^2 \exp\left\{ \int_a^t F(s)\,ds \right\},$$

where $F(s) = (A/s)(\sin 2\theta) + O(1)/s^2$ and the limits of integration refer to s. Using the expression $dt/d\theta = 1 - (A/t) \sin^2 \theta + O(1)/t^2$, derivable from the preceding display, we have

$$\int_a^t F(s)\,ds = \int_a^t \left[\frac{A}{s} + O\left(\frac{1}{s^2}\right)\right] \sin 2\theta\, d\theta.$$

The first term on the right side above can be integrated by parts:

$$\int_a^t F(s)\,ds = \left[-\frac{A}{2s} \cos 2\theta \right]_a^t - \int_a^t \frac{A}{2s^2} \cos 2\theta\, ds + \int_a^t O\left(\frac{1}{s^2}\right) \sin 2\theta\, d\theta.$$

The boundedness of the first two terms on the right side of this equation is obvious; the last term is bounded because $d\theta/ds = 1 + O(1)/s$. Hence, u^2 is bounded because $u^2 \leq r^2 \leq K^2 \exp\{\int_a^t F(s)\, ds\}$.

Combining Lemma 1 with the analogous result for negative x, we obtain

■ **THEOREM 13.** *If* $q \in \mathscr{C}$ *satisfies* $q(x) = A/x + O(1/x^2)$ *as* $x \to +\infty$ *and* $q(x) = B/x + O(1/x^2)$ *as* $x \to -\infty$, *then the spectrum of* (69) *includes the half line* $\lambda > 0$.

As regards the discrete portion of the spectrum, the key result is the following lemma, which characterizes the asymptotic behavior for large x of a wide class of DE's having nonoscillatory solutions, such as the modified Bessel equation of Chapter 9, § 7.

■ **LEMMA 2.** *In the Schroedinger equation* (69), *let* q *be continuous, let* $\lim_{x \to +\infty} q(x) = 0$, *and let* $\lambda = -k^2 < 0$. *For any* ϵ, $0 < \epsilon < k$, *there exist two solutions* $u_1(x)$ *and* $u_2(x)$ *of* (69) *such that, for all sufficiently large* x,

$$e^{(k-\epsilon)x} \leq u_1(x) \leq e^{(k+\epsilon)x}, \qquad e^{(-k-\epsilon)x} \leq u_2(x) \leq e^{(-k+\epsilon)x}. \tag{74}$$

Proof — Choose a so large that $(k - \epsilon)^2 < q(x) - \lambda < (k + \epsilon)^2$ for all $x \geq a$, and let $u_1(x)$ be the solution defined by the initial conditions $u_1(a) = e^{ka}$, $u_1'(a) = ke^{ka}$. Then $\tau(x) = u_1'/u_1$ satisfies $\tau(a) = k$ and the Riccati equation $\tau' = G(x, \tau) = q(x) - \lambda - \tau^2$. For the DE's

$$\rho' = F(x, \rho) = (k - \epsilon)^2 - \rho^2, \qquad \sigma' = H(x, \sigma) = (k + \epsilon)^2 - \sigma^2,$$

it is clear that $F(x, \tau) \leq G(x, \tau) \leq H(x, \tau)$ on the domain $\tau \geq k - \epsilon > 0$. Moreover, the solutions $\rho(x) = k - \epsilon$ and $\sigma(x) = k + \epsilon$ of the displayed DE's satisfy $\rho(a) < \tau(a) < \sigma(a)$. Hence, by the Comparison Theorem of Chapter 1, § 11, we have $k - \epsilon = \rho(x) \leq \tau(x) \leq \sigma(x) = k + \epsilon$. Integrating, we get the first inequality of (74).

We now derive the second inequality. As in Chapter 2, § 3, a linearly independent solution of the DE (69) is given by

$$u_2(x) = 2ku_1(x) \int_x^\infty \frac{ds}{u_1{}^2(s)}.$$

The first inequality of (74), applied to the integral on the right, gives the inequalities

$$\frac{1}{2(k - \epsilon)} e^{-2(k-\epsilon)x} \geq \int_x^\infty \frac{ds}{u_1(s)^2} \geq \frac{1}{2(k + \epsilon)} e^{-2(k+\epsilon)x}.$$

Multiplying through by $2ku_1(x)$, and using (74) again, we get

$$\frac{e^{2\varepsilon x}}{1 - \varepsilon/k}\, e^{-(k-\varepsilon)x} \geqq u_2(x) \geqq \frac{e^{-2\varepsilon x}}{1 + \varepsilon/k}\, e^{-(k+\varepsilon)x}. \tag{75}$$

But, for any η such that $0 < 3\epsilon < \eta < k$ we have, for sufficiently large x,

$$e^{-(k-\eta)x} \geqq \frac{e^{2\varepsilon x}}{1 - \varepsilon/k}\, e^{-(k-\varepsilon)x} \quad \text{and} \quad \frac{e^{-2\varepsilon x}}{1 + \varepsilon/k}\, e^{-(k+\varepsilon)x} \geqq e^{-(k+\eta)x}.$$

Applying these inequalities to (75), we obtain the second formula of (74) with η in place of ε. Since, for any η with $0 < \eta < k$, we can find $\varepsilon = \eta/6$ with $0 < 3\varepsilon < \eta < k$, the proof is complete.

■ COROLLARY 1.   *On* $(0, \infty)$, *let* $q(x)$ *be continuous and satisfy* $\lim_{x \to \infty} q(x) = q_0$. *Then every solution of the Schroedinger equation with* $\lambda < q_0$ *that is bounded on the interval* $(0, \infty)$ *is square-integrable.*

■ COROLLARY 2.   *Let* $q(x) \in \mathscr{C}$ *on the line* $(-\infty, \infty)$, *and let* $q(x)$ *tend to limits* q_0 *and* q_1, *respectively, as* $x \to \pm\infty$. *Then every eigenfunction with eigenvalue* $\lambda < \min(q_0, q_1)$ *is square-integrable.*

The final conclusions can be summarized in a single theorem.

■ THEOREM 14.   *Let* $q(x)$ *be as in Theorem 13. Then, for* $\lambda > 0$, *the spectrum is continuous. For* $\lambda < 0$, *the eigenfunctions are square-integrable.*

It can also be shown that, for $\lambda > 0$, the eigenfunctions are not square-integrable, and that for $\lambda < 0$, the spectrum is discrete.

EXERCISES I

1. Show that the S-L system $u'' + \lambda u = 0$, $0 \leqq x < \infty$, $\alpha u(0) + \alpha' u'(0) = 0$, $u(x)$ bounded as $x \to \infty$, has a continuous spectrum $0 < \lambda < \infty$ if $\alpha \alpha' \neq 0$.
2. Show that, if $u'' - q(x)u = 0$, $0 \leqq x < \infty$, $q(x)$ bounded, the DE cannot have two square-integrable linearly independent solutions.   [HINT: Use the Wronskian.]
3. In $u'' + [\lambda - q(x)]u = 0$, $0 \leqq x < \infty$, if $q(x) \to +\infty$ as $x \to \infty$, show that, for any λ, the DE has exactly one square-integrable solution up to a constant factor.
4*. Under the assumptions of Exercise 3, show that the S-L system corresponding to the boundary condition $u(0) = 0$, $u(x)$ square-integrable in $[0, \infty)$, has an infinite sequence of eigenvalues.
5. Show that, if the DE $u'' + q(x)u = 0$, $0 \leqq x < \infty$, $q \in \mathscr{C}$ has a solution $u_1(x)$ with $\lim_{x \to \infty} u_1(x) = 1$, it also has a solution $u_2(x)$ such that $\lim_{x \to \infty} u_2(x)/x = 1$.
6. In $u'' + q(x)u = 0$, $0 \leqq x < \infty$, suppose that $\int_0^\infty x\,|q(x)|\,dx < \infty$. Show that the DE has a solution with $\lim_{x \to \infty} u(x) = 1$.   [HINT: Show, by successive approximations, that the integral equation $u(x) = 1 - \int_x^\infty (t - x)q(t)u(t)\,dt$ has a solution.]
7. Suppose that all solutions of the DE $u'' + q(x)u = 0$ are bounded as $x \to \infty$ and that $\int_0^\infty \rho(x)\,dx < \infty$, $\rho(x) > 0$. Show that, for all λ, all solutions of the DE $u'' + (q(x) + \lambda\rho(x))u = 0$ are also bounded as $x \to \infty$.   [HINT: Consider the inhomogeneous DE $u'' + qu = -\lambda\rho u$, and show that the integral equation obtained by variation of parameters has a bounded solution.]

8. Show that, if $k^2 > 0$ and $\int_0^\infty |q(x) - k^2|\, dx < \infty$, all solutions of the DE $u'' + q(x)u = 0$ are bounded as $x \to \infty$.

9*. Show that solutions of the generalized Laguerre DE

$$u'' + \frac{2}{x}\, u' + \left[\frac{\lambda}{x} - \left(\frac{1}{4} + \frac{\alpha}{x^2}\right)\right] u = 0$$

are $u = e^{-x/2} x^{(k-1)/2} L_n^{(k)}(x)$, where $L_n^{(k)}(x) = d^k[L_n(x)]/dx^k$, for $\alpha = (k^2 - 1)/4$ and $\lambda = n - (k-1)/2$, n, k any nonnegative integers.

ADDITIONAL EXERCISES

1. Show that, if $a,\, b > 0$, the singular S-L system

$$\frac{d}{dx}\left[(1 + x)^{b+1}(1 - x)^{a+1}\frac{du}{du}\right] + \lambda(1 + x)^b(1 - x)^a u = 0, \qquad -1 < x < 1,$$

with the endpoint condition that u remain bounded as $x \to \pm 1$, has the eigenvalues $\lambda_n = n(n + a + b + 1)$ and eigenfunctions $u_n(x) = P_n^{(a,b)}(x)$ (Jacobi polynomials).

2. Obtain orthogonality relations for the Jacobi polynomials.

3. Using Rodrigues' formula, show that between any two zeros of $P_n^{(a,b)}$ there is exactly one zero of $P_{n+1}^{(a,b)}$, if $a,\, b > -1$.

4*. Derive the following identities for Legendre polynomials:

  (a) $\int_{-1}^1 P_n^{\,2}(x)\, dx = 2/(2n + 1)$,   (b) $\int_{-1}^1 x P_n(x) P_n'(x)\, dx = 2n/(4n^2 - 1)$.

[HINT: Use Rodrigues' formula and integrate by parts.]

5*. Show that the Legendre DE, with the endpoint condition

$$\lim_{x \to \pm 1} [(1 - x^2)u'(x)] = 0,$$

has the Legendre polynomials as eigenfunctions, and no other eigenfunctions.

6. Show that there exists a bounded differentiable function g on $a < x < b$, satisfying the inequality $g' + g^2/P(x) + Q(x) \leqq 0$, if and only if no solution of $(Pu')' + Qu = 0$ has more than one zero on $a \leqq x \leqq b$.

7*. Show that, if $\int_a^b |Q(x)|\, dx \leqq 4/(b - a)$, no nontrivial solution of $u'' + Q(x)u = 0$ can have more than one zero in $a \leqq x \leqq b$. [HINT. By Theorem 3, it can be assumed that $Q \geqq 0$. Changing coordinates so that $a = 0$, $b = 1$, use Exercise 6 with

$$g(x) = \int_x^1 Q(t)\, dt + \begin{cases} (1/x) - 4, & 0 < x \leqq \frac{1}{2}, \\ 1/(x - 1), & \frac{1}{2} \leqq x < 1. \end{cases}$$

8*. (Fubini) Show that if, for $a \leqq x \leqq b$,

$$p'(x) + p(x)^2 - q(x) \leqq p_1'(x) + p_1(x)^2 - q_1(x),$$

then, between any two zeros of a solution of $u'' + 2p_1u' + q_1u = 0$, there is at least one zero of $u'' + 2pu' + qu = 0$. [HINT: See Chapter 2, Exercise B4.]

9. For a regular S-L system with $\alpha\alpha' < 0$, and $\beta\beta' < 0$, and λ less than the smallest eigenvalue, show that the Green's function is negative.

▌▌ *Expansions in Eigenfunctions*

1 Fourier series

One of the major mathematical achievements of the nineteenth century was the proof that all sufficiently smooth functions can be *expanded* into infinite series, whose terms are constant multiples of the *eigenfunctions* of any S-L system with discrete spectrum. The present chapter will be devoted to proving this result for regular S-L systems and explaining some of its applications.

The most familiar example of such an expansion into eigenfunctions is expansion into Fourier series. We begin by recalling† from the advanced calculus two basic results about Fourier series. The first of these is the following.

■ FOURIER'S CONVERGENCE THEOREM. *Let $f(x)$ be any continuously differentiable periodic function of period 2π, and let*

$$a_k = \frac{1}{\pi} \int_{-\pi}^{\pi} f(x) \cos kx \, dx, \qquad b_k = \frac{1}{\pi} \int_{-\pi}^{\pi} f(x) \sin kx \, dx. \qquad (1)$$

Then the infinite series

$$a_0/2 + a_1 \cos x + b_1 \sin x + a_2 \cos 2x + b_2 \sin 2x + \cdots \qquad (2)$$

converges uniformly to $f(x)$.

Though there exist continuous functions whose Fourier series are not convergent, the following sharpened form of Fourier's Convergence Theorem applies to all continuous periodic functions.

---

† Fourier's theorem is proved in Courant and John, p. 594 ff; Fejér's Theorem is proved in Widder, p. 423.

■ FEJÉR'S CONVERGENCE THEOREM.   *Let $f(x)$ be any continuous periodic function of period 2π, and let*

$$\sigma_N(x) = \frac{1}{N} \left\{ \sum_{n=0}^{N-1} \left[\frac{a_0}{2} + \sum_{k=1}^{n} (a_k \cos kx + b_k \sin kx) \right] \right\}$$

$$= \frac{a_0}{2} + \sum_{k=1}^{N-1} (\alpha_k^N \cos kx + \beta_k^N \sin kx),$$

where $\alpha_k^N = (1 - (k/N))a_k$, $\beta_k^N = (1 - (k/N))b_k$, be the arithmetic mean of the first N partial sums of the Fourier series of $f(x)$. Then the sequence of functions $\sigma_N(x)$ converges uniformly to $f(x)$.

The preceding results, which we will assume as known, yield as corollaries the following statements about cosine series and about sine series. Let $f(x)$ be continuous on $0 \le x \le \pi$; define a function $g(x)$ for $-\pi \le x \le \pi$ by the equation $g(x) = f(|x|)$. Since $g(-\pi) = g(\pi)$, $g(x)$ can be extended to an even periodic function of period 2π, defined and continuous for all real x. By symmetry, all coefficients b_k are zero in the Fourier series of $g(x)$. Applying Fejér's and Fourier's Convergence Theorems, we have

■ COROLLARY 1.   *Any continuous function on $0 \le x \le \pi$ can be approximated uniformly arbitrarily closely by linear combinations of cosine functions. If the function is of class $\mathscr{C}^1$ and $f'(0) = f'(\pi) = 0$, then it can be expanded into a uniformly convergent series of cosine functions:*

$$f(x) = (a_0/2) + a_1 \cos x + a_2 \cos 2x + \cdots. \tag{2'}$$

By a linear transformation of the independent variable, the preceding result can be extended to any closed interval $[a, b]$; the required cosine functions are the functions $\cos[k\pi(x - a)/(b - a)]$.

Similarly, if $f(0) = f(\pi) = 0$, define $h(x)$ as $f(x)$ on $0 \le x \le \pi$, and as $-f(-x)$ on $-\pi \le x \le 0$. This gives an odd continuous periodic function of period 2π, in whose Fourier series all a_k vanish.

■ COROLLARY 2.   *Any function of class $\mathscr{C}^1$ on $0 \le x \le \pi$ which satisfies $f(0) = f(\pi) = 0$ can be expanded into a uniformly convergent series of sine functions.*

The preceding corollaries are examples of expansions into the eigenfunctions of the two regular S-L systems defined by the DE $u'' + \lambda u = 0$ and the separated endpoint conditions $u'(0) = u'(\pi) = 0$ and $u(0) = u(\pi) = 0$, respectively. We will prove below that analogous expansions are possible into the eigenfunctions of *any* regular S-L system.

2 Orthogonal expansions

Let $\phi_1(x)$, $\phi_2(x)$, $\phi_3(x)$, ... be any bounded functions on an interval $I: a < x < b$, square-integrable and orthogonal with respect to a positive weight function $\rho(x)$, so that

$$\int_I \phi_h(x)\phi_k(x)\rho(x)\,dx = 0 \qquad \text{if} \quad h \neq k. \tag{3}$$

Suppose that a given function $f(x)$ can be expressed as the limit of a *uniformly* convergent series of multiples of the ϕ_k, so that

$$f(x) = c_1\phi_1(x) + c_2\,\phi_2(x) + c_3\,\phi_3(x) + \cdots = \sum_{h=1}^{\infty} c_h\,\phi_h(x). \tag{4}$$

Multiplying both sides of (4) by $\phi_k(x)\rho(x)$, and integrating term-by-term over the interval—as is possible for uniformly convergent series—we get from the orthogonality relations (3) the equation

$$\int_I f(x)\phi_k(x)\rho(x)\,dx = \sum_{h=1}^{\infty} \int_I c_h\,\phi_h(x)\phi_k(x)\rho(x)\,dx = c_k \int_I \phi_k{}^2(x)\rho(x)\,dx.$$

Hence, the coefficients c_h in (4) must satisfy the equation

$$c_h = \left\{ \int_I f(x)\phi_h(x)\rho(x)\,dx \right\} \Big/ \left\{ \int_I \phi_h{}^2(x)\rho(x)\,dx \right\}. \tag{5}$$

When the ϕ_k are the trigonometric functions, from this identity we obtain, as a special case, the coefficients $c_1 = a_0/2$, $c_2 = a_1$, $c_3 = b_1$, ... of the Fourier series (1)–(2) with $\rho = 1$, using the familiar integrals

$$\int_{-\pi}^{\pi} dx = 2\pi, \qquad \int_{-\pi}^{\pi} \cos^2 kx\,dx = \int_{-\pi}^{\pi} \sin^2 kx\,dx = \pi,$$

for any nonzero integer k.

We can summarize the preceding result as follows.

■ THEOREM 1. *If a function $f(x)$ is the limit $f(x) = \sum c_k\,\phi_k(x)$ of a uniformly convergent series of constant multiples of bounded square-integrable functions $\phi_k(x)$ which are orthogonal with respect to a weight function $\rho(x)$, the coefficients c_h are given by* (5).

The preceding conclusion holds provided that one can integrate the series $\sum c_h\,\phi_h(x)\phi_k(x)\rho(x)$ term-by-term on the interval I. This holds much more generally than for uniform convergence, e.g., for mean-square convergence as defined below.

The preceding conclusion was justified by using the fact that uniformly convergent series can be integrated term-by-term on any finite interval I. Many other series of orthogonal functions can also be integrated term-by-term, and formula (5), therefore, also holds for them, as we shall prove in the sequel.

3 Mean-square approximation

So far, we have considered only uniformly convergent series, because these can be integrated term by term. The notion of convergence most appropriate for orthogonal expansions is, however, not uniform convergence but *mean-square convergence*, which we now define.

■ DEFINITION. *Let f and the terms of the sequence $\{f_n\}$ $(n = 1, 2, 3, \ldots)$ be square-integrable real functions. The sequence $\{f_n\}$ is said to converge to f in the mean square on I, with respect to the positive weight function $\rho(x)$, when*

$$\int_I [f_n(x) - f(x)]^2 \rho(x)\, dx \to 0 \qquad \text{as} \quad n \to \infty. \tag{6}$$

Now, suppose that $\phi_1, \phi_2, \phi_3, \ldots$ form an infinite sequence of square-integrable functions on the interval I, *orthogonal* with respect to the weight function ρ, and let $f_n(x) = \gamma_1 \phi_1(x) + \cdots + \gamma_n \phi_n(x)$ be the nth partial sum of the series $\sum_{k=1}^{\infty} \gamma_k \phi_k(x)$. To make the partial sums f_n converge in the mean square to f as rapidly as possible, we choose the coefficients γ_k so as to minimize the expression

$$E = E(\gamma_1, \ldots, \gamma_n) = \int_I \left[f(x) - \sum_{k=1}^{n} \gamma_k \phi_k(x) \right]^2 \rho(x)\, dx. \tag{7}$$

Expanding (7), and using the orthogonality relations (3), the function E of the variables $\gamma_1, \gamma_2, \ldots, \gamma_n$ is given by the expression

$$E = \int_I f^2 \rho\, dx - 2 \sum_{k=1}^{n} \gamma_k \int_I f \phi_k \rho\, dx + \sum_{k=1}^{n} \gamma_k^2 \int_I \phi_k^2 \, \rho\, dx. \tag{7'}$$

Now, consider the numbers $\gamma_1, \gamma_2, \ldots, \gamma_n$ which minimize the function E. Since E is differentiable in each of its variables, the minimum can be attained only by setting $\partial E / \partial \gamma_k = 0$. That is, a necessary condition for a minimum is that the γ_k satisfy the equations

$$0 = -2 \int_I f \phi_k \rho\, dx + 2 \gamma_k \int_I \phi_k^2 \, \rho\, dx.$$

Solving for γ_k, we get $\gamma_k = \{\int f \phi_k \rho\, dx\} / \{\int \phi \rho^2 \, dx_k\}$, which is the same as equation (5) for the c_k, in another notation.

We now show that the choice $\gamma_k = c_k$, where, as in (5),

$$c_k = \left\{ \int_I f(x)\phi_k(x)\rho(x)\ dx \right\} \Big/ \left\{ \int_I \phi_k{}^2(x)\rho(x)\ dx \right\}, \qquad (8)$$

does indeed give a minimum for E. A simple calculation, completing the square, gives for E the expression

$$E = \int_I [f - \sum \gamma_k\,\phi_k]^2\rho\ dx = \int_I f^2\rho\ dx + \sum_{k=1}^{n} [-c_k{}^2 + (\gamma_k - c_k)^2] \int_I \phi_k{}^2\rho\ dx. \tag{8'}$$

The right side shows that the minimum is attained if and only if $\gamma_k = c_k$. This proves the following result, for any interval I.

■ THEOREM 2.   *Let $\{\phi_k(x)\}$ be a sequence of orthogonal square-integrable functions, and let f be square-integrable. Then, among all possible choices of $\gamma_1, \ldots, \gamma_n$, the integral (7) is minimized by selecting $\gamma_k = c_k$, where c_k is defined by (8).*

The coefficients c_k are called the *Fourier coefficients* of f relative to the orthogonal sequence ϕ_k.

The partial sum $c_1\phi_1(x) + \cdots + c_n\,\phi_n(x)$ in Theorem 1 is thus, for each n, the *best mean-square approximation* to $f(x)$ among all possible sums $\gamma_1\phi_1(x) + \cdots + \gamma_n\,\phi_n(x)$; it is often called the *least square approximation* to $f(x)$ because it minimizes the mean square difference (7). The remarkable feature of least-square approximation by orthogonal functions is that the kth coefficient γ_k in the list $(\gamma_1, \ldots, \gamma_n)$ which gives the best mean-square approximation to f *is the same for all $n \geq k$.* This "finality property" does not hold, for example, in the case of least-squares approximation by nonorthogonal functions, or of the approximations in Fejér's Theorem, or of best *uniform* approximation minimizing $\sup_{a<x<b} |f(x) - \sum_{k=1}^{n} c_k\,\phi_k(x)|$.

Orthonormal functions.   The preceding formulas become much simpler when the orthogonal functions ϕ_k are *orthonormal*, in the sense that $\int \phi_k{}^2\rho\ dx = 1$. For a sequence of orthonormal functions, the formula for the Fourier coefficients is $c_k = \int_I f\phi_k\,\rho\ dx$. We can easily construct from any sequence ϕ_k of orthogonal functions an orthonormal sequence ψ_k by setting $\psi_k = \phi_k/[\int_I \phi_k{}^2\rho\ dx]^{1/2}$. For example, the functions

$$\frac{1}{\sqrt{2\pi}}, \qquad \frac{1}{\sqrt{\pi}} \cos kx, \qquad \frac{1}{\sqrt{\pi}} \sin kx$$

are orthonormal on $-\pi \leq x \leq \pi$ with respect to the weight function $\rho(x) \equiv 1$.

Substituting the condition $\int \phi_k{}^2\rho\ dx = 1$ into (8') and remarking that E is nonnegative, we obtain the important

■ COROLLARY 1.   *Let $\sum_1^n c_k \phi_k$ be the least square approximation to f by a linear combination of orthonormal functions ϕ_k. Then*

$$\sum_1^n c_k{}^2 \leqq \int_I f^2(x)\rho(x)\, dx. \tag{9}$$

For the right member of (9) to be finite, it is necessary that $f^2\rho$ be integrable, that is, that f be *square-integrable* with respect to the weight function ρ. When this is the case, the integrals (8) are also well-defined by the Schwarz inequality. Under these circumstances, since the right side of (9) is independent of n, if we let n tend to infinity, we will still have

$$\sum_1^\infty c_k{}^2 \leqq \int_I f^2(x)\rho(x)\, dx < +\infty \qquad \text{(Bessel inequality)}. \tag{10}$$

That is, *the Fourier coefficients of any square-integrable function f form a square-summable sequence of numbers if the ϕ_k are orthonormal.*

EXERCISES A

1. Show that $a_k \cos kx + b_k \sin kx = (1/\pi) \int_{-\pi}^{\pi} f(t) \cos (k(t-x))\, dt$.
2. Show that $\frac{1}{2} + \sum_{k=1}^n \cos kx = \sin [(2n+1)x/2]/(2 \sin (x/2))$.
3. Using Exercise 2, infer that

$$\frac{a_0}{2} + \sum_{k=1}^n (a_k \cos kx + b_k \sin kx) = \frac{1}{\pi} \int_{-\pi}^{\pi} f(t)\, \frac{\sin [(2n+1)(t-x)/2]}{2 \sin [(t-x)/2]}\, dt.$$

4. (a) Prove in detail Corollaries 1–2 of Féjer's Theorem, discussing with care the differentiability at 0 and π of the periodic functions constructed.
   (b) Find necessary and sufficient conditions for a continuous function on $[0, \pi]$ to be uniformly approximable by a linear combination of functions $\sin kx$.
5. Show that, in Fejér's convergence theorem,

$$\sigma_n(x) = \frac{1}{2\pi n} \int_{-\pi}^{\pi} f(x+t) \left[\frac{\sin (nt/2)}{\sin (t/2)}\right]^2 dt.$$

6*. Prove Fejér's theorem, assuming that Exercise 5 holds.

For the regular S-L systems in Exercises 7 and 8: (a) find the eigenvalues and eigenfunctions, (b) obtain an expansion formula for a function $f \in \mathscr{C}^1$ into a series of eigenfunctions.

7. $u'' + \lambda u = 0$, $u(0) = 0$, $u'(\pi) = 0$, $0 \leqq x \leqq \pi$,
8. The same DE with $u'(0) = 0$, $u(\pi) = 0$.
9. Show that the trigonometric functions are orthogonal, for any a, in

$$-\pi - a \leqq x \leqq \pi - a.$$

4   Completeness

The most important question about a sequence of continuous functions ϕ_k $(k = 1, 2, 3, \ldots)$, orthogonal and square-integrable with respect to a weight function ρ, is the following: Can *every* square-integrable function f be expanded into an infinite series† $f = \sum_1^\infty c_k \phi_k$ of the ϕ_k? When this is possible for every continuous f,‡ the sequence of orthogonal functions ϕ_k is said to be *complete*.

Using the fundamental equation (8′) on mean-square approximation, we can reformulate the definition of completeness as follows. In order that

$$\lim_{n \to \infty} \int_I \left[f(x) - \sum_{k=1}^n \gamma_k \phi_k \right]^2 \rho(x)\, dx = 0,$$

it is necessary and sufficient that

$$\lim_{n \to \infty} \left\{ \left[\int_I f^2 \rho\, dx - \sum_1^n c_k^2 \int_I \phi_k^2 \rho\, dx \right] + \sum_{k=1}^n (\gamma_k - c_k)^2 \int_I \phi_k^2 \rho\, dx \right\} = 0.$$

Since the term in square brackets is nonnegative by the Bessel inequality (10), and since $\int \phi_k^2 \rho\, dx > 0$ for any nontrivial ϕ_k, the limit is zero if and only if $\gamma_k = c_k$ for all k, and equality holds in the Bessel inequality (10). This proves the following results.

■ THEOREM 3.   *A sequence $\{\phi_k\}$ of functions $\phi_k(x)$, orthogonal and square-integrable with positive weight $\rho(x)$ on an interval I, is* complete *if and only if*

$$\int_I f^2(x)\rho(x)\, dx = \sum_{k=1}^\infty \left[\int_I f(x)\phi_k(x)\rho(x)\, dx \right]^2 \Big/ \int_I \phi_k^2(x)\rho(x)\, dx$$

for all continuous square-integrable functions f.

■ COROLLARY 1.   *If the $\phi_k(x)$ are orthonormal, a necessary and sufficient condition for completeness is the validity of the* Parseval *equality*

$$\int_I f^2(x)\rho(x)\, dx = \sum_{k=1}^\infty \left[\int_I f(x)\phi_k(x)\rho(x)\, dx \right]^2, \tag{11}$$

for all continuous square-integrable functions f.

---

† Here and below, the equation $f = \sum_1^\infty c_k \phi_k$ is to be interpreted in the sense of mean-square convergence, namely, that the partial sums $\sum_{k=1}^n c_k \phi_k$ converge in the mean square to the function f with respect to ρ.

‡ If every continuous function can be expanded into a series $\sum_1^\infty c_k \phi_k$, then many discontinuous functions also have such an expansion, convergent in the mean square. The class of all such functions is that of all Lebesgue square-integrable functions (see § 11). We are here considering only continuous functions in order to avoid assuming a knowledge of the Lebesgue integral.

For example, take the case of Fourier series. In the notation of (1), the condition for the completeness of the functions 1, cos kx, sin kx on $-\pi \leq x \leq \pi$ is that, for all continuous functions f,

$$\pi\left[a_0{}^2/2 + \sum_{k=1}^{\infty} (a_k{}^2 + b_k{}^2)\right] = \int_{-\pi}^{\pi} f^2(x)\, dx. \tag{12}$$

It follows from Fourier's Convergence Theorem, integrating the squares of the partial sums of (2), that the identity (12) holds if f is a continuously differentiable periodic function.

We shall now prove that the identity (12) holds for all continuous periodic functions f. By Fejér's Convergence Theorem, the sums

$$\sigma_N(x) = \frac{a_0}{2} + \sum_{k=1}^{N-1}\left(1 - \frac{k}{N}\right)a_k \cos kx + \sum_{k=1}^{N-1}\left(1 - \frac{k}{N}\right)b_k \sin kx \tag{13}$$

converge uniformly $f(x)$ for $-\pi \leq x \leq \pi$ to a continuous periodic function. Therefore, $\int_{-\pi}^{\pi} \sigma_N{}^2\, dx$ converges as $N \to \infty$ to $\int_{-\pi}^{\pi} f^2\, dx$. Evaluating the integral by (13), we find that

$$\lim_{N \to \infty} \pi\left[\frac{a_0{}^2}{2} + \sum_{k=1}^{N-1}\left(1 - \frac{k}{N}\right)^2 (a_k{}^2 + b_k{}^2)\right] = \int_{-\pi}^{\pi} f^2(x)\, dx. \tag{14}$$

Now, by the Bessel inequality, we have

$$\pi\left[a_0{}^2/2 + \sum_{k=1}^{\infty} (a_k{}^2 + b_k{}^2)\right] \leq \int_{-\pi}^{\pi} f^2\, dx < \infty. \tag{14'}$$

Since $[1 - (k/N)]^2 \leq 1$, it follows that, if we replace the sum in square brackets on the left side of (14) by $a_0{}^2/2 + \sum_{k=1}^{N}(a_k{}^2 + b_k{}^2)$, we will get an increasing sequence whose limit is at least equal to $\int f^2\, dx$. But, by (14'), this limit is at most equal to $\int f^2\, dx$. Hence, the limit is exactly $\int f^2\, dx$, and (12) is proved. Since any continuous function on $-\pi \leq x \leq \pi$ can be given an arbitrarily close mean-square approximation by a continuous function satisfying $f(-\pi) = f(\pi)$, this proves

■ COROLLARY 2. *The trigonometric functions* cos kx, sin kx ($k = 0$, 1, 2, ...) *are a complete orthogonal sequence in the interval* $-\pi \leq x \leq \pi$.

Using the method of Corollary 2 of §1 and changing variables, we obtain

■ COROLLARY 3. *The functions* cos $[k\pi(x - a)/(b - a)]$ ($k = 0, 1, 2, \ldots$) *form a complete orthogonal sequence in the interval* $a \leq x \leq b$.

We conclude this section with the following criterion for completeness of a sequence of orthogonal functions, which relates the notion of completeness to that of *approximation* in the sense of mean-square convergence.

■ THEOREM 4.   *Let $\{\phi_k\}$ $(k = 1, 2, \ldots)$ be any sequence of orthogonal square-integrable functions on an interval I, relative to a weight function $\rho > 0$. The sequence is complete if and only if every continuous square-integrable function can be approximated arbitrarily closely in the mean square by a linear combination of the ϕ_k.*

Proof — The condition is clearly necessary. Conversely, suppose that, given $\epsilon > 0$, we can find a linear combination $\sum_{k=1}^{n} \gamma_k \phi_k$ such that

$$\int_I \left(f - \sum_{k=1}^{n} \gamma_k \phi_k \right)^2 \rho \, dx < \epsilon.$$

If we replace each of the γ_k by the Fourier coefficients c_k of f relative to ϕ_k—as given by formula (5)—then by Theorem 2 the square integral on the left decreases:

$$\int_I \left(f - \sum_{k=1}^{n} c_k \phi_k \right)^2 \rho \, dx < \epsilon.$$

But this is precisely what we had to prove.

5   Orthogonal polynomials

We shall now prove the completeness of the eigenfunctions of some of the singular S-L systems studied in Chapter 10. These are the S-L systems on a *finite* interval whose eigenfunctions are polynomials, such as the Legendre polynomials.

We can use any positive *weight function* $\rho(x)$ on an interval (a, b) with the property that $\int_a^b x^n \rho(x) \, dx$ is convergent for all $n \geq 0$, to construct an infinite sequence of polynomial functions $P_0(x)$, $P_1(x)$, $P_2(x)$, ... with $P_n(x)$ of degree n, which are orthogonal on (a, b):

$$\int_a^b P_m(x) P_n(x) \rho(x) \, dx = 0, \qquad m \neq n. \tag{15}$$

Equations (15) define $P_n(x)$ uniquely up to an arbitrary factor of proportionality, the normalization constant.

Given a weight function $\rho(x)$, one can compute the $P_n(x)$ explicitly from (15); the computations will not be described here.† Instead, we

---

† It is the Gram-Schmidt orthogonalization process applied to the vectors $1, x, x^2, \ldots$. This process can be applied in any Euclidean vector space (Birkhoff and Mac Lane, pp. 179–81).

shall derive some interesting general properties of orthogonal polynomials.

We shall first establish the fact that, on any *finite* interval, such sequences of orthogonal polynomials are *complete*. To prove this, we will need the following result.

■ LEMMA. *Every uniformly convergent sequence of continuous functions is mean-square convergent on any interval I, with respect to any integrable positive weight function* ($\int_I \rho \, dx < \infty$).

This follows immediately from the inequality

$$\int_I [f_n(x) - f(x)]^2 \rho(x) \, dx \leq \max \left[((f_n(x) - f(x))^2) \right] \int_I \rho(x) \, dx, \qquad (16)$$

valid when I is any finite or infinite interval. On an infinite interval, however, we must carefully check the integrability of the weight function. For instance, the functions $f_n(x) = n^{-1/2} \exp(-x^2/n^2)$ converge uniformly to the zero function on the interval $-\infty < x < \infty$, but the integrals $\int_{-\infty}^{\infty} f_n{}^2(x) \, dx$ do not converge to zero.

Using this lemma, it is easy to prove the completeness of a sequence of *orthogonal polynomials* defined on a *finite* interval I relative to any continuous integrable weight function $\rho(x)$ from the fundamental

■ WEIERSTRASS APPROXIMATION THEOREM. *Let $f(x)$ be any function continuous on a finite closed interval $a \leq x \leq b$, and let $\epsilon > 0$ be any positive number. Then there exists a polynomial $p(x)$, such that $|p(x) - f(x)| \leq \epsilon$ for all x on $a \leq x \leq b$.*†

From this theorem, and the inequality (16), we infer

■ THEOREM 5. *Let $P_n(x)$ ($n = 0, 1, 2, \ldots$) be a polynomial function of degree n. For a fixed finite interval I: $a \leq x \leq b$, let*

$$\int_a^b P_m(x) P_n(x) \rho(x) \, dx = 0 \qquad if \quad m \neq n,$$

where $\rho(x)$ is a continuous integrable positive weight function. Then the orthogonal polynomials $P_n(x)$ are complete on I.

Proof — Let $p(x)$ be any polynomial of degree n. We can find c_n such that $p(x) - c_n P_n(x)$ is a polynomial of degree $n - 1$ or less. Hence, by induction on n, we can express $p(x)$ as a finite linear combination of $P_0(x), \ldots, P_n(x)$. By the Weierstrass Approximation Theorem, we can approximate uniformly *any* continuous function arbitrarily closely by a

---

† See Widder, p. 426, or Courant-Hilbert, Vol. 1, p. 65.

suitable polynomial $p(x)$. By the preceding lemma, every continuous function can therefore be approximated arbitrarily closely in the mean square by a linear combination of the P_k. The result now follows from Theorem 4.

The completeness of Legendre, Chebyshev, Gegenbauer (or ultra-spherical), and other Jacobi polynomials (see Chapter 9, § 11) follows as a corollary. But it is harder to prove the completeness of polynomials orthogonal on semi-infinite and infinite intervals, such as the Hermite polynomials and the Laguerre polynomials introduced in the next section.

EXERCISES B

1. Using Fourier's Convergence Theorem, show that the eigenfunctions of $u'' + \lambda u = 0$ for the separated boundary conditions $u(0) = u'(\pi) = 0$ are complete on $(0, \pi)$.
2. Show that, if $f_n \to f$ in the mean square, and c_k, $c_k^{(n)}$ are the Fourier coefficients of f, f_n relative to a given orthonormal sequence ϕ_k, then $c_k^{(n)} \to c_k$ uniformly in k.
3. Using expansions into Legendre polynomials, obtain a formula for the best mean-square approximation in $|x| \leq 1$ of a square-integrable function by poly-nomials of degree $\leq n$.
4*. Using the Prüfer substitution, obtain from Fourier's theorem an expansion theorem for functions $f \in \mathscr{C}^2[-1, 1]$ into series of Chebyshev polynomials.
5*. Show that, given square-integrable functions $f_1, \ldots, f_n$, a sequence $\phi_1, \ldots, \phi_m$ of orthonormal square-integrable functions can be found for which f_k is a linear combination of $\phi_1, \ldots, \phi_k$, $1 \leq k \leq m$.

6*   Properties of orthogonal polynomials

We shall now develop some of the properties of orthogonal poly-nomials which depend only on the fact that they are orthogonal, irrespective of completeness. These properties apply to the poly-nomials whose completeness was proved in § 5 (see last paragraph). They apply also to the Hermite and Laguerre polynomials, whose completeness will not be proved in this book. All these polynomials have been met before, except the Laguerre polynomials, which we now define.

EXAMPLE 1.   Consider the singular S-L system consisting of the DE

$$(xu')' + [\alpha + (2 - x)/4]u = 0, \qquad 0 < x < \infty, \qquad (17)$$

with the endpoint conditions that $u(x)$ is bounded as $x \to \infty$ and as $x \to 0$. Setting $u(x) = v(x)e^{-x/2}$, we get the Laguerre DE

$$xv'' + (1 - x)v' + \alpha v = 0. \qquad (18)$$

Trying $v = \sum_{k=0}^{\infty} a_k x^k$, the Method of Undetermined Coefficients (Chapter 3, § 2) gives the recurrence relation $a_{k+1} = (k - \alpha)a_k/(k + 1)^2$. Hence, we have

$$a_k = (-1)^k \alpha(\alpha - 1)(\alpha - 2) \cdots (\alpha - k + 1)a_0/(k!)^2. \tag{19}$$

The series is a polynomial if and only if $\alpha = n$, a nonnegative integer; otherwise, it represents a function which grows exponentially at infinity. Normalizing the polynomial (for $\alpha = n$) by the condition $a_n = (-1)^n/(n!)$, we get the *Laguerre polynomials*†:

$$L_n(x) = \sum_{k=0}^{n} (-1)^k \binom{n}{k} \frac{x^k}{k!}. \tag{19'}$$

For example, $L_0(x) = 1$, $L_1(x) = 1 - x$, $L_2(x) = 1 - 2x + \frac{1}{2}x^2$,

$$L_3(x) = 1 - 3x + \tfrac{3}{2}x^2 - \tfrac{1}{6}x^3, \ldots.$$

Thus, the functions $L_n(x)e^{-x/2}$ are eigenfunctions of a singular S-L system. These functions are certainly square-integrable, together with their derivatives; hence Theorem 2 of Chapter 10 applies, giving the orthogonality relations

$$\int_0^{\infty} e^{-x} L_m(x) L_n(x)\, dx = 0, \qquad m \neq n.$$

We shall now consider some of the fundamental properties of an arbitrary sequence of *orthogonal polynomials* (not necessarily solutions of a DE) $P_0(x), \ldots, P_n(x), \ldots$, where P_n is of degree n. As in §5, we assume that the weight function $\rho(x)$ is such that all products $x^n\rho(x)$ are integrable on I. We do not assume that the interval I is finite.

We first derive a result similar to the Sturm Oscillation Theorem.

■ THEOREM 6.   *Let $\{P_n\}$ $(n = 0, 1, 2, \ldots)$ be any sequence of polynomials orthogonal in a given interval (a, b) where $P_n(x)$ has degree n. Then P_n has n distinct zeros, all contained in the interval (a, b).*

Proof — Suppose that $P_n(x)$ had fewer than n zeros in (a, b). Let $x_1, \ldots, x_m$ $(m < n)$ be those zeros at which $P_n(x)$ changes sign. Then the polynomial $(x - x_1)(x - x_2) \cdots (x - x_m)P_n(x)$ would be of constant sign. Hence

$$\int_a^b (x - x_1) \cdots (x - x_m)P_n(x)\rho(x)\, dx \neq 0, \qquad m < n.$$

But $(x - x_1) \cdots (x - x_m)$ is a polynomial of degree lower than n. Therefore, it can be written as a linear combination of the polynomials $P_0, \ldots, P_m$, say $\sum_{k=0}^{m} c_k P_k(x)$, $m < n$. Hence, we have

† The normalizing condition $a_n = 1$ is also often used, and makes some formulas simpler.

$$\int_a^b (x-x_1)\cdots(x-x_m)P_n(x)\rho(x)\,dx = \int_a^b \sum_{k=0}^m c_k\,P_k(x)P_n(x)\rho(x)\,dx$$

$$= \sum_{k=0}^n c_k \int_a^b P_k\,P_n\,\rho\,dx = 0,$$

a patent contradiction since the integrand is positive except at the x_i. Hence, $P_n(x)$ has at least n zeros on (a, b). Since a polynomial of degree n has, at most, n zeros, the proof is complete.

Next, we shall establish a *recursion formula* for an arbitrary system of orthogonal polynomials.

■ THEOREM 7.   *Any three orthogonal polynomials of consecutive degree satisfy a linear relation*

$$P_{n+1}(x) = (A_n x + B_n)P_n(x) + C_n P_{n-1}(x) \tag{20}$$

for suitable constants A_n, B_n, C_n.

Proof — First choose A_n such that $P_{n+1}(x) - xA_n P_n(x)$ is a polynomial of degree n or less, so that

$$P_{n+1}(x) - xA_n P_n(x) = \gamma_0 P_n(x) + \gamma_1 P_{n-1}(x) + \cdots + \gamma_n P_0.$$

Multiplying both sides by $P_k(x)\rho(x)$, integrating from a to b, and using the orthogonality relation, we find that $\gamma_k = 0$ for $k = 2, 3, \ldots, n$. Hence

$$P_{n+1}(x) - xA_n P_n(x) = \gamma_0 P_n(x) + \gamma_1 P_{n-1}(x).$$

Therefore set $\gamma_0 = B_n$ and $\gamma_1 = C_n$, q.e.d.

The numerical values of the constants A_n, B_n, C_n in Theorem 7 depend on the normalizing factors used to define the orthogonal polynomials considered. For convenience, we have listed in Table 1 the recursion coefficients for some common polynomials.

TABLE 1.   *Recursion coefficients*

Polynomial	A_n	B_n	C_n
Legendre	$\dfrac{2n+1}{n+1}$	0	$\dfrac{-n}{n+1}$
Chebyshev	2	0	-1
Gegenbauer	$\dfrac{2n+\lambda}{n+1}$	0	$\dfrac{1-n-2\lambda}{n+1}$
Hermite	2	0	$-2n$
Laguerre	$\dfrac{-1}{n+1}$	$\dfrac{2n+1}{n+1}$	$\dfrac{-n}{n+1}$

EXERCISES C

Establish the following formulas for Hermite polynomials (see Chapter 3, § 2):

1. $H_{n+1}(x) = 2x\,H_n(x) - 2n\,H_{n-1}(x)$,
2. $H'_n(x) = nH_{n-1}(x)$,
3*. $\sum_{k=0}^{\infty} H_n(x)t^k/k! = e^{xt-t^2/2}$ (generating function).
4. Establish the recursion formula for the Laguerre polynomials:

$$L_n(x) = L'_n(x) - L'_{n+1}(x).$$

[HINT: Differentiate the recursion formula for L_n.]
5. Show that the functions $\phi_n(x) = e^{x/2}\,d^n/dx^n(e^{-x}x^n)$ are orthogonal in $0 < x < \infty$.
6. Infer from Exercise 5 that $(n!)\,\phi_n(x) = e^{-x/2}\,L_n(x)$, where L_n is the nth Laguerre polynomial.
7. Show that, if $L_n(x)$ is the Laguerre polynomial of degree n, then $d^k[L_n(x)]/dx^k$ satisfies the DE

$$xv'' + (k+1-x)v' + (n-k)v = 0.$$

8. Prove the recursion formula of Table 1:

$$(n+1)L_{n+1}(x) = (2n+1-x)L_n(x) - nL_{n-1}(x).$$

9. Let $P_k(x)$ be a sequence of orthogonal polynomials with weight function ρ in $a < x < b$, and let $c_k = \int_a^b f(x)P_k(x)\rho(x)\,dx$. Show that the partial sum

$$\sigma_n(x) = \sum_{k=0}^{n} c_k P_k(x)$$

coincides with $f(x)$ in at least $n+1$ points of the interval.   [HINT: Use a method similar to the proof of Theorem 6.]
10*. Let P_n be a sequence of orthogonal polynomials in (a, b). Show that between any two zeros of P_n there is exactly one zero of P_{n+1}.
11*. Show that the Legendre polynomials are the only Gegenbauer polynomials for which the maximum of $|P_n^a(x)|$, namely $P_n^a(1)$, is independent of n.
12*. (a) Expand the function $(1 - 2xh + h^2)^{-1/2}(|x| < 1)$ into a series of Legendre polynomials, and show that the nth Fourier coefficient is $2h^n/(2n+1)$.
   (b) Obtain from (a) the formula

$$(1 - 2xh + h^2)^{-1/2} = \sum_{k=0}^{\infty} h^k P_k(x) \qquad \text{for} \quad |h| < \sqrt{2} - 1.$$

13*. Show that the generating function for the Laguerre polynomials is $g(x, t) = (1 - t)^{-1} \exp[-xt/(1 - t)]$, that is,

$$\sum_{n=0}^{\infty} t^n L_n(x)/n! = g(x, t).$$

In Exercises 14 through 17, $D = d/dx$ and $\rho(x)$ is positive. The method of proof is to find by induction a S-L equation satisfied by the expressions given.
14*. Show that the only orthogonal polynomials of the form

$$p_n(x) = K_n(\rho(x))^{-1}D^n[\rho(x)] \qquad \text{for} \quad \rho(x) \in \mathscr{C}^{\infty}$$

are the Hermite polynomials.

15*. Show that the only orthogonal polynomials of the form

$$p_n(x) = K_n(\rho(x))^{-1}D^n[\rho(x)(ax+b)]$$

are the Laguerre polynomials, after a change of independent variable.

16*. Show that the only system of orthogonal polynomials of the form

$$K_n(\rho(x))^{-1}D^n[\rho(x)(ax^2+bx+c)]$$

are the Jacobi polynomials, after a change of independent variable.

17*. Show that the only sequences of orthogonal polynomials satisfying a Rodrigues formula $p_n(x) = K_n(\rho(x))^{-1}D^n[\rho(x)p(x)]$, where p is a given polynomial, are the Jacobi, Laguerre, and Hermite polynomials.

7* Chebyshev polynomials

The Chebyshev polynomials $T_n(x)$ were introduced in Chapter 9, § 11, as solutions of the self-adjoint DE

$$[(1-x^2)^{1/2}u']' + \lambda(1-x^2)^{-1/2}u = 0, \qquad -1 < x < 1. \qquad (21)$$

The Liouville normal form of this DE is $u_{\theta\theta} + \lambda u = 0$, obtained by setting $w = u$ and $\theta = \int_{-1}^{x} d\xi/\sqrt{1-\xi^2}$, or $x = -\cos\theta$, $0 < \theta < \pi$. For integral n and $\lambda = n^2$, two linearly independent solutions of this equation are

$$\cos n\theta = T_n(\cos\theta) = T_n(x) \qquad (21a)$$

and $S_n(x)$ given by the formula

$$S_n(x) = \sin n\theta = \sin(n-1)\theta \; \cos\theta + \sin\theta \cos(n-1)\theta. \qquad (21b)$$

From the forms of the preceding explicit solutions, we see that the functions $T_n(x)$ are eigenfunctions of the singular S-L system defined from (21) by the boundary conditions that $u'(-1)$ and $u'(1)$ be finite. All solutions of (21) are bounded at the singular points $x = \pm 1$, as is apparent from inspection of explicit solutions (21a)–(21b), and also from a calculation of the roots $\nu = 0$, $\frac{1}{2}$ of the indicial equation $2\nu^2 - \nu = 0$ of the normal form of (21). But only multiples of the $T_n(x)$ have bounded derivatives at the endpoints.

Minimax property. The most striking property of the Chebyshev polynomials is contained in the following result.

■ THEOREM 8. *Among all monic polynomials* $P(x) = x^n + \sum_{k=0}^{n-1} a_k x^k$ *of degree* n, $2^{1-n}T_n(x)$ *minimizes* $\max_{-1 \leq x \leq 1} |P(x)|$ (*Minimax property*).

Proof — For $n = 1$, the result follows by inspection. For $n \geq 2$, it follows by induction from the recursion formula

$$T_n(x) = 2xT_{n-1}(x) - T_{n-2}(x),$$

which is equivalent to the trigonometric identity

$$\cos(m\theta + \theta) = 2\cos\theta\cos m\theta - \cos(m\theta - \theta), \qquad n = m + 1.$$

Next, since $T_n(\cos\theta) = \cos n\theta$, we have that

$$\max_{-1 \leq x \leq 1} |2^{1-n}T_n(x)| = 2^{1-n}.$$

In order to establish the statement, it therefore suffices to show that for any monic polynomial of degree n we have

$$\max_{-1 \leq x \leq 1} |x^n + a_{n-1}x^{n-1} + \cdots + a_0| \geq 2^{1-n}.$$

Suppose this were not so. Then, we could find a monic polynomial $p(x)$ of degree n such that $\max_{-1 \leq x \leq 1}|p(x)| < 2^{1-n}$. Now, the polynomial $2^{1-n}T_n(x) - p(x)$ is of degree $n - 1$. We shall reach a contradiction by showing that this polynomial has n distinct zeros.

To see this, notice that the polynomial $2^{1-n}T_n(x)$ takes alternately the values $\pm 2^{1-n}$ at $n + 1$ points $x_0 = -1 < x_1 < \cdots < x_n = 1$, as follows immediately from $T_n(\cos\theta) = \cos n\theta$. Since $|p(x_k)| < 2^{1-n}|T_n(x_k)|$, it follows that the polynomial $2^{1-n}T_n(x) - p(x)$ takes alternately positive and negative values at $n + 1$ points. It follows that this polynomial of degree $n - 1$ must have at least n distinct zeros, and hence, must vanish identically, q.e.d.

The *Chebyshev polynomials of the second kind* are defined by the identity $U_n(\cos\theta)\sin\theta = \sin(n + 1)\theta$. Their theory is parallel to the theory of the Chebyshev polynomials, and is developed in Exercises D3—D7.

Chebyshev Equioscillation Principle. An important partial generalization of Theorem 8 is the Chebyshev Equioscillation Principle. This states that, if $f(x) \in \mathscr{C}[a, b]$, then there is a unique polynomial $p(x)$ of degree $n - 1$ which minimizes $\max |p(x) - f(x)|$ on $[a, b]$. The difference $P(x) = p(x) - f(x)$ vanishes at $n - 1$ points on $[a, b]$, and $|P(x)|$ assumes its maximum value at n points. Setting $f(x) = x^n$, we have $P(x) = T_n(x)$.

EXERCISES D

1. Show that the DE $((1 - x^2)^{3/2}u')' + \lambda(1 - x^2)^{1/2}u = 0$ can be reduced to a DE with constant coefficients by setting $v(\theta) = (\sin\theta)u(\cos\theta)$.
2. Show that the endpoint conditions $\lim_{x \to \pm 1} \sqrt{1 - x^2}u(x) = 0$ give an S-L system with eigenvalues $\lambda_n = n(n + 2)$, from the DE of Exercise 1.
3. Show that the eigenfunction belonging to the eigenvalue λ_n is a Chebyshev polynomial of the second kind.
4. Using Exercise 3 obtain an expansion theorem of a smooth function into a series of Chebyshev polynomials of the second kind.
5. Show that $T_n(x) = U_n(x) - xU_{n-1}(x)$.

6. Show that $(1 - x^2)U_{n-1}(x) = xT_n(x) - T_{n+1}(x)$.

7. Express $U_n(x)$ in terms of the hypergeometric function.

8. Expand the function arccos x on $(-1, 1)$ into a series of Chebyshev polynomials of the first kind.

9*. Infer the Weierstrass Approximation Theorem from Fejér's Theorem.

8   Euclidean vector spaces

The concepts of mean-square convergence and completeness have suggestive geometric interpretations. These interpretations are based on the properties of inner products.

Consider the set of all real functions $f, g, h, \ldots$, continuous and square-integrable on an interval I, with respect to a fixed positive weight function ρ. The interval I may be open or closed, finite, semi-infinite, or infinite. Define the *inner product* of two such functions f, g as the integral

$$(f, g) = \int_I f(x)g(x)\rho(x)\, dx, \qquad \rho(x) > 0. \tag{22}$$

The following formulas are immediate:

$$(f + g, h) = (f, h) + (g, h), \qquad (f, g) = (g, f),$$

$$(cf, g) = c(f, g); \quad (f, f) > 0 \quad \text{unless} \quad f \equiv 0.$$

Hence, with respect to the inner product (f, g), this set of functions is a *Euclidean vector space*† (or "inner product space").

For real functions, the integral (6) in the definition of mean-square convergence, is the inner product $(f_n - f, f_n - f)$; hence it is the square of the *distance* $\|f_n - f\| = (f_n - f, f_n - f)^{1/2}$ between f_n and f in the Euclidean vector space E. Therefore, $f_n \to f$ in the *mean square*, relative to ρ, means that the Euclidean *distance* from f_n to f in E tends to zero.

This distance enjoys the properties of distance in ordinary space, including the *triangle inequality* and the *Schwarz inequality*

$$-\|f\| \cdot \|g\| \leqq (f, g) = \|f\| \cdot \|g\| \ \cos \angle(f, g) \leqq \|f\| \cdot \|g\|.$$

The Schwarz inequality shows that f and g are *orthogonal* if and only if the angle

$$\theta = \angle(f, g) = \arccos\left[(f, g)/\|f\| \cdot \|g\|\right], \qquad 0 \leqq \theta \leqq \pi,$$

is 90°; it gives a geometrical interpretation to the definition of orthogonal functions.

---

† Birkhoff and Mac Lane, Chapter 7, pp. 177–81. The reader should familiarize himself with this notion.

We shall now generalize Theorems 1, 2, 3, and 4 to an arbitrary Euclidean vector space E.

If $\{\phi_k\}$ is a sequence of orthogonal vectors in E, and $f \in E$ is given, consider the squared distance

$$E(\gamma_1, \ldots, \gamma_n) = \|f - \sum_{k=1}^{n} \gamma_k \phi_k\|^2 = \left(f - \sum_{k=1}^{n} \gamma_k \phi_k, f - \sum_{k=1}^{n} \gamma_k \phi_k\right).$$

Defining $c_k = (f, \phi_k)/(\phi_k, \phi_k)$, we obtain, as in §3,

$$\left\|f - \sum_{k=1}^{n} \gamma_k \phi_k\right\|^2 = (f, f) - \sum_{k=1}^{n} [c_k^2(\phi_k, \phi_k)] + \sum_{k=1}^{n} [(c_k - \gamma_k)^2(\phi_k, \phi_k)].$$

Geometrically, the *least-square* approximation $\sum_{k=1}^{n} c_k \phi_k$ to f appears as the *orthogonal projection* of the vector f onto the *subspace* S of all linear combinations $\gamma_1 \phi_1 + \cdots + \gamma_n \phi_n$ of $\phi_1, \ldots, \phi_n$. This is because, in the orthogonal projection onto a subspace S of a vector $\mathbf{c}$ issuing from the origin, the component of $\mathbf{c}$ perpendicular to S is the *shortest* vector from S to $\mathbf{c}$. The coefficients γ_k are given by the direction cosine formulas of analytic geometry.

Completeness of the ϕ_k is defined as in § 4, as the property that

$$\lim_{n \to \infty} \left\|f - \sum_{k=1}^{n} c_k \phi_k\right\| = 0, \qquad \text{that is,} \qquad \sum_{k=1}^{\infty} c_k \phi_k = f,$$

for every f in E. It has a simple geometric interpretation in any Euclidean vector space E. The relation $f = \sum_{1}^{\infty} c_k \phi_k$ holds if and only if the distance $\|f - \sum_{1}^{n} c_k \phi_k\|$ tends to zero as $n \to \infty$. That is, as in the proof of Theorem 3, the condition for completeness is that we can approximate any f arbitrarily closely by finite linear combinations $c_1 \phi_1 + \cdots + c_n \phi_n$ of the orthogonal vectors ϕ_k whose completeness is in question. This idea is most vividly expressed in terms of the concept of a dense subset of a Euclidean vector space.

■ DEFINITION. *A subset S of a Euclidean vector space E is* dense *in E if and only if, for any f in E and positive number $\delta > 0$, an element s can be found in S such that $\|s - f\| < \delta$.*

As in Theorem 4, a set $\{\phi_n\}$ of orthogonal elements of E is *complete* if and only if the set S of all finite linear combinations $\sum_{1}^{n} \gamma_k \phi_k$ of the ϕ_k is dense in E.

The Parseval equality is easily derived in any Euclidean vector space E. Consider the sequence of best mean-square approximations

$$f_n = \sum_{k=1}^{n} c_k \phi_k, \qquad c_k = (f, \phi_k)/(\phi_k, \phi_k)$$

to a given vector f in E. If the finite linear combinations $\sum_1^n c_k \phi_k$ are dense in E, then the squared distance

$$\left\| \sum_{k=1}^n c_k \phi_k - f \right\|^2 = (f, f) - \sum_{k=1}^n [(f, \phi_k)^2/(\phi_k, \phi_k)] \geqq 0$$

must tend to zero as $n \to \infty$. Hence, if the sequence $\{\phi_n\}$ is *complete*, then

$$\sum_{k=1}^\infty [(f, \phi_k)^2/(\phi_k, \phi_k)] = (f, f) \qquad \text{(Parseval equality)}. \qquad (23)$$

Applying Parseval's equality to the vector $f + g$ and then expanding and simplifying, we obtain more generally

$$\sum_{k=1}^\infty [(f, \phi_k)(g, \phi_k)/(\phi_k, \phi_k)] = (f, g), \qquad (23')$$

valid whenever $\{\phi_k\}$ is complete and f, g are square-integrable. Even if Parseval's equality fails, we still get

$$\sum_{k=1}^\infty [(f, \phi_k)^2/(\phi_k, \phi_k)] \leqq (f, f) \qquad \text{(Bessel inequality)}. \qquad (24)$$

If Parseval's equality fails, then strict inequality will occur in (24) for some f in E. For such an f, we have by Theorem 1

$$\left\| f - \sum_{k=1}^n \gamma_k \phi_k \right\| \geqq \left\| f - \sum_{k=1}^n c_k \phi_k \right\| \geqq \sqrt{\delta} > 0,$$

for any choice of γ_k. Since δ is independent of n, this shows that the ϕ_k cannot be a complete set of orthogonal vectors. This gives another proof of Theorem 3, which we now restate for an arbitrary Euclidean vector space as follows.

■ **THEOREM 9.** *A sequence $\{\phi_k\}$ of orthogonal vectors of a Euclidean vector space E is complete if and only if the Parseval equality (23) holds for all f in E.*

9 Completeness of eigenfunctions

The completeness of the eigenfunctions of a regular Sturm-Liouville system is a consequence of the asymptotic formulas of Chapter 10, and a geometric property of sets of orthonormal vectors in Euclidean vector spaces. This property is stated in the following theorem of N. Bary.

■ THEOREM 10.   *Let $\{\phi_n\}$ be any* complete *sequence of orthonormal vectors in a Euclidean vector space E, and let $\{\psi_n\}$ be any sequence of orthonormal vectors in E which satisfies the inequality*

$$\sum_{n=1}^{\infty} \|\psi_n - \phi_n\|^2 < +\infty. \tag{25}$$

Then the ψ_n are complete in E.

This result will be proved in §§ 10, 11. It is plausible intuitively, because it asserts that completeness is preserved in passing from a set of orthonormal vectors ϕ_n to any nearby system.

Assuming Theorem 10 provisionally, we can establish the completeness of the eigenfunctions of a regular S-L system as follows.

Consider the asymptotic formula (56) of Chapter 10:

$$u_n(x) = \sqrt{2/(b-a)} \cos\left[n\pi(x-a)/(b-a)\right] + O(1)/n.$$

If $u_n(x)$ is the nth normalized eigenfunction of a regular S-L system in Liouville normal form, and if $\phi_n(x) = \sqrt{2/(b-a)} \cos(n\pi(x-a)/(b-a))$, this gives $|u_n(x) - \phi_n(x)| = O(1)/n$. Squaring and integrating, we get

$$\|u_n - \phi_n\|^2 = \int_I [u_n(x) - \phi_n(x)]^2 \, dx = O(1)/n^2.$$

Since the series $1 + \frac{1}{4} + \frac{1}{9} + \cdots + 1/n^2 + \cdots$ converges (to $\pi^2/6$), this implies the following lemma.

■ LEMMA.   *Let $u_n(x)$ be the nth normalized eigenfunction of any regular S-L system in Liouville normal form, with $\alpha'\beta' \neq 0$, and let*

$$\phi_n(x) = \sqrt{2/(b-a)} \cos\left[n\pi(x-a)/(b-a)\right].$$

Then the ϕ_n are an orthonormal sequence, and

$$\sum_{n=1}^{\infty} \|u_n - \phi_n\|^2 < +\infty. \tag{26}$$

Since the cosine functions are complete (by Corollary 3 of Theorem 3), it follows from this lemma and Theorem 10 that the eigenfunctions of any regular S-L system in Liouville normal form with $\alpha'\beta' \neq 0$ are a complete set of orthonormal functions.

As shown in Chapter 10, § 9, the transformation to Liouville normal form, applied to the (normalized) eigenfunctions, carries the inner product

$$(\phi, \psi) = \int_I \phi(x)\,\psi(x)\,\rho(x)\,dx,$$

into the inner product

$$(u, v) = \int_a^b u(x)\,v(x)\,dx.$$

Therefore†, the change of variable leading to Liouville normal form carries complete orthonormal sequences relative to a weight function ρ into complete orthonormal sequences. Therefore, the eigenfunctions of regular S-L systems not in Liouville normal form are also complete.

Finally, since similar arguments cover the case $\alpha'\beta' = 0$, we have the following result.

■ **THEOREM 11.** *The eigenfunctions of any regular S-L system are complete, in the Euclidean vector space of square-integrable continuous functions on the interval $a \leq x \leq b$, relative to the weight function ρ.*

10* Hilbert space

The set of real numbers differs from the set of rational numbers by *completeness* the property that every Cauchy sequence of real numbers is convergent.‡ This property of *completeness* has an analog for Euclidean vector spaces (and, more generally, for metric spaces).

■ **DEFINITION.** *In a Euclidean vector space E, a* Cauchy sequence *is an infinite sequence of vectors f_n such that*

$$\|f_m - f_n\| \to 0 \qquad as \quad m, n \to \infty. \tag{27}$$

The space E is called complete *when, given any Cauchy sequence $\{f_n\}$, there exists a vector f in E such that $\|f_n - f\| \to 0$ as $n \to \infty$. A complete Euclidean vector space is called a Hilbert space.*

Any finite-dimensional Euclidean vector space is complete; but the Euclidean vector space of continuous square-integrable functions defined in § 8 is not complete, as will appear presently.

EXAMPLE 2. Let (ℓ_2) denote the Euclidean vector space of all infinite sequences $\mathbf{a} = \{a_k\} = (a_1, a_2, a_3, \ldots)$ of real numbers which are square-summable, that is, satisfy $\sum a_k^2 < +\infty$. The vector operations on these sequences are performed term-by-term, so that $\mathbf{a} + \mathbf{b}$ is the sequence $(a_1 + b_1, a_2 + b_2, a_3 + b_3, \ldots)$. Inner products are defined by the formula

$$(\mathbf{a}, \mathbf{b}) = \sum_{k=1}^{\infty} a_k b_k = a_1 b_1 + a_2 b_2 + a_3 b_3 + \cdots \tag{28}$$

■ **LEMMA 1.** *The space (ℓ_2) is a Hilbert space.*

---

† Since distance and convergence are defined in terms of inner products in any Euclidean vector space.

‡ Courant and John, p. 94 ff; Widder, p. 277.

Proof — The problem is to prove completeness. To this end, let $\{\mathbf{a}^n\}$ be any Cauchy sequence of square-summable sequences. That is, let

$$\lim_{m,\,n \to \infty} \|\mathbf{a}^m - \mathbf{a}^n\|^2 = \lim_{m,\,n \to \infty} \left\{ \sum_{k=1}^{\infty} (a_k^m - a_k^n)^2 \right\} = 0.$$

For each fixed k, the sequence of real numbers a_k^n $(n = 1, 2, \ldots)$ (the kth components of $\mathbf{a}^n$) is a Cauchy sequence and, therefore, converges to some real number a_k. Let $\mathbf{a} = \{a_k\}$ $(k = 1, 2, 3, \ldots)$. We must prove that the sequence $\mathbf{a}$ is square-summable and that $\mathbf{a}^n \to \mathbf{a}$ in the Euclidean vector space.

Since $\big|\, \|\mathbf{a}^n\| - \|\mathbf{a}^m\| \,\big| \leqq \|\mathbf{a}^n - \mathbf{a}^m\|$ by the triangle inequality, it follows that the sequence $\|\mathbf{a}^n\|$ is bounded. Let $\sqrt{M}$ be an upper bound. Then, for all integers n, we have $\sum_{k=1}^{N}(a_k^n)^2 \leqq M$. Letting $n \to \infty$ in this finite sum, we get $\sum_{k=1}^{N}(a_k)^2 \leqq M$. Since N is arbitrary, it follows that $\|\mathbf{a}\|^2 = \sum_{k=1}^{\infty}(a_k)^2 \leqq M$. Hence, $\mathbf{a}$ is a square-summable sequence. Moreover, given $\epsilon > 0$, n can be found so large that $\|\mathbf{a}^n - \mathbf{a}^m\|^2 < \epsilon$ for all $m > n$. Therefore, for every integer N we have $\sum_{k=1}^{N}(a_k^n - a_k^m)^2 < \epsilon$. Letting $m \to \infty$, we obtain $\sum_{k=1}^{N}(a_k^n - a_k)^2 \leqq \epsilon$. Since N is arbitrary, this implies $\sum_{k=1}^{\infty}(a_k^n - a_k)^2 \leqq \epsilon$, q.e.d.

The property of Hilbert space which is most useful for establishing the completeness of eigenfunctions is the following.

■ **THEOREM 12.** *An orthogonal sequence $\{\phi_k\}$ of vectors of a Hilbert space is complete if and only if there is no nonzero vector f orthogonal to all the ϕ_k.*

Proof — Let f be a vector, and let $\{\phi_k\}$ be a sequence of orthogonal vectors in a Hilbert space $\mathscr{H}$. Let $g_n = \sum_{k=1}^{n} c_k \phi_k$ be the nth least square approximation to f by a linear combination of $\phi_1, \ldots, \phi_n$. Then, as before, we have $c_k = (f, \phi_k)/(\phi_k, \phi_k)$ and, for $m > n$,

$$\|g_m - g_n\|^2 = \sum_{n+1}^{m} [(f, \phi_k)^2/(\phi_k, \phi_k)] \leqq \sum_{n+1}^{\infty} [(f, \phi_k)^2/(\phi_k, \phi_k)].$$

By the Bessel inequality (24), the series $\sum_{k=1}^{\infty}[(f, \phi_k)^2/(\phi_k, \phi_k)]$ of positive numbers is convergent; hence the last sum in the preceding display tends to zero as $n \to \infty$. That is, the sequence $\{g_n\}$ is a *Cauchy sequence*.

It follows that $\mathscr{H}$, being complete, contains a vector g to which the g_n converge; let $h = f - g = \lim_{m \to \infty}(f - g_m)$. Then, since $(f - g_m, \phi_k) = 0$ for all $m \geq k$, we have in the limit, as $m \to \infty$, $(h, \phi_k) = 0$ for all k. By Theorem 9 (Parseval's equality), $h = 0$ for all f if and only if $\{\phi_k\}$ is complete. This completes the proof.

Remark. A complete orthonormal sequence $\{\phi_k\}$ in the space (ℓ_2) is obtained by choosing $\phi_k = \mathbf{e}^k$, the kth unit vector whose kth component is 1, and whose other components are all 0.

The Euclidean vector space $\mathscr{C}[a, b]$ of all continuous functions on a finite interval $a \leq x \leq b$ is not complete; that is, it is not a Hilbert space. The following is an example of a mean-square Cauchy sequence of continuous functions which does not converge to any continuous function. In $-1 \leq x \leq 1$, let $f_n(x) = 0$ for $-1 \leq x \leq 0$, $f_n(x) = nx$ for $0 \leq x \leq 1/n$, and $f_n(x) = 1$ for $1/n \leq x \leq 1$. The limit function $f_\infty(x)$ equals 0 for $-1 \leq x \leq 0$ and 1 for $0 < x \leq 1$.

Though the Euclidean vector space $\mathscr{C}[a, b]$ is not complete, it can be embedded in the (complete) Hilbert space (l_2), as follows. First, make the change of independent variable $t = \pi(x - a)/(b - a)$, to map the interval $[a, b]$ on $[0, \pi]$. Then for each $f(x) \in \mathscr{C}[a, b]$, expand $\tilde{f}(t) = f(a + (b - a)t/\pi)$ into the *cosine series* $\tilde{f}(t) = \sum c_k \cos kt$, $k = 1, 2, \ldots$. The vector $\mathbf{f} = (c_0, c_1, c_2, \ldots)$ defines an element of the space (ℓ_2), by the Bessel inequality.

The correspondence $f \to \mathbf{f}$ maps the space $\mathscr{C}[a, b]$ into the space (ℓ_2); moreover, it preserves vector operations: $f + g \to \mathbf{f} + \mathbf{g}$ and $\lambda f \to \lambda \mathbf{f}$. By Parseval's generalized equality (23′), which is applicable since the cosine functions are complete (Theorem 3, Corollary 3), we know that

$$(\mathbf{f}, \mathbf{g}) = [\pi/(b - a)] \int_a^b f(x)g(x)\, dx = \int_0^\pi \tilde{f}(t)(t\tilde{g})\, dt$$

Hence, the correspondence $f \to \mathbf{f}$ also preserves *inner products* (up to a constant normalizing factor); therefore, it also preserves lengths $(\mathbf{f}, \mathbf{f})^{1/2}$. In particular, $\mathbf{f} = \mathbf{0}$ implies $\int_0^\pi f^2(t)\, dt = 0$—and hence, f being continuous, that $f(t) \equiv 0$. In conclusion, we have proved the following result.

■ LEMMA 2.   *The Euclidean vector space $\mathscr{C}[a, b]$ $(-\infty < a < b < +\infty)$ can be embedded in the Hilbert space (ℓ_2), with preservation of vector operations and inner products.*

More generally, let ϕ_n be a complete sequence of orthonormal vectors in an arbitrary Euclidean space E. Then the mapping $f \to \mathbf{c} = \{c_k\}$, where $c_k = (f, \phi_k)$ for f in E, defines an embedding of E as a subspace of (ℓ_2). In the same way as above we obtain the following lemma.

■ LEMMA 3.   *Every Euclidean vector space with a complete sequence of orthonormal vectors can be embedded in (ℓ_2), with preservation of vector operations and inner products.*

In view of this Lemma, it suffices to prove Theorem 10 under the assumption that the Euclidean vector space E is complete, that is, that E is a Hilbert space. We shall make this assumption from now on.

11* Proof of completeness

We are now ready to prove Theorem 10. But to bring out more clearly the idea of the proof, we first treat a special case.

We define a sequence of orthonormal vectors of a Hilbert space to be an *orthonormal basis* if and only if it is complete.

■ LEMMA.   *Let* $\{\phi_k\}$ *be an orthonormal basis in the Hilbert space* $\mathscr{H}$. *Let* $\{\psi_k\}$ *be an orthonormal sequence in* $\mathscr{H}$ *satisfying the conditions*

$$\sum_{k=1}^{\infty} \|\psi_k - \phi_k\|^2 < 1. \tag{29}$$

Then the sequence $\{\psi_k\}$ *is also an orthonormal basis in* $\mathscr{H}$.

Proof — If the sequence ψ_k were not a basis, then we could find a nonzero function h orthogonal to every ψ_k by Theorem 12. The inner product of this function with ϕ_k is given by

$$(h, \phi_k) = (h, \psi_k) + (h, \phi_k - \psi_k) = (h, \phi_k - \psi_k).$$

Squaring and using the Schwarz inequality, we have

$$(h, \phi_k)^2 = (h, \phi_k - \psi_k)^2 \leq \|h\|^2 \|\phi_k - \psi_k\|^2. \tag{29'}$$

Summing with respect to k, we get

$$\sum_{k=1}^{\infty} (h, \phi_k)^2 \leq \|h\|^2 \sum_{k=1}^{\infty} \|\phi_k - \psi_k\|^2 < \|h\|^2,$$

in evident violation of Parseval's equality (Theorem 9), since the ϕ_k are an orthonormal basis.

■ COROLLARY 1.   *Replace condition (29) above by the weaker condition*

$$\sum_{k=N+1}^{\infty} \|\psi_k - \phi_k\|^2 < 1 \tag{30}$$

for some integer N. *Then every element of* $\mathscr{H}$ *orthogonal to* $\phi_1, \ldots, \phi_N$ *and to* $\psi_{N+1}, \psi_{N+2}, \ldots$ *must vanish.*

Proof — Any such element h satisfies the inequality (29') for $k > N$. Summing over all k, we have, since $(h, \phi_k) = 0$ for $k = 1, 2, \ldots, N$,

$$\|h\|^2 = \sum_{k=1}^{\infty} (h, \phi_k)^2 = \sum_{k=N+1}^{\infty} (h, \phi_k)^2 \leqq \|h\|^2 \sum_{k=N+1}^{\infty} \|\phi_k - \psi_k\|^2 < \|h\|^2,$$

again contradicting Parseval's equality.

■ COROLLARY 2. *If ϕ_k is an orthonormal basis and ψ_k an orthonormal sequence satisfying (30), then every element of $\mathscr{H}$ orthogonal to ψ_{N+1}, $\psi_{N+2}, \ldots$ and to the elements*

$$\eta_n = \phi_n - \sum_{k=N+1}^{\infty} (\phi_n, \psi_k)\psi_k, \qquad n = 1, 2, \ldots, N, \qquad (31)$$

must vanish.

Proof — For any such element h, we have

$$(h, \phi_n) = (h, \eta_n) + \sum_{k=N+1}^{\infty} (\phi_n, \psi_k)(h, \psi_k) = 0$$

for $n = 1, 2, \ldots, N$. Thus h also satisfies the conditions of Corollary 1 and therefore vanishes.

The proof of Theorem 10 can now be completed as follows. Choose an integer N so that

$$\sum_{k=N+1}^{\infty} \|\psi_k - \phi_k\|^2 < 1.$$

By Corollary 2, any element h of $\mathscr{H}$ which is orthogonal to the elements $\psi_{N+1}, \psi_{N+2}, \ldots$ and to the elements η_n ($n = 1, 2, \ldots, N$), defined by formula (31), must vanish. Denote by S the set of all elements of $\mathscr{H}$ orthogonal to $\psi_{N+1}, \psi_{N+2}, \ldots$. Evidently S is a vector space containing $\eta_1, \ldots, \eta_N$. By virtue of the above remark, the vector space S contains only the linear combinations of these elements. In other words, S is a finite-dimensional vector space whose dimension is at most N.

But the elements $\psi_1, \psi_2, \ldots, \psi_N$ also belong to the vector space S, and they are linearly independent (they are an orthonormal sequence!). Therefore, the elements $\psi_1, \psi_2, \ldots, \psi_N$ are a *basis* for the vector space S.† Hence, the elements $\eta_1, \eta_2, \ldots, \eta_N$ are linear combinations of $\psi_1, \psi_2, \ldots, \psi_N$. It follows that any element of $\mathscr{H}$ which is orthogonal to all the ψ_k must vanish, because such an element is also orthogonal to $\eta_1, \ldots, \eta_N$ and to $\psi_{N+1}, \psi_{N+2}, \ldots$. We conclude that the sequence $\{\psi_k\}$ is complete, proving Theorem 10.

Theorem 10 implies Theorem 11, as has already been shown in § 9.

---

† As shown in Birkhoff and Mac Lane, pp. 168–169.

It is natural to ask whether the sums $\sum c_k \phi_k$ having square-summable coefficient sequences cannot also be interpreted as functions. This question can also be answered in the affirmative, by use of the Lebesgue integral. Given any complete family $\{\phi_k\}$ of orthonormal functions on $[a, b]$, the partial sums $\sum_{k=1}^{n} c_k \phi_k$ with *square-summable* coefficient sequence $\{c_k\}$ converge in the mean square to a function $f(x)$ which is *square-integrable* for the *Lebesgue integral*. Conversely, if $f(x)$ is Lebesgue square-integrable and if $c_k = (f, \phi_k)$, the partial sums $f_n = \sum_{k=1}^{n} c_k \phi_k$ converge to $f(x)$ in the mean square. That is, the metric completion of the space $\mathscr{C}[a, b]$ is precisely the Hilbert space $\mathscr{L}_2[a, b]$ of all functions on $[a, b]$ whose squares are Lebesgue integrable. It is this space which is really appropriate for the theory of expansions in eigenfunctions.

EXERCISES E

1. Show that in a finite-dimensional Euclidean vector space E a set S of elements is dense if and only if, whenever $(\phi, f) = 0$ for all $\phi \in $ S, then $f = 0$.
2. Show that an orthonormal sequence ϕ_k $(k = 1, 2, 3, \ldots)$ in a Euclidean vector space is complete if Parseval's equality (23) holds for all f in a dense subset.
3. (Vitali.) Show that an orthonormal sequence $\phi_k(x)$ $(k = 1, 2, \ldots)$ of continuous functions for $a \leqq x \leqq b$ is complete if and only if

$$\sum_{k=1}^{\infty} \left(\int_a^x \phi_k(t)\, dt \right)^2 = x - a, \qquad a \leqq x \leqq b.$$

[HINT   Show that linear combinations of the functions $f(x) = |x - c|$ form a dense subset, and apply Exercise 2.]
4*. (Dalzell.) Show that a sequence of continuous orthonormal square-integrable functions $\phi_k(x)$, $a \leqq x \leqq b$, is complete if and only if

$$\sum_{k=1}^{\infty} \int_a^b \left(\int_a^x \phi_k(t)\, dt \right)^2 dx = (b - a)^2/2.$$

[HINT   Let $q(x) = x - a - \sum_{k=1}^{\infty} (\int_a^x \phi_k(t)\, dt)^2$, and show that $q(x) \equiv 0$ by establishing $q(x) \geqq 0$ and $\int_a^b q(x)\, dx = 0$, q continuous, applying Exercise 3.]
5. Assuming the equality $\sum_{k=1}^{\infty} 1/k^2 = \pi^2/6$, infer from Exercise 4 that the trigonometric functions $\cos kx$, $\sin kx$, $k = 0, 1, 2, \ldots$, are complete on $(-\pi, \pi)$.
6. (Moment problem.) Let $f(x)$ be continuous, $a \leqq x \leqq b$, and let

$$m_n = \int_a^b x^n f(x)\, dx.$$

Show that if all the moments m_n vanish, $f(x) \equiv 0$.
[HINT: Use the Weierstrass Approximation Theorem.]
7*. Prove the completeness of the eigenfunctions of any regular S-L system with boundary conditions $u(a) = u(b) = 0$.
8*. Let $G(f_1, f_2, \ldots, f_n) = \det(a_{ij})$, where $a_{ij} = (f_i, f_j)$. Show that the minimum of $\| f - \sum c_k f_k \|$ is equal to $G(f, f_1, f_2, \ldots, f_n)/G(f_1, f_2, \ldots, f_n)$.
[HINT: Interpret the determinants as volumes.]

9. Show by a counterexample that Theorem 10 does not remain valid if the ψ_n are allowed to be nonorthogonal unit vectors.

10. Consider the orthogonal sequence ϕ_k, and let $\psi_k = \phi_k$, $k \geq 2$, $\psi_1 = 0$. Then $\Sigma \|\phi_k - \psi_k\|^2 < \infty$, but $\{\psi_k\}$ is not complete. Which hypothesis, of Theorem 10 is violated?

11. Show that the first-order complex DE $iu' + (q(x) + \lambda)u = 0$, $a \leq x \leq b$, with the boundary condition $u(a) = u(b)$ and $i = \sqrt{-1}$, has a complete sequence of eigenfunctions for any real continuous $q(x)$.

12. Show that linear combinations of the trigonometric functions $\cos kx$, $\sin kx$ are dense in $-\pi \leq x \leq \pi$ relative to any continuous positive weight function.

APPENDIX: Linear Systems

Appendix: Linear Systems

1 Matrix norm

As in Chapter 6, §4, any system of linear DE's can be reduced to a system of n first-order DE's and so written in matrix notation as

$$\mathbf{x}'(t) = A(t)\mathbf{x}, \tag{1}$$

where $\mathbf{x}(t)$ is a column vector of length n and $A(t)$ an $n \times n$ matrix, both depending on t. In Chapter 6, we proved the existence and uniqueness of solutions of (1) in any interval of continuity of $A(t)$, for any initial $\mathbf{x}(0) = \mathbf{c}$. In this Appendix, we derive some properties of solutions of linear systems (1) whose proofs depend on deeper properties of matrices.

As in Chapter 6, §2, $\mathbf{x}'(t)$ means the limit

$$\lim_{\Delta t \to 0} \Delta t^{-1}[\mathbf{x}(t + \Delta t) - \mathbf{x}(t)],$$

where the limit is taken separately in each component $\Delta x_k / \Delta t$. Here we extend this definition, calling the *norm* of any matrix A the real number:

$$\|A\| = \sup_{\mathbf{x} \neq \mathbf{0}} |A\mathbf{x}|/|\mathbf{x}|, \tag{2}$$

where

$$|\mathbf{x}| = (\mathbf{x}^T\mathbf{x})^{1/2} = (\sum x_k^2)^{1/2} \quad \text{and} \quad |A\mathbf{x}| = |\mathbf{x}^T A^T A\mathbf{x}|^{1/2},$$

similarly†. Then $A(t) \to A(t_0)$ means equivalently:

---

† We use standard notation here: A^T signifies the transpose of A, and $\mathbf{x}^T\mathbf{x}$ the inner product of $\mathbf{x}$ with itself; see Birkhoff-Mac Lane, Chapters VIII–X for the facts assumed in this Appendix.

(i) that $a_{jk}(t) \to a_{jk}(t_0)$ for all j, $k = 1, \ldots, n$, or

(ii) that $\|A(t) - A(t_0)\|$ tends to zero as $t \to t_0$.

The equation $\|I\| = 1$, the triangle inequality $\|A + B\| \leq \|A\| + \|B\|$, the multiplicative inequality $\|AB\| \leq \|A\| \cdot \|B\|$, and $\|tA\| = |t| \cdot \|A\|$ all follow quite directly from (2). From these relations, in turn, one can prove the convergence of the *exponential series*

$$\exp tA = I + tA + (t^2/2!)A^2 + (t^3/3!)A^3 + \cdots \tag{3}$$

for any matrix A and any scalar t. It suffices to copy the usual proof for real or complex exponential series, replacing absolute values by norms throughout.

2 Constant-coefficient systems

We now introduce the alternative notation e^{tA} for $\exp tA$ as defined above, and prove the differentiability relation

$$d(e^{tA})/dt = Ae^{tA} \qquad \text{for any constant matrix } A. \tag{4}$$

Because of the commutativity of all terms, we have, as in the scalar case, $e^{tA}e^{uA} = e^{(t+u)A}$ and, hence,

$$e^{(t+\Delta t)A} - e^{tA} = (e^{\Delta tA} - I)e^{tA} = \left(\sum_{k=1}^{\infty} \Delta t^k A^k / k! \right) e^{tA}.$$

Dividing the series in parenthesis through by Δt, we get the identity matrix I plus a series of matrices whose norms are bounded by $\Delta t^{k-1}\alpha^k/(k!)$, $k = 2, 3, \ldots$, where $\alpha = \|A\|$. Hence, the norm of the sum, tends to zero with Δt, proving (4).

From (4), there follows a very beautiful result.

■ THEOREM 1.   *The constant-coefficient first-order linear system* $\mathbf{x}'(t) = A\mathbf{x}$ *has the general solution* $\mathbf{x}(t) = e^{tA}\mathbf{x}(0)$.

Proof — Differentiating $e^{tA}\mathbf{x}(0) = \mathbf{y}(t)$, we get $Ae^{tA}\mathbf{x}(0) = A\mathbf{y}$ by (4), where $\mathbf{x}(0) = \mathbf{y}(0)$ trivially.

We now generalize the concept of secular equation from second-order linear systems with constant coefficients to nth-order systems. Namely, if $p_A(\lambda)$ is the characteristic polynomial of the matrix A, we define the *secular equation* of the constant-coefficient system $\mathbf{x}'(t) = A\mathbf{x}$ to be the DE $p_A(D)u = 0$, where D denotes d/dt.

■ THEOREM 2.   *Any component* $x_i(t)$ *of any vector solution of* $\mathbf{x}'(t) = A\mathbf{x}$ *satisfies the secular equation* $p_A(D)u = 0$.

Proof — We write the given DE as $D\mathbf{x} = A\mathbf{x}$. By the Cayley-Hamilton Theorem for matrices, $p_A(A) = 0$ is the zero matrix; hence, we have $p_A(A)\mathbf{x} = 0$. Since $A\mathbf{x}$ can have $D\mathbf{x}$ substituted for it throughout, we know that $p_A(D)\mathbf{x} = 0$ for any solution of the given DE.

Stability.   Theorem 2 shows that, if every eigenvalue of A has a negative real part, then by Theorem 5′ of Chapter 5 the constant-coefficient system $\mathbf{x}'(t) = A\mathbf{x}$ is *strictly stable*. A more explicit proof can be given of this result and its converse by allowing vectors and matrices to have *complex* components and replacing $\mathbf{x}^T\mathbf{x}$ and A^TA by the corresponding Hermitian formulas $\mathbf{x}^H\mathbf{x}$ and A^HA, where the superscript H signifies conjugate transpose.

This permits us to make a change of basis in the vector space of $\mathbf{x}(t)$ which replaces A by its *Jordan normal form* $J = PAP^{-1}$ (P complex nonsingular). Now consider, for example, a typical elementary Jordan block submatrix on the diagonal of J, say the 4×4 matrix

$$J_i = \begin{bmatrix} \lambda_i & 1 & 0 & 0 \\ 0 & \lambda_i & 1 & 0 \\ 0 & 0 & \lambda_i & 1 \\ 0 & 0 & 0 & \lambda_i \end{bmatrix}.$$

We can exponentiate this block explicitly, getting

$$e^{tJ_i}, \lambda_i t = \begin{bmatrix} 1 & t & t^2/2! & t^3/3! \\ 0 & 1 & t & t^2/2! \\ 0 & 0 & 1 & t \\ 0 & 0 & 0 & 1 \end{bmatrix}.$$

Since negative exponentials die out faster than any power, it follows that $e^{tJ} \to 0$ as $t \to \infty$ if and only if every eigenvalue of A has negative real part. Finally, since $e^{tA} = P^{-1}e^{tJ}P$, it follows that the same is true of e^{tA}. (The matrices A and J have the same eigenvalues.)

The Jordan normal form also gives a suggestive *canonical form* for first-order linear systems.

3   The matrizant

We next consider the general case, of variable but continuous $A(t)$ in (1). If $\mathbf{x}_1(t), \ldots, \mathbf{x}_m(t)$ is any list of m (column) vector solutions of (1), the $n \times m$ matrix $X(t)$ composed of these columns will, trivially, satisfy the matrix DE $X'(t) = A(t)X$. In particular, we can construct in this way an $n \times n$ matrix solution of

$$M'(t) = A(t)M, \qquad M(0) = I \text{ (identity matrix)}. \tag{5}$$

The matrix function $M(t)$ so defined is called the *matrizant* of the system (1). By (4), the matrizant of the constant-coefficient system $\mathbf{x}'(t) = A\mathbf{x}$ is just e^{tA}.

Since the multiplication of matrices is associative, the vector-valued function $M(t)\mathbf{c} = \mathbf{x}(t)$ will satisfy $\mathbf{x}(0) = M(0)\mathbf{c} = I\mathbf{c} = \mathbf{c}$ for any given $\mathbf{c}$. Since

$$\mathbf{x}'(t) = M'(t)\mathbf{c} = A(t)M(t)\mathbf{c} = A(t)\mathbf{x},$$

it will also satisfy (1). By the uniqueness theorem proved in Chapter 6, it follows that *every* solution of (1) has the form $M(t)\mathbf{c}$.

The determinant det $M(t)$ of the matrizant also has a remarkable property. We know by (4) that

$$M(t + \Delta t) = M(t) + \Delta M(t) = M(t) + A(t)\,\Delta t\,M(t) + o(\Delta t)$$
$$= [I + A(t)\,\Delta t]M(t) + O(\Delta t).$$

By the multiplication rule for determinants, therefore, we have

$$\det M(t + \Delta t) = \det [I + A(t)\,\Delta t]\det M(t) + o(\Delta t).$$

Expanding in minors, on the other hand, we obtain

$$\det [I + A(t)\,\Delta t] = 1 + \Delta t\,\mathrm{Tr}\,A(t) + O(\Delta t^2),$$

where $\mathrm{Tr}\,A = \sum a_{kk}$ is the *trace* of A. Combining,

$$\det M(t + \Delta t) = (1 + \Delta t\,\mathrm{Tr}\,A)\det M(t) + o(\Delta t),$$

or

$$[\det M(t + \Delta t) - \det M(t)]/\Delta t = \mathrm{Tr}\,A\,\det M(t) + o(1).$$

Now, passing to the limit as $\Delta t \to 0$, we get (using the alternative notation $|M(t)|$ for det $M(t)$):

$$d\,|M(t)|/dt = \mathrm{Tr}\,A\,|M(t)|.$$

Integrating this first-order DE by the methods of Chapter 1, we obtain our final result.

■ **THEOREM 3.** *The determinant of the matrizant of* (1) *satisfies*

$$\det M(t) = \exp\left\{\int_0^t [\mathrm{Tr}\,A(t)]\,dt\right\}. \tag{6}$$

■ **COROLLARY.** *If* $\mathrm{Tr}\,A \equiv 0$, *the matrizant of* (1) *has determinant identically* 1 (*is "unimodular"*).

This is the case, for example, with systems (1) which come from nth-order DE's of the normal form

$$u^{(n)}(t) + a_2(t)u^{(n-2)}(t) + \cdots + a_n(t)u = 0.$$

Next, we define the *adjoint* of the system (1) to be the first-order linear system

$$\mathbf{f}'(t) = -A^T(t)\mathbf{f} \quad (\text{that is,} \quad df_i/dt = -\sum_j a_{ji}f_j). \tag{7}$$

We consider the solution curves of (7) as lying in the dual space of linear functionals on the space of $\mathbf{x}(t)$, given by the linear forms

$$\mathbf{f}(\mathbf{x}) = \sum f_j x_j = (\mathbf{f}, \mathbf{x}) = \mathbf{f}^T\mathbf{x} \quad (\text{inner product}). \tag{8}$$

■ THEOREM 4.   *In order that* $(\mathbf{f}(t), \mathbf{x}(t))$ *be* constant *for every solution* $\mathbf{x}(t)$ *of the vector* DE (1), *it is necessary and sufficient that* (7) *hold.*

Proof — By straightforward differentiation, we have

$$\frac{d}{dt}\left[\sum_j f_j(t)x_j(t)\right] = \sum_j f_j(t)x_j'(t) + \sum_j f_j'(t)x_j(t)$$

$$= \sum_{j,k} f_j(t)a_{jk}(t)x_k(t) + \sum_k f_k'(t)x_k(t).$$

Since there exists a solution of (1) with $\mathbf{x}(t_0) = \mathbf{c}$ for any t_0 and $\mathbf{c}$ the, condition that $(\mathbf{f}(t), \mathbf{x}(t))$ be constant for all solutions of (1), and hence that the derivative above vanish identically, is precisely that

$$0 = \sum_j f_j(t)a_{jk}(t) + f_k'(t) \quad \text{for all} \quad k, \tag{9}$$

which is obviously equivalent to (7), as claimed.

4   Floquet theorem; canonical bases

We next consider *periodic* linear systems, that is, systems of the form (1) with

$$A(t + T) = A(t) \quad \text{for some fixed period } T. \tag{10}$$

A very special example is furnished by the Mathieu equation

$$u'' + (\lambda - 16d \cos 2x)u = 0,$$

which is equivalent in the Poincaré phase plane to

$$u' = v, \quad v' = (-\lambda + 16d \cos 2x)u = 0.$$

Equations of Hill's type,

$$u'' + p(t)u = 0, \qquad p(t + \pi) = p(t),$$

provide a more general class of examples.

In any case, let $M(T)$ be the matrizant of the first-order periodic linear system (10), and let the eigenvectors of $M(T)$ be $\mathbf{v}_1, \ldots, \mathbf{v}_r$ (hopefully, $r = n$), with $M(T)\mathbf{v}_i = \lambda_i \mathbf{v}_i$. Then, if $\mathbf{x}_i(t)$ is the solution of (10) with the initial-value vector $\mathbf{v}_i$, then by definition we have $\mathbf{x}_i(T) = \lambda_i \mathbf{x}_i(0) = \lambda_i \mathbf{v}_i$; moreover, $\lambda_i \neq 0$ since $\mathbf{x}(t) = \mathbf{0}$ is the only solution of (10) with $\mathbf{x}(T) = \mathbf{0}$ (Uniqueness Theorem). Since $A(t + T) = A(t)$, $\mathbf{x}_i(t + T)$ is, therefore, the solution of the same initial-value problem as $\mathbf{x}_i(t)$ but with the initial-value vector multiplied by λ_i. We conclude the quasi-periodic relation

$$\mathbf{x}_i(t + T) = \lambda_i \mathbf{x}_i(t). \tag{11}$$

This is essentially Floquet's Theorem. Since $\lambda_i \neq 0$, $\lambda_i = e^{\alpha_i T}$ for some real or complex constant α_i, we can define $\mathbf{y}_i(t) = e^{-\alpha_i t}\mathbf{x}_i(t)$ with the assurance that, by (11), $\mathbf{y}_i(t + T) = \mathbf{y}_i(t)$. We have proved

■ THEOREM 5. *If the matrizant $M(T)$ of (10) has r independent eigenvectors, then (10) has r linearly independent solutions*

$$\mathbf{x}_i(t) = e^{\alpha_i t}\mathbf{y}_i(t), \qquad where \quad \mathbf{y}_i(t + T) = \mathbf{y}_i(t), \tag{12}$$

and each $\mathbf{x}_i(t)$ is an exponential (scalar) function $e^{\alpha_i t}$ times a periodic function.

Finally, let $t = a$ be an isolated singular point of the matrix $A(t)$, considered as a function of the *complex* independent variable t. By this, we mean that all $a_{jk}(t)$ are analytic in some punctured disc $0 < |t - a| < r$. Much as in Chapter 9, we can consider the effect of making a simple loop $t = a + e^{i\theta}\tau$ around $t = a$ on some basis of solutions of the linear system (1); we do *not* assume periodicity. If the basis of solutions has for initial values $\mathbf{x}_i(t_0) = \mathbf{e}_i$, where $\mathbf{e}_i = (\delta_{i,1} \ldots \delta_{i,n})$ is the ith unit vector, this is given by the "matrizant" of (1) for the given loop. In any event, we can write

$$\mathbf{x}(c + e^{2\pi i}\tau) = M\mathbf{x}(c + \tau), \tag{13}$$

where M is a suitable nonsingular *circuit matrix*. An argument like that used to prove Theorem 5 (and Theorem 4 of Chapter 9) gives the following result.

■ THEOREM 6. *If the circuit matrix of $A(t)$ in (1) for the isolated singular point $t = a$ has r independent eigenvectors, then (1) has r solutions*

$$\mathbf{x}(t) = (t - a)^{\alpha_i}\mathbf{f}_i(t), \tag{14}$$

where the $\mathbf{f}_i(t)$ are holomorphic in $0 < |t - a| < r$.

BIBLIOGRAPHY

Bibliography

General references

ABRAMOWITZ, MILTON, AND I. A. STEGUN, *Handbook of Mathematical Functions.* New York: Dover, 1965.

AHLFORS, L. V., *Complex Analysis: Introduction to the Theory of Analytic Functions of One Complex Variable*, 2nd ed. New York: McGraw-Hill, 1953.

BIRKHOFF, GARRETT, AND S. MacLANE, *A Survey of Modern Algebra*, 3rd ed. New York: Macmillan, 1965.

CARRIER, GEORGE F., MAX KROOK, and C. E. PEARSON, *Functions of a Complex Variable: Theory and Technique.* New York: McGraw-Hill, 1966.

COURANT, RICHARD, *Differential and Integral Calculus, Vol. 2* (Interscience), 2nd ed. New York: Wiley, 1936.

COURANT, RICHARD, and D. HILBERT, *Methods of Mathematical Physics, Vol. 1* (Interscience). New York: Wiley, 1953.

COURANT, RICHARD, and F. JOHN, *Introduction to Calculus and Analysis, Vol. 1* (Interscience). New York: Wiley, 1965.

FLETCHER, A., J. C. P. MILLER, and L. ROSENHEAD, *Index of Mathematical Tables, Vol. I and II*, 2nd ed. Reading, Mass.: Addison-Wesley, 1962.

GRAVES, LAWRENCE M., *Theory of Functions of Real Variables*, 2nd ed. New York: McGraw-Hill, 1956.

HILDEBRAND, FRANCIS B., *Introduction to Numerical Analysis.* New York: McGraw-Hill, 1956.

HILLE, EINAR, *Analytic Function Theory, Vol. 1.* Waltham, Mass.: Blaisdell, 1959; Vol. 2, 1962.

KAPLAN, WILFRED, *Advanced Calculus.* Reading, Mass.: Addison-Wesley, 1952.

PEIRCE, B. O., and R. M. FOSTER, *Short Table of Integrals*, 4th ed. Waltham, Mass.: Blaisdell, 1957.

PICARD, E., *Traité d'Analyse*, 2nd ed. (3 vols.). Paris: Gauthier-Villars, 1922-1928.

RUDIN, WALTER, *Principles of Mathematical Analysis*, 2nd ed. New York: McGraw-Hill, 1964.

STIEFEL, E. L., *An Introduction to Numerical Mathematics*, tr. by W. C. Rheinboldt. New York: Academic, 1963.

TAYLOR, A. E., *Advanced Calculus*. Waltham, Mass.: Blaisdell, 1955.

WIDDER, DAVID V., *Advanced Calculus*, 2nd ed. Englewood Cliffs, New Jersey: Prentice-Hall, 1961.

Works on Ordinary Differential Equations

BELLMAN, RICHARD, *Stability Theory of Differential Equations*. New York: McGraw-Hill, 1953.

BELLMAN, RICHARD, and KENNETH L. COOKE, *Differential – Difference Equations*. New York: Academic, 1953.

BIEBERBACH, L., *Theorie der Differentialgleichungen*. Berlin: Springer, 1930.

BIEBERBACH, L., *Theorie der gewöhnlichen Differentialgleichungen auf Funktiontheoretischer Grundlage dargestellt*. Berlin: Springer, 1953.

BÔCHER, M. *Leçons sur les méthodes de Sturm*. Paris: Gauthier-Villars, 1917.

CESARI, L., *Asymptotic Behavior and Stability Problems in Ordinary Differential Equations*, 2nd ed. New York: Academic, 1963.

CODDINGTON, EARL A., and N. LEVINSON, *Theory of Ordinary Differential Equations*. New York: McGraw-Hill, 1955.

DAVIS, PHILIP J., and PHILIP RABINOWITZ, *Numerical Integration*. Waltham, Mass.: Blaisdell, 1966.

FORD, LESTER R., *Differential Equations*, 2nd ed. New York: McGraw-Hill, 1955.

HALANAY, A., *Differential Equations: Stability, Oscillations, Time-Lags*. New York: Academic, 1966.

HARTMAN, PHILIP, *Ordinary Differential Equations*. New York: Wiley, 1964.

HENRICI, PETER, *Numerical Integration of Ordinary Differential Equations*. New York: Wiley, 1961.

HENRICI, PETER, *Error Propagation for Difference Methods*. New York: Wiley, 1963.

HOCHSTADT, HARRY, *Special Functions of Mathematical Physics*. New York: Holt, 1961.

HUREWICZ, WITOLD, *Lectures on Ordinary Differential Equations*. M.I.T., 1958.

INCE, E. L., *Ordinary Differential Equations*, 4th ed. New York: Dover, 1953.

KAMKE, E., *Differentialgleichungen: Lösungsmethoden und Losungen*. Leipzig: Akademische Verlagagesellschaft, 1943.

KAMKE, E., *Differentialgleichungen reeller Funktionen*. Leipzig: Akademische Verlagagesellschaft, 1930.

KAPLAN, WILFRED, *Ordinary Differential Equations*. Reading, Mass.: Addison-Wesley, 1958.

LEFSCHETZ, SOLOMAN, *Differential Equations, Geometric Theory*, 2nd ed. (Interscience). New York: Wiley, 1963.

LIAPOUNOFF, A., *Problème Générale de la Stabilité de Mouvement*. Kraus, 1947.

MAGNUS, WILHELM AND S. WINKLER, *Hill's Equation* (Interscience). New York: Wiley, 1966.

MCLACHLAN, N. W., *Ordinary Non-Linear Differential Equations in Engineering and Physical Sciences*, 2nd ed. New York: Oxford, 1956.

NEMYTSKII, V. V., AND V. V. STEPANOV, *Qualitative Theory of Differential Equations*. Princeton, New Jersey: Princeton, 1960

PETROWSKI, I. G,. *Ordinary Differential Equations*. New York: Prentice-Hall, 1966.

PICARD, E., *Leçons sur Quelques Problèmes aux Limites de la Théorie des Equations Différentielles*. Paris: Gauthier-Villars, 1930.

PLISS, V. A. *Nonlocal Problems of the Theory of Oscillations*. New York: Academic, 1966. (Russian ed., 1964)

POINCARÉ, H., *Les Méthodes Nouvelles de la Mécanique Céleste, Vol. I-III*. New York: Dover, 1957.

SANSONE, G., *Equazioni Differenziali nel Campo Reale, Vol. I, II*. Bologna: Zanichelli, 1948.

SANSONE, G., AND R. CONTI, *Non-Linear Differential Equations*. New York: Pergamon, 1952.

STOKER, J. J., *Nonlinear Vibrations in Mechanical and Electrical Systems* (Interscience). New York: Wiley, 1950.

TITCHMARSH, E. C., *Eigenfunction Expansions Associated with Second-Order Differential Equations, Vol. I*. Oxford, England: Clarendon, 1962; *Vol. II*, 1962.

TRICOMI, F. G., *Equazioni Differenziali*, 3rd ed. Turin: Einaudi, 1961.

WASOW, W., *Asymptotic Expansions for Ordinary Differential Equations* (Interscience). New York: Wiley, 1966.

WILCOX, C. (editor), *Asymptotic Solutions of Differential Equations*. New York: Wiley, 1964.

INDEX

Index

A B C D E F G H I J   5 4 3 2 1 7 0 6 9